VENTURE INTO SPACE

NASA SP-4301

VENTURE INTO SPACE

EARLY YEARS OF
GODDARD SPACE FLIGHT CENTER

ALFRED ROSENTHAL

NASA Center History Series

Scientific and Technical Information Division
OFFICE OF TECHNOLOGY UTILIZATION   1968
NATIONAL AERONAUTICS AND SPACE ADMINISTRATION
Washington, D.C.

For Sale by the Superintendent of Documents,
U.S. Government Printing Office, Washington, D.C. 20402
Price $2.50 (Paper Cover)
Library of Congress Catalog Card Number 67-60096

Mrs. Robert H. Goddard and James E. Webb, Administrator of the National
Aeronautics and Space Administration, unveiled the sculpture of the late rocket
pioneer at the dedication of the Goddard Space Flight Center, March 16, 1961.

Foreword

SINCE ITS INCEPTION the Goddard Space Flight Center has magnificently fulfilled its mission to become a symbol of the aims and dedication of my late husband, Robert H. Goddard. As an active division of the National Aeronautics and Space Administration, the Goddard Center has already made many significant contributions to man's knowledge of the upper atmosphere and outer space—the precise goals of my husband's life. Through its televised tracking activities, the name of Goddard has become commonplace in the American home.

Like most scientists, my husband kept a careful and detailed account of his experiments and theories, with occasional summaries and forecasts. It is therefore most appropriate that the Goddard Space Flight Center pause, at intervals, to sum up its activities, evaluate its successes, and plan for even more effective work in the future.

At the dedication of this Center, I remarked that my husband was an extremely happy man, doing what he most wanted to do, with adequate funds in optimum surroundings; and I expressed the hope that many of those who would work at the Goddard Center might be similarly blessed. I feel that this hope is being realized. I also called attention to the opportunities for the "straight thinker and the hard worker," with the wish that the Center would attract such people, and keep them. This, too, has come to pass. With such personnel I have no doubt that this great living memorial will continue to play a vital role in the coming Space Age.

ESTHER C. GODDARD

Preface

THE GODDARD SPACE FLIGHT CENTER is a partnership of many people—scientists, engineers, project managers, and administrators—whose combined efforts are needed to carry on and bring to fruition scientific and technological expeditions into outer space.

While the Goddard Center came into being with the establishment of the National Aeronautics and Space Administration, its antecedents extend much further. Indeed, the Center inherited much scientific and operational competence from groups and individuals who had already achieved professional distinction. Under the guidance of Dr. Harry J. Goett, the Center's first director, 1959–1965, a most competent team came into being. This team successfully developed and launched a wide variety of scientific spacecraft, sent into orbit this Nation's first weather and synchronous communications satellites, and provided the tracking links for America's first man-in-space missions.

The purpose of this preliminary historical report is to describe the Center's historical origins and traditions, as well as the projects and activities which the men and women of Goddard were privileged to make their contribution to the U.S. space program. In doing so, they not only opened a new path of exploration but were carrying on a tradition of scientific and technical curiosity envisioned two generations earlier by a then unknown New England professor—Dr. Robert H. Goddard.

JOHN F. CLARK
Director, Goddard Space Flight Center

Contents

LIST OF ILLUSTRATIONS

LIST OF ILLUSTRATIONS (Cont'd)

LIST OF ILLUSTRATIONS *(Cont'd)*

PAGE

LIST OF ILLUSTRATIONS (Cont'd)

Introduction

THIS HISTORICAL REPORT represents a preliminary record of the efforts of this NASA Center, from its antecedents through 1963. Any cutoff date for such a report must be necessarily arbitrary; 1963 has been selected as terminal date because that year saw the culmination of many of the early efforts: the organization achieved the form its planners had envisioned; many of the physical facilities were completed; and, perhaps most important, scientific findings produced by "first generation" satellites began to be returned to curious scientists. As a consequence of the new scientific knowledge and technological advances, the years beyond 1963 would feature more advanced missions, utilizing "second generation" spacecraft with more sophisticated instrumentation. Weather and communications satellites developed during the early years had by 1963 demonstrated such utility as to make operational systems a reality. The Goddard-operated manned space flight tracking network contributed to the successful completion of Project Mercury, the United States' first man-in-space program. In brief, for Goddard Space Flight Center the year 1963 could be considered the end of Act One of the Space Age, and the curtain raiser of Act Two.

This volume is a mosaic of what was considered to be reliable information, gleaned from many sources. Historical documents, a GSFC chronology, and a bibliography are included as appendixes. In its preparation, valuable assistance and advice was received from numerous officials at the National Aeronautics and Space Administration Headquarters—particularly Dr. Eugene M. Emme, NASA Historian; his deputy, Dr. Frank W. Anderson, Jr.; and Mr. Thomas E. Jenkins, NASA Management Reports Director, formerly of the Goddard Space Flight Center—and from the entire Center staff. Without the considerate support from virtually every element of the agency, the preparation of this document would have been an almost impossible task. Comments, suggestions, or corrections of fact are sincerely invited so as to assist our historical efforts.

ALFRED ROSENTHAL
Historian, Goddard Space Flight Center

PART ONE

ORIGINS OF THE GODDARD SPACE FLIGHT CENTER

No single thing abides;
*   but all things flow.*
Fragment to fragment clings
*   —the things thus grow*
Until we know them
*   and name them.*
                    —HALLOCK

From Robert H. Goddard to the International Geophysical Year

1

THE HISTORICAL TRADITIONS of the Goddard Space Flight Center have antecedents in a period long before America's awakening to the Space Age. Named in honor of Dr. Robert H. Goddard, the Center continues in the scientific tradition of this New England scientist, who has been recognized not only as the "Father of American Rocketry" but also as one of the pioneers in the theory of space exploration.[1]

Dr. Goddard was one of those rare combinations occasionally appearing in the history of science and technology; he was a theoretical scientist and a practical and exacting engineer, but he was also a dreamer who was considerably ahead of his own time. His particular dream was the scientific conquest of the upper atmosphere and ultimately of the void of space through the use of rocket propulsion. To the fulfillment of this dream Dr. Goddard devoted his talents, his energies, and his life. He had the drive and single-mindedness found among those who today are probing the innermost secrets of the space environment.

The Life of Dr. Goddard

Robert Hutchings Goddard was born in Worcester, Massachusetts, on October 5, 1882. Childhood illnesses prevented the young boy from expressing his energy in the usual boyish activities. As a consequence, he developed his imagination and read voraciously. He was greatly influenced by H. G. Wells' *War of the Worlds*.[2] Jules Verne also stimulated his imagination. Dr. Goddard is known to have read Verne's *From the Earth to the Moon* annually and ultimately to have rewritten it to include a rocket launch instead of a cannon-powered flight.[3]

A germ of his later work might be seen in his effort in the spring of 1898 to construct a hydrogen-filled balloon made of thin aluminum. Although

5

it was too heavy to fly, Goddard was not discouraged; he turned his attention to such other things as "how birds fly" (which also interested two brothers named Wright, in Ohio) and the marvels of electricity. This was the situation when, on the afternoon of October 19, 1899, he found himself high in a cherry tree, assigned the duty of clipping its dead limbs. It was, he said, "one of those quiet, colorful afternoons of sheer beauty which we have in October in New England . . . as I looked toward the fields to the east, I imagined how wonderful it would be to make some device which had even the *possibility* of ascending to Mars, and how it would look on a small scale if sent up from the meadow at my feet . . . I was a different boy when I descended the ladder. Life now had a purpose for me." [4]

The young Robert Goddard began to construct models of his own design and devoted himself, in high school, to the study of physics and mathematics. By the time he graduated, he had, he said, "a set of models which would not work and a number of suggestions which, from the physics I had learned, I knew were erroneous." He gathered up all his models and his carefully catalogued notes and burned them.

"But the dream would not go down," wrote Dr. Goddard in later years, "and inside of two months I once again caught myself making notes of further suggestions, for even though I reasoned with myself that the thing was impossible, there was something inside me which simply would not stop working." As early as 1909, Goddard conceived the multiple-stage rocket, the general theory of hydrogen-and-oxygen rocket propulsion, and the use of a plane-like structure for rocket guidance. [5]

By this time, Goddard had graduated from Worcester Polytechnic Institute with a B.S., holding high honors in physics and mathematics. All through college the young scientist had been absorbed by his obsession with propulsion. Near the end of his senior year, he filled the basement of the Worcester Polytechnic Institute physics building with smoke, the result of a static test of a small rocket. [6]

The years between graduation from Worcester Polytechnic Institute and 1919 were full and arduous ones for Goddard. He stayed on at Worcester as an instructor in physics while doing graduate work at Clark University, where he received his A.M. in 1910 and his Ph.D. in physics in 1911. He then spent a year at Clark as an honorary fellow in physics, where he worked on various rocket methods. In 1912 he went to Princeton as a research fellow and worked on electrical theory (the subject of his Ph.D. dissertation) during the day and on rocket propulsion theory during the evenings. Through 1913–1914 illness prevented him from teaching but did not hinder his speculations on rocketry. In fact, during his convalescence Dr. Goddard laid the foundations for two patents, received in July 1914, which developed his idea of a multistage rocket and liquid propellants. [7]

In the autumn of 1914, Dr. Goddard returned to Clark University as an instructor and began his basic work on rocketry, which led to the now-famous 1919 Smithsonian publication. It was during this period that he proved his theory, by static laboratory test, that a rocket would perform in a vacuum and was therefore capable of operating in space. By the middle of 1916, he had reached the limit of what he could accomplish on his own funds. He wrote up his experiments, entitled the manuscript "A Method of Reaching Extreme Altitudes," and sent it to three organizations that he thought might be interested enough to aid him financially. The only encouraging reply he received was from the Smithsonian Institution, which was looking for a very-high-altitude device to extend meteorological research and asked for further details. This was in December 1916. After receiving the Smithsonian's commendation for his work, Dr. Goddard requested $5,000 to continue his experiments. The next letter from Washington granted the $5,000 and enclosed an advance of $1,000.[8]

Thus began, in January 1917, the years of experimentation which Dr. Goddard continued unceasingly for the remainder of his life. When the United States entered World War I in 1917, he volunteered to direct his rocket research toward ends which might prove useful to the military. This work led to the development of a solid-fuel prototype that became the World War II "bazooka"; however, the war ended five days after he demonstrated it. During World War II, Dr. Goddard's invention was to be "dusted off" by his colleague, Dr. Clarence N. Hickman, and was perfected to provide the American soldier with the first effective hand weapon against the tank.[9]

After returning to Clark in 1919, Dr. Goddard persuaded the Smithsonian to publish his revised "Method of Reaching Extreme Altitudes"—a rather dry and factual report on his experiments during the preceding several years which had been designed to show the Smithsonian where its money was going. The Smithsonian agreed, provided the cost of publication came from the $5,000 grant to Goddard. The study was released on January 11, 1920, as Smithsonian Miscellaneous Publication Number 2540. In this publication, Dr. Goddard mildly referred to the space potential of rocket thrust and suggested the possibility that someday a rocket such as the one he was designing might be used to hit the moon. The newspapers picked up the story, some portrayed him as a crackpot, others as an amateur who did not know that reactive thrust would not work in a vacuum. This adverse publicity had a deep and lasting effect on Dr. Goddard. From that day forward, he rarely spoke of anything which might pertain to space flight, and he avoided publicity for himself and his work. In private, however, he continued to speculate on the possibilities of the rocket in space, on possible manned and unmanned missions, on methods of navigating in space, and on the potentialities of a solar-powered engine. All this he kept locked away in a cabinet in a folder marked "Formulae for Silvering Mirrors."[10]

In the early 1920s Dr. Goddard began his pioneering experiments with liquid-fuel propulsion. He had considered the idea of a hydrogen and oxygen fuel supply as early as 1909. After several experiments he discovered that liquid oxygen and gasoline made the most practical fuel, and the first static test of liquid-fuel propulsion was made on November 1, 1923. After overcoming numerous problems with the apparatus, the fuel pumps in particular, he was ready to try again. On March 16, 1926, Professor Goddard, his wife Esther, and two assistants drove to "Aunt Effie" Ward's farm near Auburn, Massachusetts, and prepared his rocket for launch. Ignition was accomplished by a blowtorch attached to a pole. The rocket rose from the ground, traveled a distance of 184 feet, reached an average speed of 60 miles per hour, and stayed in the air for 2½ seconds. It was the first liquid-fuel rocket flight in the world, an event comparable to Kitty Hawk in its significance. Not a word reached a newspaper.[11]

Dr. Goddard continued his experiments at Auburn. In 1928, after another test, he reported to the Smithsonian that he had demonstrated the rocket's potential for study of the ultraviolet; upper air composition, electrical conditions, and movement; and mapmaking by several simultaneous ground observations of high-altitude light flashes. Then on July 17, 1929, he launched a scientific payload of a barometer, a thermometer, and a camera. On that date his rocket was mistaken for an airplane crashing in flames, which caused the State fire marshal to forbid Goddard to conduct any more launches in Massachusetts. The Smithsonian succeeded in persuading the Army to allow him to launch his rockets on Federal property at Camp Devens, Massachusetts; but as a precaution against fires he could experiment only after a rain or a snowfall. The "moon-rocket man" publicity from this affair brought Goddard an unexpected windfall. Up to this time he had been relying on the steady but relatively small grants from the Smithsonian for the necessary financial assistance. Charles A. Lindbergh, who was at the height of his popularity, read the unfavorable press accounts of Goddard's work. Lindbergh was interested in the use of rockets to provide emergency thrust for airplanes. He visited Dr. Goddard and was impressed with his work. Lindbergh took Goddard's cause to Daniel and Harry Guggenheim. Subsequently the Daniel and Florence Guggenheim Foundation began to supply him with money for his experiments. Between 1929 and 1941, Dr. Goddard received over $150,000 from this source.[12]

The first Guggenheim grant enabled Dr. Goddard to leave Massachusetts for a more suitable testing ground. He moved his work to Roswell, New Mexico, which was to be his headquarters for the remaining fifteen years of his life. All through the 1930s Dr. Goddard and his small staff worked at improving his rockets and their components. While at Roswell, he devised and patented a gyroscopic control for rockets and an ingenious system for cooling the combustion chamber, called "curtain cooling," in which the fuel of the rocket acted as the cooling agent. "There was never so much invention with so little manpower," remarked one of Dr. Goddard's mechanics.[13]

When war broke out in Europe in 1939, Dr. Goddard visited the U.S. War Department and tried to interest the military in his work, but nothing tangible came of it. After the United States became involved in 1941, the Navy and the Army Air Corps asked him to work for them, not to develop his rocket as an offensive or defensive missile but merely to develop a jet-assisted takeoff (JATO) device for helping aircraft take off from short runways or aircraft carriers. Dr. Goddard's repeated efforts to convince the American military of the potential of the rocket were to no avail. So it happened that JATO and the revived 1918 "bazooka" were the major contributions which this genius was allowed to make to the American war effort.[14]

The Germans, however, had not neglected their rocket technicians as had the Americans. By September 1944, German V–2 ballistic rockets began to fall on Britain. The Allies were startled at the great lead of German rocket technology. When details of the V–2 reached Annapolis, where Dr. Goddard was working in the Navy's research laboratories, he noted the similarity between the German missile and his own liquid-fuel rocket. Although the $5\frac{1}{2}$-ton V–2 was much larger than anything that Dr. Goddard (or anyone in the U.S.) had ever constructed, the two rockets were almost identical in basic design. Out of this similarity arose a controversy over the extent to which the Germans may have worked from Goddard's patent designs.[15]

Finally illness took its toll. In Baltimore, in 1945, Dr. Goddard was operated on for throat cancer. His lungs, already weakened from an earlier attack of tuberculosis, gave out and the American rocket pioneer died on August 10, 1945. His passing went practically unnoticed except among his faithful small group of family and friends.[16]

The Goddard Legacy

Robert Hutchings Goddard's rocket research was perhaps as fundamental to the opening of the Space Age as was the Wright Brothers' research to the Air Age. Yet his work attracted little serious attention during his lifetime and he did not encourage it. When the United States began to prepare for the conquest of space in the 1950s, American rocket scientists began to recognize the enormity of the early debt which their science owed to the New England professor. They discovered that it was virtually impossible to construct a rocket or launch a satellite without acknowledging the work of Dr. Goddard. This great legacy was covered by more than 200 patents, many of which were issued after his death.

Belated honors have begun to pour upon the name of Robert Goddard in recent years. On September 16, 1959, the Congress of the United States authorized the issuance of a gold medal in his honor. The Smithsonian

Dr. Goddard and colleagues holding the rocket used in the successful experimental flight of April 19, 1932. They are, from left to right, L. Mansur, A. Kisk, C. Mansur, Dr. R. H. Goddard, and N. L. Jungquist.

Dr. Robert H. Goddard and colleagues at Roswell, New Mexico, after the successful test of May 19, 1937. Dr. Goddard is holding the cap and the pilot parachute.

Dr. Goddard at work on his rocket in his shop at Roswell, New Mexico, October 1935.

Institution, long familiar with his work, awarded him its coveted Langley Medal, in honor of his discoveries in rocketry, on June 28, 1960. Subsequently Clark University, Worcester, Massachusetts, which was made the depository of his papers, established the Robert H. Goddard Memorial Library. In 1964 a commemorative airmail postage stamp was issued in his honor.

On May 1, 1959, the National Aeronautics and Space Administration named its new Space Flight Center at Greenbelt, Maryland, the Goddard Space Flight Center.[17] It is hardly a coincidence or accident that his name was chosen to inspire the work being done by this team of scientists and engineers engaged in the scientific exploration of space. It is perhaps one of the most fitting of the many belated honors which have come to the name of Goddard, because it established a Center which is realizing the dream of space exploration the young Goddard had conceived at the turn of the century.

The essence of his philosophy, as he expressed it in his high school oration in 1904, serves well as the motto of the Goddard Space Flight Center:

It is difficult to say what is impossible, for the dream of yesterday is the hope of today and the reality of tomorrow.

From Project Vanguard to the Goddard Space Flight Center

2

A FTER WORLD WAR II, interest in rocket technology gradually developed in the United States.[18] This was generated mainly by the impact of the German V–2 rocket upon American military and scientific circles during and after the war. At the end of the war, a number of the German rocket experts and almost 100 V–2 rockets were brought to the United States. Few realized their full potential. Scientists saw the rocket as a new tool of high-altitude research, while military considerations aroused the interest of the Army, the Air Force, and the Navy.

Early Rocket Development

In January 1946, the U.S. Army announced that a firing program for the V–2 rockets would begin later that year at White Sands, New Mexico. Government agencies and several universities were invited to consider using the V–2s for high-altitude (sounding rocket) research and experimentation.[19] The first V–2 to be used in the sounding rocket research program was launched in June 1946, and in the next 6 years over 60 were launched. As the result of the V–2 program in the United States, valuable knowledge was gained in two areas. First, the rockets enabled soundings to be made to an altitude of about 100 miles, and measurements of high-energy particle radiation, found at high altitudes but absorbed at lower levels, were made. Second, a great deal was learned about rocket technology and men were trained so that similar-size American rockets could be built as the supply of V–2s became depleted.[20]

Several organizations, partially staffed with personnel who had engaged in United States V–2 research, began to develop rockets. The first of these rockets was the Aerobee, designed by the Applied Physics Laboratory (APL) of The Johns Hopkins University. It was capable of carrying a small payload to an altitude of about 80 miles.[21]   In 1947 the Naval Research Laboratory (NRL), in Washington, D.C., proposed the construction of a rocket which would replace the V–2 in the American sounding rocket program.   This rocket, at first called Neptune but later identified as Viking, was smaller than the V–2, but more powerful.[22]   It could lift a larger payload to a height of about 150 miles with a high order of stability.   In the 6 years between 1949 and 1955, 12 of these rockets were launched, carrying payloads as high as 158 miles.   None attained the hoped-for altitude, but new altitude records were established and valuable scientific information was gained.[23]   Other groups benefiting from the experience of the American V–2 program were the Army, which began work on its Redstone missile after 1950, and the U.S. Air Force, which began work on the Atlas ICBM in 1954.[24]   In addition, the Jet Propulsion Laboratory (JPL) of the California Institute of Technology developed the WAC Corporal research rocket.[25]

Early U.S. Satellite Proposals

Although the main emphasis in these years was on the development of an improved rocket-powered vehicle, a germinal program was initiated in earth satellites.   The U.S. Navy's Bureau of Aeronautics was one of the first Government organizations to initiate a satellite study program.   In October 1945, a committee of the Bureau of Aeronautics recommended that an earth satellite development program be undertaken for scientific purposes.   The Aerojet Corporation and the California Institute of Technology were given the task of determining whether such a project was technically feasible using the single-stage rocket vehicle which the Navy had proposed.[26]

In March 1946, the Navy took its proposal to the Army Air Force, suggesting a joint satellite program to aid funding.   Although the first effort at such a program appeared promising, the Air Force informed the Navy that it could not cooperate.   In the meantime, the Air Force had established Project RAND (later to become the RAND Corporation) to begin a satellite feasibility study.   RAND drew up a proposal for the Air Force entitled "Preliminary Design of an Experimental World-Circling Spaceship."   The RAND proposal ruled out the satellite as a military weapon because no rocket could be constructed which could lift the heavy A-bomb into orbit and no explosive force short of an atomic one would inflict enough damage to warrant the expense of putting it into orbit.   The problem was not one of capability (it was assumed that the U.S. could launch a 500-pound satellite by 1951) but rather one of devising a useful function for the satellite to perform once it was in orbit.   Because a satellite was not a potential weapon, there were no funds available for its development.[27]

The RAND-Air Force proposal, like its Navy counterpart, urged the early adoption of a satellite program for scientific purposes.   They argued for its capabilities in the fields of meteorology, communications, and astronomy. In October 1946, RAND issued an additional study entitled "The Time Factor in The Satellite Program," in which they emphasized the psychological and political factors which could result from the first satellite launch. Even this dramatic prognosis was insufficient to overcome the factor that the satellite was not a potential weapon.

When the Department of Defense (DOD) was created in 1947, none of the three military services was authorized to continue development of a rocket with satellite capability. The Air Force discontinued its satellite studies in mid-1947, but did resume them in 1949. By that time, the Navy had discontinued its studies because of lack of funds. Early in 1948, DOD reviewed the existing satellite proposals but again concluded that "neither the Navy nor the USAF has as yet established either a military or a scientific utility commensurate with the presently expected cost of a satellite vehicle." The work was so neglected at DOD that, in November 1954, the Secretary of Defense remarked publicly that he knew of no American satellite program.[28]

The RAND Corporation proved to be prophetic in its prediction of the great psychological-propaganda impact of the first satellite launching. They had emphasized, as early as 1946, that a satellite would be an "instrument of political strategy." When the Soviet Union launched *Sputnik I* in October 1957, it had exactly the impact that RAND had said it would have —only in reverse. It was the United States which did the soul searching and suffered a drop in world opinion. It was only after this 1957 propaganda defeat that the U.S. Government fully understood the wider significance of these early satellite studies.[29] Yet, at the time of the first Sputniks, there actually was a satellite program in the United States.

The International Geophysical Year

While missile development and satellite proposals were progressing within the military services, an important boost was given to the scientific use of rocket technology. By 1951, the American Rocket Society (ARS) had grown to a point where its voice could be heard. In the winter of that year, Commander Robert Truax, who had been championing rocket propulsion in the Navy, strongly and bluntly told the members at their annual meeting that they were too complacent in their attitude toward space flight, that time was catching up with them, and that definite action was called for. As a consequence of this meeting, the American Rocket Society formed an Ad Hoc Committee on Space Flight.[30]

In 1954, this ARS committee proposed that the Government sponsor the development of a small scientific satellite and use available military hardware to launch it. This proposal was informally submitted to Dr. Alan T. Waterman of the National Science Foundation. The satellite idea was alive in many forms in many scientific circles. The International Scientific Committee of the National Academy of Sciences, in making plans for the International Geophysical Year (IGY),[31] recommended that the launch of small scientific satellites be considered by individual groups preparing their own programs for the IGY. The United States National Committee for the IGY, formed by the National Academy of Sciences, also studied the possibility of having an earth satellite launched as part of the U.S. contribution to IGY. Interest in satellite projects had also been revived among the military; the Army and the Navy had proposed in early 1955 a joint program (Project Orbiter) to launch an elementary, uninstrumented satellite in 2 or 3 years.[32]

It was in 1954 that the International Geophysical Year (1957–1958) was proposed. Its American spokesmen were among those scientists who had participated in the V–2 sounding rocket program. That summer, the International Scientific Radio Union and the International Union of Geodesy and Geophysics adopted resolutions calling for the launch of an artificial earth satellite during the forthcoming IGY. Both the United States and the Soviet Union picked up this proposal. On July 29, 1955, the White House announced that the United States would launch "small, unmanned, earth-circling satellites as a part of the U.S. participation in IGY." The next day the Soviet Union made a similar announcement.[33]

The Vanguard Project

The White House announcement of the proposed satellite launchings was the product of coordinated efforts within the National Academy of Sciences (NAS), the National Science Foundation (NSF), and the Department of Defense. The announcement stated that NAS would determine the experiments to be orbited, NSF would supply the necessary funds, and DOD would launch the satellite. A Committee on Special Capabilities was established in DOD to determine the means for launching the U.S. satellite. This Committee, chaired by Dr. Homer J. Stewart, had three proposals from which to select.[34] One proposal was based on the as yet incomplete Atlas missile, one on the Army's Redstone (Project Orbiter), and one on the Naval Research Laboratory's Viking. The Navy proposal was based on sounding rocket research experience of the Naval Research Laboratory (NRL) and the Martin Company, builders of the Viking. In essence it would use the Viking as a first stage, the Aerobee as a second stage, and an as yet undetermined rocket as a third stage.[35] After lengthy deliberation, a majority of the Stewart Committee recommended the NRL satellite proposal in August 1955. The recommendation was accepted and endorsed by the Policy Committee of DOD. The U.S. IGY satellite program under Navy management and DOD monitoring was established and designated "Project Vanguard."

PROJECT VANGUARD

Objectives:

- To develop and procure a satellite-launching vehicle.

- To place at least one satellite in orbit during IGY.

- To accomplish one scientific experiment with the satellite.

- To track the satellite's flight to demonstrate that it had actually attained orbit.

Criteria:

- The first stage was to be based on the Viking rocket, which had been developed by the Navy to replace the dwindling supply of captured V–2s.

- The second stage was to be an improved Aerobee rocket.

- The third stage was to be a solid-fuel rocket weighing about 500 pounds, necessitating a real advance in the existing solid-fuel rocket technology.

- On top of this vehicle would be placed a nose cone weighing 20 pounds, including the IGY scientific experiment to be orbited.

On September 9, 1955, Project Vanguard was officially authorized when the Department of Defense notified the Secretary of the Navy to proceed with the project. Project Vanguard was to be accomplished without a specific appropriation from Congress. All funds came from the emergency fund of the Secretary of Defense. Only after *Sputnik I* had been launched and the Vanguard project had reached its final stages of completion did Congress authorize the Secretary of Defense to make available additional funds for Vanguard by reprograming the Defense budget. Two years, 6 months, and 8 days after the Department of Defense authorized the project the first successful Vanguard satellite was launched (March 17, 1958).[36]

At NRL, a special task force, headed by Dr. John P. Hagen, was assembled to handle the Vanguard program.[37] In a letter to the Navy Department, this group clarified its definition of what Project Vanguard really would be: "a complete system for space exploration." They had a difficult task before them. In addition to the development of a new satellite launching rocket, they had to place a reliable scientific experiment into earth orbit

Project Vanguard staff members meet with Dr. John P. Hagen, Director of Project Vanguard, at the U.S. Naval Research Laboratory, Washington, D.C. Left to right: Dr. J. W. Siry, Head of the Theory and Analysis Staff; D. G. Mazur, Manager of the Vanguard Operations Group at Cape Canaveral, Fla.; J. M. Bridger, Head of the Vehicle Branch; Cdr. W. E. Berg, Navy Program Office; Dr. Hagen; Dr. J. P. Walsh, Deputy Project Director; M. W. Rosen, Technical Director; J. T. Mengel, Head of the Tracking and Guidance Branch; and Dr. H. E. Newell, Jr., Science Program Coordinator. L. Winkler, Engineering Consultant, was not present when this picture was taken.

and not only prove that it was in orbit but gather data from the satellite via telemetry. This had never been done before.

Dr. Hagen's small NRL team had mountains of problems to overcome. One difficulty might be used for illustration. At the Martin Company, which NRL had selected to build the Vanguard missile, the original NRL-Viking engineering team had been broken up. Unknown to the Navy, the Martin Company had received a prime contract from the Air Force to develop the second-generation ICBM, the Titan. Some of the leading Viking engineers already had been put on this project. This was, Dr. Hagen noted, "a shock, as we had cleared our intentions with the DOD before letting our letter of intent." The Navy stuck with the Martin Company, but "things could have been much easier for the Vanguard group if the original Viking team of Martin had remained intact." [38]

While the NRL was busy preparing the launch vehicle, the National Academy of Sciences established a technical panel, under its IGY committee, to select the experiments to be launched. The Vanguard group, through the liaison of Dr. Homer E. Newell, insisted on only one requirement for each experiment: that it must have a very high reliability of performance and must be tested thoroughly to prove this reliability.[39]

The National Academy of Sciences requested the Vanguard group to make the satellite spherical in shape; in fact, a 30-inch sphere was requested. This caused some concern, as it originally had been planned that Vanguard would orbit merely a simple nose cone. The Vanguard group agreed that they could change their design to launch a 20-inch sphere, but this would require a complete redesign of the second stage, which would have to have a large diameter. Therefore, in the fall of 1955, a redesign of the Vanguard vehicle was undertaken to fulfill the new requirements.[40] Since Vanguard was scientific in purpose, there was no alternative.

By March 1956, the redesign of the Vanguard rocket was completed and a full schedule of six test vehicles and seven satellite-launching vehicles was prepared. As prime contractor for the launch vehicle, the Martin Company was constructing the first stage; Aerojet Corporation had received a subcontract for the second stage; and the Grand Central Rocket Company and the Allegany Ballistics Laboratory were each building separate third stages based on different designs. Two major problems remained to be solved: choosing a launch site, and constructing the necessary satellite tracking system.[41]

With the rocket thrust then attainable, it was virtually mandatory that the satellite be launched eastward in order to gain, rather than lose, the earth's rotational velocity of some 1,300 feet per second (about 1,000 mph). An eastward launching could be made only from the east coast, lest the spent rocket stages fall on inhabited areas. This ruled out the otherwise most natural launch site, White Sands, New Mexico, where the Viking launch facilities were available. The best available site was Cape Canaveral, Florida, which then was being expanded to accommodate the testing of large, liquid-fuel ballistic missiles. The only other serious "competitor" was Roosevelt Roads, in Puerto Rico. Cape Canaveral was selected for many reasons, the main one being financial. However, a number of problems arose from this selection. When the Navy requested that the Army Ballistic Missile Agency (ABMA) share its launch facilities at the Cape with the Vanguard operation, the Army refused on the grounds that it would interfere with the Redstone program and thus be detrimental to the Nation's ballistic missile program. It was then decided that Vanguard would construct its own checkout hangar, blockhouse, and launch pad at Cape Canaveral. This was an 18-month program but was still within the limited time remaining to complete a satellite launching during IGY. Additional down-range facilities also had to be constructed. Unlike the ballistic missile of that day, Vanguard was multistage, requiring command and control points as far away as a thousand miles from the launch site to inject a satellite into orbit. Even a gantry (service tower) was unavailable; the Vanguard group had to disassemble the Viking gantry at White Sands, transport it to the Cape, and reassemble it there. By the time of the first launch, the Vanguard group had constructed the Nation's first complete satellite launch facility, almost from the ground up.[42]

Tracking facilities proved to be a problem. Two types of tracking were necessary—electronic and optical. The electronic tracking system had to have a series of ground stations equipped with radio transmitting and receiving equipment, timing facilities, and data-acquisition (telemetry) equipment. These facilities had to be constructed before the launch could take place and had to be located in various parts of the world to provide the degree of orbital coverage considered necessary. A contract was awarded to the Bendix Corporation to construct this system, which later became known as Minitrack (for *Minimum weight tracking*, because it required only the simplest and lightest transmitter in the satellite). A system of optical tracking stations was established and managed by the Smithsonian Astrophysical Observatory. A communications network centered at the Naval Research Laboratory, Washington, D.C., tied the 13 Minitrack and 12 SAO stations together.[43]

Twelve Vikings had been built and fired in the normal course of NRL's upper atmosphere research. Viking 13 was at White Sands awaiting preparation for launch when the Navy was given the Vanguard mission. Viking 14 was modified by adding an ejectable sphere and a solid-fuel second stage to test its ignition and separation at altitude. This vehicle was designated as Test Vehicle 1 (TV–1). It was then decided to use Viking 13 to check out the new launch facilities at Cape Canaveral. To make this the first of the Vanguard series and to avoid having to renumber all the vehicle designations, Viking 13 was placed ahead of the rest of the planned series and designated Test Vehicle 0 (TV–0).[44]

On December 8, 1956, TV–0 was successfully launched at Cape Canaveral. It reached an altitude of 126 miles and dropped into the ocean 183 miles away.[45] TV–1 was launched on May 1, 1957; this was a redesigned rocket and the only one of its kind flown. The first stage was the Viking 14; the second stage (which was actually the Vanguard third stage) ignited, separated successfully, and flew 450 miles farther, carrying a heavy instrumented nose cone. A milestone had been reached; a solid-fuel upper stage had been ignited in flight, and the feasibility of the Vanguard rocket had been proven.[46]

In July 1957, an important change was made in the Vanguard program; NRL directed that the Vanguard team replace the instrument test packages previously flown on its test vehicles with small (6-inch) satellite spheres. The 6-inch spheres had orginally been developed to give an extra margin of reliability over the heavier 20-inch sphere when used on the launch vehicles. The decision to use the 6-inch sphere on the test vehicles was an indication that emphasis was being shifted from the testing of the vehicles to the earlier launching of satellites. This alteration was not made on TV–2, the first of the true Vanguard vehicles. This rocket was already on the launch stand going through prelaunch checkout when, on October 4, it was announced that the Soviet Union had launched an earth satellite at 7:30 in the evening from the Tyuratam Range in Kazakhstan, U.S.S.R.[47]

After Sputnik

The launch of *Sputnik I* caused a great deal of turmoil in the United States. Great pressure was exerted on the Vanguard team to get an American satellite into orbit.[48] The launch of TV–2 on October 23, 1957, seemed anticlimactic, since the launch was not designed to place a satellite in orbit but simply to test the vehicle. The vehicle consisted of the first of the new Viking first stages and dummy second and third stages, with some of the control system of the last two stages operational. *Sputnik II* was launched on November 3, 1957. On December 6, an attempt was made to launch TV–3; this was the first test of the complete live three-stage vehicle and control system and was the first Vanguard rocket with potential orbital capabilities. The first-stage engine lost thrust after two seconds, and the

Technicians mate the *Vanguard I* satellite to its slender booster rocket in preparation for its successful flight on March 17, 1958.

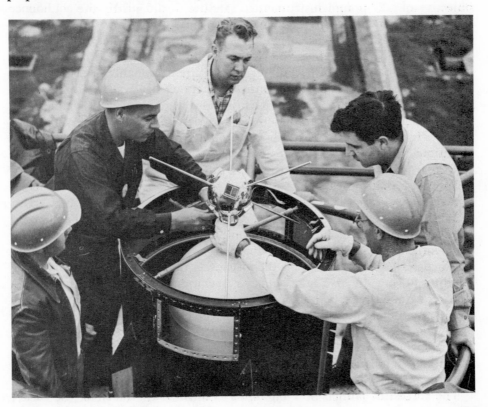

vehicle burned up on the launching pad. Because of the Russian first with *Sputniks I* and *II* and because a White House statement that the next Vanguard launch would place an American satellite in orbit was wrongly construed to apply to this test launch, news of the Vanguard failure reverberated around the world.[49]

The unfortunate turn of events in the early Vanguard test launches, which reflected the troubles inevitable in development of a new three-stage booster, plus the "space race" pressure generated by the Sputniks, led to a relaxation of the ban on use of military missiles for the IGY satellite project. The Army Ballistics Missile Agency was authorized in November to attempt a satellite launching with its proven Redstone missile. As a result, the Army and the Jet Propulsion Laboratory were able to launch the first U.S. satellite, *Explorer I,* on January 31, 1958. The *Explorer I* and its IGY experiment of James A. Van Allen boosted the prestige of the U.S. space program. But this event, as well as the breakup of the TV–3 backup Vanguard on February 5, brought more unkind comments in public about the Vanguard satellite program.[50]

On March 17, 1958, TV–4 successfully launched into orbit *Vanguard I,* a 6-inch sphere weighing 4 pounds. Although this was far from the final objective of a 20-pound instrumented satellite, it did justify the confidence which had been placed in the Vanguard project. Primary purpose of the launch was a test of the performance of the Vanguard rocket, but the small sphere it carried achieved such a remarkably stable orbit that it proved one of the Nation's most important early satellites. Probably the most noteworthy of its many major contributions to knowledge was the discovery of the "pear shape" of the Earth. Scientists also were able to study and measure the density of the atmosphere in a region some 465 miles above the Earth. It provided extensive observation and measurements of air density variations associated with solar activity and the first quantitative data on how solar radiation pressure affects a satellite's orbit.

For more than 6 years it transmitted radio signals from space on its assigned 108-megacycle frequency, powered only by six quartz-covered arrays of solar cells. Officially known internationally as 1958 Beta 2, *Vanguard I* is still circling the globe every 134 minutes and has an apogee of about 2,400 miles and a perigee of about 400 miles.

When NASA phased out the 108-megacycle radio band used for scientific satellites during the IGY, the agency's tracking and data acquisition facilities were gradually converted to the internationally allocated 136-megacycle band. At the close of 1964, the station near Quito, Ecuador, was the only NASA station still monitoring on the 108-megacycle frequency, and the signals from *Vanguard I* had degraded to the extent that Quito was unable to detect any signals, even at optimum conditions (when the satellite was in sunlight at the time of its perigee).

The successful launch of *Vanguard I* confirmed the merit of the rocket

The liftoff of *Vanguard I* on March 17, 1958.

design; it also demonstrated that the Vanguard group had become a well-integrated professional and technical team. Three other Vanguard rockets were launched before the Vanguard team was transferred from NRL to the newly created civilian space agency, NASA. The first satellite launch vehicle (SLV–1), launched May 27, 1958, was successful except for a premature second-stage burnout; in the second (SLV–2), launched June 26, 1958, the second stage cut off prematurely; the third (SLV–3), launched September 26, 1958, reached an altitude of 265 miles.[51]

Vanguard and NASA

The launch of *Sputnik I* in the fall of 1957 was a real jolt to the complacency of the American people. In true American tradition, a great clamor went up as to why the Soviet Union was ahead of the United States, who was to blame for the situation, and what was to be done about it. The people engaged in existing satellite programs had a difficult time explaining that their best efforts had been slowed by limitations over which they had no control.   The end results of the new "space consciousness" were beneficial, since there developed a general realization that the American effort had to be greatly expanded and financially supported.

About 6 months after the launch of *Sputnik I*, the President's Science Advisory Committee and the President's Advisory Committee on Governmental Organization recommended the establishment of a civilian agency to direct nonmilitary space activity.   President Eisenhower delivered a message to Congress on April 2, 1958, which stated that "aeronautical and space science activities sponsored by the United States should be conducted under the direction of a civilian agency except for those projects primarily associated with military requirements."   As a result of this message and with a clear public demand for such action, Public Law 85–568, the National Aeronautics and Space Act, was enacted and signed by the President on July 29, 1958.   This law established the National Aeronautics and Space Administration and gave the new agency the responsibility for conducting the scientific exploration of space for peaceful purposes.   The law also gave the

Vanguard III, launched September 18, 1959.

President the authority to transfer to NASA "any function of any other department or agency of the United States, or of any officer or organizational entity thereof, which relate primarily to the functions, powers, and duties of . . . NASA." NASA opened its doors on October 1, 1958. Project Vanguard was transferred to NASA, with other DOD space projects.[52]

The Vanguard project was continued under the direction of NASA. *Vanguard II* (SLV–4), launched on February 17, 1959, was the first full-scale (21-pound) Vanguard payload to achieve orbit. It was also the first satellite designed to observe and record the cloud cover of the earth and was a forerunner of the Television Infrared Observation Weather Satellites (Tiros). *Vanguard III* (SLV–7), launched on September 18, 1959, was a 20-inch sphere weighing about 50 pounds.[53]

Vanguard Helped Shape the Future

As it happened, Vanguard did not put the first U.S. satellite into orbit. Nonetheless its contributions to the U.S. space effort were great indeed. Vanguard research became the basis for later launch vehicles, particularly the remarkably reliable Delta. Vanguard pioneered the use of advanced state-of-the-art techniques, including the first utilization of solar cells, which have since become commonplace components of American satellites. The scientific experiments which were flown on the Vanguard satellites increased the amount of scientific knowledge of space and opened the way for more sophisticated experiments.[54]

Perhaps the most significant achievement of Project Vanguard was to bring together a group of dedicated and talented scientists and engineers who came to understand the complexities and challenges of the space sciences program. This team was assimilated into the National Aeronautics and Space Administration, where it became the human core of the Goddard Space Flight Center and served as the foundation for the distinguished space sciences programs which were to emerge.[55]

Establishment of the
Goddard Space Flight Center
3

O**N SEPTEMBER** 25, 1958, Administrator T. Keith Glennan announced the activation of the National Aeronautics and Space Administration (NASA), effective October 1, 1958.[56] Approximately 8,000 people and five laboratories of the 43-year-old National Advisory Committee for Aeronautics (NACA) were to be assimilated into the new agency. NACA's facilities would then become NASA's facilities, including Wallops Station (Wallops Island, Va.), and four research centers: Langley Research Center (Hampton, Va.), Lewis Research Center (Cleveland, Ohio), Ames Research Center (Moffett Field, Calif.), and the Flight Research Center (Edwards, Calif.).

On October 1, 1958, an executive order of the President effected the transfer to the National Aeronautics and Space Administration of the responsibilities involving several space research projects, including the Navy's Vanguard project.[57]

By this executive order, about 150 Project Vanguard personnel were transferred from the U.S. Naval Research Laboratory to the National Aeronautics and Space Administration.[58] The transfer became effective on November 30, 1958, and this group became known as the NASA-Vanguard Division. In December 1958, this group was transferred from the Naval Research Laboratory to the Space Science Division of NASA. During December 1958 and January 1959, 15 people from the Naval Research Laboratory were transferred to the Theoretical Division of NASA. Early in 1959, these elements, with others, were designated by NASA Headquarters to serve as the nucleus of a new Space Projects Center. Its staff was temporarily housed at the Naval Research Laboratory, Washington, D.C., and at the Colemont Building, Silver Spring, Maryland.

This assemblage was composed of some of the most experienced men engaged in space research. It included upper atmosphere scientific research teams and scientists and engineers from all three military services, the Project Mercury (manned satellite) team culled from the experienced staff of the former NACA laboratories, and the Navy's Project Vanguard staff. These groups gave immediate, mature capabilities in many vital areas of space flight research and development, since each was a "going concern" when transferred. From these and other groups, the initial team of senior personnel, around which was built the organization of the new Space Center, was assembled.

NASA Deputy Administrator Dr. Hugh L. Dryden appears to have been a key figure in selection of the Beltsville site. When the need for the new Space Center became apparent, he remembered the availability of surplus Government land near the Beltsville Agricultural Research Center. Believing that most of the Project Vanguard staff lived in Maryland, he had encouraged consideration of the Beltsville site. "Later, I learned that I may have been mistaken, since many of the Vanguard people actually lived in Virginia," Dr. Dryden recalled.

The New Beltsville Space Center

On August 1, 1958, Senator J. Glenn Beall of Maryland announced in a press release that the new "outer space agency" (NASA) would establish a laboratory and plant at Greenbelt, Maryland. This was the first time public notice was drawn to what was to become Goddard Space Flight Center.[59]

Planning of the new Center continued through the rest of 1958 and by the end of the year events were ripening. On January 15, 1959, by action of the NASA Administrator, four divisions (Construction Division, Space Sciences Division, Theoretical Division, and the Vanguard Division) of NASA were designated as the new Beltsville Space Center.[60]

On January 22, 1959, a NASA General Notice announced the establishment of the Beltsville Space Center to be operated under the direction of the Director of Space Flight Development in NASA Headquarters, Dr. Abe Silverstein.[61]

In a meeting held on February 12, 1959, for the purpose of surveying the organization and functions of the Beltsville Space Center, it was generally agreed that the Center probably would perform five major interrelated space science functions on behalf of NASA:[62]

- Project management
- Research
- Development and fabrication
- Advanced planning
- Operations

At the meeting it was agreed that the Beltsville Space Center should conduct an active space science program, launch six or seven vehicles for communications and meteorological satellites, and carry out research with geodetic satellites as well as fulfill other Vanguard Division follow-on

28

programs. In addition to the scientific satellites and the meteorological and communications programs, the Beltsville center was to assume administrative responsibility for the early phases of the Mercury project—the first U.S. man-in-space program. Vehicles under consideration in these activities, in addition to the Center-managed Delta vehicle, were the Vega, Centaur, Thor-Vanguard (which became Thor-Delta), Juno V, and the Nova. Another extremely important function of the Beltsville center would be the global tracking operation which included tracking, data acquisition, and data reduction for both NASA's manned and scientific space missions.

Beltsville Becomes Goddard

On May 1, 1959, Dr. T. Keith Glennan, NASA Administrator, in a public release, formally announced that the Beltsville Space Center would be redesignated the Goddard Space Flight Center "in commemoration of Dr. Robert H. Goddard, American pioneer in rocket research." The Center would be under the overall guidance of Dr. Abe Silverstein, then Director of Space Flight Development at NASA Headquarters.

The organization of Goddard Space Flight Center (GSFC) was to include a director, not yet appointed; three major research and development groups, each headed by an assistant director; and business administration and technical services departments.

In the announcement, Dr. John W. Townsend, Jr., Chief of NASA's Space Sciences Division and previously Chief of the Rocket Sonde Branch of the Naval Research Laboratory, was named Assistant Director for Space Science and Satellite Applications. John T. Mengel, who was responsible for the development of the Project Vanguard Minitrack satellite tracking system, was named Assistant Director for Tracking and Data Systems. Dr. Robert R. Gilruth, who would become Director of Project Mercury and who had been Chief of the Pilotless Aircraft Research Division, Langley Research Center, was named Assistant Director for Manned Satellites. The three Assistant Directors temporarily reported to Dr. Silverstein. The announcement also stated that the Office of Business Administration would be headed by Dr. Michael J. Vaccaro, transferring from the NASA Lewis Research Center, Cleveland, Ohio, where he had served as Director of Organization and Personnel. This was the first formal announcement of the Goddard organization, mission, and appointment of key personnel.[63]

Two other key appointments followed a few months later. In May 1959 Leopold Winkler, who had transferred to NASA with the Vanguard program, was appointed Chief, Technical Services. And in September 1959, Dr. Harry J. Goett was named Director of Goddard Space Flight Center. Goett came from Ames Research Center, where he had been Chief of the Full Scale and Flight Research Division.

GODDARD SPACE FLIGHT CENTER RESPONSIBILITIES, 1959

- Conducting advanced planning and theoretical studies
- Conducting necessary supporting research
- Developing payloads for approved programs
- Supervising GSFC flight operations
- Supervising tracking, data acquisition, communications, and computing operations
- Interpreting results of flight programs
- Furnishing technical management of projects
- Exercising procurement and contract administration authority
- Providing support of space program activities of other organizations
- Reporting status of approved programs
- Providing administrative and management support

With the new space agency, NASA, specifically responsible for activities in space devoted to peaceful purposes, the question arose as to which space programs initiated by the Department of Defense under its Advanced Research Projects Agency should be continued by NASA.[64] Spacecraft and meteorological satellites had been developed by the Army Signal Corps' Research and Development Laboratory, Fort Monmouth, New Jersey; vehicle development had progressed under the Army's Ballistic Missile Agency. Upon transfer of the meteorological program to NASA (April 1959), the mission was assigned to the Goddard Space Flight Center. The space communications program also had been a military project. One phase of it—indeed, the earliest phase—had been the passive balloon technique, with experiments conducted by the Army Signal Corps at Fort Monmouth and at NACA's Langley Laboratory. The other phase was the experimental hardware for active repeater communications satellites. With creation of NASA and the establishment of Goddard, both projects were assigned to the new Center.

Having acquired programs and people from other agencies, Goddard immediately needed money to operate. Some money had been inherited along with the programs and people. The executive order transferring Project Vanguard to NASA also transferred remaining project funds totaling approximately $6 million, plus about $300,000 earmarked for special equipment ordered earlier by the Navy's Vanguard staff. Also available to the newly established Center were certain funds which had been appropriated to NACA. These resources were not enough to meet the new Center's needs. Since the Fiscal Year 1959 Independent Offices Appropriations Bill already had cleared the House of Representatives, the Bureau of the Budget authorized the budget request to be included in the 1959 Independent Offices Appropriations Bill as a supplemental item while the bill was being considered by the Senate. The item was subsequently considered by the House-Senate Conference Committee without further referral to the House.

The Fiscal Year 1960 budget without the manned space flight program totaled somewhat less than $100 million (the manned flight program was about $140 million, giving the Center a total budget of about $240 million). The program mushroomed in Fiscal Year 1961 to about $160 million, plus an additional $140 million designated for the manned space missions. The Center's scientific and technical programs for Fiscal Year 1962 came to about $250 million; for Fiscal Year 1963 it was about $354 million.

During the early period of its development, contractual operations, which became a vital and integral part of Goddard's business operations, were handled for the Center by NASA Headquarters.

Meanwhile on April 24, 1959, construction of the new space laboratory began on a site located on a 550-acre tract formerly part of the U.S. Department of Agriculture's Agricultural Research Center at Beltsville, Maryland. By September 1960, Building 1 was fully occupied and other buildings were well underway. Although much of the occupancy was on a temporary basis and the personnel complement was widely scattered from Anacostia, D.C., to Silver Spring, Maryland, and points between, the Goddard Space Flight Center had become a physical reality.

The Dedication

On February 8, 1961, Dr. Harry J. Goett, the Director, announced dedication ceremonies to be held on March 16, 1961. A committee with Dr. Michael J. Vaccaro as chairman and Robert C. Baumann as co-chairman planned the ceremonies.

The dedication included opening remarks by Dr. Goett and a welcoming address by James E. Webb, NASA Administrator. The event also marked the presentation of a Congressional Medal awarded posthumously to Dr. Robert H. Goddard, which was accepted by his widow, Mrs. Esther C. Goddard. In presenting the Medal, Representative Overton Brooks said:[65] "From the Congress of which I am Chairman of the House Committee on Space and Aeronautics, we present this medal, but truly it comes not from the Congress of the United States but from the heart . . . of the American people as a whole." Senator Robert S. Kerr, Chairman of the Committee on Aeronautical and Space Sciences of the Senate, was unable to be present but sent the following message to Mrs. Goddard:

Mrs. Goddard, I am more than honored to have the opportunity of joining my good friend, Overton Brooks, in presenting to you this Congressional Medal in recognition of the creative achievements of your late husband. It was just 35 years ago today that he launched the world's first successful liquid fuel rocket and it is most appropriate that we make this presentation on this auspicious anniversary. It is only through the genius of a man like Dr. Goddard, who was not afraid to work for what he believed in, that we shall maintain the spirit and vitality that has made our country great. This medal, authorized by Congress on behalf of all the people, is but a small token from a grateful nation.

Dr. Hugh L. Dryden, Deputy Administrator of NASA, introduced Dr. Detlev W. Bronk, President, National Academy of Sciences, who made the dedication address. Dr. Bronk said in part:

There are two quotations I would like to repeat. The one appropriate to the mission of this institution, the other with regard to the man we honor. The first is from Louis Pasteur, speaking at a time when his beloved country was not doing well. "Oh, my country," said he, "You who so long held the sceptre of thought, why did you neglect your noblest creations? Take interest, I beseech you, in those sacred institu-

Dedication ceremony, March 16, 1961.

Dignitaries and guests attending the Center's dedication.

tions which we designate under the expressive name of laboratories. Demand that they be multiplied and adorned for they are the temples of wealth and of the future. There it is that humanity grows, becomes stronger and better . . . it learns to read in the work of nature symbols of progress with universal harmony." And from Pliny the Younger, "It is a noble employment to save from oblivion those who deserve to be remembered."

A bronze bust of Dr. Goddard was unveiled by his wife, assisted by Dr. Abe Silverstein, NASA Director of Space Flight Programs. The bust was created by the Washington sculptor Joseph Anthony Atchison, noted for his creative work in the Shrine of the Immaculate Conception in Washington, the World Flight Memorial for the Smithsonian Institution, and the Second Inaugural Medal of President Franklin D. Roosevelt.

Responding to the recognition paid her late husband, Mrs. Goddard remarked: "I hope that this bust and the man it represents will serve as an inspiration not only to the brilliant and dedicated people who are now at work at this tremendous Space Flight Center but to all who may work here in years to come. My husband would be deeply proud and happy for this very great tribute."

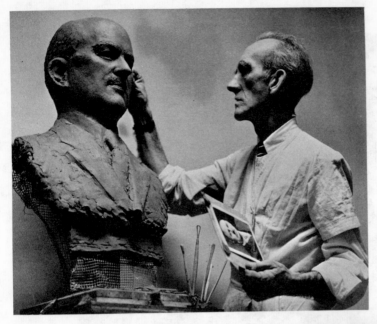

Joseph Anthony Atchison at work on the bust of Dr. Robert H. Goddard.

Mrs. Robert H. Goddard participating in the dedication of the NASA Center named in honor of her late husband.

Tours of the Center were conducted for invited guests, and "open house" was held for employees and their families. Included was a Control Room demonstration with simulation of prelaunch and countdown procedures, followed by a simulated satellite injection into orbit.

Lectures reviewed the Center's operation of global satellite networks, including Minitrack and Project Mercury. The cooperative role of the Center in the international exploration of space was explained. Guests saw an animated miniature tracking station and a scale model of the forthcoming United States-United Kingdom spacecraft, *Ariel I,* the first international satellite to be flown under Goddard project direction. There were also displays of spacecraft instrumentation and Goddard's family of sounding rockets, including an Aerobee 150A with a new attitude control system.

Other models on display included the Tiros weather satellites; *Explorer X,* the magnetometer spacecraft; *Explorer VIII,* the Direct Measurement Satellite; and *Vanguard I.* There was also a demonstration of a micrometeoroid detector, and vacuum, vibration, and spin-balancing equipment used to simulate space environmental conditions was shown.

Under authorization for construction at the time of dedication were eight buildings, representing a $27 million investment. They would provide the necessary facilities for 2,000 scientific, technical, and administrative personnel. The 550-acre tract once devoted to agricultural research was rapidly assuming a new role—the peaceful exploration of space.

PART TWO

GODDARD SPACE FLIGHT CENTER GOES TO WORK

Nature to be commanded must be obeyed.

—Francis Bacon

The Early Years
4

THE OPERATIONAL CONCEPTS which have been developed and applied at the Goddard Space Flight Center go beyond the traditional men, money, and machines concept of management. Although the early years of Goddard were deeply concerned with men (or manpower), money (in terms of budgetary activity, procurement activity, and operational costs), and machines (in terms of buildings and support equipment resources), other factors had far-reaching effects. These included such elements as Goddard's approach to project organization, its plan for uniting different disciplines into a group serving a common purpose, its program for disseminating scientific information, and many others.

Dr. T. Keith Glennan, then NASA Administrator, said: "We are not an operating organization in the ordinary sense of that term. We do not expect to operate meteorological or communications systems. Our product is knowledge—new and fundamental knowledge—the techniques, processes, and systems by means of which we acquire that knowledge. The rocket-powered launch vehicles we design and buy are not an end in themselves—they are cargo-carrying trucks of space, discarded when their fuel is exhausted." [66]

While the direct relation between some particular element or effort of Goddard and the acquisition of space knowledge sometimes appeared tenuous, the fact remained that the primary reason for the Center's existence was to acquire new knowledge. To do so required the coordinated effort of many scientists, engineers, technicians, and support personnel—often located in remote areas throughout the world—as well as buildings, equipment, and facilities.

The Center's growth may be measured by several factors: (1) the rapidity with which it expanded its work force from a few people formerly with the Vanguard project at NRL to a staff of some 3,000 with widely varied skills and backgrounds; (2) the growth of its physical plant from a wooded area near Greenbelt, Maryland, to a complex of modern space science laboratories, testing facilities, and worldwide tracking, data acquisition, and reduction facilities; and (3) the growth in financial responsibility from the

The wooded site selected for the Space Center.

approximately $6,300,000 transferred by the Navy to an R&D budget of about $354.03 million for Fiscal Year 1963.

A Nucleus Goes to Work

The first employees of the activity later designated as the Goddard Space Flight Center were some 150 individuals of the Vanguard group, transferred from the Navy to the newly created National Aeronautics and Space Administration. By mutual agreement between DOD and NASA it was decided that this cadre would remain physically at the Naval Research Laboratory "until suitable space is available at the projected NASA Space Projects Center in Beltsville."

In December 1958 another 46 employees were transferred to the Beltsville Center from NRL's Space Sciences group. By the end of 1958 the new Center had a total of 216 employees. By June 1959 the Center had grown to 391 people in the Washington area. In 1959 recruitment activities were stepped up significantly, and by the year's end there were 579 employees. By June 30, 1960, through transfer and recruitment the personnel complement had grown to 707 people.

First computers are moved to the Goddard Space Flight Center.

As previously indicated, NASA's manned space flight program was an integral part of the early Goddard mission. For this mission, the Center had the talent and technical capabilities from the early Vanguard days, including the worldwide Minitrack network. Increasing emphasis on scientific, meteorological, and communications satellite projects, together with recognition that the manned space flight program demanded an independent organization, led to the Space Task Group (STG) at Langley being separated from its organizational assignment to Goddard as of January 3, 1961. Goddard retained its responsibilities in connection with the Project Mercury tracking network. As a result of this transfer, 667 people left the Goddard roster to form the nucleus of what later became NASA's Manned Spacecraft Center, at Houston, Texas.[67]

Organizing for Space Science
5

The secret of good administration . . . lies not in the administrator's vast and exact knowledge, but in his skill in navigating areas of ignorance. . . . It is the daily experience of an administrator that he make decisions in areas outside his expertise on what a scholar would consider to be insufficient evidence.[68]

EVEN AS THE INVESTIGATION AND EXPLORATION of space became a national goal, the effective direction and administration of the space program became an urgent necessity for the newly created agency. Here was a national effort which was to be conducted under the closest scrutiny of the public, the Congress, and the scientific community. It was a program involving vast human and financial resources which had to be given sound, and in many ways, novel, direction and guidance.

The national commitment to space did not come as a smooth, steady, acceleration of effort, but instead as a series of challenges and responses. We have seen in earlier chapters the experiments of one New England professor, how such efforts were multiplied many times during World War II, received postwar government and scientific endorsement and support in the IGY, blossomed into a national space program with civil and military components in the wake of *Sputnik I*, and leapfrogged into the exclusive bracket of top Federal program expenditures following the shock of the world's first manned space flight, made by the Soviet Union's Cosmonaut Gagarin in April 1961. It was then that President John F. Kennedy and his administration rallied the Nation; he said on May 25, 1961: "Now it is time to take longer strides—time for a great new American enterprise —time for this Nation to take a clearly leading role in space achievement which in many ways may hold the key to our future on earth."[69] Later President Kennedy predicted that this major expansion of the space program would be considered "as one of the most important decisions that will be made during my incumbency."[70] The goal was not only to land a man on the moon within the decade, but also to gain American competence and preeminence in all space activities.

Responsible for three distinct phases of the U.S. space program—scientific investigation of cislunar space, applications satellites (weather and communications), and space tracking of manned and scientific satellites (tracking, data acquisition, and data reduction)—Goddard Space Flight Center's missions were vital to the U.S. position in space. Within four years after its establishment, the Goddard Space Flight Center had an annual research and development budget of some $354.03 million—about one million dollars per day. The accompanying charts graphically illustrate the rapid growth in expenditures at Goddard.

With the establishment of the Goddard Center from the Vanguard project and the Upper Atmosphere group of the Naval Research Laboratory, varied capabilities, practices, and management concepts were brought together. The early organization did not fit neatly into simple categories

Funding at Goddard Space Flight Center, 1959–1963
[All amounts are in millions of dollars]

Year	Sounding rockets	Satellites			Tracking and data acquisition	Delta launch vehicle	Total
		Scientific	Meteor-ological	Communi-cations			
1959	3.56	21.31	0.99	3.57	3.10	12.93	45.46
1960	9.68	20.24	7.93	3.05	16.19	12.48	69.57
1961	8.25	35.14	17.50	31.15	29.65	9.58	131.27
1962	7.29	67.64	26.97	21.42	45.13	0.70	169.15
1963	9.51	89.87	42.43	31.30	86.59	0.70	261.40

Major GSFC missions

Year	Salaries and plant support				Advanced research and technology
	Salaries and expenses	Construction and equipment (on site and tracking)	Plant support	Total	
1959	2.02	3.95	0.14	6.11	0
1960	11.40	17.74	3.56	32.70	0
1961	16.31	14.63	4.97	35.91	0
1962	26.68	32.46	11.47	70.61	2.78
1963	38.83	35.41	13.81	88.05	4.58

of programs, disciplines, or functions. It contained most of the needed "across-the-board" capability with many specialized skills. This in-house competence, further increased by those who joined the staff later, was one of the Center's greatest assets. It provided the basic capability to assure intelligent control of its programs and to conduct enough in-house research and development of a significant and challenging nature to ensure the professional excellence of its scientific and technical staff.

The complexity of the Center's missions made for intricate patterns of communications and decision-making, calling for new skills in management and in conduct of organizational relations. Since some 90 percent of the Center's research and development funds were expended with private industry, nonprofit and educational institutions, and other Government agencies, the need for effective management techniques became increasingly important. Also needed were effective communications with the scientific community; new scientific knowledge was the fundamental objective of Goddard's space program. Suggestions and proposals for scientific experiments were evaluated by subcommittees of the NASA Headquarters Space Sciences Steering Committee for: (a) scientific merit; (b) the capabilities of the proposer and his institution. The experimenter chosen by the Committee could elect to build the hardware himself or subcontract to industry.

Where management responsibility for a major space project was assigned to the Goddard Center, project groups were created and became the backbone of the Center's management structure. Headed by a project manager, each project group included support elements from the Center's Office of Administration (for fiscal, procurement, scheduling, and other administrative details) and representatives for test and evaluation (reliability) and tracking (data acquisition and data reduction). It was the project manager's responsibility to ensure that Goddard's resources, both internal and contractual, were effectively used to serve the needs of a particular project.

The Center management considered the following relationships essential to effective project operations:

- Project needs must be communicated to line supervisors.
- Project manager must have rapid and direct access to top management to report how adequately requirements are being served.
- Top management must be able to step in to resolve such problems as arise from conflict between the needs of the various projects, between project demands and the more general discipline activity.
- Engineers and scientists in the project groups must keep in constant touch with the contractors and major subcontractors to follow the progress of project elements.
- A project support staff must assist the project group by performing such functions as procurement, financial management, PERT analysis, progress reporting.

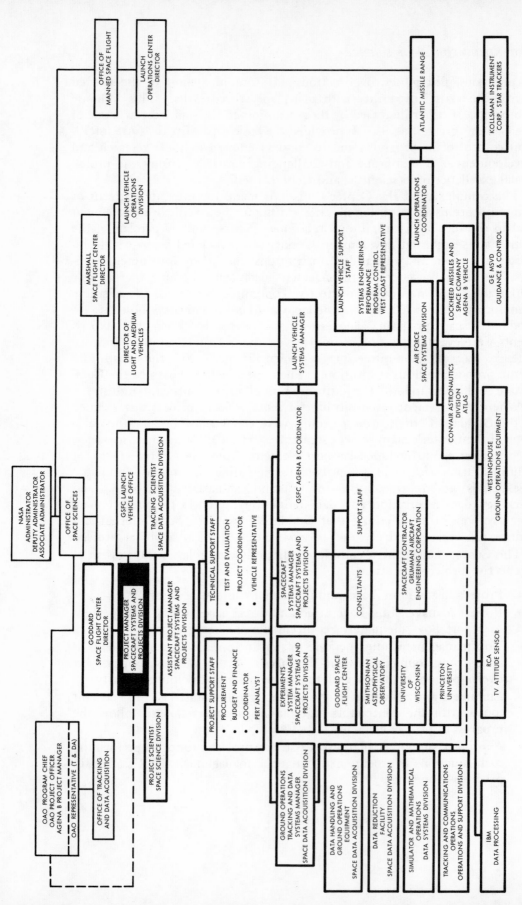

Orbiting Astronomical Observatory project management chart.

The director and key staff elements kept themselves informed through weekly staff meetings and weekly reports, issued every Friday, became "weekend reading material" in preparation for the next staff conference.

But whatever the technique, the management of the Center's complex research and development programs was no easy task; project management developed into a new and important art which affected virtually every level of the organizational strata. Solutions had to be found to such questions as to how NASA Headquarters would deal effectively with the Center; how the Center management would manage the project manager; and how the project manager in turn would manage a multimillion dollar contract with the aerospace industry, again involving a variety of contract managers. The formal management organization at Goddard is shown in accompanying illustrations.

In these early years, a major consideration was the amount of contract assistance which the Center should seek in carrying out its projects. It was obvious that only a relatively small portion could be done in-house. According to Eugene W. Wasielewski, Associate Center Director: "We try to have at least one small satellite under development in-house, at all times. Sometimes we have two in process. We also attempt to do a major share of the work on one of the large satellites. . . . While it is difficult to generalize, we feel we are barely doing enough in-house work to enable us to carry out our programs effectively."[71]

If a major project was to be accomplished through a prime contractor, specifications and requests for proposals were issued. Soon the program involved such prime contractors as Radio Corporation of America (*Relay I* and *II*), Hughes Aircraft Corporation (Syncom), General Electric (Nimbus), Ball Brothers (Orbiting Solar Observatory), Grumman Aircraft Corporation (Orbiting Astronomical Observatory), Thompson Ramo Wooldridge Space Laboratories (*Pioneer V*, Orbiting Geophysical Observatory), and many others. In the area of tracking, data acquisition, and data reduction, there were such industrial giants as International Business Machines, Western Electric, Bell Telephone Laboratories, and Bendix Corporation.

Contracting with industry on a multimillion dollar scale required the Center to seek the highest quality of American scientific and industrial skill, as well as the best capabilities of other Government laboratories. Each experiment in space was characterized by a high degree of attention to individual design and assembly. Even in a series of projects having the same general purpose, the payload packages varied according to the experiments conducted. Seldom, if ever, were any two payloads identical.

Procurement problems were complicated by the fact that in many instances the experiment or spacecraft hardware to be bought had never before been manufactured, indeed had never before been on the drawing board. More often than not, materials of a rare or "exotic" nature and

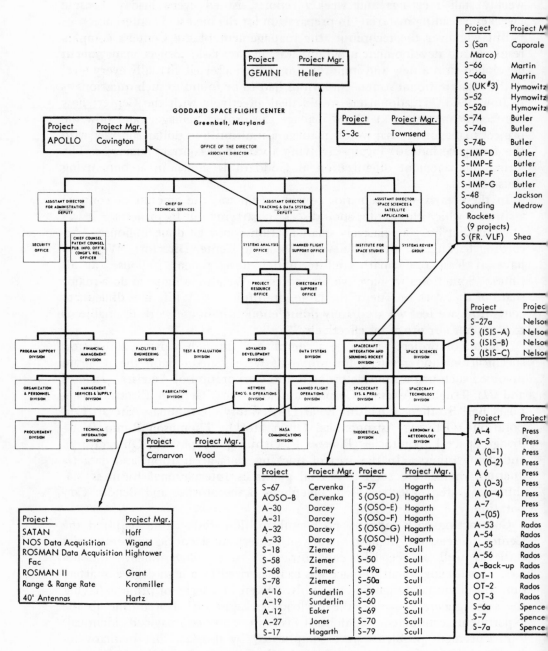

Goddard Space Flight Center project assignments as of September 20, 1963.

Personnel—the Center's most important resource. Here William Cahill discusses Goddard computer operations with a group of new employees.

limited availability were required. This called for extensive knowledge of supply sources, capabilities, and past performance of industrial firms and other vendors.

From January 1, 1960, to June 30, 1960, procurement actions totaled over $61 million; during Fiscal Year 1961, procurement actions totaled $375 million; and during Fiscal Year 1962 the procurement actions totaled over $418 million. (See Appendix E for detailed breakdown.) "Space" became a big and complicated business.

Personnel

The nucleus of Goddard Center personnel was drawn from several NACA laboratories and from the various satellite programs transferred to NASA in 1958 (see ch. 2). But as the Center's missions expanded and the physical plant neared completion, more and more skilled people of various descriptions were needed.

In a labor market which was extremely tight because of the nationwide shortage of scientists and engineers, Goddard had the additional problem of finding interested individuals possessing the specific and unique experience demanded by its programs. Experience with the college recruitment programs was rewarding. Although NASA entrance salaries may have been somewhat below the national average, the challenge of Goddard's mission, facilities, and progressive educational programs attracted high-quality graduates. The critical recruitment was for jobs in which highly specialized experience was necessary: for example, senior people with solid experience in satellite instrumentation, communications systems, systems integration, and spacecraft project management. It was somewhat paradoxical that for this group of personnel the Center was in effect in competition with itself; it competed with the personnel needs of industrial concerns which, with government contracts, were also engaged on space projects. One incentive particularly attractive at Goddard was the opportunity provided by the Center to participate in a major space science project from its inception to completion. The Center's mission frequently called for the "universal type" scientist, capable in areas beyond his immediate scientific discipline, knowledgeable in such fields as aerodynamics, electrical engineering, data transmission, etc.

Rather than establishing positions such as physicist, electrical engineer, etc., NASA categorized and identified positions directly with the nature of the work to be done. Since the areas of academic training did not always correspond with the fields of advanced research and development, the aero-

Aerial view of Goddard Space Flight Center, June 1962.

space technology concept was applied. Under this plan, the title "Aero Space Technologist" was used to cover the broad field of research and development specialties.[72] Specifically, the titles of positions had the symbol AST followed by the specialty.

Five separate categories of employees composed the overall Goddard team: scientists and engineers; "blue collar" craftsmen; technical support personnel; administrators; and clerical personnel. Almost 42 percent of the Center's work force consisted of scientists and engineers, while NASA-wide the ratio was approximately one-third scientists and engineers to two-thirds support personnel.

As previously indicated, the scientists and engineers who had been associated with Project Vanguard and other Government space programs formed the nucleus of the GSFC personnel complement. This group grew rapidly:[73]

1959:   782 (including Space Task Group staff later transferred to
              Manned Spacecraft Center)
1960: 1,265 (including Space Task Group staff later transferred to
              Manned Spacecraft Center)
1961: 1,497
1962: 2,850
1963: 3,494 (December 31, 1963)

Sources from which scientists and engineers were recruited during the period of December 1958 to December 1963 were:

Government: 916   (50.8 percent)
Private industry: 495   (27.4 percent)
Schools: 264   (14.5 percent)
Other: 128   (7.07 percent)

Scientists were selected from virtually every source and from many geographic regions. The recruiting program was conducted with the aid of extensive publicity campaigns and through the cooperation of colleges and universities.

For staff personnel, Goddard sponsored graduate study programs and undergraduate cooperative courses with several colleges and universities. Select students who had completed their sophomore year could attend school one semester and work at Goddard the next, alternating in this way until they got their degrees. Under another plan, graduate students could take three-quarter-credit courses at a local university, wherein they worked 3 days a week at Goddard and attended classes on alternate days.

Likewise, scientists and engineers were encouraged to augment their education in one of several local graduate school programs. Because the field of space technology was unique and developed so rapidly, Goddard had a program of seminars, colloquia, and specialized courses.

Goddard also assisted employees who, having completed their studies at the master's degree level, were striving for greater competence and stature. Each year a limited number of carefully selected scientists and engineers were offered an opportunity to spend up to one year in research and study fellowship programs at institutions of their choice. This program enabled an employee to conduct advanced study and to do research under the direction of men with international reputations.

Location plan of Center, June 1962.

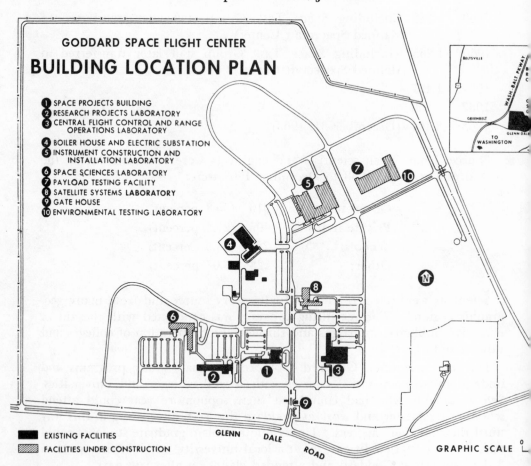

GODDARD SPACE FLIGHT CENTER

BUILDING LOCATION PLAN

1 SPACE PROJECTS BUILDING
2 RESEARCH PROJECTS LABORATORY
3 CENTRAL FLIGHT CONTROL AND RANGE
   OPERATIONS LABORATORY
4 BOILER HOUSE AND ELECTRIC SUBSTATION
5 INSTRUMENT CONSTRUCTION AND
   INSTALLATION LABORATORY
6 SPACE SCIENCES LABORATORY
7 PAYLOAD TESTING FACILITY
8 SATELLITE SYSTEMS LABORATORY
9 GATE HOUSE
10 ENVIRONMENTAL TESTING LABORATORY

BELTSVILLE
GREENBELT
GLENN DALE
TO
WASHINGTON

GLENN DALE ROAD

EXISTING FACILITIES
FACILITIES UNDER CONSTRUCTION

GRAPHIC SCALE

Physical Plant

The physical plant of Goddard Space Flight Center was established with an eye to immediate and future requirements. An engineering master plan was developed by Voorhees, Walker, Smith, Smith & Haines of New York City. It envisioned a "campus type" layout, conducive to effective management and creative activity.

The first construction contract was let on April 10, 1959, to Norair Engineering Corporation, Washington, D.C. This contract called for construction of Buildings 1 and 2, together with access roads and parking areas. The first construction began early on the morning of April 24,

Location plan of Center, 1963 estimates.

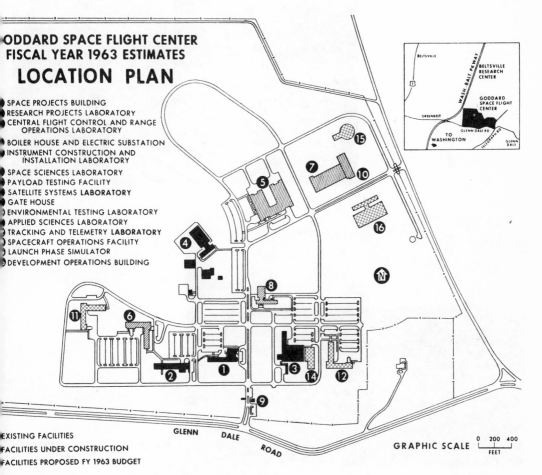

GODDARD SPACE FLIGHT CENTER
FISCAL YEAR 1963 ESTIMATES
LOCATION PLAN

- SPACE PROJECTS BUILDING
- RESEARCH PROJECTS LABORATORY
- CENTRAL FLIGHT CONTROL AND RANGE OPERATIONS LABORATORY
- BOILER HOUSE AND ELECTRIC SUBSTATION
- INSTRUMENT CONSTRUCTION AND INSTALLATION LABORATORY
- SPACE SCIENCES LABORATORY
- PAYLOAD TESTING FACILITY
- SATELLITE SYSTEMS LABORATORY
- GATE HOUSE
- ENVIRONMENTAL TESTING LABORATORY
- APPLIED SCIENCES LABORATORY
- TRACKING AND TELEMETRY LABORATORY
- SPACECRAFT OPERATIONS FACILITY
- LAUNCH PHASE SIMULATOR
- DEVELOPMENT OPERATIONS BUILDING

EXISTING FACILITIES
FACILITIES UNDER CONSTRUCTION
FACILITIES PROPOSED FY 1963 BUDGET

GLENN DALE ROAD

GRAPHIC SCALE 0 200 400 FEET

1959, when brush and trees were cleared in the area which was to become the Center's main entrance.

The computer and switchboard rooms were occupied on April 28, 1960. By July of the same year, the remainder of Building 1 was completely occupied, although steam for operation of the heating system and refrigeration compressors for air conditioning were provided by a temporary boiler outside the building. September 16, 1960, saw the full occupation of Building 2.

Site for Building 1, June 1959.

Building 1 under construction, October 1959.

Building 1.

Humphreys & Harding, Inc., began construction of the Central Flight Control and Range Operations Building (Building 3) on September 21, 1959. Installation of computer equipment was completed on March 1, 1961, while other portions of the computer and communications area were occupied in November and December of the same year.

Building 4, housing service shops, central power-plant, refrigeration plant, cooling tower, emergency power generators, and office areas, was started on May 23, 1960, under contract with Norair Engineering Corporation. Parking lots and roads were also included under this contract. Steam service lines, temporary boiler, and service shops were completed in November; office space, parking lot, and boilers were placed in operation on December 20, 1960. Construction and installation of refrigeration equipment were completed on May 29, 1961.

The Instrument Construction and Installation Laboratory, Building 5, under contract with Norair Engineering Corporation, was started on November 26, 1960. Initial phases of this structure accommodated many administrative and scientific personnel formerly housed in temporary quarters. In early 1962 it was necessary to modify the machine shop and upper floor areas to house personnel pending completion of Buildings 6, 8, and 11. Building 5 was completed on March 20, 1962.

Arthur Venneri Co. was low bidder on a contract to build the Space Science Laboratory, Building 6. Construction was begun on November 19,

1960. By February 1962, the lower floors were completed and sections A and B were ready for occupancy. The remaining portion of the building required one additional month, and the staff took possession on March 2, 1962.

The contract for Buildings 7 and 10 went to United Engineers and Constructors, Inc., on January 31, 1961. Notice to proceed with the construction of Building 7 was given in May 1961; construction started May 22, 1961. Occupancy by the Test and Evaluation Division, formerly housed in Building 4 and in numerous trailers, began April 28, 1962, and was completed a month later. Construction of Building 10 was started on October 19, 1961, by United Engineers and Constructors, Inc., with a scheduled contract completion date of September 1, 1962. Sufficient portions of the building, together with the overhead crane, were completed by March 2, 1962, so that installation of the Space Environmental Simulator and Dynamic Test Chambers by Minneapolis-Honeywell Corporation could begin.

The Satellite Systems Laboratory, Building 8, under contract with Arthur Venneri Co., was begun on September 16, 1961, and was targeted for occupancy by spring 1963. Featuring a 500-seat auditorium, it also included provisions for a presentation-type stage, multipurpose projection

Aerial view of Buildings 1, 2, 3.

booth, and wide-range sound facilities. Building 8 would house the Director, Associate Director, Assistant Directors, and supporting administrative services offices of the Center.

Building 11, an Applied Sciences Laboratory, was begun by the Norair Engineering Corporation of Washington, D.C., on August 16, 1962, and completed during September 1963. A contract for the construction of Building 12 was awarded to the Piracci Construction Company of Baltimore. This building, a Tracking and Telemetry Laboratory, was to augment such facilities in Building 3. Construction was begun on October 22, 1962, and was completed during November 1963. Each of the buildings have laboratory and office space for approximately 350 employees.

The assignment of space for the most effective administration of the Center continued to be a critical problem, and occupancy in many areas was on a temporary basis. This particularly applied to Buildings 1 and 5. Many of the administrative officers which eventually were scheduled to be located elsewhere at the Center were housed in rented space in the Jackson Building, Bladensburg, Maryland; at Lawrence St., Bladensburg, Maryland; at Litton Industries, College Park, Maryland; at Beltsville; and in the Colemont Building, Silver Spring, Maryland.

Building 8 under construction, July 1962.

Occupancy by Directorate and Location, July 12, 1962

Building [a]	1	2	3	4	5	6	7	8	Jac	Law	CFO	Litton	ARC	Cole	Litton 2A	Cape	NYC
Dir. and Asst. Dir. OA—585:																	
84 Dir., Asst. Dir.—OA	25						1	5	12								
82 Fin Mgmt	12				70												
81 O and P	2				79												
57 Mgmt Ser	39				18												
219 P and S	16								100	103							
62 TID	30				32												
Office of Tech. Serv.—456:																	
2 Chief OTS							2										
140 Fac Eng				115							25						
188 Test and Eval				30			158										
126 Fab Div		4			113	5	4										
Track and Data Sys.—725:																	
17 Asst. Dir.			17														
130 Track Sys			125				22						5				
116 OP and Sup			94														
219 Data Sys			219														
164 Spa Data Acq			6			20						138					
79 MSFS			19		60												
Space Sci. and Sat. App.—1,123:																	
11 Asst. Dir.						11											
284 Spa Sci		213				10								12			
185 Spa Sys and Proj					50	105									49	30	
175 Aero and Mete	16	137			22												
326 Spac Tech		5		16		305											
142 Theo	86	5															56
	226	359	480	161	485	456	187	5	112	103	25	138	5	12	49	30	56

[a] Jac—Jackson St.   CFO—Construction Field Office   Cole—Colemont   NYC—Institute for

Law—Lawrence St.   ARC—Agricultural Research Center   Cape—Cape Canaveral   Space Studies, N. Y.

Organizational Growth

A review of the organization charts (see Appendix F) gives an indication of how the Center grew while, at the same time, adhering to its original concepts. The manned satellite function shown in the first two charts was transferred from Goddard to the Manned Spacecraft Center at Houston, Texas. The other four major elements—Administration (formerly Business Administration), Tracking and Data Systems, Space Science and Satellite Applications, and Technical Services—remained basically the same with further refinements. The Office of Technical Services expanded to include such divisions as Facilities Engineering, Test and Evaluation, and Fabrication.

The Office of Space Science and Satellite Applications, while retaining essentially the same functions, recognized the need for the creation of a separate division for aeronomy and meteorology. The responsibilities of the Office of Tracking and Data Systems grew to the point where the original breakdown of a Theory and Analysis Staff, a Tracking Systems Division, and an Operations Division no longer was adequate. It expanded to include a Space Projects Integration Office, an Operations and Support Division, a Tracking Systems Division (with a plans office), a Space Data Acquisition Division, a Data Systems Division (with a theory and analysis office), and a Manned Space Flight Support Division.

Goddard Institute for Space Studies

To provide a point of contact between the national space program and an area rich in universities and scientific talent, the Goddard Institute for Space Studies was established in New York City in May 1961 as a part of the Goddard Space Flight Center.

The Institute's primary mission was to assist in the analysis and interpretation of data from NASA probes. It was concerned with basic theoretical research in a broad variety of fields, including the structure of the earth, the moon, and other planetary bodies in the solar system; the atmospheres of the earth and other planets; the origin and evolution of the solar system; the properties of interplanetary plasma; sun-earth relations; and the structure and evolution of stars.

The second major mission of the Institute was to arouse the interest of university scientists and students in the space program and to enlist their participation in some of the theoretical problems of space research. With its location in New York, the Institute had a unique opportunity for direct contact with the metropolitan university community. In its first year it developed associations with Princeton University, Yale University, Columbia University, New York University, the City College of New York, and Brooklyn Polytechnic Institute.

Drs. Robert Jastrow, Jackson Herring, Hong Yee Chiu, and Albert Arking of the Goddard Institute for Space Studies in New York.

The Institute was originally designated as a New York office of the Theoretical Division of the Goddard Space Flight Center. Dr. Robert Jastrow was named Director and also continued as Chief of the Theoretical Division. In July 1962, the Institute was separated from the division.

Goddard Launch Operations

Much of the early success of the Goddard satellite program has stemmed from the efforts of its launch teams, organized under the Directorate for Space Science and Satellite Applications, with personnel at both the Eastern and Western Test Ranges (ETR and WTR). The ETR team provided the management and technical direction of the field efforts involving the successful Delta launch vehicle. Under the Field Projects Branch, Goddard scientists and engineers closely supervised, monitored, and directed the launch vehicle preparations, launch operations, and coordination for spacecraft checkout. A similar team at WTR was responsible for the field integration of the spacecraft and launch vehicle and for coordinating and directing mission operations originating from the Pacific coast.

Fabrication and Testing

A scientific satellite was not a mass-produced item, but usually a one-of-a-kind spacecraft containing delicate scientific and electronic equipment. It required the best engineering talents to build and test these spaceborne laboratories. Manufacture of these space vehicles was accomplished either in-house by the Center's staff of skilled fabricators, under contract with American industry, or by a combination of both. The Center's fabrication staff was composed of a small but highly specialized team of engineers and technicians skilled in machining, forming, optics, electronics, satellite assembly, etc.

In its lifetime, each spacecraft would have to survive environmental stresses during ground handling, launching, and then operate effectively in space for its expected lifetime. The task was not a simple one, since these spacecraft contained equipment heretofore used only under the ideal environment of a laboratory. In space, these instruments had to operate reliably at distances and under conditions where they were subjected to solar radiation, space vacuum, extreme temperatures, radiation belts, and solar flares. Unlike a laboratory, there could be no experienced experimenter in attendance, making adjustments and taking readings.

Goddard's Spacecraft Test Facility served as a large-scale laboratory to

The welding of circuitry for use in a scientific satellite.

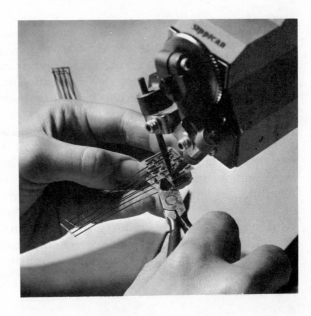

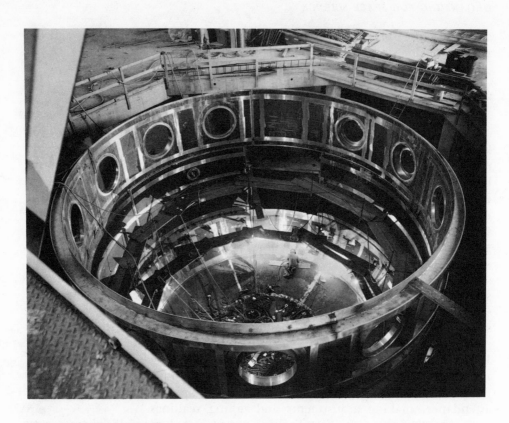

Space environment simulator under construction at Goddard.

test Goddard-developed spacecraft and probes. It was the Center's conscience. Here a satellite was exposed to man-made conditions of extreme temperature, humidity, shock, vibration, structural loadings, and various combinations to assure that the spacecraft and equipment could take the punishment which they were to face on their orbital mission. These facilities were capable of handling one 4,000-pound payload, plus two 1,000-pound loads simultaneously, measuring up to 25 feet.

Two major items in the Center's Spacecraft Test Facility were a dynamic test chamber and a space environment simulator. These chambers simulated some of the forces that converge on a spacecraft from initial ground handling through launch and flight. The dynamic test chamber consisted of a stainless-steel structure $33\frac{1}{2}$ feet in diameter and 58 feet high. Powerful mechanical pumps reduced inside pressure to 0.1 mm mercury. Here, dynamic balancing, solar paddle erection, spacecraft orientation, etc., could be tested. In the space environment simulator, a spacecraft could be exposed to simulated conditions of cold outer space, extreme vacuum, and solar radiation.

A review of scientific satellite failures detected by means of environmental test programs was made for the calendar year 1962. Five satellites were selected for this review, all of which were launched and successfully operated in space during 1962. These satellites were chosen to represent several factors that might influence their complexity. For example, weights varying from less than 100 to over 300 pounds and three launch vehicles were represented. The scientific discipline represented by the on-board experiments covered electron density; galactic noise; corpuscular, solar, and cosmic radiation; magnetic fields; ionospheric relations; and communication experiments. The telemetry systems were typically pulse-frequency modulated, although one system included traveling-wave tubes. Only one of the systems used batteries exclusively; the other four included solar cells for power. The satellites reviewed included those developed by NASA, by industry, and through international cooperation. They all, however, were tested under the same philosophy.

The ratio of electrical to mechanical failures was 4:1 (80 versus 20 percent). The mechanical problems were chiefly concerned with antenna designs, subsystem mounting, and local resonances. Stronger and stiffer designs, together with damping (often by potting), were general solutions to these problems. Electrical problems were erratic and spurious, requiring much troubleshooting. Solid-state components often were found to be faulty. Local overheating was often corrected by providing improved heat sinks and heat conduction paths. The failure distribution seemed reasonably consistent between the satellites. Nearly one-half of the failures reviewed occurred during the thermal-vacuum test, which simulated space conditions. However, nearly one-sixth of the failures occurred during

Failure Distribution by Spacecraft

Space-craft	Weight, lb	Vehicle	Failures during test					
			Electrical		Mechanical		Total	
			No.	Percent	No.	Percent	No.	Percent
A	94	Scout	10	71	4	29	14	12
B	170	Delta	15	83	3	17	18	16
C	86	Delta	18	78	5	22	23	20
D	150	Delta	42	86	7	14	49	43
E	310	Thor-Agena	6	60	4	40	10	9
Total			91	80	23	20	114	100

Failure Distribution by Test Condition

Failure category	Failure during test [a]															
	Electrical							Mechanical							Total	
						Total								Total		
	A	B	C	D	E	No.	Per-cent	A	B	C	D	E	No.	Per-cent	No.	Per-cent
Checkout	---	2	3	5	2	12	13	---	---	1	4	1	6	26	18	16
Vibration	7	5	3	4	1	20	22	4	3	3	1	3	14	61	34	30
Temperature	---	1	1	---	1	3	3	---	---	---	---	---	---	---	3	3
Vacuum	---	1	3	1	---	5	5	---	---	---	---	---	---	---	5	4
Thermal-vacuum	3	6	8	32	2	51	56	---	---	1	2	---	3	13	54	47
Total	10	15	18	42	6	91	100	4	3	5	7	4	23	100	114	100

[a] Test conditions for spacecraft A, B, C, D, and E in table above.

checkout, and about one-third during vibration. One observation made from these data was the importance of completing the entire system and checking it out early in the project life. One-sixth of the errors noted were primarily indicative of the interaction of subsystems and the many interface problems. Cabling and connectors were particular offenders at this stage of checkout. Each of these failures was detected, corrected, tested, and evaluated. The final result—in space flight—was a successful satellite.[74]

Tracking, Data Acquisition, and Data Reduction
6

THE FIRST FUNCTIONAL TRACKING SYSTEM to be constructed for satellites was the Minitrack network. This network grew directly out of arrangements originally made by the United States with agencies abroad as part of the program for the International Geophysical Year. Among the overseas stations tied in with the satellite tracking network were Antigua, West Indies Federation; Quito, Ecuador; Lima, Peru; Antofagasta and Santiago, Chile; Woomera, Australia; and Esselen Park, Union of South Africa. These countries, in a program originally established in 1957 by the U.S. Naval Research Laboratory in cooperation with other agencies here and abroad, were all part of Minitrack.[75]

On January 10, 1959, representatives of NASA and DOD met to coordinate the separate requirements of the two agencies, and arrived at an agreement for a "National Program to Meet Satellite and Space Vehicle Tracking and Surveillance Requirements for FY 1959 and FY 1960." The agreement, signed by Secretary of Defense Neil H. McElroy and NASA Administrator T. Keith Glennan, established respective responsibilities and mutual use of tracking data wherever possible and led to the formation of the continuing NASA–DOD Space Flight Tracking Resources Committee.

The basic responsibilities of the network included: tracking, orbit computation, data acquisition (environmental and scientific telemetry), and data reduction.

The network consisted of three major functional parts. The first, the Minitrack Net, has been used to track all U.S. satellites containing a suitable beacon since the beginning of the space programs in 1957 and 1958.

The Minitract network comprised an organization of fixed ground stations, located throughout the world, to provide precision tracking, command, and telemetry reception from satellites and space probes together with a communications system to transmit this information to a computing facility.

A large percentage of the original stations were located along the 75th

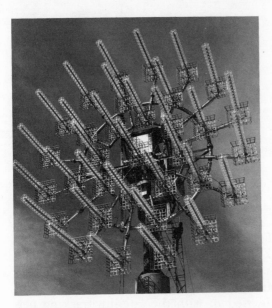

A Wallops Island helical antenna that receives video signals from the Tiros weather satellites.

meridian to intercept satellite orbits with inclinations of less than 45 degrees. New stations were added in higher latitudes to cope with more nearly polar orbits. Furthermore, ten of the stations were supplemented with additional antennas aligned specifically for polar orbit. (As of December 1962, the Minitrack system included the following stations: Blossom Point, Maryland; Fort Myers, Florida; Quito, Ecuador; Lima, Peru; Antofagasta, Chile; Santiago, Chile; Woomera, Australia; Esselen Park, South Africa; Goldstone, California; St. John's, Newfoundland; East Grand Forks, Minnesota; Fairbanks, Alaska; and Winkfield, England.)

The prime Minitrack satellite tracking system consisted of radio interferometers [76] operating in conjunction with a transmitting beacon in the payload itself. Since the establishment of the network, certain enhancements have been added to the original station equipment to provide tracking capability by optical and Doppler means as well. While the original tracking equipment operated on or near 108 megacycles (Mc), the frequency assigned for IGY activities, additional equipment has been provided, tunable over the 136–137-Mc region.

Many of the satellites launched by NASA used very wide bandwidths for transmission of data from the satellite to the ground stations. Since the receiver and sky noise in the telemetry link is proportional to the bandwidth used for reception, either a very high transmitter power or a very high antenna gain, or both, had to be used in a wideband telemetry link to achieve good signal-to-noise ratios. Since transmitter powers were restricted for technical reasons, it became necessary to develop very high gain antennas at the ground stations for receiving the wideband telemetry signals. The

66

Fairbanks, Alaska, tracking station.

antenna that best satisfied the requirements for high gain and multiple frequency operation was a parabolic antenna 85 feet in diameter.

The first satellite to require a large data acquisition facility for wide bandwidth reception was the Nimbus weather satellite. Nimbus was also one of the first NASA satellites that was to have a polar orbit. So the first station for wideband data acquisition was constructed on Gilmore Creek, 12 miles north of Fairbanks, Alaska; it was completed in May 1962. A contract was awarded the University of Alaska for operation of the station, to provide coverage for 70 percent of the passes of a satellite in a polar orbit. A contract for construction of a second station located near Rosman, North Carolina, was placed in July 1962; this station picked up an additional 20 percent of the passes of a polar satellite. Thus these two stations formed a network which provided coverage of 90 percent of the orbits of a satellite with a very high inclination.

The main antenna for the Alaskan station was an 85-foot-diameter paraboloid of revolution with a focal length of 36 feet. Its surface consisted of double-curved aluminum sheet panels. The surface was separate from the reflector structure so it could be independently adjusted. The antenna reflector was mounted on an X–Y-type mount designed specifically for tracking satellites. It was capable of tracking at rates from 0 to 3 degrees per second, with accelerations up to 5 degrees per second per second.[77]

Tracking Project Mercury [78]

The first Mercury-Redstone flight occurred December 19, 1960. In this flight, the unmanned capsule reached a peak altitude of 135 miles, a range of 235 miles, and encountered 5½ minutes of zero gravity. The flight was a success. The capsule control system, retrorockets, separation rockets, communications equipment, and recovery equipment functioned properly. The capsule was recovered soon after landing by a helicopter dispatched from an aircraft carrier.

Tracking, data acquisition, and communications for this project were the responsibility of the Goddard Space Flight Center. For the Project Mercury flights, Goddard operated a worldwide tracking network, spanning three oceans and three continents. In their location and equipment configuration, these tracking sites were prescribed by the character of the onboard electronics systems and by facilities existing throughout the world, which were used to the maximum extent possible. This maximum utilization of existing facilities was mandatory if the rapid pace set for the project was not to outstrip the development of the ground tracking system.[79]

Since the major requirement was one of safety, a highly reliable command system for backup of the astronaut functions by ground command was installed at strategic points around the earth. This requirement also made it mandatory that the onboard spacecraft systems be carefully monitored during all phases of the flight; this was accomplished by providing real-time telemetry display data at the sites.

Goddard was the focal point for receipt of real-time radar data from the sites. Two IBM 7090 computers provided launch and orbital computing during the flight; real-time display data were then transmitted to the Mercury Control Center at GSFC. An air-to-ground communications system was established together with remote site-to-control-center voice and teletype communications, to maintain network contact with the astronaut during all phases of the flight.

A special facility for testing and evaluation was established at Wallops Island, Virginia. Here a typical site was constructed during the early phases of equipment procurement to evaluate the performance of the systems, determine the interface problems, develop detailed equipment testing procedures, establish calibration techniques and equipment, and perform early training exercises. This proving ground was invaluable in providing a rapid evaluation of contractor-developed equipment and testing procedures. Here also the criteria were established for ultimate acceptance testing of the equipment as it was to be installed at each of the remote sites.

Late in 1961, an industrial team headed by the Western Electric Company turned over this $60 million global network to NASA. Other team members were Bell Telephone Laboratories, Inc.; the Bendix Corporation; Burns & Roe, Inc.; and International Business Machines Corporation. The Lincoln Laboratory of the Massachusetts Institute of Technology had advised and assisted on special technical problems related to the network. The contract had involved extensive negotiations with Federal agencies, private industry, and representatives of several foreign countries in the establishment of tracking and ground instrumentation.

This worldwide network consisted of tracking and instrumentation sites (sixteen land-based sites and two ships), a control center, and a computing and communications center. The network was capable of performing real-time analysis of both the powered phase and orbiting flight. From orbital insertion until landing, the network provided continuous prediction of the capsule location, monitored the status of the capsule and astronaut, and initiated the command functions necessary for the mission.

In view of the fact that the computing system, located at GSFC, required a reliable input of tracking data to assure accurate location of the capsule at all times, two types of radar were incorporated. Because the spacecraft was

The two tracking ships of the Mercury network.

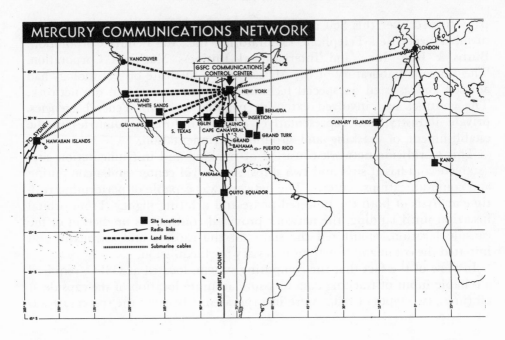

Mercury

of such a size that skin tracking with conventional radar would not be entirely reliable, two radar beacons were placed on board the spacecraft. The frequencies, selected on the basis of the available existing tracking facilities, had C-band as well as S-band tracking capabilities. This provided a degree of redundancy in case one of the onboard beacons failed during an orbital flight.

Of almost equal importance in the early consideration of the orbital flight was the capability of backing up the astronaut by ground command. At strategic sites throughout the network, dual FRW–2 command systems were installed. As it turned out, the command system was required more often during unmanned ballistic and unmanned orbital flights.

For intelligent ground command, a high degree of real-time ground monitoring capability had to be provided for the flight controllers located at the various sites. The spacecraft was designed to incorporate a dual telemetry system operating at separate carrier frequencies. Consequently the ground system had to have the capability of receiving two separate telemetry carriers with the attendant demodulation equipment associated with each.

To assure high reliability of spacecraft-to-ground communications under unknown conditions which might be experienced at approximately 100 miles altitude, again a dual communications system was incorporated into the spacecraft. This consisted of both ultra-high-frequency and high-fre-

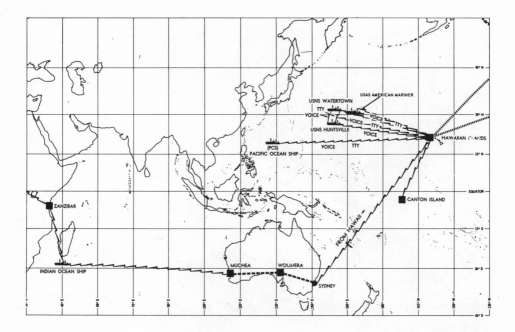

network map.

quency communications systems.   Each ground tracking site had associated receiving and transmitting equipment for these frequencies.

To interconnect the network tracking sites with a reliable intercommunications system, two means of communication between sites and with the control center were established.   The first and basic type consisted of the teletype communications facilities.   Not only did the teletype communications system have to carry the load of communications among the flight controllers located at various sites around the network during the mission, but this system also was designed to deliver the radar tracking data from the radar tracking sites to the central computers.   The second type of ground communications network provided the capability to communicate by voice between the control center and all sites.

To further enhance the reliability of the tracking systems, such as radar, command, communications, and telemetry, early and reliable acquisition of the spacecraft as it approached each tracking site was of major importance. Therefore a great deal of emphasis was placed on the system which could reliably provide pointing information to the various tracking antennas as the spacecraft appeared above the horizon.   In addition, the provision of accurate radar tracking data, the reliable transmission of commands at a predetermined time, and tagging the received telemetry data with an accurate time reference made it necessary that a universal time system be installed at all sites.   This system utilized the time signals of radio stations

71

Goldstone antenna.

WWV, Beltsville, Maryland, and WWVH, Hawaii, operated by the National Bureau of Standards, for calibration.

The Ground Communications Network was an automatic communications system connecting the Mercury sites around the world with GSFC. All intelligence pertaining to the Mercury capsule, except on life support equipment, passed through GSFC. The system carried telephone, teletypewriter, and high-speed data (1,000 bits per second) information to and from the worldwide network on a real-time basis. It accepted a message from a distant site and delivered it to the final destination, regardless of location, in a little over one second. The voice communications system was essentially a private-line telephone system which terminated in SCAMA (Switching, Conferencing, and Monitoring Arrangement) at GSFC, where it could be interconnected or switched over various lines.

Altogether the Mercury system involved approximately 60,000 route-miles of communications facilities to assure an integrated network with worldwide capability for handling satellite data. It comprised 177,000 actual circuit-miles—102,000 miles of teletype; 60,000 miles of telephones; and over 15,000 miles of high-speed data circuits.

The various tracking and telemetry stations throughout the world were integrated into a coordinated network through a communications system terminating in the GSFC Space Operations Control Center.

The Space Operations Control Center had multiple functions:

• Control the operation of all tracking, command, data acquisition, and data transmission facilities utilized in support of scientific space vehicles.

• Coordinate the operation of other ground instrumentation facilities utilized in support of scientific space vehicles, with the exception of certain launch site installations.

• Ensure that operational activities required in support of any spacecraft were properly executed according to the operations plan. In case of inability to fulfill the plan, the control center was to recommend alternative courses of action to the project manager and make certain his decision was properly implemented.

• Provide facilities for monitoring the status of the network and the space vehicle at all times.

• Ensure that the project manager was informed of any departures from normal in the status of the network or of the satellite which might affect the conduct of the operation.

• Coordinate data reduction facilities, both for reduction of tracking data for determination and refinement of the orbit, and also for performance of such computations on the telemetered data as were requested by the project manager. The control center was directly responsible for converting tracking data into formats suitable for data processing.

• Schedule network activities to ensure that the requirements imposed were within the operational capability of the network and avoid conflicts between individual projects insofar as possible.

• Provide facilities in which interested officials could follow the critical phases of specific operations and rapidly obtain information on the status of any satellite during its useful lifetime.

In the performance of these functions the control center utilized a number of special facilities:

Communications.—Ten telephone toll lines, two local voice loop circuits, two special external point-to-point circuits, and ten dial intercom positions provided voice contact between external and internal groups performing functions essential to a given operation. There was also a special voice line to other agencies to pass on satellite orbital data. In addition to the routine in-house routing system for printed messages, the center was tied into the worldwide teletype network via three quasi-real-time data lines and two monitor lines providing minimum delay on circuits of operational importance.

Displays.—Three large edge-lit plexiglass boards were available for display of status, schedules, and graphical data of general interest and importance. An opaque projector presented teletype messages and infor-

In the photograph above, James Donegan (seated second from left), Goddard Mercury Operations Director, and staff monitoring the progress of the MA–6 (John Glenn) flight. Below, the GSFC communications area.

mation of interest on a screen. Digital clocks displayed time (GMT): time to lift-off (countdown), and elapsed time of a hold. The clocks could be preset and controlled to indicate the status of proceedings. A world-map display indicated the nominal orbit on a Mercator projection; and active sites were illuminated to indicate status, acquisition, etc. Doppler launch data were superimposed on a nominal curve on a plotting board, indicating launch vehicle performance after lift-off.

Computation.—Three small computers were available: the CDC–160, the LPG–30, and an RPC–4000. These machines processed data of various types and of particular interest into a form for optimum presentation. For example, teletype data were edited and stored on IBM-style magnetic tape for rapid and easy handling. These machines lent themselves to expeditious solution of last-minute data changes. They were also used to perform various studies to aid in operational planning.

The communications network centering on GSFC included 36 full-period leased teletype lines serving 50 continental and foreign stations in the Minitrack and Deep Space networks, other data acquisition and command stations for scientific satellites, and other agencies in the scientific community engaged in the exploration of space. The 36 circuits (later expanded to 42-line capacity) terminated in a Western Union 111B switching center which combined tape relay, message-switching, and circuit-switching capabilities. Circuit combining facilities permitted the interconnection of

During Project Mercury's MA–6 mission.

Goddard computer room.

any station in the network in any combination for direct conference or real-time data exchange as needed. In addition, six full-period off-net lines were brought into the center. Three TWX, RCA, and Western Union commercial refile services were available. These circuits were used to carry all types of administrative and logistics information, satellite tracking data, satellite prediction and orbital data, and certain types of telemetry data.

All equipment and circuits in the Operations Room were arranged on a patch panel which permitted complete flexibility in interchange or substitution of equipments and links. One of the page printers was equipped with a keyboard for use in keyboard-to-keyboard coordination of data runs with remote stations in the network. Each of the circuits could be directly connected to any station in the network by leg-combining repeaters under switch control. An off-line 19/14 teletype set was provided for special tape preparation.

In the Control Room, two page printers were provided for monitoring purposes. Any lines in the network could be monitored upon request, and outbound traffic from the Control Room was carried by courier to the communications room. Voice communication in the Control Room was handled by standard telephone equipment. Each of 12 operating positions had the capability of using an outside exchange line, local interposition extensions, or a general conference loop; selected positions had the capability of point-to-point connection for immediate contact to facilities such as the communications room. The Operations Director, the Project Coordinator, and the Network Controller were able to select any of the lines in the room. Headset transceivers were generally used, leaving the operators' hands free.

Data Reduction Center.—A data processing center was established for determining the orbital parameters of earth satellites and reducing the scientific data obtained by the experiments contained in these satellites. Computer facilities available at the center included four large-scale general-purpose scientific computers (IBM 7090s) with associated peripheral equipment, as well as a variety of small digital computers, such as the CDC–160 and LPG–30. Scientific data obtained by the satellites were processed by special-purpose equipment developed to handle the many different telemetry formats in use. Underlying principles stressed semiautomatic operation with optimum improvement in the signal-to-noise ratio. Conversion to digital format was a one-step operation, allowing rapid entry into a large-scale computer for the complete reduction and analysis phase. Quick-look facilities in the form of tabulation or strip charts gave the experimenters the opportunity to evaluate their data prior to the final reduction and analysis and thereby determine optimum handling procedures to suit their individual needs.

The objective of the GSFC orbital calculation programs was to determine and predict the orbits of satellites on the basis of observational data. Initially the programs were written by the IBM Vanguard group for the Vanguard IGY project. These were subsequently replaced by programs written by GSFC personnel incorporating improvements in methods and efficiency. Orbit prediction could be done in four ways: Hansen theory, Keplerian ellipse, Brouwer theory, and numerical integration of equations of motion. The output of these orbit-prediction programs could be supplied in a variety of local frames at arbitrary times and in any form required. Output forms used included geodetic latitude, longitude, and height above subsatellite points; azimuth, elevation, and range; local hour angle, declination, right ascension, and direction cosines—all with reference to an arbitrarily selected site on the earth's surface.

Data acquired at the many remote stations had to be processed and reduced. Some of these data were not uniform in quality; therefore, the central data reduction facility had to be extremely flexible and capable of taking into account operational errors. The central facility also had to be able to handle many categories of data and the many variations created by a lack of standardization of all missile ranges and data acquisition networks. Almost without exception, telemetry data were recorded at the stations on magnetic tape.

The first step in the operation was an inspection and evaluation of the tapes received. Selection for further processing was based on the general requirements that the tapes had signals with adequate signal-to-noise ratio and usable timing, standard frequency, and tape-speed controls. The data were then digitalized and stored on digital magnetic tape. In cases where experimenters demanded analog records such as film or strip-chart recordings, these were supplied. In some instances, these were the only means by which the data could be presented. But since digitalizing did allow rapid entry of the data in a computer, it was usually suggested as the preferable method.

The final reduction and analysis of the data in a computer allowed insertion of calibration, linearization, smoothing, selection, correlation, and other data and, finally, merging of the data with orbit and aspect data. Mathematical operations on the data, such as insertion into equations relating measured values to other quantities, were easily performed; and the final output to the experimenter could be in the form of tabulation or graphs as desired.

Goddard-Managed Satellites and Space Probes
7

WHEN THE GODDARD SPACE FLIGHT CENTER was established, its basic mission within the NASA structure was the scientific exploration of space—"to meet the gaps in current knowledge . . . and research in space in all the scientific disciplines as dictated by the expanding knowledge of space phenomena." [80] By December 31, 1963, Goddard had launched some thirty satellites and space probes and performed experiments with over three hundred sounding rockets.

Specific emphasis was placed on experimentation in several scientific areas: atmospheric structure, electric and magnetic fields, astronomy, energetic particles, gravitation, ionospheric structure and behavior, and satellite meteorology, and communications. As a result of investigation in these areas, man's knowledge of the upper atmosphere would be increased and the groundwork would be laid for operational systems of meteorological and communications satellites.

Although much can already be written about the results of the explorations carried out at Goddard before 1964, it must be emphasized that the story here is incomplete. At this point in time, the interpretation of space research is an open-end task. It has not yet been possible to fully interpret all of the mass of data that has already been transmitted. Some satellites are still orbiting and transmitting data that will undoubtedly alter present concepts. Finally, discussion continues among scientists about the significance and interpretation of the data that have already been studied. For these reasons, intrinsic in the nature of scientific advances, the following account of satellites, probes, and sounding rockets must necessarily be incomplete. [81]

Early Satellites Related to the Center Mission

The Center considers *Explorer VI*, launched in August 1959, as its first satellite. Prior to that time, the United States had placed eight satellites in orbit and launched one major space probe as a result of pre-NASA programs.   Although not directly connected with the work at Goddard Space Flight Center, they have been listed here as precursors of the Center's program.

Explorer I

This satellite was launched on January 31, 1958, under the project direction of the Army Ballistic Missile Agency and was the first U.S. satellite placed in earth orbit.   Its IGY experiment was responsible for the discovery of the Van Allen radiation belt—believed by many to be the most significant finding of the International Geophysical Year.   It demonstrated the feasibility of temperature control by satellite surface treatment and showed that micrometeoroids are not necessarily a major hazard in space navigation near the earth.   The satellite ceased transmission on May 23, 1958.

Vanguard I

Launched March 17, 1958, *Vanguard I* was a test of the Vanguard launch vehicle and satellite ejection mechanism under the management of the Naval Research Laboratory.   In an earth orbit, it determined atmospheric density at great altitudes and conducted geodetic measurements.   It revealed that the earth is slightly pear-shaped, and the extensive information gained from it was useful in correcting geophysical map errors.   It revealed much about the pressure of solar radiation and pioneered the use of photocells as a solar power source.   Its lifetime, originally estimated at 200 years, is now believed to be about 2,000 years.   One of its transmitters functioned until January 1965.

Explorer III

Explorer III, launched by the Army on March 26, 1958, went into an orbit slightly more elliptical than planned.   It yielded valuable data on radiation belts and micrometeoroid impacts as well as external and internal temperatures and transmitted for about two months before reentry on June 28, 1958.

Explorer IV

The Advanced Research Projects Agency of the Department of Defense launched *Explorer IV* on July 26, 1958, for the purpose of studying radiation belts detected by *Explorers I* and *II* and to measure artificial radiation created by previous experiments.   It collected data that helped to establish detailed spatial relations and many of the properties of artificial radiation;

and it aided in analysis of the earth's magnetic field. Transmitting until October 1958, it decayed about a year later.

Project Score

Launched December 18, 1958, also under the direction of the Advanced Research Projects Agency, Project Score tested the Atlas ICBM as a launch vehicle. It also tested the feasibility of voice and teletype relay via satellite. For the first time a human voice (President Eisenhower's) was beamed from outer space. It was the first known satellite to be guided into orbit by a radio-inertial system. Its beacon signal terminated December 19, 1958, and the voice signal stopped on December 31, 1958. It reentered the atmosphere on January 21, 1959.

Vanguard II

This satellite, launched under NASA direction on February 17, 1959, was placed in orbit for the purpose of studying the earth's cloud cover. While the satellite was successfully placed in orbit, a wobble which developed in the satellite's orientation prevented interpretation of the cloud-cover data from the two optical telescopes. The payload configuration consisted of a sphere with a shell of highly polished silicon-monoxide-coated magnesium. The two transmitters functioned for 19 days.

Discoverer I

Discoverer I was launched by the Air Force under the direction of the Advanced Research Projects Agency on February 28, 1959. Its objective was to demonstrate the orbital capability of the Discoverer satellite with the Thor-Agena booster and the capability of the ground-support equipment. The satellite was the first to be placed in near-polar orbit. Difficulty with stabilization caused tumbling, which hampered continuous tracking. Transmitters included telemetry and a tracking beacon. The satellite reentered the atmosphere and decayed in mid-March 1959.

Pioneer IV

Launched by NASA on March 3, 1959, this instrumented probe was placed in an earth-moon trajectory to measure radiation in space, to test the photoelectric sensor in the vicinity of the moon, to sample the moon's radiation, and to test long-range tracking.

Pioneer IV, the first U.S. solar satellite, achieved an earth-moon trajectory, and yielded important radiation data in space. An injection below the planned velocity caused it to pass 37,300 miles from the moon and prevented near-lunar experiments. The configuration of this spacecraft was conical with a shell of gold-washed fiber glass, which served as a conductor and antenna. It was tracked for 82 hours to a distance of about 407,000 miles. It is in orbit around the sun.

Discoverer II

Launched on April 13, 1959, by ARPA, its objectives were to maintain a life-supporting temperature and oxygen environment and provide data on propulsion, communications, recovery techniques, and the measurement of cosmic radiation. It achieved a near-circular polar orbit and stabilization was controlled. The timer malfunctioned and caused a premature capsule ejection, preventing a recovery attempt.

Discoverer II was the first satellite to carry a recoverable instrument package. Telemetry was received until April 14, 1959, and the tracking beacon functioned until April 21, 1959. The capsule made impact in the vicinity of the Spitsbergen Islands (Arctic Ocean) on April 26, 1959, and was lost.

Goddard Satellites Leave the Launching Pads

With the launching of *Explorer VI* on August 7, 1959, Goddard Space Flight Center began a series of NASA satellite launchings that was to provide an accumulation of new data so significant and detailed that it would give man new perspective on his environment and solidify the foundation for operational weather and communications satellites. The following presentation of Goddard launchings is primarily chronological, but summary discussions have been inserted in appropriate places to give a clearer picture of some of the achievements of satellite-derived scientific research.

Explorer VI

Explorer VI, launched by an Air Force Thor-Able booster on August 7, 1959, was the first scientific satellite under the project direction of Goddard Space Flight Center. In addition to Goddard personnel, several universities and one private laboratory participated in equipping the satellite with experiments and interpreting the data received.[82]

The Universities of Chicago and Minnesota and the Space Technology Laboratories (STL) developed the instruments for measurement of the Van Allen radiation belt. STL also provided instrumentation for measuring the earth's magnetic field and for a type of one-line television scanning of the earth's cloud cover. NASA and the Air Force Cambridge Research Laboratories provided micrometeoroid experiments. Stanford University provided all equipment for the observation of very-low-frequency radio signals.

Explorer VI, launched from AMR August 7, 1959.

This "paddle wheel" satellite stopped transmitting on October 6, 1959, and reentered the earth's atmosphere sometime before July 1961. During its active lifetime, *Explorer VI* transmitted much valuable data. The most significant results can be briefly summarized.

The University of Chicago, using a triple coincidence telescope—an electronic device for measuring particles—reported that there appeared to be high-energy radiation of 10–20 million electron volts (MeV) on the inner side of the Van Allen radiation belt. It is apparently a narrow proton band, 330 miles thick, at about 1,240 miles from the earth. The total counting rate maximum was about 1,400 counts per square centimeter per second. They detected no protons with energies greater than 75 MeV, or electrons with energies greater than 13 MeV in the vast outer low-energy radiation region. There was some indication that radiation intensity varied with time.

The University of Minnesota also made measurements on the radiation belt but used an ionization chamber and Geiger counter. These measurements were compared with measurements of the University of Chicago and with those made by other spacecraft. Although instruments differed, the University of Chicago and the University of Minnesota measurements showed the same region of hard radiation. At times the radiation intensities at great distances dropped to a level about 5,000 times less than those measured by *Pioneer IV* and 10 times lower than *Pioneer III*.

Variations of radiation with respect to time were noted. In August, radiation at great distances had increased to a point consonant with the

Pioneer III measurements. In general, the measurements showed that the radiation belt had a complicated and variable structure. There appeared to be some correlation between the variations in pockets of radiation at large distances and solar outbursts.

The Space Technology Laboratories installed five instruments on *Explorer VI* that measured various kinds of radiation and magnetic fields and televised the earth's cloud cover. Although the intensity of the radiation fields did not increase with solar activity in readings taken August 16, August 20 readings seemed to indicate correlation between solar activity and increased radiation. One hundred and forty traverses of the radiation belt region indicated that the low-energy radiation zone has a gross structure similar to the radiation belts reported by Van Allen, but fluctuations in intensity indicated that both the inner and outer zones are much more complicated than had been previously indicated.

The data from the magnetic field experiment were quite involved, but there were no unexpected findings. The television scanner data gave only a crude image of the cloud cover, but they did correlate roughly with data from meteorological maps and are of historical significance in that they formed the first satellite-originated, complete, televised cloud-cover picture.

The micrometeoroid counting rate, as conducted by NASA and the Air Force Cambridge Research Laboratories, was somewhat lower than that found in earlier experiments. Stanford University's very-low-frequency detecting experiments showed that the Navy's 15.5-kilocycle-per-second transmitting station was received clearly below the D-region of the ionosphere and dropped out after passage through the D-region at 43.4 miles altitude.

Vanguard III

Vanguard III was launched on September 18, 1959, marking the end of the Vanguard launching activities. The 50-pound satellite achieved the desired orbit of 2,329 miles apogee and 319 miles perigee. The satellite was equipped by the Naval Research Laboratory to measure solar x-radiation and by Goddard Space Flight Center to measure magnetic fields, micrometeoroid impacts, and satellite temperatures. The ionization chambers from the Naval Research Laboratory were saturated most of the time because of the high apogee of the satellite. But the information enabled scientists to refine their determinations of the lower edge of the Van Allen radiation belt.

GSFC's magnetometer worked well; it showed there were systematic variations from the predicted fields. The micrometeoroid experiment showed from 4 to 15 impacts of particles 10^{-9} g or larger per square meter per hour. The thermistors showed that the temperature of the satellite varied between 6° and 27° C. The satellite ceased transmitting on December 11, 1959; it is expected to remain in orbit about 40 years.[83]

Explorer VII

The seventh Explorer satellite was launched by an ABMA Juno II booster on October 13, 1959. The 91.5-pound satellite achieved a successful orbit with an apogee of 680 miles and a perigee of 342 miles. It was the last ARPA originated satellite under NASA cognizance. The Naval Research Laboratory experiment measured Lyman-alpha and solar x-rays. The Research Institute for Advanced Study of the Glenn L. Martin Company installed Geiger tubes for heavy primary cosmic rays; total cosmic-ray counts were made by the University of Iowa. The radiation balance in the earth's atmosphere was measured by the University of Wisconsin. Goddard Space Flight Center conducted micrometeoroid and temperature experiments. Information was received about solar x-ray and Lyman-alpha radiation, heavy cosmic radiation, and cosmic radiation counts. Of special interest was the intense radiation recorded on one orbit as the satellite passed through an aurora.

Some of the experiments were coordinated to show correlations between atmospheric and solar activity. The Geiger-tube radiation counts indicated a correlation during periods of high activity between solar activity and optical emissions from the lower atmosphere. University of Wisconsin experiments indicated correlation between the earth's atmospheric temperature and space temperature.

The heavily instrumented satellite was spin-stabilized and carried two sets of radiation detectors, one an integrating ionization chamber and a Geiger-Mueller tube combined in a single package, and the other a proportional counter telescope. The vehicle also carried a magnetometer to measure the component of the ambient magnetic field perpendicular to the spin axis of the vehicle. A micrometeoroid detector and a device for determining the attitude of the vehicle relative to the sun were also included, but failed to function properly.

The Goddard instrumentation recorded the first penetration of a sensor in flight by a micrometeoroid. The tracking beacon became inoperative on December 12, 1959. Several of the instruments, although designed for short-term transmission, were still transmitting data in 1961.[84]

Pioneer V

One of the most dramatic space launchings in 1960 was that of *Pioneer V,* on March 11. This 94.8-pound interplanetary probe was placed into a successful orbit around the sun by an Air Force Thor-Able booster. Communication was lost soon after launch as the result of a malfunctioning diode, but was restored on April 24.

Pioneer V set a communications distance record that stood until the fall of 1962 when *Mariner II* set a new record on its flight toward

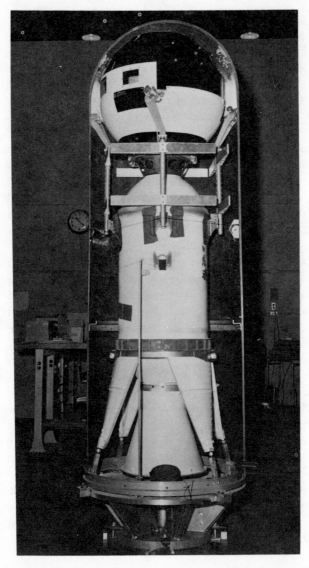

Pioneer V in final checkout.

Venus. *Pioneer V* continued to transmit interplanetary data up to a distance of 17,700,000 miles and its tracking signal was received from a distance of 22,500,000 miles from the earth.

Some of the scientific achievements of *Pioneer V* can be briefly summarized.

Galactic Cosmic Rays.—The frequently observed sharp decreases in the intensity of galactic cosmic rays, called Forbush decreases, are phenomena of solar origin and are not caused by the earth or its magnetic field.[85]   This fact was determined by a comparison of data from *Pioneer V* with simultaneous observations obtained from ground-based neutron monitors. The comparison showed that the magnitude of the large Forbush decreases of April 1, 1960, in the vicinity of the earth was almost identical with that observed at the position of *Pioneer V*, 3,100,000 miles (5 million km) closer to the sun.

The mechanism which produces the 11-year variation in cosmic-ray intensity is centered in the sun, and the size of the volume of space in which the intensity is reduced is greater in radius than one astronomical unit during that part of the solar cycle which was covered by the *Pioneer V* measurements.[86] This result is inferred from the fact that the reduction in intensity produced by this mechanism was nearly the same at the earth and at *Pioneer V*.

Solar Cosmic Rays.—Cosmic rays were observed in space, completely free of any effects due to the earth. Instruments aboard *Pioneer V* directly detected particles accelerated by solar flares, which constitute a potential hazard to man in space. Numerous bursts of such particles were observed with the ionization chamber-Geiger tube package. The correlation between these observations and data from ionosondes at Thule and Resolute Bay on the minimum ionospheric reflection frequency indicates that the particles detected in the bursts were solar protons, with energies probably between 10 and 50 MeV, and that very few, if any, solar electrons above 50 MeV result from flares.[87] Many of these proton events were detected by the counter telescope also. However, the threshold of this instrument for proton detection was about 75 MeV, whereas that for the ionization chamber-Geiger tube package was about 20 MeV.

These solar flare particles, which produce ionization in the polar atmosphere for many successive hours, are not stored in the geomagnetic field. This fact was established by a comparison of data received from *Pioneer V* with polar cap absorption data acquired simultaneously.[88]

The energetic electrons in the earth's outer radiation zone arise from an acceleration mechanism within the geomagnetic field rather than from direct injection of energetic electrons into the field. This conclusion was based on the fact that the flux of electrons of energies in the 50-billion-electron volt (BeV) range reached very high levels in the outer radiation zone, according to *Explorer VII* data, while few, if any, electrons of these energies were detected at *Pioneer V*.[89]

Bremsstrahlung-producing radiation (electromagnetic radiation produced by the sudden retardation of a charged particle), evidently accelerated by solar activity, is present in interplanetary space during the periods of such activity.[90] This type of radiation was detected by the proportional counter telescope on numerous occasions.

The Geomagnetic Field.—The termination of the geomagnetic field was observed at about 14 earth radii on the daylight side of the earth, at least during periods of little geomagnetic activity.[91]   The distance from the earth of this termination was considerably greater than that predicted by most theories.

An anomaly in the geomagnetic field was observed at about 6 earth radii on the daylight side of the earth.[92]   This deviation from the assumed dipolar character of the field was similar to that observed with the earth satellite on the night side of the earth.[93]   The anomalous component of the field is believed to be produced by a ring current circling the earth with its axis parallel to the geomagnetic axis.[94]

The existence of rapid fluctuations in the geomagnetic field between 10 and 14 earth radii was confirmed.[95]   This phenomenon was first observed with instruments aboard the space probe *Pioneer IV* in October 1959.[96] These fluctuations may be produced by the interaction of the geomagnetic field and the ionized particles therein with the interplanetary medium.[97]

Magnetic Fields in Interplanetary Space.—During periods of low solar activity, the interplanetary magnetic field was found to be about 2.7×10^{-5} gauss and nearly perpendicular to the plane of the ecliptic.[98]   During periods of solar activity, fields greater than 50×10^{-5} gauss were observed.   The direction of the fields at such times could not be determined.   The correlation of these increases in the interplanetary field with solar and terrestrial effects leads the experimenters to conclude that these high fields accompany the plasma ejected from the sun during active periods.   Further, these comparatively intense fields are believed to be responsible for the exclusion of galactic cosmic rays from regions of the solar system during Forbush decreases.[99]

Measurement of the Astronomical Unit.—The astronomical unit, expressed in the terms of solar parallax, was found to be 8.79738 ± 0.00082 seconds of arc.[100]   This result, determined from the long-range tracking of *Pioneer V,* is in good agreement with the value of 8.79835 seconds of arc obtained from optical observations of the asteroid Eros.

Tiros I

Tiros I, the first meteorological satellite, was launched into a near-circular orbit of 428.7 miles (690 km) perigee and 465.9 miles (750 km) apogee on April 1, 1960.[101]   Shaped like a hat box, it was about 21 inches high and 42 inches in diameter and weighed about 270 pounds.   The top and sides were covered with solar cells, the primary source of power.   Its main sensors were two TV camera systems.   When viewing the earth vertically, one camera took pictures about 700 to 800 miles on the side, while the other took more detailed pictures about 80 miles on the side.   Since it was spin-stabilized, the cameras could view the earth during only part of each orbit.   Tape recorders made it possible to store pictures taken over areas distant from the United States and to read them out as the satellite passed over the command and data acquisition stations at Fort Monmouth, New Jersey, and Kaena Point, Hawaii.

Tiros I had a useful lifetime of 78 days (1302 orbits). On June 16, 1960, a stuck relay in the satellite drained the batteries, and continued operation caused general failures. During its operational lifetime, *Tiros I* provided 22,952 exciting pictures of the earth's cloud cover, of which an estimated 60 percent were of meteorological interest. Weather patterns over the earth lying roughly between 50° N and 50° S latitude were photographed. These weather patterns, compared with data provided by conventional observations, showed that the satellite data provided more complete and more accurate information than had been possible in the past.

Studies of *Tiros I* pictures indicate that distinct cloud vortex characteristics are probably associated with individual storm types. Striking patterns of large spiral cloud formations, some as much as 1,550 miles in diameter, were observed. Jet streams, thunderstorms, fronts, and regions of moist and dry air were discernible in some photographs. In the absence of obscuring clouds, large ice packs were sometimes seen.[101]

Echo I

Echo I was a 100-foot-diameter, aluminized-plastic inflatable sphere that was placed into orbit on August 12, 1960. The initial orbital parameters were: apogee, 1,049 miles (1,689 km); perigee, 945 miles (1,522 km); period, 118.3 minutes; inclination, 47.2 degrees. The Mylar polyester sphere, including subliming powders, weighed approximately 124 pounds and had been designed by the Langley Research Center. Initial inflation was accomplished by the expansion of residual entrained air when the packaged sphere was ejected from the payload. Inflation was maintained by the use of subliming chemicals. The sphere carried two 10-milliwatt tracking beacons, powered by chemical batteries and solar cells. It was the first passive communications satellite.

The specific objectives of the launch were: to orbit a 100-foot-diameter, aluminized-plastic sphere to be used as a passive reflector of electromagnetic waves; to study the effects of the space environment on large area-to-mass-ratio structures; to measure the reflective characteristics of the sphere and the electromagnetic propagation characteristics of space; and to conduct experiments to determine the feasibility of using such satellites as passive relays in worldwide communication systems.

The principal communications experiments were conducted by the Jet Propulsion Laboratory (JPL) station at Goldstone, California; the Bell Telephone Laboratory (BTL) station, Holmdel, New Jersey; and the Naval Research Laboratory (NRL) station, Stump Neck, Maryland. Goldstone and Holmdel carried out the first communication experiment; JPL transmitted at 2,390 Mc and received at 960.05 Mc; at the other end of the

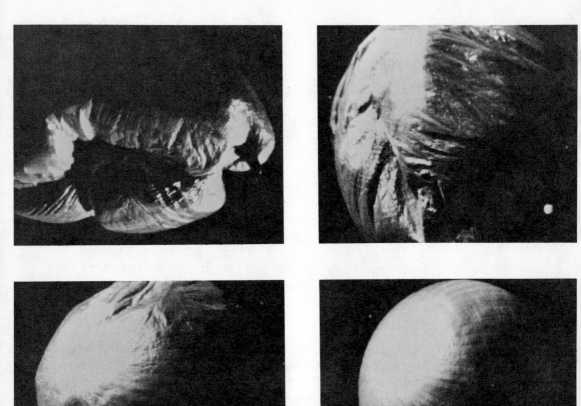

Echo inflation test sequence.

link, BTL received at 2,390 Mc and transmitted at 960.5 Mc. Voice messages were transmitted over the two-way link utilizing wideband frequency modulation with special demodulation techniques developed by BTL. NRL received JPL transmissions at 2,390 Mc, and transmitted at either 2,390 or 2,390.4 Mc, using 2,390 Mc when JPL was not transmitting and 2,390.4 Mc for differentiation from JPL transmissions when JPL was transmitting simultaneously. In addition to experimenting with voice modulation, tests were made with continuous wave "sine wave" modulation, etc., to provide further data for evaluation of the characteristics of the passive satellite transmission media. At a secondary priority on later passes of the satellite, experiments were conducted utilizing narrow-band phase modulation, narrow-band frequency modulation, and single sideband.

Immediately after launch, and for a few days thereafter, beacon function was completely satisfactory. Suitable orbital elements were determined; and the highly directional antennas at NRL, JPL, and BTL were directed at the satellite to well within the required accuracies of 0.2°, 0.2°, and 0.4°, respectively. After a period of time, orbital data points became increasingly uncertain because of several causes. The first of these was the failure of the battery system; this limited beacon power to that supplied directly by the solar cells, so the beacons could function only when the satellite was in sunlight. A second cause was the progressive darkening of the epoxy resin with which the solar cells were coated. This darkening was a design feature which would cause the cells to become inactive within a period of approximately 6 months to 1 year, so that beacon transmissions would eventually cease. Finally, *Echo I*'s gradual change in its aspect with relation to the sun meant that it passed through the earth's penumbra for more extended periods. This development precluded beacon function; the Minitrack orbital data were based on fewer data points, with a consequent loss of accuracy. Antenna-pointing accuracy requirements no longer could be met. Minitrack stopped tracking *Echo I* on December 28, 1960.

Significant information has been gained from *Echo I*.[102]

- The use of a sphere as a passive reflector has been effectively demonstrated. System and space transmission losses did not differ substantially from those anticipated.
- With good reflector sphericity there was no appreciable cross-polarization of reflected signals. However, as wrinkling occurred, there was increasing cross-polarization of signal components.
- The uniquely large area-to-mass ratio of *Echo I* has made it possible to determine the effect of solar pressure on its motion, and a quantitative measure of such effects has been applied to orbit predictions.
- *Echo I* provided data for air drag in the upper atmosphere measurements. Thirty-fold diurnal changes in density in the upper atmosphere at the altitude of about 620 miles (1,000 km) and changes produced by solar disturbances on high-altitude atmospheric density have been reported. The density of the atmosphere at the altitude of the *Echo I* orbit has been calculated from the drag and is reported as about 10^{-17} at about 620 miles (1,000 km) altitude and about 10^{-18} at about 992 miles (1,600 km) altitude.
- An interesting use has been made of observations of *Echo I* to acquire information on the ozone distribution in the atmosphere. An experimenter reported he found the maximum of ozone content between 12.4 miles (20 km) and 18.6 miles (30 km) altitude, with the number of molecules per cubic centimeter as $2 \times 10^{12}/cm^3$ and decreasing 10^{11} molecules/cm^3 at the altitude of 40.3 miles (65 km).
- Another experimenter reported that he had used a special radar tracking technique to search for ionization surrounding *Echo I* but that he

found no evidence of such ionization in the case of either *Echo I* or *Sputnik III*.

- The whole process of tracking, determining orbits, and pointing narrow-beam antennas using computed drive tapes has been demonstrated successfully; this means a satellite can be used in synchronized fashion for communication relay between two remotely located sites.
- Radar cross-sectional measurements have been made on the satellite. They have indicated a gradual decrease in average area which, presently, appears to be about one-half of the original value.

At the time of publication, *Echo I* was still in orbit, visible to the naked eye in the night sky, and still capable of reflecting radio signals. Although the satellite was slightly crumpled and had lost much of its original shape as the result of micrometeoroid punctures, its orbit and condition were better than had been anticipated. The satellite was expected to reenter the earth's atmosphere in 1968.

Explorer VIII

This satellite was launched on November 3, 1960, with the objective of studying the temporal and spatial distribution of ionospheric parameters by direct measurement. The 90-pound satellite was launched into an orbit of 50° inclination with a 258-mile (415 km) perigee and a 1,423-mile (2,290 km) apogee. Spin stabilization at 30 rpm was used. Data transmissions stopped on December 27, 1960, the approximate date estimated for exhaustion of the chemical batteries. No solar cells were used.

The instruments included a radio frequency (RF) impedance probe for determination of electron concentration, four ion traps for measurements of positive-ion concentration and mass distribution, two Langmuir probes for measurement of electron temperature, an electric-field meter for determination of satellite charge distribution, and two instruments for determining micrometeoroid impacts. All the instruments operated continuously with the exception of the electric-field meter, which operated only by command.

One of the micrometeoroid detectors consisted of two microphones with a maximum detectable sensitivity of 10^{-4} dyne-second and a dynamic range of 3 decades. This detector reported frequency and momenta of impacts. The second micrometeoroid detector used a photomultiplier tube with a 1000A evaporated layer of aluminum on the window. Light flashes generated by micrometeoroid impacts on the aluminum were translated into pulses of varying length and amplitude by the photomultiplier. The pulses were interpretable in terms of the kinetic energy of the impinging particle. Sensitivity was estimated to be sufficient to detect particles of $< 10^{-15}$ g having a velocity of 20 km/sec.

The radio frequency impedance probe experiment could be connected to the antenna upon command, to study ion sheath effects.

Two of the four ion traps were single-grid models and thus sensitive to photoemission. The remaining two ion traps were multiple-grid models not sensitive to photoemission. Comparison of the data from the two experiments gives the magnitude of the photoemission current.

The Langmuir probe measured both electron and positive-ion currents. The electric-field meter was of the rotating-shutter type and capable of measuring fields up to 10,000 volts/meter. Its noise equivalent was less than 5 volts/meter and residual drift less than 5 volts/meter.

Explorer VIII data have disclosed a number of interesting discoveries. It measured the diurnal electron temperatures between altitudes of 244 miles (400 km) and 1,364 miles (2,200 km) and found the daytime temperature to be about 1,800° K and the nighttime temperature to be about 1,000° K. In its orbit it measured an electron concentration of 1.3×10^4 electrons/cm³. Its ion probe reported the mean mass of the ions as 16 atomic mass units, indicating the predominance of atomic oxygen in the ions. The ion density profile determined by *Explorer VIII* up to 465 miles (750 km) was similar to that determined before, but, in addition, showed the upper atmosphere to be isothermal. Another interesting and important result found by *Explorer VIII* was the ratio of helium to hydrogen ions. Above 496 miles (800 km) the helium ion was found to be an important constituent of the ionosphere, and at the altitude of 1,364 miles (2,200 km) there was a heavy predominance of helium ions over hydrogen ions. This discovery explains the high air densities encountered by *Echo I* in its high-altitude orbit. The instruments carried by *Explorer VIII* also revealed that the spacecraft was charged and that, as the altitude of the craft increased, the negative charge changed to positive.[103]

Tiros II

Launched November 23, 1960, into an orbit of 431 miles (730 km) apogee and 406 miles (625 km) perigee, *Tiros II* was similar to *Tiros I* but carried, in addition, infrared sensors to observe the radiation from the earth and its atmosphere, and a magnetic coil for partial control of orientation. The magnetic coil was included on the basis of experience with *Tiros I*, whose spin axis had moved in an unexpected manner (but fortunately remained more favorable for observations). These motions were caused by the interaction of an induced magnetic field in the satellite with the magnetic field of the earth. The new coil allowed some control of satellite orientation and camera pointing.

Presumably because of a malfunction associated with the lens of the wide-angle camera, the pictures from this *Tiros II* camera failed to show the detail that was so striking in the *Tiros I* photographs. They did disclose large cloud masses or clear areas, and proved useful in day-to-day weather analyses and forecasting. The narrow-angle camera pictures were of excellent quality.

Prior to the launching of *Tiros II,* 21 countries were offered the necessary orbital data if they wished to conduct special meteorological observations to be correlated with the satellite observations. Ten of the 17 countries which indicated a desire to participate chose to proceed with their programs even though the wide-angle camera picture quality proved poorer than expected.

The measurements made by the infrared detectors on *Tiros II* were: temperature of the top of the water vapor layer (6.3 microns (μ)); surface temperatures or cloud-top temperatures (8 to 12 μ), which help to distinguish cloudy areas at night; the amount of reflected radiation (0.2 to 5 μ); the amount of emitted radiations (7 to 30 μ); and low-resolution cloud pictures (0.5 to 0.7 μ).

The magnetic orientation coil, on several separate occasions, functioned as planned. The sensor instrumentation worked properly until mid-January 1961 when a malfunction in the clock control system forced discontinuance of remote wide-angle pictures to reduce the danger of a power drain that would disable the entire satellite.

The operation of *Tiros II* continued during most of 1961, but with a more or less progressive deterioration in the quality of data obtained. The blackbody sensor of the wide-angle radiometer failed in March. Of the scanning radiometer channels, the 6.3-μ channel had degraded early in the year, the 7- to 30-μ channel in early April; and no useful infrared data were obtained after April 23, 1961. The infrared electronics and tape recorder continued to function until the satellite was shut off in early December after more than a year in orbit. Except for temporary suspensions, the cameras had been programed to operate regularly until the *Tiros III* launch on July 12, 1961, and from then until August 8, 1961, on an average of two orbits per day. Cloud pictures of operationally significant meteorological value were obtained in early August. After August 8, camera programing was sporadic because of power limitations. The last pictures, in November 1961, were still not completely useless although obviously degraded. A total of 36,156 pictures was obtained.

The third pair of spin-up rockets was fired with partial success in mid-September 1961. The fourth pair was successfully fired on September 28 after more than 10 months in orbit. The magnetic orientation coil worked well until late November 1961. In early December 1961, the satellite no longer appeared to be responding to orientation coil commands and was so oriented that the sun shining on the base plate produced excessive heating and very little power. The beacons were shut off on December 3, 1961, but the satellite is still in orbit. Case studies have clearly demonstrated the expected correlation between the 8- to 12-μ atmospheric window data and the concurrent patterns of cloud cover and cloud-top altitude.

During the fall of 1961, a *Tiros II Radiation Data User's Manual* was published, along with Volume I of the *Tiros II Radiation Catalog.* Volume I of this catalog contains analyzed grid point data for fifty orbits of the *Tiros II* scanning radiometer data.[104]

Perhaps the most striking of the *Tiros II* picture data were several examples of narrow-angle camera photographs of sea ice in the area of the Gulf of St. Lawrence. One series of such examples was obtained in January 1961; the second in late March. The March pictures included coverage from the Gaspé Peninsula to east of Newfoundland and show significant changes in the ice patterns, particularly in the vicinity of Anticosti Island.

Explorer IX

Explorer IX, a 12-foot inflatable sphere made of Mylar and aluminum foil, weighed 15 pounds. It was launched on February 16, 1961, for the purpose of obtaining atmospheric densities from drag measurements. A project of Langley Research Center with GSFC participation, *Explorer IX* went into orbit with a perigee of 395 miles, an apogee of 1,605 miles, and an inclination of 39°. The tracking beacon carried by the sphere failed to operate after the sphere was placed in orbit, but optical tracking from the ground was successful. By means of this satellite, density of the atmosphere at an altitude of 434 miles was calculated from drag for comparison with values calculated from *Echo I* at about twice this altitude. The sphere was sensitive to changes in the density along relatively small segments of its orbit and was thus able to reveal the effect of solar disturbances on upper-atmosphere density.

The results obtained by *Explorer IX,* combined with those of *Echo I* and other satellites such as *Vanguard I,* showed that the upper atmosphere is a dynamic region of changing density caused by the diurnal variation of sunlight and by the smaller changes of energy associated with solar disturbances.[105] The satellite reentered April 9, 1964.

Explorer X

This spin-stabilized earth satellite, weighing about 79 pounds, was launched on March 25, 1961. It entered a highly eccentric orbit with an apogee of about 186,000 miles located at an angle of 140° to 150° from the sun-earth line, and a perigee of about 100 miles.

The highly eccentric orbit was selected for the purpose of studying the properties of the magnetic field and the solar interplanetary plasma over a region extending from close to the earth out to a point where the effects of the earth's magnetic field should be negligible. The scientific payload consisted of an extremely sensitive rubidium-vapor magnetometer, two flux-gate saturable-core magnetometers to measure the spatial and temporal var-

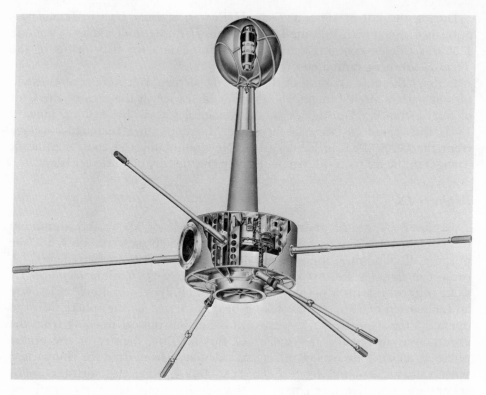

Explorer X, an interplanetary probe, launched March 25, 1961.

iations of the geomagnetic and interplanetary fields, and a multigrid plasma probe to determine the flux, energy spectrum, and directionality of very low energy protons in the plasma. Since the satellite was spin-stabilized, a sun sensor was used to provide information about the orientation of the instruments relative to the sun. Power for the satellite was provided by batteries having an active life of about 60 hours, sufficient to permit continuous measurements to be made on the first outward pass to apogee.

Quiet magnetic conditions prevailed prior to and during the first day of the satellite's outward pass to apogee; solar activity was confined to Class 1 and 1— flares. However, at 10:15 Universal Time on the second day after launch, a Class 3 flare occurred near the east limb of the sun, producing disturbed magnetic conditions in the vicinity of the satellite and at the earth. Significant findings are:

Magnetic Fields.—The measured geomagnetic field between 1.8 and 5 earth radii over the South Atlantic Ocean was found to be less than the computed field.[106] The discrepancy was attributed to the existence of the field source having its maximum strength at an altitude between 1.8 and 3 earth radii at the geomagnetic equator. From 5 to 6.6 earth radii, the measured geomagnetic field was in agreement with the computed field. Superposition of the earth's field and the interplanetary field was detected between 11 and 19 earth radii. Beyond 19 earth radii the earth's field was negligible.

The interplanetary field between 20 and 21.5 earth radii was found to be stable. However, its magnitude was more than anticipated. The field was approximately radial from the sun. An abrupt change in the character of the interplanetary field was detected simultaneously with the first detection of the solar interplanetary plasma at 21.5 earth radii. Large fluctuations both in magnitude and direction were encountered for five hours after the onset of the abrupt change and were attributed to the passage of shock waves.[107]

When the satellite was at 37.1 earth radii, an increase in the interplanetary field intensity occurred at about the same time that a sudden commencement was observed at the earth's surface, indicating that little if any delay was associated with the arrival of the sudden commencement disturbance at the earth's surface from outside the earth's field.

Solar Interplanetary Plasma.—The *Explorer* X satellite provided the first experimental observation of a plasma in interplanetary space.[108] A strongly spin-modulated signal was present at all energies near the earth, from 1.3 to 2.9 earth radii. The interplanetary plasma was first detected at 21 earth radii, and its presence was confirmed out to 38.5 earth radii.

Correlation of the plasma data with the magnetic field data indicated that the presence of the plasma was coincident with a relatively weak field which fluctuated in magnitude and direction. Absence of plasma was associated with strong steady fields directed away from the sun. Large fluctuations in plasma intensity were detected between a minimum detectable value of less than 5×10^6 and about $10^{10}/cm^2$-sec.

Explorer XI

Explorer XI, the gamma-ray astronomy satellite, was launched on April 27, 1961, into an orbit with an apogee of 1,113.2 miles, perigee of 304 miles, an inclination of 28.8°, and period of 108.1 minutes. The objective of this satellite was the detection of extraterrestrial high-energy gamma rays, such as result from the decay of neutral π mesons. The experiment was designed to detect and map the direction and intensity of the galactic gamma rays above the earth's atmosphere. Earlier balloon experiments had been limited by the background radiation produced in the residual atmosphere.

Explorer XI resembled an old-fashioned street lamp with the payload constituting the lamp and the attached burned-out fourth stage the post. Before being put into orbit, the payload and the fourth stage were spun about the longitudinal axis at 6 cps, but the whipping of the external loop antennas and the nutation damper included in the satellite converted the rotation into an end-to-end tumbling that was desired for scanning the entire sky. Storage batteries carried the major portion of the power load.

The instrumentation consisted of a gamma-ray telescope and sensing devices in the forward end of the payload. The latter reported the position of the satellite relative to the earth's horizon and to the sun. The telescope consisted of a sandwich of scintillation crystals and of a Cerenkov detector contained in an anticoincidence shield. The use of crystals with different fluorescent decay rates—namely, CsI (Tl) and NaI (Tl)—permitted differentiation between gamma rays and neutrons. When the instrumentation was not in the anticoincident mode, primary cosmic-ray protons could be observed. These particles have known energy and can be used as a calibration standard for the energy of the gamma rays.

The energy spectrum of the positive particles was found to be peaked at 500 electron volts even though the shape of the energy spectrum showed large variations. The number density of the plasma protons ranged from 6 to 20 cm³. The plasma arrived from the general direction of the sun.

The aluminum housing of the satellite, serving as a micrometeoroid shield, emitted secondary neutrons and gamma rays, the background counts from which could obscure the results if the intensity of celestial gamma rays was low.

Explorer XI achieved too high an apogee and consequently reached into the inner Van Allen belt, which masked the gamma-ray counts in that portion of the orbit. As a result, useful data were supplied only about five percent of the time in orbit. Preliminary results of the analysis of these data have been given by the Massachusetts Institute of Technology, based on some 23 hours of useful observing time in a period of 23 days.

During this period 127 events which could have been gamma rays occurred. Of these, 105 were shown by analysis to have come from the direction of the earth and were presumably produced in the earth's atmosphere; the remaining 22 came from a variety of directions. The analysis of arrival directions was complicated by the fact that all portions of the sky were not scanned for the same length of time. Therefore use was made of an idealized model of the galaxy. It was assumed to be a disk 100,000 light years in diameter and 1,000 light years in thickness, filled uniformly with a gas of one hydrogen atom per cubic centimeter, and having a cosmic-ray density equal to its value in the vicinity of the earth. By means of this model, "predicted" intensities were used to evaluate an expected number of counts in each of the cells into which the sky was divided. Comparison of the "predictions" with the observations showed a good degree of consistency with regard to spatial distribution and to the number of events. The results are consistent with a source strength of gamma rays in the galaxy of the order of 10^{-24} cm^{-3}-sec^{-1}.[109]

Tiros III

This satellite was launched on July 12, 1961, into an orbit with an apogee of 506.44 miles, a perigee of 461.02 miles, and a 48.2° inclination. Both TV cameras were of the wide-angle type. *Tiros III* was basically the same as *Tiros II* except that a third set of infrared sensors developed by V. Suomi, of the University of Wisconsin, was added; these sensors, very much like his experiment on *Explorer VII*, consisted of two pairs of hemispheres (each pair consisting of one black and one white hemisphere), mounted on mirrors, on opposite sides of the spacecraft.

The satellite was commanded from, and data were acquired at, stations located on St. Nicolas Island, California, and Wallops Island, Virginia. An auxiliary command (only) station at Santiago, Chile, permitted obtaining more hurricane and other cloud-picture data over the tropical Atlantic Ocean than would otherwise have been possible.

Tiros III proved a worthy successor to the earlier satellites in the series, especially with regard to the discovery and tracking of Atlantic hurricanes and Pacific typhoons. The cloud-picture data from these and other weather situations were made available for operational weather analysis and forecasting through internationally disseminated operational nephanalyses.

On more than 50 separate occasions, *Tiros III* photographed tropical cyclones in all stages of development. Five hurricanes (Anna through Esther, inclusive) and one tropical storm were seen in the Atlantic; two hurricanes and a tropical storm were seen in the data-sparse Pacific near Baja California. Typhoons Kathy through Tilda, nine storms in all, were followed in the central and western Pacific.

On a single day (September 11, 1961), *Tiros III* photographed Hurricane Betsy (in a dissipating stage), Carla (as it hit the Texas coast), and Debbie; discovered the tropical storm later designated as Hurricane Esther; and photographed Typhoons Nancy and Pamela.

One of the two *Tiros III* cameras ceased operation on July 27, 1961, apparently because of a stuck shutter, confirming the desirability of redundant wide-angle cameras. Some deterioration of the quality of the TV pictures of the second camera was noted as early as the second week in August, and became progressively worse. Routine preparation of operational nephanalyses was stopped in late November 1961, when the picture quality became too poor. Few nephanalyses were transmitted after that date, and archiving of the pictures was terminated. The tape recorder on the second camera ceased to function on December 5, 1961, preventing further data acquisition in remote mode. It was possible to resume direct picture taking in early January 1962, but quality remained poor and the pictures were of little, if any, practical value. Over 35,000 pictures were obtained through the end of December 1961.

Degradation of the 6.3-μ and 7- to 30-μ infrared channels was noted as early as August 5, 1961. No useful infrared data were obtained after October 30, 1961; for several weeks before then, about 50 percent of the data were lost because of problems with the tape recorder playback mechanism.[110]

Explorer XII

Explorer XII, an Energetic Particles Satellite, was launched on August 15, 1961, in an orbit with an apogee of 47,800 miles, a perigee of 180 miles, and an inclination of 33°. The highly eccentric orbit permitted measurements both in interplanetary space and inside the earth's magnetosphere. About 90 percent of the time of the satellite was spent in the Van Allen belt region. The objectives of this satellite were to describe the protons and electrons trapped in the Van Allen radiation belt; to study the particles coming from the sun, including the occasional very intense bursts of high-energy protons which present a hazard to manned flight; to study the cosmic radiation from outside the solar system; and to correlate particle phenomena with the observed magnetic field in space about the earth.

Explorer XII was octagonal in shape, 19 inches from side to side, and 27 inches long, including a magnetometer boom. It carried four laterally extended paddles, carrying solar cells. Prior to injection into orbit, the satel-

Explorer XII, an energetic particles satellite, was launched on August 15, 1961.

lite and third stage were spun to 150 rpm for stabilization. After burnout of the third stage, a yoyo despin device slowed the rate down to 31 rpm. Further despinning to 18 rpm occurred as the solar paddles were extended just prior to separation of the spacecraft from the third stage.

Seven experiments were carried in the satellite:

(1) A proton analyzer was used to measure the proton flux and distribution of energies in the space beyond 6 earth radii. Although the mass of the particles was not measured, the particles were assumed to be protons, since the latter probably constitute at least 85 percent of the positive-ion population in space.

(2) A three-core flux-gate magnetometer, sensitive to a few gammas, was used to measure the earth's vector magnetic field at distances of 3 to 10 radii.

(3) The trapped-radiation experiment (four Geiger counters and three CdS cells) measured the fluxes and energies of particles emitted by the sun, the galactic cosmic rays, as well as trapped Van Allen belt particles.

(4) The cosmic-ray experiment monitored cosmic rays beyond the effect of the earth's magnetic field during the apogee portion of the orbit. The instrumentation consisted of a double telescope for cosmic rays, a single crystal detector of energetic particles, and a Geiger-Mueller telescope for cosmic rays. The group of instruments was capable of obtaining data on the flux of moderate to very energetic protons 1 to 700 MeV, on the flux of low-energy alpha particles, and on the differential spectrum of proton energy.

(5) An ion-electron detector was carried to measure particle fluxes, types, and energies in and above the Van Allen belt. This device consisted of a photomultiplier tube coated with a powder phosphor, $ZnS(Ag)$, in combination with absorbing screens for the detection of energetic particles and with a scattering block for the detection of electrons. The energy flux could be measured for protons with energies below 1 MeV and for electrons below 100 KeV.

(6) An experiment was carried to determine the deterioration of solar cells resulting from direct exposure to the radiation in the Van Allen belt, and to compare the effectiveness of glass filters in preventing degradation of solar cells.

(7) An optical aspect experiment was carried to determine the orientation in space of the spacecraft as a function of time. Six photodiodes gave the position of the spin axis of the satellite relative to the sun's elevation with an accuracy of about 5° in azimuth and elevation.

The launch occurred as planned, and all experiments functioned normally until December 6, 1961, when the satellite ceased transmitting; telemetry coverage of nearly 100 percent was maintained until then. By September 12 the spin rate of the satellite had increased from the initial value of 27.8 to 28.63 rpm as a result of the solar-radiation pressure on the solar cell paddles. The unprotected cells in the solar cell experiment suffered a major degradation when the spacecraft passed through a point of high proton concentration in the Van Allen belt. Degradation for the test cell patches covered by glass was not noticeable.

The instrumentation carried in this satellite indicated that the level of electron flux in the outer portion of the Van Allen belt was about three orders lower than what had previously been considered to be present. The ion-electron detector, which was capable of measuring protons of low energy, showed that protons are present in the outer Van Allen belt. This region was at one time thought to contain only electrons. The instrumentation on board this satellite detected electrons out to a boundary of 8 earth radii, with a maximum flux at 6 to 7 earth radii. The data from the satellite confirmed existence of a low-energy proton current ringing the earth in an east-to-west direction, perpendicular to perpetual north-south spiraling motion along geomagnetic field lines.[111]

Explorer XIII

The effects of micrometeoroids or cosmic dust in collisions with spacecraft, and the degree of likelihood of collisions, were unknown, but the possibility that the particles constitute a hazard to travel in the space environment was very real and required investigation. The micrometeoroid satellite, *Explorer XIII,* a project of the Langley Research Center with GSFC participation, was designed to provide an improved estimate of the danger of penetration of spacecraft by cosmic dust by securing direct measurements of the puncture hazards in spacecraft structural skin specimens at satellite altitudes. In addition, the satellite carried instruments to measure micrometeoroid flux rates and to obtain data regarding the erosion of spacecraft materials.

The satellite was launched on August 25, 1961, failed to obtain a high enough perigee, and all the data collected during its 2½ days of life were telemetered during 13 minutes of time. It reentered August 27, 1961.

Explorer XIII carried a group of experiments installed around the fourth stage of a Scout launch vehicle. The satellite was cylindrical in shape, 76 inches in length, and 24 inches in diameter; the overall weight was about 187 pounds. Five types of detectors were carried. One consisted of a battery of pressurized cells in which the pressure was released upon puncture. In the second type, foil gauges showed impact of micrometeoroids by a change in resistance. A third type of experiment showed a change of resistance in wire grids when a wire was broken by impact. Another detector used photoelectric cells which detected the light transmitted through the aluminized Mylar sheets. The fifth experiment recorded impacts on piezoelectric crystals.

The satellite was spin-stabilized during the last stage of burning. It was expected that interaction of the satellite with the magnetic field of the earth would cause the original spin to turn into a tumbling motion after 10 days. Two separate telemeters were used for storing and telemetering data. Both used Goddard's Minitrack telemetry and coding system.[112]

P–21 Electron Density Profile Probe

The P–21 space probe was launched on October 19, 1961, from Wallops Island by means of a Scout rocket in a nearly vertical trajectory. The altitude achieved was 4,261 miles. The payload itself was in the form of an eight-sided frustrum and weighed 94 pounds. The heat shield had been selected for low electrical conductivity, to permit an attempt to use the stored antennas during the propulsion period.

The flight of the probe was about 2 hours in duration. It was launched near mid-day at a time when the ionosphere appeared quiet. The payload was spin-stabilized about its axis before fourth-stage separation. Telemetry of the swept-frequency r-f probe data made use of the 73.6-Mc frequency. The instrumentation carried consisted of: (1) a continuous-wave (CW) propagation experiment to measure the ionosphere profile; (2) an r-f probe experiment to measure the ionospheric electron density, especially at altitudes above 620 miles where data are particularly scarce; and (3) a swept-frequency probe to provide information on the power absorbed by electron pressure waves. Two CW signals were transmitted from the rocket to the ground, one at 12.27 Mc and one at 73.6 Mc. They were controlled to an exact 6 to 1 ratio. Comparison of the two frequencies for Faraday rotation gave the columnar electron density in the path traversed by the beam; this experiment was of value only during the ascent of the rocket and only below 2,480 miles. A new instrument was used with the dual purpose of providing information on electron densities in the ionosphere and information concerning the behavior of the probes themselves.

It was planned to calibrate the r-f probe during ascent to 2,480 miles by means of the CW experiment and to use the probe measurements for the remainder of the flight. The r-f probe made use of a capacitor in which the dielectric constant of the gas between the plates was affected by the ionization of the gas. Comparison of the capacity of the probe when in the ionosphere and when outside supplied the information necessary to determine electron density in the ionosphere. The heat shield had been selected for low electrical conductivity to permit an attempt to use the stored antennas during the propulsion period.

Tiros IV

This satellite was launched on February 8, 1962, into an orbit with a 48.29° inclination, an apogee of 525 miles, and a perigee of 471 miles.   One of the TV cameras was a standard Tiros wide-angle type; the second carried a Tegea Kinoptik lens not previously used on Tiros.   In the scanning radiometer, the 7- to 30-μ sensor had been dropped to provide a channel for picture-timing data.   Beacon frequencies had been transferred from the 108-Mc to the 136-Mc band.   Otherwise the satellite was basically the same as *Tiros III*.   Vidicon picture transmission ceased on June 11, 1962, after some 30,000 pictures were transmitted.[113]

OSO I

The Orbiting Solar Observatory satellite, designed for the study of radiations from the sun with instrumentation located above the earth's atmosphere, was launched on March 7, 1962.   *OSO I* weighed about 458 pounds.   It reached an orbit with an apogee of 369 miles and a perigee of 343.5 miles, an inclination of 32.8°, and a period of 96.15 minutes.   The measurements included ultraviolet radiation studies using narrow-band detectors, a gamma-ray experiment to study solar emission in the 0.1- to 500-MeV region, neutron flux measurements from the earth and the sun, and studies of the time variation of solar ultraviolet, x-ray, and gamma-ray emissions.   An instrument obtained spectral and spatial variations in the 1A and 10A radiation region as the instrument's look-angle scanned across the inner corona and the solar disk.   Gamma rays in the 0.1- to 5-MeV region were detected by a combination of scintillation counters.   An electronic pulse height analysis of the counter pulses yielded the energy spectrum of the rays.   To measure gamma rays in the 100- to 500-MeV region, a Cerenkov detector viewed from four directions by multiplier tubes in conjunction with an anticoincident scintillator was used.   The neutron experiment, using BF_3 counters, monitored the neutron flux from the earth

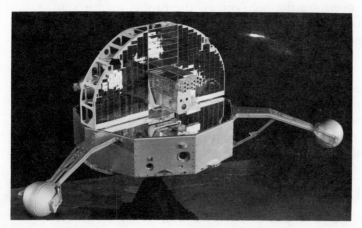

Orbiting Solar Observatory I, launched March 7, 1962.

and the sun.   One objective of this experiment was to determine whether the lower radiation belt arises from the decay of neutrons emitted from the earth's atmosphere.

The satellite consisted of a spinning portion for gyroscopically stabilizing the payload in space and a servo-driven instrumentation section providing azimuth and partial elevation control.   This instrumentation section was oriented within one minute of arc.   It housed about 173 pounds of instrumentation requiring a stabilized view of the sun for operation.   Additional instrumentation was carried in the spinning wheel portion of the satellite. Power for the servosystems and the instruments was furnished by solar cells and rechargeable chemical storage cells.

After May 22, 1962, contact was lost with *OSO I*.   Then contact was reestablished on June 24, 1962, and satisfactory data were received until August 6, 1963, thereby exceeding the expected life of the satellite by almost a year.   The satellite is still in orbit.

All experiments transmitted as programed, resulting in a significant increase in knowledge about the composition and behavior of the sun.   Data revealed tentative evidence that solar flares may be preceded by a series of microflares whose sequence and pattern may be predictable.   *OSO I* reported at least four of these series during a year in orbit.[114]

P–21a Electron Density Profile Probe

A second electron density profile probe, P–21a, was launched on March 29, 1962.   (See the account of the launch of P–21 on October 19, 1961, for more details on the mission and instrumentation of the electron density probes.)   In addition to equipment carried on P–21, P–21a had a swept-frequency radio-frequency probe and a positive-ion detector.   Like P–21, the second probe was to measure electron density profile and intensity of ions in the atmosphere.   However, it was launched so the measurements could be made at night.   The probe achieved an altitude of 3,910 miles and transmitted good data.   The 12.3-Mc transmission failed, but Faraday rotation data were obtained by 73.6 Mc to give electron density profile at nighttime.   As a result of P–21a data, it was concluded that the characteristics of the ionosphere differ drastically from the daytime state when the temperature of the ionosphere is much cooler.

The data from the P–21 and P–21a probes and from satellites were combined with sounding rocket data to enable scientists to map in greater detail the structure of the upper atmosphere.   These data show that there are two transition regions (from O^+ to He^+ and from He^+ to H^+) in the upper ionosphere rather than a single transition from O^+ to H^+ as was previously believed.   The O^+/He^+ transition, i.e., $O^+/He^+=1$, was between 800 and 1,400 kilometers, depending on the atmospheric temperature.   The measured temperature in the upper ionosphere was found to be constant with altitude within a few percent and consistent with a previously developed empirical relation which predicts the temperature as a function of diurnal time and of solar activity. The determined altitudes of the ion transition levels were in good agreement with a theoretical model which describes these altitudes as a function of atmospheric temperature.

Ariel I

On April 26, 1962, the first international satellite was launched as a joint United Kingdom-United States project. The satellite was designated *Ariel I,* the International Ionosphere Satellite. The spacecraft transmitted regularly until November 1963, when its transmission became intermittent.

The satellite had an overall diameter of 23 inches, was 22 inches high, and weighed 136 pounds. It was spin stabilized at a rate of 12 to 36 rpm. Solar cells and nickel-cadmium batteries supplied the power. Data were stored on a 100-minute tape recorder. Orbital parameters were: apogee, 754.2 miles; perigee, 242.1 miles; inclination, 53.86°; period, 100.9 minutes; eccentricity, 0.057.

This project developed from proposals made in 1959 to NASA by the British National Committee on Space Research. These proposals were in response to a United States offer to the Committee on Space Research (COSPAR) of the International Council of Scientific Unions to launch

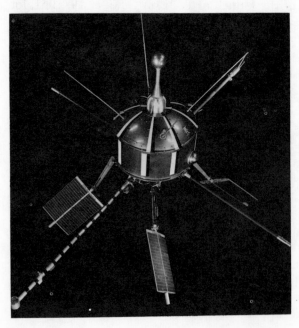

Ariel I, launched April 26, 1962.

scientific experiments or complete satellites prepared by scientists of other nations. The content of the program and the division of responsibility between NASA and the British Committee were agreed to during discussions that took place in late 1959 and early 1960. Subsequently the NASA Administrator assigned project responsibility for the United States to the Goddard Space Flight Center.

This assignment included the design, fabrication, integration, and testing of the spacecraft structure, power supply telemetry, command receiver, thermal control, and data storage. GSFC supplied the vehicle, was responsible for launch, performed data acquisition via the worldwide Minitrack network, and provided data processing. The United Kingdom had the responsibility for the design, fabrication, and testing of all flight sensors and their associated electronics up to the telemetry encoder input. The United Kingdom also was responsible for data analysis and interpretation.

The University College, London, carried out a number of experiments that included an electron temperature and density determination based on Druyvesteyn's modification of the Langmuir probe to determine the electron density and temperature near the satellite. Ion mass, composition, and temperature instrumentation was essentially the same as the electron temperature experiment with another method of temperature measurement, a solar Lyman-alpha emission measurement. This last experiment measured two parts of the solar spectrum to enable simultaneous and nearly continuous observations of the state of the ionosphere and of the solar atmosphere. In addition, University College installed instruments to measure solar x-ray emission, latitude and longitude of the sun with respect to the satellite, and satellite spin rate.

Imperial College, London, installed instrumentation to make accurate measurements of the primary cosmic ray energy spectrum and the effects of interplanetary magnetic field modulation of this spectrum. The University of Birmingham conducted ionosphere electron density measurements with instruments that differed from those of the University College, London, to provide checks on the measurements.

Goddard Space Flight Center provided subsystems that accommodated telemetry, data encoder, tape recorder, power system, and spacecraft parameters (housekeeping) system.[115]

Tiros V

Tiros V was launched from the Atlantic Missile Range on June 19, 1962. The infrared sensor had not functioned in a prelaunch test, but the launch was not delayed to repair the sensor; the satellite was needed for observations, during the August-September tropical storm season. The orbit, with a 367-mile perigee and a 604-mile apogee, was more elliptical than planned, but good picture transmission was still possible.

Tiros V is mated to second stage of launch vehicle.

Tiros V liftoff from Cape Canaveral, June 19, 1962.

The first camera ceased transmitting data on July 6, 1962, and the second on May 4, 1963. During its 10½ operational months, *Tiros V* transmitted 57,857 pictures, about 80 percent of which were usable for cloud cover analysis.

Of the ten major tropical storms in the 1962 season, *Tiros V* observed five of them. In addition, it supplied data that were used in weather analysis for the orbital flights of Project Mercury Astronauts Walter Schirra and Gordon Cooper. *Tiros V* data were used by Australia in the first instance of international use of weather satellite data. On September 6, 1962, data from *Tiros V* satellite were sent to France via the *Telstar I* communication satellite.[116]

Telstar I

A dramatic new era in world communications was inaugurated on July 10, 1962, when a Goddard Space Flight Center team launched the world's first active communications satellite. *Telstar I* was a product of private industry, American Telephone & Telegraph Company, launched for AT&T by NASA on a reimbursable basis. Here was a satellite which enabled a whole continent to "see" across oceans. Television programs from and to Europe, for instance, brought new, real-time sights and sounds into the homes of millions. Even though Telstar's "mutual visibility"—the time during which signals could be sent and received—was relatively short (approximately 15 to 20 minutes), the portents of this new communications medium was immediate. With an elliptical orbit that crossed the Van Allen belts, *Telstar I* taught engineers a great deal about radiation damage to communications equipment.

Telstar I, launched July 10, 1962.

A legislative debate soon ensued on Capitol Hill as to how this new communications system was to be used operationally—by private industry, by a public utility, or by a Governmental agency. On August 31, 1962, President John F. Kennedy signed Public Law 87–624, the "Communications Satellite Act of 1962" (Exhibit 16). This law created a "communications satellite corporation for profit which will not be an agency or establishment of the United States Government, but which would have government representation on its Board of Directors and have many of its activities regulated by Government." A space-age development now became a new business enterprise and marked a new form of Government-business collaboration.[117]

Tiros VI

Tiros VI was launched on September 18, 1962. Good coverage of a large portion of the earth's cloud cover was possible because the satellite went into an almost circular orbit with an inclination of 58.3°. The launch was originally scheduled for November but was pushed forward to September so that *Tiros VI* could serve as a backup for *Tiros V* during the last half of the tropical storm season. It also was used for weather observations for the Project Mercury flights of Astronauts Walter Schirra and Gordon Cooper.

Transmission was such that *Tiros VI* was able to aid in the detection of hurricanes and typhoons in both the 1962 and 1963 tropical storm seasons. Data from this satellite were used by the U.S. Weather Bureau in daily forecasts.

On December 1, 1962, the medium-angle camera ceased to function, and it was announced on October 17, 1963, that the satellite was no longer transmitting data. During its 13 months of active lifetime, *Tiros VI* transmitted over 67,000 pictures.[118]

Alouette I

On September 29, 1962, a second international satellite, the *Alouette I*, was launched. A United States-Canadian project, it was NASA's first satellite launched from the Pacific Missile Range and into polar orbit.

Alouette I was a project of the Canadian Defence Research Board, and a part of NASA's Topside Sounder Program. The primary objective was to examine the structure of the ionosphere from above in a manner similar to that being used by ground-based sounding stations. In particular, information was desired about the ionosphere in the region above the maximum electron density of the F layer, usually about 188 to 250 statute miles above the earth's surface.

The topside sounder was carried in a satellite traveling at 638-mile apogee and 620-mile perigee. It was launched with a Thor-Agena vehicle. The satellite provided radio transmissions (downward and via the Echo

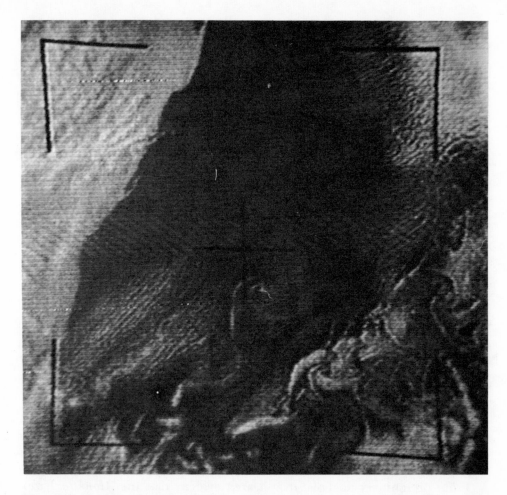

Tiros VI photographed Cape Blanc, Africa, the clearly discernible ocean, and eddy pattern from Canary Islands, April 23, 1963.

satellite) over a frequency range of about 2 to 15 Mc. The data were telemetered to Canadian, United States, and United Kingdom sites.

After having been in orbit for one year, all four experiments—ionospheric sounder, energetic-particle counters, VLF receiver, and cosmic-noise-intensity equipment—continued to provide data without degradation of quality since launch. Energetic photons and corpuscles, together with micrometeoroids, were gradually decreasing the efficiency of the solar cells. The solar-cell charging power was down to 58 percent of its initial value, but the efficiency was declining at a much slower rate, confirming predicted rate of decrease.

Canadian scientists check *Alouette I*, which was launched September 29, 1962.

The control center for the *Alouette I* satellite was at the Defence Research Telecommunications Establishment (DRTE) in Ottawa, Canada. The magnetic tape was processed at DRTE and topside ionograms were filed at the World Data Center, Boulder, Colorado.

From preliminary analysis, it appeared evident that the *Alouette I* topside sounder not only clarified many of the earlier concepts about the structure of the topside ionosphere, but at the same time raised a number of new questions concerning the relative importance of solar, magnetic, and corpuscular control of the topside ionosphere.

The analysis of *Alouette I* data has led to the publication of numerous scientific papers. About two-thirds of these were of Canadian origin, the remaining one-third were by scientists of the United Kingdom and United States.[119]

Explorer XIV

This Energetic Particles Satellite, launched on October 2, 1962, contained a cosmic-ray experiment, an ion detector experiment, a solar cell experiment, a plasma probe and analyzer, a trapped radiation experiment, and a magnetometer experiment. Its objectives were to describe the trapped

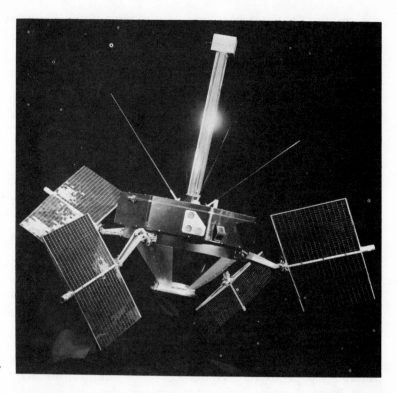

Explorer XIV.

corpuscular radiation, solar particles, cosmic radiation, and the solar wind and to correlate the particle phenomena with the magnetic field observations. This satellite was to continue and extend the energetic-particles study undertaken by *Explorer XII*.

The 89-pound *Explorer XIV* satellite was launched into a highly elliptical orbit with an apogee of 61,090 miles and a perigee of 174 miles. The satellite transmitted data from the six experiments and tracking beacon regularly until January 1963, when stabilization difficulties caused the loss of about 15 days of data. On January 29, transmission was resumed and continued until mid-August when all usable signals except the tracking beacon ceased. In 10 months the satellite had transmitted 6,500 hours of usable data.

Instruments enabled scientists to chart the boundaries of the magnetosphere with more precision than had been previously possible, and it was found that it flared away from the earth in a definite shape.

The effects of magnetic fields on particles and radiation, and variations in the magnetic field during the day-night cycle were observed. There was possible confirmation of *Explorer VI's* claim of a ring current on the night side of the earth. Dr. James Van Allen said that *Explorer XIV* and *Explorer III* data indicated the radiation from high-altitude nuclear tests that was trapped in the ionosphere would remain much longer than he had previously estimated.[120]

Explorer XV

This satellite was launched October 27, 1962, for the purpose of studying the new artificial radiation belt created by nuclear explosions. Instrumentation was similar to *Explorer XII* and included p-n junction electron detectors, scintillator detectors, a scintillator telescope, and a triaxial fluxgate magnetometer.

The satellite went silent in February 1963, after transmitting 2,067 hours of data. Digitized data were sent to the five experimenters, who used it to determine more exactly the intensity and location of the artificial radiation.[121]

Relay I

Relay I, NASA's first active communications satellite, was launched by Goddard Space Flight Center on December 13, 1962. The objective of the 172-pound satellite was to investigate wideband communications between ground stations by means of a low-altitude satellite. *Relay I* was placed in an orbit with an apogee of 4,612 miles and perigee of 819 miles. Although *Relay I* was primarily a communications satellite, the major portion of its instrumentation was designed to evaluate the satellite's circuitry and equipment and transmit this information to earth. Seven instruments were designed to measure energetic particles and the effects of these particles on *Relay I*'s instrumentation.

Communications signals to be evaluated were an assortment of television signals, multichannel telephone, and other communications. Wideband stations used in the experiment were located at Rumford, Maine; Pleumeur-Bodou, France; Goonhilly Downs, England; and Weilheim, West Germany. Narrowband stations were located at Nutley, New Jersey, and Rio de Janeiro, Brazil.

Some of the most noteworthy of the transmissions made on *Relay I* were the first three-way link between North America, South America, and Europe; first simultaneous TV transmission to London, Paris, and Rome (March 11, 1963); first known color transmission (March 19, 1963); and transmission of the coverage of President Kennedy's tragic death (November 22 to 26, 1963).

Transmission difficulty was experienced during the week after launch and for about a week during March 1963, but long-term performance of the satellite was considered excellent. Although all planned experiments had been completed by March 1963, *Relay I* was still transmitting at the end of 1963. At that time it had completed 2,880 orbits, performed 1,330 wide-

Relay I, which was launched December 13, 1962.

band experiments, 720 narrowband experiments, and 157 demonstrations (TV and narrowband). The transponder had been operated for 288 hours over a period of 720 operations.[122]

Syncom I

Syncom I was launched on February 14, 1963. The objective was to place in orbit a 24-hour (synchronous) active communications satellite with the Delta rocket. The booster functioned well, but 20 seconds after the apogee motor fired to place the satellite in a near-synchronous orbit, all communications were lost. Optical sightings of the satellite were made after some days; it was found to be in a near-synchronous orbit traveling eastward at about 2.8° per day. The firing of the apogee motor may have damaged the satellite.[123]

Explorer XVII

This Explorer satellite, launched on April 3, 1963, was to make studies of the earth's upper atmosphere. Specifically, it was designed to make direct samplings of atmospheric constituents such as helium, nitrogen, and oxygen. Measurements were made with two mass spectrometers, four vacuum-pressure gauges, and two electrostatic probes. Telemetry was performed with a new pulse-code-modulation system—a solid-state system

Syncom I.

providing output power of 500 milliwatts and capable of supplying 40 separate channels of information in digital form.

After a few days of operation *Explorer XVII* had more than tripled all previous direct measurements of the neutral gases in the earth's upper atmosphere. Among the data was confirmation that the earth is surrounded by a belt of neutral helium at an altitude of 150 to 60 miles. The satellite became inactive on July 10, 1963.[124]

Telstar II

On May 7, 1963, *Telstar II* was launched into orbit from Cape Canaveral. This medium-altitude, active communications satellite was designed to provide additional information on TV, radio, telephone, and data transmission, as well as experiments on the effects of radiation on the on-

Explorer XVII readied for launch.

board communications equipment.   It was a project of AT&T launched by a Goddard Center launch team.   The Center also participated in some of the experiments.   It was successfully used for transmitting TV, color TV, and voice messages between the United States, France, and England.   The transmitter failed after some 60 days in orbit.[125]

Tiros VII

Tiros VII was launched June 19, 1963, into an orbit designed to provide maximum Northern Hemisphere hurricane coverage for the 1963 season.   The satellite was equipped with two vidicon cameras with wide-angle lenses, a five-channel medium-resolution radiometer to measure infra-red radiation, an electron temperature probe, and a magnetic attitude coil.

Coverage extended to 65° N and 65° S latitudes, and included Hurricanes Arlene through Ginny during the 1963 hurricane season.   The electron temperature probe malfunctioned 26 days after launch, but the two cameras and the infrared subsystems remained active for over two years.   Spacecraft reliability had truly made great strides and the Goddard team and its contractors had laid the foundation for an operational system of weather satellites.[126]

Syncom II

Syncom II communications satellite was launched July 26, 1963, and by September had been maneuvered into a near-perfect synchronous orbit. Firings of hydrogen peroxide jets on August 11 slowed *Syncom II* from 7° drift per day to 2.7° drift per day, and on August 12 the drift was reduced to 1.2° per day. By September 7 the satellite was in orbit over Brazil and the South Atlantic Ocean at an altitude of more than 22,000 miles in an orbit that varied from an absolute circle by no more than 4.5 miles. Orbital period was 23 hours, 55 minutes and 54 seconds—only 0.09 second shorter than the mean sidereal day. The satellite had a drift of about one degree per month that was corrected by a periodic figure-eight carrying the satellite along the 55° meridian to points 33° north and south of the equator. NASA Administrator James E. Webb called completion of the positioning maneuvers the culmination of "one of the outstanding feats in the history of space flight."

The satellite was equipped with a spin-stabilized active repeater consisting of a 7,200-Mc receiver and an 1,800-Mc transmitter with an output of 2 watts. A vernier velocity-control system was installed for orientation of spin axis and adjustment of the orbit. In addition, onboard instrumentation could measure the effect of radiation on the solar cells that powered the spacecraft. Measurement of power loss resulting from radiation damage confirmed the desirability of changing the next Syncom satellite to n/p cells with 0.012-inch quartz cover slides.

A telephone conversation between President John F. Kennedy and Nigerian Prime Minister Sir Abubaker Tafawa Balewa on August 23, 1963, was the first transmission of the satellite. The success of this project confirmed the feasibility of earth-synchronous satellite systems, a technical achievement of major significance.[127]

The success of Goddard's work on the synchronous satellite development was to pave the way for the world's first commercial communications satellite, *Early Bird*. After its NASA research and development role was completed, *Syncom II* continued its useful service. NASA transferred operation of the satellite to DOD on January 1, 1965; DOD used it for communications with the armed forces in Vietnam.

Explorer XVIII

Explorer XVIII, an Interplanetary Monitoring Platform (IMP), was launched on November 27, 1963. The satellite carried ten experiments designed to study the radiation environment of cislunar space and to monitor this region over a significant portion of a solar cycle. Special emphasis was placed on the acquisition of simultaneous data to aid in the determination of interdependent effects of magnetic and ion fields. In addition, it was hoped that knowledge could be gained for the further development of a simple, relatively inexpensive, spin-stabilized spacecraft for interplanetary investigation.

An elliptical orbit of 121,605-mile apogee and 122-mile perigee, with

Useful Lifetimes of Goddard Satellites

Project	Other name	Useful life, days	Remarks
Explorer VI	S–2	68	
Explorer VII	S–1a		
Explorer VIII	S–30	55	
Explorer X	P–14	2	Satellite achieved estimated useful lifetime.
Explorer XI	S–15	180	
Explorer XII	S–3	112	Transmission ceased abruptly.
Explorer XIII	S–55a	2	
Explorer XIV	S–3a	310	
Explorer XV	S–3b	95	
Explorer XVII	S–6	100	Power supply designed for 3 months.
Explorer XVIII	IMP–I	300	Survived 9-hour shadow at 160 days.
Echo I	A–11	250	Number of days useful as a communications satellite; number of days useful for scientific information indefinite.
Tiros I	A–1	77	Number of days TV data meteorologically useful.
Tiros II	A–2	231	
Tiros III	A–3	145	Number of days TV system useful.
Tiros IV	A–9	146	Number of days IR system provided useful meteorological data.
Tiros V	A–50	330	Number of days TV system useful.
Tiros VI	A–51	388	
Tiros VII	A–52	920[a]	
Tiros VIII	A–53	740[a]	
Ariel I	S–51	320	Some damage from Starfish event (74 days); useful data continued at a decreasing rate.
Alouette I	S–27	1,185[a]	
Relay I	A–15	924	
Syncom I	A–25	0.25	
Syncom II	A–26	900[a]	
Vanguard III		85	Achieved estimated useful lifetime.

[a] Still functioning December 31, 1965.

an orbital period of 93 hours, was achieved. All experiments and equipment operated satisfactorily except for the thermal ion experiment, which gave only 10 percent usable data. The satellite was the first to accurately measure the interplanetary magnetic field and shock front, and to survive a severe earth shadow of 7 hours and 55 minutes. One year later, on December 15, 1964, Dr. Norman F. Ness, speaking at a Goddard Scientific Symposium, discussed some of the findings produced by the IMP satellite.

Dr. Ness compared the earth to a comet, explaining the presence of a long magnetic tail extending to an unknown distance out beyond the dark (night) side of the earth.

The new theory was drawn from the results of the first detailed mapping of the earth's magnetic field on the nighttime side of the magnetosphere by this satellite. Earlier, scientists had believed the earth's magnetic field on its dark side was draped out far beyond the earth in a massive closed teardrop. Under the new theory countless magnetic lines of force stretch out like the tail of a comet to a still-to-be-determined distance in space, possibly beyond the moon. Within this vast comet-like tail the lines of force in the Northern Hemisphere are directed toward the sun; in the Southern Hemisphere, away from the sun. In between there is a neutral zone.

Dr. Ness characterized this neutral zone—which had been hypothesized but never before detected—as a thin sheet, which is a permanent part of the earth's environment and virtually void of magnetic activity. Though the neutral zone's exact role was unknown, it may be responsible for speeding particles into the earth's polar region, either directly or via the Van Allen belt to cause aurora. The neutral zone may even play a major role in the development of the Van Allen belt. Because of its location, it may give rise to gegenschein, a slight but noticeable increase in the luminosity of the night sky.[128]

Tiros VIII

The eighth Tiros weather satellite was launched on December 21, 1963. The satellite went into a successful orbit, and proved for the first time the feasibility of automatic picture transmission (APT) for direct facsimile readout from the satellite. This system allowed weathermen around the world, using inexpensive ground equipment, to receive an almost real-time photo of the weather in their area.

Recognizing the continuing success of the Tiros weather satellite program, the U.S. Weather Bureau in late 1962 began discussions with NASA to continue this program on an operational basis. This follow-on effort was named Tiros Operational Satellite System (TOSS). On May 23, 1963, TOSS was formally implemented when the Weather Bureau issued a $9,132,000 purchase order to NASA providing for three Tiros spacecraft, two Thor-Delta launch vehicles, plus associated launch, data acquisition programing, and data analysis services. The first two TOSS spacecraft would be identical to *Tiros VI* with its two wide-angle cameras. The third would embody a "cart wheel" configuration producing vertically oriented pictures taken by cameras looking out from the spacecraft rim.[129]

Boosters and Sounding Rockets

8

SATELLITES WERE THE BACKBONE of the Goddard Space Flight Center research program, but no account of the Center would be complete without discussing the boosters that placed these satellites into orbit and the sounding rockets with their complementary research.

Delta

By far the most important of the launch vehicles has been the Delta. It was important to the entire U.S. space program because of the frequency of its use and its proven reliability. It is also important in a study of the Goddard program because its development was closely associated with the efforts of the Goddard Space Flight Center. Like the original core of Goddard personnel, the Delta evolved, in part, from the Vanguard project at the Naval Research Laboratory.

In September 1955, NRL was given a green light for the development of a rocket capable of launching a satellite into orbit. This project, known as Project Vanguard, was to be part of the International Geophysical Year and was not to interfere with the Department of Defense rocket program. The development of the Vanguard vehicle and the orbiting of Vanguard satellites has already been discussed (see ch. 2).

Although the Delta is generally considered the progeny of the Vanguard, there is another thread of the Delta development that must be picked up. Near the end of 1955, the U.S. Air Force awarded Douglas Aircraft Company a contract to develop a 1,500-mile Intermediate Range Ballistic Missile (IRBM). While this vehicle, known as the Thor, was still in development, it was augmented by mating the Thor with two upper stages that were essentially the upper stages of the Vanguard. The new vehicle was fired as the Thor-Able in April 1958 and was widely used in the early period of the Air Force space program.

Just one year later a NASA contract was signed for the Delta, a rocket with satellite launching capability. This rocket, which was patterned after the Air Force Thor-Able, first successfully launched a satellite on August 12, 1960.

The Delta was originally conceived as an "interim launch vehicle" for satellite launching through 1961 or 1962—a rocket to serve until larger-thrust rockets were developed. But the Delta proved so reliable that it became an "off the shelf" item. Although some programs, such as manned space flight, had to wait until larger rockets were available, most of NASA's satellite needs could be met satisfactorily and economically with a Delta-size vehicle. The Delta was continuously modified so that it kept pace with the demands made on a medium-weight satellite launch vehicle. It thus achieved exceptional reliability and versatility under the guidance of its Goddard project managers.

These improvements not only included innumerable modifications but a general upgrading of the capabilities of the rocket. The Delta rockets used through 1960 and 1962 lifted payloads of less than 300 pounds into relatively low orbits. Later Deltas were capable of placing satellites of over 800

DELTA CONFIGURATION

Stages: 3

Propellants: 1st stage, liquid oxygen and kerosene; 2d stage, unsymmetrical dimethylhydrazine and inhibited red fuming nitric acid; 3d stage, solid

Thrust: 1st stage, 170,000 lb at sea level; 2d stage, 7,700 lb; 3d stage, 2,800 lb

Maximum Diameter: 8 ft, excluding fins

Height: 88 ft, less spacecraft

Payload: 800 lb in 350 n.mi. orbit; 130 lb escape

---

pounds into orbits of around 1,000 nautical miles. Changes included stretching the second stage propellant tank by three feet in 1962 and replacing the X–248 solid propellant third stage in 1963 with the higher performance X–258.

It is ironic that Delta's remarkable flight record started with a failure. In its debut at Cape Canaveral on May 13, 1960, Delta No. 1 failed to put a 100-foot-diameter Echo balloon into orbit. A circuitry problem in the second stage was diagnosed as the problem. The circuitry subsystem was redesigned, more severely tested, and installed in the second stage for another flight. On August 12, 1960, 3 months after the first failure, Delta No. 2 successfully launched a backup Echo passive communications satellite into orbit. Delta No. 2 was the start of a successful launch string that would last for 2½ years and include 21 successful space missions.

Among the satellite "firsts" boosted into orbit by Delta were: the first passive communications satellite, *Echo I*; the first international satellite,

Delta Growth (1962 to 1963)

Delta configuration	Earth orbit (300 miles)	Escape
DM19 (1960)	525 lb	70 lb
DSV–3A and 3B (1962) 3-foot longer second stage tanks	800 lb[a]	95 lb
DSV–3C (1963) X–258 motor replaced X–248 motor	800 lb[a]	115 lb

[a] Structural limits of the second stage limit spacecraft weight to 800 pounds.

Delta Launch Vehicle Record, 1960 to 1963

Vehicle No.	Mission	Results	Launch	Weight, pounds
1	Echo	Failed	May 13, 1960	132
2	Echo I	Successful	August 12, 1960	200
3	Tiros II	"	November 23, 1960	280
4	Explorer X	"	March 25, 1961	80
5	Tiros III	"	July 12, 1961	280
6	Explorer XII	"	August 16, 1961	90
7	Tiros IV	"	February 8, 1962	280
8	OSO I	"	March 7, 1962	500
9	Ariel I	"	April 26, 1962	160
10	Tiros V	"	June 19, 1962	300
11	Telstar I	"	July 10, 1962	171
12	Tiros VI	"	September 18, 1962	280
13	Explorer XIV	"	October 2, 1962	89
14	Explorer XV	"	October 27, 1962	98
15	Relay I	"	December 13, 1962	172
16	Syncom I	"	February 14, 1963	150
17	Explorer XVII	"	April 3, 1963	150
18	Telstar II	"	May 7, 1963	410
19	Tiros VII	"	June 19, 1963	300
20	Syncom II	"	July 26, 1963	150
21	Explorer XVIII (IMP I)	"	November 27, 1963	138
22	Tiros VIII	"	December 21, 1963	265

Delta on launch pad; Scout launches *Explorer XVI*.

Ariel I; the first privately owned satellite, *Telstar I;* the first synchronous orbiting satellite, *Syncom II;* the Orbiting Solar Observatory; the Tiros weather satellites; and *Explorer XVIII*, the first Interplanetary Monitoring Platform.

The Delta was used to launch 21 of the 33 satellites discussed in chapter 7. The first launch (the attempted Echo launch on May 13, 1960) was the only failure that the Delta experienced in the 22 launches. With its outstanding record of reliability and extensive use, the Delta was truly the workhorse of the NASA scientific satellite program.

In addition to the Delta, other boosters have been used to launch Goddard satellites, including the Delta precursor, the Vanguard, for the launch of *Vanguard III*, and the four-stage Scout. This Scout solid-fuel rocket, managed by NASA's Langley Research Center, was used to launch smaller satellites and two space probes. Several Department of Defense rockets were also available for Goddard's use. The Juno II, an Army Redstone-derived vehicle, was used for three of the Explorer satellites. The Air Force's Thor-Able launched three early Goddard satellites and its Thor-Agena was used to launch *Alouette I*.[130]

Sounding Rockets

In addition to its satellite program, Goddard-managed sounding rocket experimentation made many contributions to the space science program. By December 31, 1963, the Center had fired 292 sounding rockets. Of these, 203 were considered successful, 31 partially successful, and 58 failures —either because the rocket failed or the payload was not recovered.[131] (It should be pointed out that classification of a sounding rocket flight as successful, partially successful, or failure, involves some arbitrary decision, and that the above totals are subject to further interpretation.) This program supported astronomy, solar physics, energetic particles and fields, ionospheric physics, and planetary atmosphere and meteorology. Many sounding rocket launchings also served to flight-test equipment intended for use on satellites.[132]

The sounding rocket program also enabled many foreign countries to participate in atmospheric and space research. Frequently the Goddard Center assisted other nations in these cooperative efforts.

While the sounding rocket program has never caught the public imagination as have the more dramatic satellite programs, these activities have played an important role in Goddard Center's scientific investigation of space, and no account of the early years at Goddard would be complete without some discussion of them.

As a practical matter, satellites cannot orbit below 100 miles because of atmospheric drag. Balloons and aircraft were not effective above about 20 miles. A device was needed to take measurements in the upper atmosphere, particularly in the zone between 20 and 100 miles. This was the early impetus to the development of sounding rockets. A statement made by Dr. Homer E. Newell, Jr., before a Senate committee serves as a brief background to the Goddard sounding rocket program:

> The United States has been using sounding rockets for upper air research and rocket astronomy since the close of World War II. WAC Corporal, V–2, Viking, Aerobee, Aerobee-Hi, Nike-Deacon, Nike-Cajun, Nike-Asp, and Rockoons were used. Altitudes attained were below 200 miles for the most part. Many hundreds of rockets were fired prior to the start of the International Geophysical Year; an additional 200 were

Sounding rocket readied for launch at Fort Churchill, Canada.

On April 26, 1962, the Japanese electron temperature experiment was launched from Wallops Island by a Nike-Cajun sounding rocket.

fired as part of the International Geophysical Year program.   Current rate of rocket soundings is somewhat below 100 per year.   Higher altitude rockets are being introduced into the work to extend the atmospheric observations to one to several thousands of miles altitude. Launchings have been carried out at White Sands, N. Mex.; Wallops Island, Va.; San Nicolas Island, Calif.; Cape Canaveral, Fla.; Fort Churchill, Canada; Guam; and from shipboard in the North Atlantic, the Mid-Pacific and South Pacific, and the vicinity of Antarctica.[133]

Most Goddard sounding rockets were launched from Wallops Island, Virginia, and Fort Churchill, Canada.

Immediately after the end of World War II, the United States began an upper atmosphere research program using V–2 rockets.   As the supply of V–2s ran out and the need for rockets specifically designed for research purposes became evident, the development of the Viking, the Aerobee, and the Nike-Deacon rockets was undertaken.   The latter two rockets played prominent roles in NASA's sounding rocket program.

The Nike-Deacon consisted of a Nike-Ajax first stage and a Deacon second stage.   From 1947 on, one or another version of the Aerobee served as the principal sounding rocket workhorse.   The Aerobee came in two configurations: the Aerobee 150 and the Aerobee 300.   The Aerobee 150 was a two-stage system consisting of a solid-propellant booster and a liquid-propellant sustainer stage.   Both burned for the duration of the launch and the booster merely provided assistance at takeoff.   The Aerobee 300 was the Aerobee 150 propulsion system with the addition of a third stage.   While the Aerobee 150 had a three-fin configuration, the Aerobee 150A was four-finned.   There was also an Aerobee 300A, which used a 150A second stage.

Nike-Apaches and Nike-Cajuns were perhaps the most heavily used rockets in the United States sounding rocket program.   Identical in appearance, the Apache propellant provided more power than the Cajun and thus took a given payload to a higher altitude.

The Javelin was the largest sounding rocket used with any frequency.   This four-stage rocket was designed primarily for the researcher who wished to place a payload experiment of between 90 and 150 pounds at altitudes between 500 and 650 miles.   The largest scientific sounding rocket was the Journeyman.   It lifted a payload of between 50 and 150 pounds to altitudes between 900 and 1,300 miles, although its usefulness could be extended to heavier payloads and higher altitudes.

Other sounding rockets included: the Astrobee 200, a two-stage solid-propellant rocket, similar to the Aerobee 150 but with a higher acceleration to the payload; the Astrobee 1500, a two-stage solid-propellant rocket capable of reaching 1,500 miles altitude; and the Black Brant II built by Canadian Bristol Aerojet Limited.

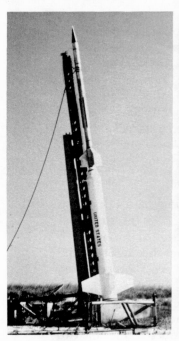  

Nike-Cajun; Javelin; Nike-Apache.

A closeup of the sounding rocket used in the first joint flight effort by the United States and Japan being checked by a Japanese scientist.

Major Sounding Rockets

NIKE-APACHE/NIKE-CAJUN

Overall:
Total length: 28 ft
Gross weight: 1,600 lb
Propellant: Solid fuel
Payload weight:
    Minimum: 40 lb
    Nominal: 60 lb
    Maximum: 120 lb
First stage: Nike (M5E1) booster
Length: 12.4 ft
Principal diameter: 16.5 in.
Thrust: 42,500 lb
Burning time: 3.5 sec

Second stage: Apache (TE 307–2)
    Length: 8.9 ft
    Principal diameter: 6.5 in.
    Thrust: 5,000 lb
    Burning time: 6.4 sec
Second stage: Cajun (TE 82–1)
    Length: 8.9 ft
    Principal diameter: 6.5 in.
    Thrust: 8,500 lb
    Burning time: 4 sec

JOURNEYMAN

Overall:
Stages: 4
Total length: 62 ft
Gross weight: 14,079 lb
Payload weight:
    Minimum: 75 lb
    Nominal: 125 lb
    Maximum: 175 lb
First stage: Sergeant
Maximum diameter: 31 in.
Thrust: 50,000 lb
First stage booster:
2 Recruits
Thrust: 36,000 lb (each)

Second and third stages: Lance
    Length: 16 ft
    Maximum diameter: 15 in.
    Thrust: 44,000 lb
    Burning time: 6.4 sec
Fourth stage: X–248
    Length: 6 ft (plus 3-ft payload)
    Maximum diameter: 19 in.
    Thrust: 3,000 lb
    Burning time: 42 sec

JAVELIN

Overall:
Total length with nominal payload:
    Approximately 49 ft
Gross weight less payload:
    Approximately 7,500 lb
Fuel: Solid
Payload weight:
    Minimum: 20 lb
    Normal: 125 lb
    Maximum: 175 lb
First stage: Honest John (M–6) booster
Diameter: 22.9 in.
Length: 16 ft
Thrust: 82,000 lb
Burning time: 5 sec

Second and third stages: Nike (M5E–1) motor
    Diameter: 16.5 in.
    Length: 11.2 ft
    Thrust: 42,500 lb
    Burning time: 3.3 sec
Fourth stage: X–248 rocket motor
    Diameter: 19 in.
    Length: 6 ft (plus 2.4-ft payload)
    Thrust: 3,000 lb
    Burning time: 42 sec

129

Goddard Space Flight Center fired about 100 sounding rockets per year from 1959 through 1963, so it is impractical to discuss each firing. This program was a significant element of the Center's scientific and technological endeavor. Not only do sounding rockets continue to fulfill the early purpose of taking measurements in the upper atmosphere but they also serve a variety of specialized scientific and meteorological purposes at other altitudes. Furthermore they are economical testing devices for equipment and systems that will later fly in expensive satellites.

Goddard Looks to the Future
9

THE CENTRAL IDEA of the scientific exploration of space has been expressed by the first Director of Goddard Space Flight Center (1959 to 1965), Dr. Harry J. Goett:

> The characteristic of space science is such that it spreads across many disciplines, and a very broad segment of the scientific fraternity is helping unravel the meaning of the new scientific data being brought back from outer space. You must recognize the efforts of the orbital mechanicians, physicists with various areas of specialization, astronomers, geologists, and geodesists in the analysis of the results. . . . Each of these disciplines is finding that it has a new frontier. New areas of research are being created by the data which rockets and satellites provide. We surely have just started to realize their potentials.
>
> The job of putting together the cosmic jigsaw of space from the bits and pieces of data obtained from our satellites is one that engages the efforts of many people throughout the scientific community; and this jigsaw puzzle goes together so gradually that there are no singular events which merit a headline.[134]

At the end of 1963, many pieces of the jigsaw puzzle had been fitted together and scientists were able to plan for the future. The Vanguard and Explorer satellites were the forerunners of complex "second generation" observatory spacecraft containing as many as 30 individual experiments. Soon the data flow from these space-borne laboratories would be measured literally in miles of magnetic tape daily. By 1964 some 15 to 20 satellites were being interrogated every day, producing some 50 miles of data tapes daily and tens of thousands of data bits per second. Somehow the future had arrived sooner, much sooner, than engineers, scientists, and managers had dared to expect. The chain reaction of space-related scientific inquiry was to continue.

Vanguard II (SLV–4), launched in February 1959, gave impetus to the Tiros weather satellites, which within the brief span of 4 years would develop into the Tiros Operational Satellite System (TOSS). The Nimbus weather satellite program would promise further breakthroughs in space-borne meteorology.

Rapid strides were also made by NASA in the area of improved communication techniques. Technological advances produced by AT&T's Telstar, NASA's Echo, Relay, and Syncom systems soon found further applications. In 1965 the control of *Syncom II* and *Syncom III* would be transferred to the Department of Defense for operational communications and for study in design of military communications systems. *Early Bird*, the world's first commercial communications satellite, would be built by the Syncom contractor, Hughes Aircraft Co., for the Communications Satellite Corporation and would be closely patterned on the earlier Syncom.

Facilities and experience gained in space tracking, especially in support of Project Mercury, would provide a readily adaptable base for the tracking of Projects Gemini and Apollo.

Years ahead of man's first travels to the moon and to other planets, Goddard communication links from far-flung tracking stations would carry the first closeup photographs of the moon and Mars.

Splash crater on the moon.

Goddard's top management staff, 1962. From left to right: Dr. M. J. Vaccaro, Assistant Director for Administration; J. T. Mengel, Assistant Director for Tracking and Data Systems; E. W. Wasielewski, Associate Director; Dr. H. J. Goett, Director; Dr. J. W. Townsend, Assistant Director for Space Science and Satellite Applications; and L. Winkler, Chief of Technical Services.

The vast investment of talent and money had begun to pay off. New scientific knowledge and technology poured in as returns to a Nation which some five years earlier had embarked on a new national purpose—the exploration of space. Now a new debate developed: How fast? How much?

NASA Administrator James E. Webb, sensing the Nation's feeling, remarked: "In the years ahead, we can expect continuing and necessary debate on the rate and 'mix' of the space investment."[135] He considered it extremely important that the country strive to maintain a well-balanced effort, duly recognizing the potential returns from manned exploration, scientific investigations, practical applications, and possible military uses of space, with a substantial share of attention to basic research in each area.

What was required, in the national interest, was a judicious evaluation of the Nation's new opportunities produced by the Space Age. If the United States was to ensure its security and position as leader of the Free World and gain the scientific and economic benefits which space would surely produce, it had an opportunity it could not afford to neglect. At Greenbelt, Maryland, a team of 3,500 engineers and scientists was ready to contribute to this endeavor.

The Center's management staff in 1965. From left to right: Robert E. Bourdeau, Assistant Director for Projects; Herman E. LaGow, Assistant Director for Systems Reliability; John T. Mengel, Assistant Director for Tracking & Data Systems; Eugene W. Wasielewski, Associate Director; Dr. John F. Clark, Director; Dr. John W. Townsend, Jr., Deputy Director; Dr. Michael J. Vaccaro, Assistant Director for Administration and Management; William G. Stroud, Chief, Advanced Plans Staff; Daniel G. Mazur, Assistant Director for Technology; Dr. George F. Pieper, Assistant Director for Space Sciences.

Goddard's past and its hopes for the future were summed up by the Center's second director, Dr. John F. Clark:

> We who are engaged in the hectic task of space exploration have little time to reminisce about past accomplishments and little inclination to speculate about future achievements beyond, at the most, a few years.... Looking back at our early years of space exploration, one fact becomes paramount: We have telescoped time and emerged with the means to explore space, to use it for the benefit of not only this nation, but of the world. The capabilities that we have built up have not just been placed in space, but rather have been anchored on the solid earth in laboratories, launch facilities, and in the dedication of the men and women who make up this cooperative team.
>
> One can speculate—but it is only speculation—about what the future may bring. There are many avenues of exploration open: the moon, the space environment near earth, the planets, and even the galaxies. But without knowing what constraints we may encounter in the availability of people, dollars or objectives, such speculation can be a rather academic exercise. It is certain, however, that the years immediately

ahead will be filled with intense activity in space, just as they have been in the past decade. We shall be expanding our knowledge and operational capability constantly. Only the rate of progress is uncertain.[136]

Somehow the dream of a lonely New England professor had become the commitment of a new generation.

Footnotes

Chapter 1

[1] For a discussion of the relative role of Dr. Goddard among the space pioneers see: Willy Ley, *Rockets, Missiles and Space Travel*, New York: 1961; Eugene M. Emme, ed., *History of Rocket Technology*, Detroit: 1964.

[2] Milton Lehman, *This High Man: The Life of Robert H. Goddard*, New York: 1963, pp. 14, 22–23.

[3] E. R. Hagemann, "Goddard and His Early Rockets," *Journal of the Astronautical Sciences*, Summer 1961, pp. 51–52; Shirley Thomas, "Robert H. Goddard," *Men of Space*, Philadelphia: 1960, I, 23.

[4] Robert H. Goddard, "An Autobiography," *Astronautics*, April 1959, p. 27.

[5] *Ibid.*

[6] Lehman, pp. 40–50.

[7] Lehman, pp. 56–70.

[8] G. Edward Pendray, "Pioneer Rocket Development in the United States," Hagemann, pp. 53–54. In *History of Rocket Technology*, p. 22. For the best account of Dr. Goddard's relationship with the Smithsonian Institution, see Bessie Zaban Jones, *Lighthouse of the Skies: The Smithsonian Astrophysical Observatory: Background and History, 1846–1955*, Washington: 1965, pp. 241–276. Dr. Charles G. Abbott of the Smithsonian in 1958 still considered Goddard's 1916 proposal " 'the best presentation of a research in progress that I have ever seen.' "

[9] Lehman, pp. 96–97.

[10] *Ibid.*, pp. 102–112; Hagemann, pp. 54–56; Jones, pp. 254–258.

[11] Lehman, pp. 139–144.

[12] Eugene M. Emme, "Yesterday's Dream . . . Today's Reality," *The Airpower Historian*, October 1960, pp. 219–220; Jones, pp. 266–272.

[13] Robert H. Goddard, *Rocket Development: Liquid Fuel Rocket Research, 1929–1941*, New York: 1948.

[14] Lehman, pp. 341–353.

[15] *Ibid.*, pp. 378–390. See Arthur C. Clarke, *Man and Space*, New York: 1964.

[16] *Ibid.*, pp. 395–399.

[17] The Center was formally dedicated on March 16, 1961.

Chapter 2

[18] The pre-World War II activities of the American Rocket Society are briefly discussed in G. Edward Pendray, "Pioneer Rocket Development in the United States," in Eugene M. Emme (ed.), *The History of Rocket Technology*, Detroit: 1964, pp. 10–28.

[19] James A. Van Allen, John W. Townsend, Jr., and Eleanor C. Pressley, "The Aerobee Rocket," in Homer E. Newell, Jr. (ed.), *Sounding Rockets*, New York: 1959, pp. 54–56.

[20] John P. Hagen, "The Viking and the Vanguard," in Emme, *op. cit.*, pp. 122–141.

[21] Van Allen, Townsend, and Pressley, *op. cit.*, pp. 54–70.

[22] Milton Rosen, *The Viking Rocket Story*, New York: 1955; Homer E. Newell, Jr., "Viking," in *Sounding Rockets*, pp. 235–242.

[23] Newell, "Viking," pp. 239–242. The upper atmospheric research group of the Naval Research Laboratory consisted largely of people who were to transfer to NASA a decade or so later—Dr. Homer E. Newell, Milton W. Rosen, Dr. John W. Townsend, Leopold Winkler, Daniel G. Mazur, and others. (Statement of T. E. Jenkins, formerly Administrative Officer of the Beltsville Space Center, July 15, 1963.)

[24] Wernher von Braun, "The Redstone, Ju-

piter, and Juno," in Emme, *op. cit.*, pp. 108–109; Robert L. Perry, "The Atlas, Thor, Titan, and Minuteman," in Emme, *op. cit.*, pp. 144–145.

[25] Frank J. Malina, "Origins and First Decade of the Jet Propulsion Laboratory," in Emme, *op. cit.*, pp. 63–65.

[26] R. Cargill Hall, "Early U.S. Satellite Proposals," in Emme, *op. cit.*, pp. 67–93.

[27] *Ibid.*, pp. 28–33.

[28] *Ibid.*, pp. 35–37.

[29] *Ibid.*, pp. 40–41.

[30] Kurt R. Stehling, *Project Vanguard*, Garden City, N. Y.: 1961, pp. 37–42.

[31] The origins of the IGY are discussed in Walter Sullivan, *Assault on The Unknown; The International Geophysical Year*, New York: 1961, pp. 20–35.

[32] R. Cargill Hall, "Origins and Development of the Vanguard and Explorer Satellite Programs," Goddard Historical Essay Winner for 1963, published in *The Airpower Historian* (October 1964), pp. 101–112.

[33] *Documents on International Aspects of the Exploration and Use of Outer Space, 1954–1962*, Staff Report Prepared for the Committee on Aeronautical and Space Sciences, U.S. Senate, 88th Congress, 1st Session, Washington, D.C.: 1963, p. 27.

[34] The activities of the Stewart Committee are reported in Hall, "Origins and Development of the Vanguard and Explorer Satellite Programs," *The Airpower Historian* (October 1964), pp. 101–112.

[35] Stehling, *op. cit.*, p. 50. The Office of Naval Research actually was a cosponsor with the Army of the "Project Orbiter" proposal, and also of the NRL proposal.

[36] Hagen, pp. 439, 449–450.

[37] On Dr. Hagen, see: Stehling, pp. 69–71.

[38] Hagen, p. 440.

[39] *Ibid.*, pp. 440–441.

[40] Hall, "Origins and Development of the Vanguard and Explorer Satellite Programs,"

op. cit., 101–112.

[41] Hagen, pp. 441–442.

[42] Hagen, pp. 442–444; Milton W. Rosen, "Placing the Satellite in its Orbit," *Proceedings of the XLIV IRE, XLIV* (1956), 749.

[43] *Ibid.*, pp. 444–446; John T. Mengel, "Tracking the Earth Satellite, and Data Transmission, By Radio," *Proceedings of the IRE, XLIV* (1956), 755.

[44] Stehling, p. 79.

[45] *Ibid.*, pp. 80–81.

[46] Hagen, p. 447.

[47] *Ibid.*

[48] *Ibid.*, pp. 447–448; Stehling, pp. 123, 142, 143.

[49] Stehling, *op. cit.*, pp. 25, 181.

[50] David S. Akens, *Historical Origins of the George C. Marshall Space Flight Center*, Huntsville, Alabama: 1960, pp. 44–47; Stehling, pp. 142–143; Wernher von Braun, "Redstone, Jupiter, and Juno," in Emme, *op. cit.*, pp. 107–121, and Eric Bergaust, *Reaching for The Stars*, Garden City, N.Y.: 1960. Studies of Air Force rocket technology during this same period include: Robert L. Perry, "The Atlas, Thor, and Titan," *Technology and Culture* (Fall 1963), pp. 466–477; and John L. Chapman, *Atlas: The Story of a Missile*, New York: 1960.

[51] Hagen, *op. cit.*, pp. 448–449.

[52] Eugene M. Emme, *Historical Sketch of NASA*, NASA EP–29. Washington, D.C.: 1965, pp. 5–13; *Documents on International Aspects of the Exploration and Use of Outer Space, 1954–1962*, pp. 66–80.

[53] See: *First Semiannual Report to the Congress of the National Aeronautics and Space Administration*, Washington, D.C.: 1959, 18–19; *Second Semiannual Report of the National Aeronautics and Space Administration*, Washington, D.C.: 1960, pp. 13–15.

[54] Hagen, pp. 449–450.

[55] *Ibid.*, p. 451.

Chapter 3

[56] "NASA General Directive No. 1," September 25, 1958. (Appendix H, Exhibit 2.)

[57] "Executive Order 10783," October 1, 1958. (Appendix H, Exhibit 4): "White

House Press Release," October 1, 1958. (Appendix H, Exhibit 3.)

[58] "NASA Release," October 1, 1958 (Appendix H, Exhibit 5.)

[59] Senator J. Glenn Beall, "Press Release," August 1, 1958. (Appendix H, Exhibit 1.)

[60] "NASA General Notice No. 1," January 15, 1959. (Appendix H, Exhibit 6.)

[61] "NASA General Notice," January 22, 1959. (Appendix H, Exhibit 7.)

[62] Thomas E. Jenkins, "Memorandum for the Record," February 15, 1959. (Appendix H, Exhibit 8.)

Thomas E. Jenkins, "Memorandum for All Concerned," March 6, 1959. (Appendix H, Exhibit 9.)

[63] T. Keith Glennan, "Memorandum from the Administrator," May 1, 1959; Abe Silverstein, "Memorandum to Assistant Directors and Division Chiefs," May 1, 1959; NASA Release No. 59–125, May 1, 1959; GSFC Release No. 3–10–61–5, March 12, 1961; GSFC Release No. 3–14–61–1, March 14, 1961. (Appendix H, Exhibits 10 through 14.)

[64] The Advanced Research Projects Agency (ARPA) of the Department of Defense, created in February 1958, was the first organizational response to the challenge of Sputnik. This agency was directly in charge of the entire U.S. space effort between the time of its creation and the activation of NASA in October 1958. When NASA was activated, ARPA turned over to the new agency Project Vanguard and several other projects in a germinal stage. Many of NASA's most successful programs, such as Tiros, originated in ARPA. The role ARPA played in the origins and development of the U.S. space program has not yet been fully analyzed. Such an analysis must be undertaken before the history of the U.S. effort in space can be considered complete.

[65] This and the following quotations from speeches at the dedication are taken from the respective speakers' texts.

Chapter 4

[66] Address of Dr. T. Keith Glennan, Administrator, National Aeronautics and Space Administration, to Science, Engineering, and New Technology Committee, Oregon State Department of Planning and Development at Portland, Oregon, on October 12, 1960.

[67] James M. Grimwood, *Project Mercury: A Chronology*, NASA SP–4001, Washington, D.C.: 1963, p. 120.

Chapter 5

[68] Sir Eric Ashby, *Daedalus*, XCI (Spring 1962), 269.

[69] H. Doc. No. 174, 87th Congress, 1st Sess., p. 11.

[70] Speech at Rice University, Houston, Texas, Sept. 12, 1962.

[71] Eugene Wasielewski, text of speech delivered at the National Rocket Club, Washington, D.C., December 19, 1962.

[72] For the concept and origin of this personnel series, see Robert L. Rosholt, *An Administrative History of NASA, 1958–1963*, NASA SP–4101, pp. 141–144.

[73] When President Eisenhower assigned responsibility for the development and execution of a manned space flight program, the National Aeronautics and Space Administration was in the process of being organized. Studies and plans for the manned satellite program were presented to Dr. T. Keith Glennan, Administrator, NASA; and on October 7, 1958, he gave orders to proceed with them. In November 1958, the Space Task Group was officially established to conduct the manned space flight program to be known as Project Mercury. The Space Task Group was organized under the Goddard Space Flight Center but was administratively supported by the Langley Research Center and physically located there. It later became evident that the scope and size of the manned space flight program required an entirely separate center, which subsequently led to the creation of the new Manned Spacecraft Center at Houston, Texas. Responsibilities for the Project Mercury worldwide tracking and data complex remained with the Goddard Space Flight Center.

[74] J. C. New, "Scientific Satellites and the Space Environment," NASA Technical Note D–1340, June 1962; J. H. Boeckel, "The Purposes of Environmental Testing for Scientific

Satellites," NASA Technical Note D–1900, 1963; A. R. Trimmins and K. L. Rosette, "Experience in Thermal-Vacuum Testing Earth Satellites at Goddard Space Flight Center," NASA Technical Note D–1748, 1963.

Chapter 6

[75] William R. Corliss, "The Evolution of STADAN," GSFC Historical Note No. 3, 1967, pp. 13–33.

[76] The radio interferometer measures two of the three direction cosines of a line from the center of the station to a satellite as a function of time while the satellite passes through the beam pattern of the receiving antennas. The third direction cosine is thus defined, and the angular position of the satellite is determined. From a series of independent angle measurements from various ground stations, satellite orbital elements may be computed.

Phase comparison techniques are used to measure the differences in arrival time of the wavefront of a distant point source at pairs of receiving antennas separated by known distances in wavelengths of the transmitted frequency. Measurement of this radio path difference is accomplished by a comparison of the phase angle of the signal received at one antenna to that received at another.

The antennas are aligned along baselines in the east-west and north-south directions. Since the phase measurement system is capable of indicating phase difference to a small fraction of a wavelength, two pairs of antennas are aligned along orthogonal baselines many multiples of a wavelength long to obtain good angular resolution. These are termed *fine* antennas. As a radio source passes through the antenna pattern, the relative phase will cycle from 0 to 360 degrees for each wavelength added to the radio path difference. The phase meters repeat their readings every 360 electrical degrees, so a number of different space angles will produce identical phase readings during a satellite transit. This ambiguity is resolved by employing several progressively shorter baselines, which produce fewer integral numbers of wavelength change as the radio source passed through the antenna beam. These are termed *medium* and *coarse* antennas. Ambiguity antenna information determines the number of full wavelengths to be added to the relative phase angle measured at the fine antennas to define a data point. See Corliss, *op. cit.*, pp. 10 ff.

[77] *Ibid.*, pp. 50–60.

[78] For the overall story of Project Mercury, see James M. Grimwood, *Project Mercury: A Chronology*, NASA SP–4001, Washington, D.C.: 1963; Loyd S. Swenson, Jr., James M. Grimwood, and Charles C. Alexander, *This New Ocean: A History of Project Mercury*, NASA SP–4201, Washington, D.C.: 1966.

[79] For the story of Mercury network development and equipment, see William R. Corliss, "The Beginnings of Manned Space Flight Tracking," unpublished GSFC Historical Note No. 4, 1967.

Chapter 7

[80] Memorandum for the Record, Feb. 16, 1959. (Appendix H, Exhibit 8.) See Appendix A on the objectives of the United States space program.

[81] This compilation is based primarily on the following annual reports to the Committee on Space Research (COSPAR): *Goddard Space Flight Center Contributions to the COSPAR Meeting, May 1962*, Washington, D.C.: National Aeronautics and Space Administration, 1962 (TN D–1669); *United States Space Science Program Report to COSPAR, Sixth Meeting, Warsaw, Poland, June, 1963*, Washington, D.C.: National Academy of Sciences-National Research Council, 1963; *Goddard Space Flight Center Contributions to the COSPAR Meeting, June, 1963*, Washington, D.C.: National Aeronautics and Space Administration, 1963 (G–545); *United States Space Science Program Report to COSPAR, Seventh*

Meeting, Florence, Italy, May, 1964, Washington, D.C.: National Academy of Sciences-National Research Council, 1964. In addition to the COSPAR reports, much information in Goddard Space Flight Center's *Goddard Projects Summary: Satellites and Sounding Rockets* has been used. Also see Appendix B, "Chronology of Major NASA Launchings, October 1, 1958 through December 31, 1962," in House Committee on Science and Astronautics, *Astronautical and Aeronautical Events of 1962,* Washington: 1963, pp. 299–305.

82 For results of *Explorer VI,* see, among others, C. Y. Fan, P. Meyer, and J. A. Simpson, *Journal of Geophysical Research,* LXVI, No. 9 (September 1961); A. Rosen and T. Farley, *Journal of Geophysical Research,* LXVI, No. 7 (July 1961); A. Rosen. T. Farley, and C. P. Sonett, in *Space Research, Proceedings of the First International Space Science Symposium, Nice, 11–16 January 1960,* ed. by H. K. Kallmann Bijl, Amsterdam: North-Holland Publishing Co., 1960, pp. 938–980; C. P. Sonett, E. J. Smith, D. L. Judge, and P. J. Coleman, Jr., *Physical Review Letters,* IV, No. 4 (February 1960), 161–163.

83 "Geomagnetic-Field Studies Using Earth Satellites," *IGY Bulletin,* XCVI (April 1961), 6–12; J. P. Heppner, J. C. Cain, I. R. Shapiro, and J. D. Stolarik, "Satellite Magnetic Field Mapping," NASA TN D-696, May 1961; "IGY Satellite 1959 Eta," *IGY Bulletin,* XXVIII (October 1959), 10–14; H. E. LaGow and W. M. Alexander, "Recent Direct Measurements of Cosmic Dust in the Vicinity of the Earth Using Satellites," *Space Research, Proceedings of the First International Space Science Symposium, Nice, 11–16 January 1960,* ed. by H. K. Kallmann Bijl, Amsterdam: North-Holland Publishing Co., 1960.

84 "IGY Satellite 1959 Iota," *IGY Bulletin,* XXIX (November 1959); W. C. Lin, "Observation of Galactic and Solar Cosmic Rays, October 13, 1959 to February 17, 1961 with Explorer VII (Satellite 1959 Iota)," SUI–61–16, Department of Physics and Astronomy, State Univ. of Iowa (August 1961); G. H. Ludwig and W. A. Whelpley, "Corpuscular Radiation Experiment of Satellite 1959 Iota (Explorer VII)," *Journal of Geophysical Research,* LXV, No. 4 (April 1960), 1119; J. A. Van Allen and W. C. Lin, "Outer Radiation Belt and Solar Proton Observations with Explorer VII During March–April 1960," *Journal of Geophysical Research,* LXV, No. 9 (September 1960), 2998.

85 C. Y. Fan, P. Meyer, and J. A. Simpson, *Physical Review Letters,* V, No. 6 (September 1960), 269.

86 *Ibid.,* p. 272.

87 R. L. Arnoldy, R. A. Hoffman, and J. R. Winckler, unpublished communication.

88 C. Y. Fan, P. Meyer, and J. A. Simpson, *Journal of Geophysical Research,* LXV, No. 6 (June 1960), 1862.

89 R. L. Arnoldy, R. A. Hoffman, and J. R. Winckler, *Journal of Geophysical Research,* LXV, No. 9 (September 1960), 3004.

90 C. Y. Fan, P. Meyer, and J. A. Simpson, *Physical Review Letters,* p. 269.

91 P. J. Coleman, Jr., C. P. Sonett, D. L. Judge, and E. J. Smith, *Journal of Geophysical Research,* LXV, No. 6 (June 1960), 1856.

92 *Ibid.*

93 C. P. Sonett, E. J. Smith, D. L. Judge, and P. J. Coleman, Jr., *Physical Review Letters,* IV, No. 4 (February 1960), 161.

94 E. J. Smith, P. J. Coleman, Jr., D. L. Judge, and C. P. Sonett, *Journal of Geophysical Research,* LXV, No. 6 (June 1960), 1858.

95 J. P. Coleman, Jr., C. P. Sonett, D. L. Judge, and E. J. Smith, *Journal of Geophysical Research,* LXV, No. 1 (January 1960), 1856.

96 C. P. Sonett, D. L. Judge, A. R. Sims, and J. M. Kelso, *Journal of Geophysical Research,* LXV, No. 1 (January 1960), 55.

97 C. P. Sonett, *Physical Review Letters,* V, No. 2 (July 1960), 46.

98 P. J. Coleman, Jr., L. Davis, Jr., and C. P. Sonett, *Physical Review Letters,* V, No. 2 (July 1960), 43.

99 P. J. Coleman, Jr., C. P. Sonett, and L. Davis, Jr., *Journal of Geophysical Research,* LXVI, No. 7 (July 1961), 2043.

100 J. B. McGuire, E. R. Spangler, and L. Wong, *Scientific American,* CCIV, No. 4 (April 1961), 64.

101 For this and other Tiros satellites, see John Ashby, "A Preliminary History of the Evolution of the Tiros Weather Satellite Program," unpublished GSFC Historical Note No. 1, 1964; Richard Chapman, "Tiros-Nimbus: Administrative, Political, and Technological Problems of Developing U.S. Weather Satellites," unpublished study in the Inter-Univer-

sity Case Study Program, Inc., Syracuse, N.Y., 1966. For *Tiros I* results, see *IGY Bulletin*, No. 51 (September 1961), pp. 14–17, 23–24; "Roundup on *Tiros I*," *Astronautics*, V (June 1960, 32–44.

[102] For results of *Echo I*, see R. Bryant, *Journal of Geophysical Research*, LXVI (1961), 3066–3069; *IGY Bulletin*, No. 39 (September 1960) pp. 13–17; L. Jaffe, "Project Echo Results," *Astronautics*, VI, No. 5 (May 1961), 32–33, 80; W. C. Jakes, Jr., "Project Echo," *Bell Laboratories Record*, XXXIX, No. 9 (September 1961), 306–311.

[103] For *Explorer VIII* results, see "Ionosphere Direct Measurement Satellite," *IGY Bulletin*, No. 42 (December 1960), pp. 10–13; M. Melin, "Observing the Satellites," *Sky and Telescope*, XXI (January 1961), 11–12; R. E. Bourdeau and J. E. Donley, "*Explorer VIII* Measurements in the Upper Ionosphere," NASA TN D–2150, June 1964.

[104] The *Manual*, the *Catalog*, and copies of the magnetic tape data tabulations are available from the National Weather Records Center. For general information on the Tiros program, see footnote for *Tiros I*. For results of *Tiros II*, see W. R. Bandeen, R. A. Hanel, John Licht, R. A. Stampfl, and W. G. Stroud, "Infrared and Reflected Solar Radiation Measurements from the *Tiros II* Meteorological Satellite," *Journal of Geophysical Research*, LXV, No. 10 (October 1961), 3169–3185; *Proceedings of the International Meteorological Satellite Workshop, November 13–22, 1961*, Washington: NASA and U.S. Department of Commerce, Weather Bureau, 1962; "The *Tiros II* Cloud-Cover and Infrared Satellite." *IGY Bulletin*, No. 43 (January 1961), pp. 9–13.

[105] For *Explorer IX* results, see *IGY Bulletin*, No. 46 (April 1961), pp. 12–16; *STL Space Log*, I, No. 5, June 1961; W. J. O'Sullivan, C. W. Coffee, and G. M. Keating, "Air Density Measurements from the *Explorer IX* Satellite," *Space Research III*, ed. by W. Priester. New York: John Wiley and Sons, Inc., 1963, pp. 89–95.

[106] J. P. Heppner, N. F. Ness, T. L. Skillman, and C. S. Scearce, *Goddard Space Flight Center Contributions to 1961 Kyoto Conference on Cosmic Rays and the Earth Storm*, Washington: NASA, 1961. The previous field

computations are to be found in H. F. Finch and B. R. Leaton, *Monthly Notices Royal Astronomical Society, Geophysical Supplement*, VII, No. 6 (November 1957), 314.

[107] For other *Explorer X* results, see *IGY Bulletin*, No. 48 (June 1961), pp. 1–4; *STL Space Log*, I, No. 5 (June 1961).

[108] H. S. Bridge, C. Dilworth, A. J. Lazarus, E. F. Lyon, B. Rossi, and F. Scherb (Massachusetts Institute of Technology), "Plasma Measurements from *Explorer X*," *1961 Kyoto Conference on Cosmic Rays and the Earth Storm.*

[109] For *Explorer XI* results, see *IGY Bulletin*, No. 50 (August 1961), pp. 10–13; *STL Space Log*, I, No. 5 (June 1961).

[110] For general information on the Tiros program, see footnote to *Tiros I*. For results of *Tiros III*, see *IGY Bulletin*, No. 51 (September 1961), pp. 14–17; *Sky and Telescope*, XXII, No. 3 (September 1961), 143–145.

[111] For *Explorer XII* results, see Air Force Special Weapons Center Report No. TN–61–34; State University of Iowa Report No. 61–23.

[112] For *Explorer XIII* results, see "Explorer 13 Micrometeoroid Satellite," *IGY Bulletin*, No. 50 (October 1961), pp. 14–16; *STL Space Log*, I, No. 6 (September 1961); "The Micrometeoroid Satellite, Explorer 13 (1961 Chi)," NASA TN D–2468; "Micrometeoroid Satellite (Explorer XIII) Stainless Steel Penetration Experiment," NASA TN D–1986 (October 1962).

[113] For Tiros program information, see footnote to *Tiros I*. For *Tiros IV* results, see *IGY Bulletin*, No. 58 (April 1962) and No. 62 (August 1962); *U.S. Space Science Program* (Report to COSPAR), National Research Council, 1 May 1962; *Sky and Telescope*, XXIII (May 1962), 256–259; F. Bartko, V. Kunde, C. Catoe, and M. Halev, "The TIROS Low Resolution Photometer," NASA TN D–614 (September 1964).

[114] For *OSO I* results, see F. P. Dolder, O. E. Bartoe, R. C. Mercure, Jr., R. H. Gablehouse, and J. C. Lindsay, "The Orbiting Solar Observatory Spacecraft," *Space Research III*, ed. by W. Priester, New York: John Wiley and Sons, Inc., 1963; W. A. White, "Solar X-Rays: Slow Variations and Transient Events," GSFC Report No. X–614–63–195, presented at the

4th International Space Science Symposium, Warsaw, Poland, June 1963; W. M. Neupert, W. E. Behring, and J. C. Lindsay, "The Solar Spectrum from 50 Angstroms to 400 Angstroms," GSFC Report No. X–614–63–196, presented at the 4th International Space Science Symposium, Warsaw, Poland, June 1963; W. M. Neupert and W. E. Behring, *Solar Observations with a Soft X-Ray Spectrometer,* NASA TN D–1466, September 1966; J. C. Lindsay, "Scientific Results of the First Orbiting Solar Observatory," *Transactions of the American Geophysical Union,* XLIV (September 1963), 722–725.

[115] For *Ariel I* results, see "Ariel-Joint United Kingdom-United States Ionosphere Satellites," *IGY Bulletin,* No. 59 (May 1962), pp. 1–5; Elliott, Quenby, Mayne, and Durney, "Cosmic Ray Measurements in the U.K. Scout 1 Satellite," *Journal of British Institute of Radio Engineers,* XXII (September 1961), 251–256; M. O. Robins, "The *Ariel 1* Satellite Project and Some Scientific Results," paper presented at 9th Anglo-American Conference, held at Cambridge, Mass., October 16–18, 1963, and Montreal, Canada, October 21–24, 1963; *Ariel 1: The First International Satellite,* NASA SP–43, 1963 (revised 1964).

[116] For general information on the Tiros program, see the footnote for *Tiros I.* For results of *Tiros V,* see *IG Bulletin,* No. 62 (August 1962); "Weather Satellite Systems," *Astronautics and Aerospace Engineering,* I (April 1963).

[117] For *Telstar I* results, see *IG Bulletin,* No. 62 (August 1962); *Space/Aeronautics,* XXXVIII (January 1963), 41; "Project Telstar: Communications Experiment," *Journal of the Society of Motion Picture and Television Engineers,* LXXII (February 1963), 91–96; D. S. Peck, R. R. Blair, W. L. Brown, F. L. Smits, "Surface Effects of Radiation on Transistors," *The Bell System Technical Journal,* XLII (January 1963), 95–129.

[118] For general information on the Tiros program, see the footnote for *Tiros I.* For results of *Tiros VI,* see *IG Bulletin,* No. 66 (December 1962), 584–585.

[119] For *Alouette I* program information, see Jonathan Casper, "History of Alouette: NASA Case-Study of an International Program," unpublished NASA Historical Note No. 42, 1965;

for *Alouette I* results, see J. O. Thomas, "Canadian Satellite: The Topside Sounder Alouette," *Science,* CXXXIX (January 18, 1963), 229–232; E. S. Warren, "Sweep-Frequency Radio Soundings of the Topside of the Ionosphere," *Canadian Journal of Physics,* XL (1962), 1692.

[120] For *Explorer XIV* results, see Franck, Van Allen, Whelpley, and Craven, "Absolute Intensities of Geomagnetically Trapped Particles with *Explorer XIV,*" State University of Iowa Report No. 62–31 (December 1962), and *Journal of Geophysical Research,* LXVIII (March 1963), 1573–1579; "Collected Papers on the Artificial Radiation Belt from the July 9, 1963 Nuclear Detonation," *Journal of Geophysical Research,* LXVIII (February 1, 1963), 605ff.; "*Explorer XIV* Energetic Particles Satellite," *IG Bulletin,* No. 66 (December 1962), p. 585; H. Meyerson, "Energetic Particles Satellite, S–3a, Spacecraft Description and Preliminary Project Results," NASA Report N–90–013 (February 1963).

[121] For *Explorer XV* results, see *IG Bulletin,* No. 68 (February 1963); *Study of the Enhanced Radiation Belt,* Goddard Space Flight Center, Greenbelt, Md., 1962.

[123] For *Syncom I,* see "Syncom 1," STL "Communications Satellites," paper presented at the First World Conference on World Peace Through Law, Athens, Greece, June 30–July 7, 1963; R. C. Waddel, "Radiation Damage to Solar Cells on *Relay I* and *Relay II,*" *Radiation Effects on Solar Cells and Photovoltaic Devices,* I, Proceedings of the Fourth Photovoltaic Specialists Conference, NASA-Lewis Research Center, Cleveland, Ohio, June 2, 1964; R. E. Warren and J. R. Burke, "Project Relay," *British Communications and Electronics,* VIII (August 1962), 582–583.

[123] For *Syncom I,* see "Syncom I," STL *Spacelog* (June 1963), pp. 31–33, (September 1963), pp. 41–42; "Syncom Lost and Found," *Sky and Telescope* (April 1963), pp. 210–212; Donald D. Williams, "Control of the 24-hour Syncom Satellite," *Missiles and Space* (February 1963), pp. 14, 15, 58.

[124] For *Explorer XVII* results, see "Preliminary Results of Explorer 17 Announced," NASA News Release No. 63–79, April 18, 1963; Spencer, Newton, Reber, Brace, and Horowitz, "New Knowledge of the Earth's Atmosphere

from the Aeronomy Satellite," paper presented at the Fifth International Space Science Symposium, Florence, Italy, May 1964 (also GSFC Report No. X–651–64–114, May 1964) .

[125] For *Telstar II* results, see *Electronics*, XXXVI (May 10, 1963) , 29; *Bell Laboratories Record*, XLI (April 1963) , 181; *Aviation Week and Space Technology*, LXXXI (May 6, 1963) , 30.

[126] For *Tiros VII* results, see Sigmund Fritz, "Pictures from Meteorological Satellites and Their Interpretation," *Space Science Reviews*, III (November 1964) , 541–580; W. R. Bandeen, B. J. Connath, and R. A. Hanel, "Experimental Confirmation from the *Tiros VII* Meteorological Satellite of the Theoretically Calculated Radiance of the Earth within the 15-micron Band of Carbon Dioxide," *Journal of the Atmospheric Sciences*, XX (November 1963) , 609–614; W. Nordberg, W. R. Bandeen, G. Warnecke, and V. Kunde, "Stratospheric Temperature Patterns Based on Radiometric Measurements from *Tiros VII* Satellite," GSFC Report No. X–651–64–115 (May 1964) ; *Sky and Telescope*, XXVI (August 1963) , 76.

[127] For *Syncom II* results, see G. E. Mueller and E. R. Spangler, *Communications Satellites*, New York: John Wiley and Sons, Inc., 1964; R. M. Bentley and A. T. Owens, "Syn-

com Satellite Program," *Journal of Spacecraft*, I (July–August 1964) , 395–399; "*Syncom II* Satellite," *1964 IEEE International Convention Record* (March 23–26, 1964) , pp. 71–153.

[128] For *Explorer XVIII* results, see T. L. Cline, G. H. Ludwig, and F. B. McDonald, "Detection of Interplanetary 3- to 12-MeV Electrons," GSFC Report X–611–64–362, November 1964; E. Ehrlich, "NASA Particles and Fields Spacecraft," AIAA Paper 64–337, First AIAA Annual Meeting, Washington, D.C., June-July 1964; "Initial Results from the First Interplanetary Monitoring Platform *(IMP 1)*," *International Geophysical Bulletin*, No. 84, June 1964; "Interim Status Report, Interplanetary Monitoring Platform, *IMP 1*, Explorer 18," GSFC Report X–672–64–33, February 1964; F. B. McDonald and G. H. Ludwig, "Measurement of Low-Energy Primary Cosmic-Ray Protons on *IMP–1* Satellite," *Physical Review Letters*, XIII (December 1964) , 783–785; N. F. Ness and J. M. Wilcox, "Extension of the Photospheric Magnetic Field into Interplanetary Space," GSFC Report X–612–65–79, February 1965.

[129] On *Tiros VIII*, see M. Tepper and D. S. Johnson, "Toward Operational Weather Satellites," *Astronautics and Aeronautics*, III (June 1965) , 16–26.

Chapter 8

[130] *Launch Vehicles of the National Launch Vehicle Program* (NASA SP–10) , November 1962; *Goddard Projects Summary: Satellites and Sounding Rockets*, Goddard Space Flight Center; William S. Beller, "New Delta May Prove Most Economical," *Missiles and Rockets* (August 16, 1965), pp. 24–29.

[131] See Arnold W. Frutkin, *International Cooperation in Space*, Englewood Cliffs, N.J.: Prentice-Hall, 1965, pp. 51–59.

[132] For further information on sounding rockets, see *Goddard Space Flight Center Contributions to the COSPAR Meeting, May 1962*, GSFC Technical Note D–1669, 1962; *United*

States Space Science Program: Report to COSPAR, Sixth Meeting, Warsaw, Poland, June, 1963, Washington: National Academy of Sciences–National Research Council, 1963; *United States Space Science Program: Report to COSPAR, Seventh Meeting, Florence, Italy, May, 1964*, Washington: National Academy of Sciences-National Research Council, 1964.

[133] *NASA Authorization for Fiscal Year 1961 —Part I*. 86th Congress, 2d Session—Senate. Testimony of Homer E. Newell, Jr., Deputy Director, Office of Space Flight Programs, NASA, pp. 23–24.

Chapter 9

[134] Harry J. Goett, "Scientific Exploration of Space," paper presented before the Franklin Institute, Philadelphia, Pa., March 8, 1962.

[135] James E. Webb, Address before Ameri-

can Institute of Aeronautics and Astronautics, New York Lecture, October 21, 1963.

[136] *Sperryscope*, Sperry Rand Corporation, October 1966.

APPENDIXES

Man, being the servant and interpreter of Nature, can do and understand so much and so much only as he has observed in fact or in thought of the course of nature: beyond this he neither knows anything nor can do anything.

—FRANCIS BACON

Appendix A

Introduction to the United States Space Sciences Program*

Excerpts from the report of the National Academy of Sciences dated March 12, 1959, to the Committee on Space Research

. . . A space sciences program is being developed by the U.S. National Aeronautics and Space Administration on as broad a basis as possible. In the planning and programing, advantage is being taken of the advice of the National Academy of Sciences' Space Science Board and also of specialists and experts in the scientific community. In the conduct of satellite and space probe experiments broad participation of the scientific community and industry, along with government, is planned, and steps are being taken to secure such participation. The developing program uses and will increase the momentum in space research developed during the International Geophysical Year. . . .

Although the program planning is still in its preliminary stages, it is hoped that in each of the next 2 years between 75 and 100 sounding rockets may be launched and on the order of one or two satellite or space probes every two months.

In the rocket sounding program, emphasis will be placed upon experiments relating to atmospheric structure, electric and magnetic fields, astronomy, energetic particles, and the ionosphere.

The satellite program will emphasize atmospheres, ionospheres, astronomy, energetic particles, electric and magnetic fields, and gravitation.

Space probes will investigate energetic particles, fields, and ionospheres.

Although the approximate magnitude and emphasis of the program has been described, much remains uncertain regarding the special vehicles to be used, their orbits or trajectories, their specific schedules, launching sites, tracking and telemetering support, and special technology support.

I. Atmospheres

Objectives

To determine and understand the origin, evolution, nature, spatial distribution, and dynamical behavior of the atmospheres of the earth, moon, sun, and planets; and their

---

* Report on the second meeting of the Committee on Space Research, held at The Hague, March 12–14, 1959.

relations to the medium of interplanetary space; to investigate atmospheric phenomena associated with interactions between photons, energetic particles, fields, and matter; to understand the relations between the earth's upper atmosphere and its surface meteorology; to evaluate atmospheric effects on space flight.

Program

(a) Long range

Long-range plans for achieving the above objectives include: (1) instrumented satellite stations around other planets; (2) rocket probes deep into the atmospheres of other planets including soft landings onto the surface with automatic and eventually manned recording stations; (3) probes deep into the solar atmosphere; (4) special probes for measuring the density and nature of gas and dust particles in interplanetary space and within comets; and (5) extensive theoretical studies to understand the basic natural phenomena taking place within the atmospheres.

(b) Immediate

Short-range plans include extensive and intensive studies of the structure and composition of the earth's atmosphere by direct measurements with sounding rockets and with satellites. Diurnal, latitudinal, and temporal variations in these parameters will be studied and will be correlated with energy and momentum balances in the earth's upper atmosphere. Models of the earth's atmosphere will be formulated for (1) providing basic data needed in understanding ionospheric, auroral, and other phenomena; and (2) providing guidance in the study of the atmospheres of other planets.

Short-range plans for studies up to about 50 miles include scores of synoptic rocket flights and several cloud cover satellites to establish the relationships between surface meteorology and the structure and dynamics of the upper atmosphere.

II. Ionospheres

Objectives

To determine and understand the source, nature, spatial distribution, and dynamical behavior of the ionized regions of the solar system, including the ionospheres of the earth, moon, and planets; to investigate ionospheric phenomena resulting from interactions between photons, particles, ions, and magnetic, electrostatic, and electromagnetic fields; to understand the relationship between solar activity and the terrestrial and other planetary ionospheres, magnetic fields, and upper atmospheric current systems; to evaluate ionospheric effects on space flight, including communications.

Program

(a) Long range

The long-range program will exploit present techniques for determining the terrestrial ionospheric structure, its propagation characteristics, and its influence on space flight by observation from below, within, and above. New techniques for evaluating the least known parameters will be developed. All of the applicable methods will then be used for the study of other planetary ionospheres. Eventually, propagation sounding stations may be established on the surface of the moon. All the data will then be applied to understand the interrelations between solar activity, magnetic fields, the aurora, the Great Radiation Belt, and other phenomena.

(b) Immediate

The immediate program is concerned with obtaining electron density profiles at altitudes above the F_2 layer by inclusion of proven propagation experiments in space probes. Concurrently latitude and temporal variations of this parameter will be obtained by use of a polar orbiting satellite beacon. Topside sounders in satellite will be used for synoptic studies of electron density in the outer ionosphere. This technique promises less ambiguity than that obtainable from satellite beacons. Present knowledge of electromagnetic propagation will be extended by inclusion of very low frequency receivers in polar-orbiting satellites. Ion spectrum studies will be extended to lower mass numbers and higher altitudes by inclusion of rf mass spectrometers in space probes and satellites. Direct measurements using devices such as antenna probes, ion probes, and electric field meters will be made in rockets and satellites, to better define ionospheric structure and to study the interaction between the ionosphere and space vehicles.

III. Energetic Particles

Objectives

To determine and understand the origin, nature, motion, spatial distribution, and temporal variation of particles having energies appreciably greater than thermal; to understand their relation to the origin of the universe; to understand interactions between such particles, fields, photons, and matter; to evaluate possible hazards to life and other effects of energetic particles and photons in space.

Program

(a) Long range

Measurements using deep space probes will be made from the close proximity of the sun to the limits of the solar system. Extensive measurements in the vicinity of the planets, especially the earth, will be made to determine the interactions of the energetic particles with the atmospheres and fields of these bodies. These measurements will require satellite orbits around the earth, the moon, and other planets. The establishment of an observatory on the surface of the moon or on some other planet might be desirable, depending on the data previously acquired by artificial satellites.

(b) Immediate

In the near future the measurement of energetic particles will be pursued with satellites and rockets in the vicinity of the earth and with interplanetary probes. These measurements will be aimed at determining the interactions of these particles with the earth's atmosphere and field, their interactions with interplanetary fields, the types and energies of these particles, their spatial distribution, and the origin of the energetic particles.

The immediate program includes specifically measurements of the cosmic ray intensity in interplanetary space; of time and latitude cosmic ray intensity variations; of the composition and spatial extent of the Great Radiation Belt; of the cosmic ray energy and charge spectrum; and of the nature of the particles producing auroras.

IV. Electric and Magnetic Fields

Objectives

To determine and understand the origin, nature, method of propagation, spatial distribution, and temporal variation of magnetic and electric fields throughout the universe; to understand interactions between these fields and matter in space, and the influence of existing fields on solar and planetary atmospheres; to use these fields in the investigation of the internal constitution of astronomical bodies; to evaluate their effects and interactions on space flights.

Program

(a) Long range

Results from satellites, probes, and rockets to be flown in 1959 will be an important factor in determining the long-range program for studying the earth's fields. One can, however, anticipate that an important item will be establishing an earth satellite observatory which will include instruments for measuring particle flux and solar radiations as well as magnetic and electric field instruments such that direct correlations can be made between the various phenomena. Also rocket soundings into the ionosphere will continue to study details of ionospheric currents more thoroughly.

Attempts will be made to measure the fields of the moon, Mars, and Venus from probes making those approaches and eventually from packages landing and serving as observatories.

Probes will be launched toward the sun to obtain solar field measurements as close to the sun as feasible.

Theoretical analyses and correlations between electric and magnetic field phenomena and other phenomena will be an integral part of the program.

(b) Immediate

The short-range magnetic field program includes the use of sounding rockets, satellites, and space probes to carry magnetometers for investigation of the existence of ring currents above the ionosphere during magnetic storms, ionospheric currents, information on radiation belt currents, for measuring electric currents and the form of the earth's field at great distances, interplanetary fields, and the moon's magnetic field, and to study the complete spectra of field variations and for comprehensive field mapping.

It is also anticipated that simple magnetometers which can detect only the existence of a perceptible field will be placed in several rockets and space vehicles as secondary experiments. The short-range electric field program includes the use of electric field meters and Langmuir probes to explore satellite charging and ion sheath characteristics.

V. Gravitational Fields

Objectives

To determine and understand the origin, nature, method of propagation, spatial distribution, temporal variation, and effect of gravitational fields throughout the universe; to determine and understand the external form and internal constitution of the earth, planets, and stars; to determine and understand the relations between gravitational and electromagnetic fields; to evaluate effects of gravitational fields of different magnitudes, including weightlessness, on space flights.

Program

(a) Long range

For the study of the fundamental nature of the gravitational fields, two avenues are opened by the ability to launch satellites and space probes. The first of these is the ability to try experiments on a scale of hundreds and thousands of kilometers by probing the fields of planetary masses with bodies capable of being accurately observed. This is significant because gravitational fields, except that of the earth, are almost unmeasurable in laboratory-scale experiments. In the second place, the periods of artificial satellites are so much shorter than those of the moon and other natural satellites that in a few years a number of revolutions corresponding to thousands of years for natural satellites may be observed.

By the first avenue, it is possible to seek the links which must exist between the theory of the electromagnetic field and gravitational field. It is planned in particular to test the equality of gravitational and inertial masses by experiments in space which are a repetition of the experiment of Galileo in the Leaning Tower of Pisa. An attempt will be made to devise experiments which will reveal the velocity of propagation of gravitation, if any.

It is planned to determine the masses of the inner planets by direct observation of probes passing near them or possibly around them. These probes will at the same time help to determine the value of the astronomical unit.

It is planned to test the hypothesis that gravitational attraction depends on the average density of matter in the universe and that it therefore is slowly weakening as the universe expands. For this purpose, it is planned to compare an atomic clock on the ground with a gravitational clock of some kind. A proposal for a gravitational clock consisting, in effect, of a high satellite with a very well measured orbit is being studied.

It is planned to employ moon probes to obtain improved values for the overall mass of the moon and for the moments of inertia about its three principal axes. It is planned to attempt to determine the strength of the materials in the moon's interior from this information.

It is planned to measure the mass of Venus and of Mercury in order to test Bullen's ideas about the nature of the cores of the planets.

Using the second avenue, it is planned to observe the motions of close satellites of the earth over a long period and to make precise comparison with theory, searching for systematic trends in the inclination and the eccentricity, which might shed light on the history of the solar system.

(b) Immediate

(1) Studies are now being made on existing satellites with the object of determining the low harmonics of the earth's field from tracking data.

(2) It is also planned to put into orbit a special geodetic satellite which will be capable of refining the observations on the harmonics, and of determining intercontinental distances with high precision. It should be possible to carry the study of the form of the geoid much further than has been possible to date.

The information developed in (1) and (2) above will be applied to the question of the basic hypothesis of geodesy. This hypothesis, as formulated by some theorists, is in essence that the low harmonics of the earth's gravitational field have amplitudes of a meter or so. The hypothesis is not universally accepted; other theorists consider that the amplitudes are on the order of scores of meters. A decision between these two hypotheses is important because Heiskanen, in particular, proposes extensive work revolving around the Stokes' Theorem—work which is only warranted if the basic hypothesis is satisfied. This information will also be used in an attempt to evaluate hypotheses of convection in the mantle. These hypotheses seem to go with the ideas of the first-mentioned school of theorists, and it may be possible to decide between these hypotheses and the alternative contraction hypothesis on the basis of our information.

(3) It is planned to put in orbit a satellite carrying a very precise clock in order to test the theory of Einstein which predicts a change in the clock's speed depending upon the strength of the earth's gravitational field.

VI. Astronomy

Objectives

To determine the spatial distributions of matter and energy over the entire universe, and to understand their cosmological origins, evolutions, and destinies; to observe from above the earth's atmosphere the spectral distributions of energy radiated from objects in the solar system, in this and other galaxies, and in the intervening space, with emphasis on observations that are prevented or comprised by the absorption, background emission, and differential refraction of the earth's atmosphere; to determine and understand the geology of the planets; to determine the effects of meteors, radiations, and other astronomical influences on space flights.

Program

(a) Long range

The first phase of the long-range program will be the development of an orbiting and stabilized platform. With such a platform, it will be possible to orient a wide range of telescopic instruments so as to make detailed observations of specific quantities of interest at selected locations on the celestial sphere. Command control for the platform will be incorporated so that redirection of the instrumentation will be possible. The obvious advantages of observations made beyond the earth's atmosphere will be available to us with such an orbiting observatory. There will still remain some observational difficulties because of the backscattered light of the sun and the Doppler shifts resulting from the high velocity of the satellite.

(b) Immediate

The immediate program will continue and extend to the Southern sky the survey of the newly discovered nebulosities in the far ultraviolet by means of rockets. These measurements are being undertaken to determine the nature and sources of these emissions. Concurrently stellar photometry measurements will be made in the near and far ultraviolet spectrum region to extend magnitude systems to ultraviolet. Emphasis is being given to extending observations into the previously unexplored far infrared and high energy gamma-ray spectral regions by means of scanning satellite and rockets. Apart from their intrinsic value, these surveys are essential as ground work for the satellite observatory program.

Studies of the solar ultraviolet and x-ray spectra will be extended to include long term variations, line profiles, distribution across the disk, and the spectra of the coronal x-ray flux. These studies will be carried out in a series of rocket firings and with satellite-borne pointing devices.

Deep space probes will be used to determine the nature of the interplanetary medium.

Satellites will be used to map the emissions of the high atmosphere which arise from charged particle interactions and photochemical reactions.

VII. Biosciences

Objectives

To determine the effects on living terrestrial organisms of conditions in the earth's atmosphere, in space and in other planetary atmospheres, and of flight through these regions; to investigate the existence of life throughout the solar system, and to study such life forms in detail; to develop information necessary to achieve and maintain healthful artificial environments for terrestrial organisms, including man, throughout the solar system.

Appendix B

Goddard Space Flight Center
Satellite and Space Probe Projects

GODDARD SPACE FLIGHT CENTER satellite launchings for 1959 through 1963 are given in the following table. The listings include the name of the satellites, their international designation (the international designation changed after 1962), the NASA designation, the project manager, and project scientist. The tabulation also gives the date of launch, the date on which the satellite became silent, the launch vehicle, and launch site. The period of the satellite is given in minutes, unless otherwise designated, and the perigee and apogee are given in statute miles. Orbital elements change over time. Any inconsistencies between text and appendixes derive from the date of measurement. The following abbreviations have been used.

Affiliations:

AFCRL	Air Force Cambridge Research Laboratories
ARC	Ames Research Center
BTL	Bell Telephone Laboratories
CRPL	Central Radio Propagation Laboratory
DRTE	Defence Research Telecommunications Establishment
DSIR	Department of Scientific and Industrial Research
ETR	Eastern Test Range
GSFC	Goddard Space Flight Center
JPL	Jet Propulsion Laboratory
MIT	Massachusetts Institute of Technology
NRC	National Research Council
NRL	Naval Research Laboratory
TRW/STL	Thompson Ramo Wooldridge/Space Technology Laboratories
WTR	Western Test Range

Scientific disciplines:

R Aeronomy
E Energetic Particles and Fields
I Ionospheric Physics
A Astronomy
P Planetary Atmospheres
S Solar Physics

Goddard Space Flight Center

Designation	Objectives	Launch and orbit data					Project manager and project scientist
		Launch date/ silent date	Vehicle and launch site	Period, min.	Statute miles		
					Perigee	Apogee	
Explorer VI 1959 Delta 1 S–2	To measure three specific radiation levels of earth's radiation belts; test scanning equipment for earth's cloud cover; map earth's magnetic field; measure micrometeoroids; study behavior of radiowaves.	Aug. 7, 1959 Oct. 6, 1959	Thor-Able ETR	12.5 hours	156	27,357	Dr. John C. Lindsay Dr. John C. Lindsay
Vanguard III 1959 Eta 1	To measure the earth's magnetic field, X-radiation from the sun, and several aspects of the space environment through which the satellite travels.	Sept. 18, 1959 Dec. 11, 1959	Vanguard ETR	130	319	2,329	
Explorer VII 1959 Iota 1	Variety of experiments, including solar ultraviolet, X-ray cosmic-ray, earth radiation, and micrometeoroid experiments.	Oct. 13, 1959 Aug. 24, 1961	Juno II ETR	101.33	342	680	H. E. LaGow

Satellite and Space Probe Projects

Experiment data				Remarks
Instrumentation summary	Experiment and discipline	Experimenter	Affiliation	
Equipment to measure radiation levels; TV-type scanner; micro-meteoroid detector; two types of magne-tometers and devices for space communi-cation experiments.	Triple coincidence tele-scopes—A Scintillation counter—E Ionization chamber Geiger counter—E Spin-coil magnetometer—E Fluxgate magnetometer—E Aspect sensor Image-scanning television system Micrometeoroid detector —P	J. A. Simpson C. Y. Fan P. Meyer T. A. Farley Allan Rosen C. P. Sonett J. Winckler E. J. Smith D. L. Judge P. J. Coleman	U. of Chicago TRW/STL U. of Minne-sota TRW/STL TRW/STL TRW/STL TRW/STL AFCRL TRW/STL	Orbit achieved. All experi-ments performed. First complete televised cloud-cover picture was ob-tained. Detected large ring of electrical current circling earth; first de-tailed study of region now known as the Van Allen radiation belt. Weight: 142 lb Power: Solar
Proton precession magnetometer, ioni-zation chambers for solar X-rays, micro-meteorite detectors and thermistors.	Proton magnetometer—E Ionization chambers—E Environmental measure-ments	J. P. Heppner H. Friedman H. E. LaGow	GSFC NRL GSFC	Orbit achieved. Provided comprehensive survey of earth's magnetic field over area covered; surveyed location of lower edge of Van Allen radiation belt. Accurate count of micro-meteoroid impacts. Power: Solar
Sensors for measure-ments of earth-sun heat balance; Ly-man-alpha and X-ray solar radiation detectors; micro-meteoroid detectors, Geiger-Mueller tubes for cosmic ray count; ionization chamber for heavy cosmic rays.	Thermal radiation balance Solar X-ray and Lyman-alpha—S Heavy cosmic radiation—E Radiation and solar-proton observation—E Ground-based ionosphere observation—I	V. Suomi H. Friedman R. W. Kreplin T. Chubb G. Groetzinger P. Schwed M. Pomerantz J. Van Allen G. Ludwig H. Whelpley G. Swenson C. Little C. Reid O. Villard, Jr. W. Ross W. Dyke	U. of Wiscon-sin NRL Martin Co. Bartol Research St. U. of Iowa U. of Illinois Nat. Bu. of Standards U. of Alaska Stanford U. Penn. State U. Linfield Res. Inst.	Orbit achieved. Provided significant geophysical information on radiation and magnetic storms; demonstrated method of controlling internal tem-peratures; first micro-meteoroid penetration of a sensor in flight. Weight: 91.5 lb Power: Solar

Goddard Space Flight Center

Designation	Objectives	Launch and orbit data					Project manager and project scientist
		Launch date/ silent date	Vehicle and launch site	Period, min.	Statute miles		
					Perigee	Apogee	
Explorer VII —Cont.							
Pioneer V 1960 Alpha 1	To investigate interplanetary space between orbits of earth and Venus, test extreme long-range communications, study methods for measuring astronomical distances.	Mar. 11, 1960 Jun. 26, 1960	Thor-Able ETR	311.6 days	Perihelion 74.9 million from sun	Aphelion 92.3 million from sun	Dr. John C. Lindsay Dr. John C. Lindsay
Tiros I 1960 Beta 2 A-1	To test experimental television techniques leading to eventual worldwide meteorological information system.	Apr. 1, 1960 June 17, 1960	Thor-Able ETR	99.1	428.7	465.9	W. G. Stroud H. I. Butler S. Fritz (U.S. Weather Bureau)
Echo I 1960 Iota 1 A-11	To place 100-foot inflatable sphere into orbit; measure reflective characteristics of sphere and propagation; study effects of space environment.	Aug. 12, 1960 Passive satellite	Thor-Delta ETR	110.3	945	1,049	R. J. Mackey
Explorer VIII 1960 Xi S-30	To investigate the ionosphere by direct measurement of positive ion and electron composition; collect data on the frequency, momentum,	Nov. 3, 1960 Dec. 28, 1960	Juno II ETR	112.7	258	1,423	Robert E. Bourdeau Robert E. Bourdeau

Satellite and Space Probe Projects (Cont.)

Experiment data				Remarks
Instrumentation summary	Experiment and discipline	Experimenter	Affiliation	
	Micrometeoroid penetration—P	H. LaGow	GSFC	
High-intensity radiation counter, ionization chamber Geiger-Mueller tube to measure plasmas, cosmic radiation, and charged solar particles. Magnetometer and micrometeoroid measurements.	Triple coincidence proportional counter cosmic-ray telescope—E Search-coil magnetometer and photoelectric cell aspect indicator—E Ionization chamber and G-M tube—E Micrometeoroid counter—P	J. Simpson D. Judge J. Winckler E. Manring	U. of Chicago TRW/STL U. of Minnesota AFCRL	Highly successful exploration of interplanetary space between orbits of earth and Venus; established communication record of 22.5 million miles on June 26, 1960; made measurements of solar flare effects, particle energies and distribution, and magnetic-field phenomena in interplanetary space. Weight: 94.8 lb Power: Solar
One wide and one narrow angle camera, each with tape recorder for remote operation. Picture data can be stored on tape or transmitted directly to ground stations.	TV camera systems (2)			Provided first global cloud-cover photographs (22,952 total) from near-circular orbit. Weight: 370 lb Power: Solar
Two tracking beacons 107.94 Mc and 107.97 Mc.	Communications		JPL BTL NRL	Demonstrated use of radio reflector for global communications; numerous successful transmissions. Visible to the naked eye. Orbit characteristics perturbed by solar pressure due to high area-to-mass ratio. Still in orbit. Weight: 124 lb (including inflation powder) Power: Passive
RF-impedance probe using a 20-foot dipole sensor; single-grid ion trap; four multiple-grid ion traps; Langmuir probe experiment, rotating shutter electric field meter; photomultiplier and micrometeoroid microphone; thermistors for reading internal	RF impedance—I Ion traps—I Langmuir probe—I Rotating-shutter electric field meter—I Micrometeoroid photomultiplier—I	J. Cain R. Bourdeau G. Serbu E. Whipple J. Donley R. Bourdeau G. Serbu E. Whipple J. Donley J. Donley M. Alexander C. McCracken	GSFC GSFC GSFC GSFC GSFC	The micrometeoroid influx rate was measured. Weight: 90.14 lb Power: Battery

Goddard Space Flight Center

Designation	Objectives	Launch and orbit data					Project manager and project scientist
		Launch date/ silent date	Vehicle and launch site	Period, min.	Statute miles		
					Perigee	Apogee	
Explorer VIII —Cont.	and energy of micro-meteoroid impacts; establish the altitude of the base of the exosphere.						
Tiros II 1960 Pi 1 A-2	To test experimental television techniques and infrared equipment leading to eventual worldwide meteorological information system.	Nov. 23, 1960 July 12, 1961	Delta ETR	98.2	406	431	R. A. Stamfl
Explorer IX 1961 Delta 1 S-56a (A project of the Langley Research Center with GSFC participation)	To study performance, structural integrity, and environmental conditions of Scout research vehicle and guidance controls system. Inject inflatable sphere into earth orbit to determine density of atmosphere.	Feb. 16, 1961 April 9, 1964 Passive satellite	Scout Wallops Island	118.3	395	1,605	
Explorer X 1961 Kappa 1 P-14	To gather definite information on earth and interplanetary magnetic fields and the way these fields affect and are affected by solar plasma.	Mar. 25, 1961 Mar. 27, 1961	Thor-Delta ETR	112 hours	100	186,000	J. P. Heppner J. P. Heppner

Satellite and Space Probe Projects (Cont.)

Experiment data				Remarks
Instrumentation summary	Experiment and discipline	Experimenter	Affiliation	
and surface temperatures of the spacecraft, and despin mechanisms to reduce spin from 450 to 30 rpm.	Micrometeoroid microphone—I	O. Berg M. Alexander C. McCracken	GSFC	
Included one wideangle and one narrow-angle camera, each with tape recorder for remote operation; infrared sensors to map radiation in various spectral bands; attitude sensors; experimental magnetic orientation control.	Two TV camera systems Widefield radiometer Scanning radiometer	W. Nordberg R. Hanel	GSFC GSFC	Orbit achieved. Narrow-angle camera and IR instrumentation sent good data. Transmitted 36,156 pictures. Weight: 277 lb Power: Solar
Radio beacon on balloon and in fourth stage.				Vehicle functioned as planned. Balloon and fourth stage achieved orbit. Transmitter on balloon failed to function properly requiring optical tracking of balloon. Weight: 80 lb Power: Passive
Included rubidium vapor magnetometer, two fluxgate magnetometers, a plasma probe, and an optical aspect sensor.	Rubidium-vapor magnetometer and fluxgate magnetometers—E Plasma probe—E Spacecraft attitude	J. P. Heppner T. L. Skillman C. S. Scearce H. Bridge F. Scherb B. Rossi J. Albus	GSFC MIT GSFC	Probe transmitted valuable data continuously for 52 hours as planned. Demonstrated the existence of a geomagnetic cavity in the solar wind and the existence of solar proton streams transporting solar interplanetary magnetic fields past the earth's orbit. Weight: 79 lb Power: Battery

Goddard Space Flight Center

Designation	Objectives	Launch and orbit data					Project manager and project scientist
		Launch date/ silent date	Vehicle and launch site	Period, min.	Statute miles		
					Perigee	Apogee	
Explorer XI 1961 Nu 1 S–15	To orbit a gamma-ray astronomy telescope satellite to detect high-energy gamma rays from cosmic sources and map their distribution in the sky.	Apr. 27, 1961 Dec. 6, 1961	Juno II ETR	108.1	304	1,113.2	Dr. J. Kupperian, Jr. Dr. J. Kupperian, Jr.
Tiros III 1961 Rho 1 A–3	To develop satellite weather observation system; obtain photos of earth's cloud cover for weather analysis; determine amount of solar energy absorbed, reflected and emitted by the earth.	July 12, 1961 Feb. 1962	Delta ETR	100.4	461.02	506.44	Robert Rados
Explorer XII Energetic Particles Explorer 1961 Upsilon 1 S–3	To investigate solar wind, interplanetary magnetic fields, distant portions of earth's magnetic field, energetic particles in interplanetary space and in the Van Allen belts.	Aug. 15, 1961 Dec. 6, 1961	Thor-Delta ETR	26.45 hours	180	47,800	Paul Butler Dr. F. B. McDonald
Explorer XIII 1961 Chi 1 (A project of the Langley Research Center with GSFC	To test performance of the vehicle and guidance; to investigate nature and effects on	Aug. 25, 1961 Aug. 28, 1961	Scout Wallops Island	97.5	74	722	C. T. D'Aiutolo

Satellite and Space Probe Projects (Cont.)

Experiment data				Remarks
Instrumentation summary	Experiment and discipline	Experimenter	Affiliation	
Gamma-ray telescope consisting of a plastic scintillator, crystal layers, and a Cerenkov detector; sun and earth sensors; micrometeoroid shields; temperature sensor; damping mechanism.	Gamma-ray telescope—E	W. Kraushaar G. Clark	MIT	Orbit achieved. Detected first gamma rays from space. Directional flux obtained. Disproved one part of "steady-state" evolution theory. Weight: 82 lb Power: Solar
Two wide-angle cameras, two tape recorders and electronic clocks, infrared sensors, five transmitters, attitude sensors, magnetic attitude coil.	Omnidirectional radiometer Widefield radiometer Scanning radiometer Two TV cameras	V. Suomi R. Hanel W. Nordberg	U. of Wisconsin GSFC GSFC	Orbit achieved. Cameras and IR instrumentation transmitted good data. Transmitted 35,033 pictures. Weight: 285 lb Power: Solar
Ten particle detection systems for measurement of protons and electrons and three orthogonally mounted fluxgate sensors for correlation with the magnetic fields, optical aspect sensor, and one transmitter. PFM telemetry transmitting continuously.	Proton analyzer—E Magnetometer—E Cosmic ray—E Ion-electron—E Solar cell	M. Bader L. Cahill B. O'Brien F. B. McDonald L. Davis G. Longanecker	ARC U. of New Hampshire St. U. of Iowa GSFC GSFC GSFC	Orbit achieved. All instrumentation operated normally. Ceased transmitting on Dec. 6, 1961, after sending 2,568 hours of real-time data. Provided significant geophysical data on radiation and magnetic fields. Weight: 83 lb Power: Solar
Micrometeoroid impact detectors; transmitters.	Cadmium sulfide photoconductor—A Wire grid	M. W. Alexander L. Secretan	GSFC	Orbit was lower than planned. Reentered Aug. 28, 1961. Weight: 187 lb including 50-lb 4th stage and 12-lb transition section. Power: Solar

Designation	Objectives	Launch and orbit data						Project manager and project scientist
		Launch date/ silent date	Vehicle and launch site	Period, min.	Statute miles			
					Perigee	Apogee		
participation) S–55a	space flight of micro-meteoroids.							
P–21 Electron Density Profile Probe P–21	To measure electron densities and to investigate radio propagation at 12.3 and 73.6 Mc under daytime conditions.	Oct. 19, 1961 Oct. 19, 1961	Scout Wallops Island					John E. Jackson Dr. S. J. Bauer
Tiros IV 1962 Beta 1 A–9	To develop principles of a weather satellite system; obtain cloud and radiation data for use in meteorology.	Feb. 8, 1962 June 19, 1962	Delta ETR	100.4	471	525		Robert Rados
OSO I 1962 Zeta 1 OSO–1	To measure solar electromagnetic radiation in the ultraviolet, X-ray and gamma-ray regions; to investigate effect of dust particles on surfaces of spacecraft.	Mar. 7, 1962 Aug. 6, 1963	Delta ETR	96.15	343.5	369		Dr. John C. Lindsay Dr. John C. Lindsay
P–21a Electron Density Profile Probe	To measure electron density profile, ion density, and intensity	Mar. 20, 1962 Mar. 20, 1962	Scout Wallops Island					John E. Jackson Dr. S. J. Bauer

Satellite and Space Probe Projects (Cont.)

Experiment data				Remarks
Instrumentation summary	Experiment and discipline	Experimenter	Affiliation	
Continuous-wave propagation experiment for the ascent portion of the trajectory, and an RF-probe technique for the descent.	RF probe—I CW propagation—I	H. Whale G. H. Spaid J. E. Jackson	GSFC GSFC GSFC	Probe achieved altitude of 4,261 miles and transmitted good data. Electron density was obtained to about 1,500 miles, the first time such measurements had been taken at this altitude. Weight: 94 lb Power: Battery
Two TV camera systems with clocks and recorders for remote pictures, infrared sensors, heat budget sensors, magnetic orientation control horizon sensor, north indicator.	Omnidirectional radiometer Widefield radiometer Scanning radiometer Two TV camera systems	V. Suomi R. Hanel W. Nordberg	U. of Wisconsin GSFC GSFC	Orbit achieved. All systems operated properly. Tegea Kinoptic lens used on one camera, Elgeet lens on the other. Supported Project Mercury. Weight: 285 lb Power: Solar
Devices to conduct 13 different experiments for study of solar electromagnetic radiations; investigate dust particles in space and thermoradiation characteristics of spacecraft surface materials.	X-ray spectrometer—S 0.510 MeV gamma-ray monitoring; 20–100 keV X-ray monitoring; 1–8A X-ray monitoring—S. Dust particle—E Solar radiation and solar ultraviolet—A Solar gamma rays, high-energy distribution—A Solar gamma rays, low-energy distribution—A Solar gamma rays, high-energy distribution—A Neutron monitor—E Lower Van Allen belt—E Emissivity stability of surfaces in a vacuum environment—E	W. Behring W. Neupert K. Frost W. White M. Alexander C. McCracken W. White K. Hallam W. White K. Frost J. R. Winckler L. Peterson M. Savedoff G. Fazio W. Hess S. Bloom G. Robinson	GSFC GSFC GSFC GSFC GSFC U. of Minnesota U. of Rochester U. of California U. of California ARC	Orbit achieved. Experiments transmitted as programed. Weight: 458 lb Power: Solar
A continuous-wave propagation experiment to determine electron density and associated param-	CW propagation—I RF probe—I Ion traps—I	S. Bauer H. White R. Bourdeau E. Whipple J. Donley	GSFC GSFC GSFC	Probe achieved altitude of 3,910 miles. Afforded nighttime observations. Determined that characteristics of the iono-

Goddard Space Flight Center

Designation	Objectives	Launch and orbit data					Project manager and project scientist
		Launch date/ silent date	Vehicle and launch site	Period, min.	Statute miles		
					Perigee	Apogee	
P–21a Electron Density Profile Probe— Con.	of ions in the atmosphere.						
Ariel I International Satellite 1962 Omicron 1 (UK–1) S–51	To study the relationships between ionosphere and cosmic rays.	Apr. 26, 1962 Nov. 9, 1964	Delta ETR	100.9	242.1	754.2	R. C. Baumann Robert E. Bourdeau
Tiros V 1962 Alpha Alpha 1 A–50	To develop principles of a weather satellite system; obtain cloud-cover data for use in meteorology.	June 19, 1962 May 4, 1963	Delta ETR	100.5	367	604	Robert Rados
Telstar I (A project of AT&T) 1962 Alpha Epsilon 1 A–40	Joint AT&T–NASA investigation of wideband communications.	July 10, 1962 Feb. 21, 1963	Delta ETR	157.8	592.6	3,503.2	C. P. Smith, Jr.

Satellite and Space Probe Projects (Cont.)

Experiment data				Remarks
Instrumentation summary	Experiment and discipline	Experimenter	Affiliation	
eters of ionosphere. A swept-frequency probe for direct measurements of electron density and a positive ion experiment to determine ion concentration under nighttime conditions.		G. Serbu		sphere differ drastically from daytime state when the temperature of the ionosphere is much cooler. (See P-21) Weight: 94 lb Power: Battery
Electron density sensor, electron temperature gauge, solar aspect sensor, cosmic-ray detector, ion mass sphere, Lyman-alpha gauges, tape recorder, X-ray sensors.	Electron density sensor—I Electron temperature gauge—I Cosmic-ray detector—E Ion mass sphere—I Lyman-alpha gauge—I X-ray emission—I	J. Sayers R. L. F. Boyd H. Elliot R. L. F. Boyd R. L. F. Boyd R. L. F. Boyd	U. of Birmingham (U.K.) U. College, London (U.K.) Imperial College, London (U.K.) U. College, London (U.K.) U. College, London (U.K.) U. College, London (U.K.)	Orbit achieved. First international satellite. Contained six British experiments launched by American Delta vehicle. All experiments except Lyman-alpha transmitted as programed. Lyman-alpha gauge failed during launch, ion mass sphere, Sept. 1962; X-ray emission, Oct. 1962; cosmic-ray detector, Dec. 1962, and electron density sensor, Mar. 1963. Tracking and data acquisition stopped on request of the project on June 30, 1964. Restarted on Aug. 25, 1964, for a 2-month period. Good data were acquired from electron temperature gauge.
Two TV camera systems with tape recorders for recording remote picture areas, magnetic orientation control, horizon sensor, north indicator.	Two TV camera systems			Launched at a higher inclination (58°) than previous Tiros satellites, to provide greater coverage. Time of launch chosen to include normal hurricane season for South Atlantic. One TV system transmitted good data for 10½ months. Weight: 285 lb Power: Solar
The system provided TV, radio, telephone and data transmission via a satellite repeater system.	Included electron detector for range 0.25–1 MeV; proton detectors in the following energy ranges: 2.5–25.0 MeV, ranges greater than 50 MeV.	W. Brown	BTL	Orbit achieved. Television and voice transmissions were made with complete success. BTL provided spacecraft and ground stations facilities. Government was reimbursed for cost incurred.

Designation	Objectives	Launch and orbit data					Project manager and project scientist
		Launch date/ silent date	Vehicle and launch site	Period, min.	Statute miles		
					Perigee	Apogee	
Telstar I— Cont.							
Tiros VI 1962 Alpha Psi 1 A–51	To study cloud cover and earth heat balance; measurement of radiation in selected spectral regions as part of a program to develop meteorological satellite systems.	Sept. 18, 1962 Oct. 11, 1963	Delta ETR	98.73	425	442	Robert Rados
Alouette I Swept Frequency Topside Sounder (Canada) 1962 Beta Alpha 1 S–27	To measure the electron density distribution in the ionosphere between the satellite height (620 miles) and the F2 peak (approx. 180 miles) and to study for a period of one year the variations of electron density distribution with time of day and with latitude under varying magnetic and auroral conditions with particular emphasis on high-latitude effects. To obtain galactic-noise measurements, study	Sept. 29, 1962	Thor-Agena WTR	105.4	620	638	John E. Jackson

Satellite and Space Probe Projects (Cont.)

Experiment data				Remarks
Instrumentation summary	Experiment and discipline	Experimenter	Affiliation	
				Conducted more than 300 technical tests and over 400 demonstrations; 50 TV programs—5 in color. Weight: 175 lb Power: Solar
Two TV camera systems (78° and 104° lens), clocks and tape recorders for remote operation, infrared and attitude sensors, magnetic-attitude coil.	Two TV camera systems			Inclination 58.3°; velocity at perigee 16,822; apogee, 16,756. Medium-angle camera failed Dec. 1, 1962, after taking 1,074 pictures. TV camera provided good data for 13 months after launch. Weight: 300 lb Power: Solar
The satellite was spin-stabilized and contained a swept-frequency pulse sounder covering the frequency range 1.6 to 11.5 Mc. Sounder data were transmitted via a 2-watt FM telemetry system. Data from the other experiments and housekeeping data were transmitted through a ¼-watt PM-telemetry system. There were two sets of sounder antennas, the longest set measuring 150 ft. tip to tip. Data were acquired on command and in real time only.	Topside sounder—I Energetic particle counters—E VLF receiver (whistler) —I Cosmic noise—A	E. S. Warren G. L. B. Nelms G. E. Lockwood E. L. Hagg L. E. Petrie D. B. Muldrew R. W. Knecht T. E. Van Zandt W. Calvert J. W. King S. J. Bauer L. Blumle R. Fitzenreiter J. E. Jackson D. C. Rose I. B. McDiarmid J. S. Belrose T. R. Hartz	DRTE CRPL NBS DSIR England GSFC NRC Canada DRTE DRTE	The Alouette satellite was a project of the Canadian Defence Research Board. This international project was a part of NASA's topside sounder program and was the first NASA-launched satellite from the WTR. Alouette had the distinction of being the first spacecraft designed and built by any country other than the U.S. and the U.S.S.R. Weight: 320 lb Power: Solar

Designation	Objectives	Launch and orbit data					Project manager and project scientist
		Launch date/ silent date	Vehicle and launch site	Period, min.	Statute miles		
					Perigee	Apogee	
Alouette I— Cont.	the flux of energetic particles, and investigate whistlers.						
Explorer XIV Energetic Particles Satellite 1962 Beta Gamma 1 EPE-B S-3a	To correlate energetic particles activity with observations of the earth's magnetic fields; to monitor the existence of transient magnetic fields associated with plasma streams.	Oct. 2, 1962 Feb. 1964	Delta ETR	36.58 hours	174	61,090	Paul G. Marcotte Dr. F. B. McDonald
Explorer XV 1962 Beta Lambda 1 EPE-C S-3b	To study artificial radiation belt created by nuclear explosion.	Oct. 27, 1962 Feb. 9, 1963	Delta ETR	5 hours	195	10,950	Dr. John W. Townsend Dr. Wilmot Hess
Relay I 1962 Beta Upsilon 1 A-15	To investigate wideband communications between ground stations by means of low-altitude orbiting spacecraft. Communications signal to be evaluated will be an assortment of TV signals, multichannel telephony,	Dec. 13, 1962	Delta ETR	185.09	819.64	4,612.18	Wendell Sunderlin Dr. R. Waddel

Satellite and Space Probe Projects (Cont.)

Experiment data				Remarks
Instrumentation summary	Experiment and discipline	Experimenter	Affiliation	
A low-energy (0.1 to 20 keV) proton analyzer; a three-core magnetometer; one omnidirectional and three directional electron-proton detectors; a cosmic-ray package; an ion-electron scintillation detector; and devices to determine the effects of radiation on solar cells and the effects of space on electrolytic timers.	Proton analyzer—E Magnetic field (magnetometer)—E Trapped-particle radiation—E Cosmic-ray, ion-electron detector, solar-cell, and electrolytic timer—E	M. Bader L. Cahill J. A. Van Allen B. J. O'Brien F. B. McDonald L. R. Davis U. Desai	ARC U. of New Hampshire State U. of Iowa GSFC	Velocity at apogee 1,507 mph; perigee 23,734 mph. Inclination to equator 33°. Weight: 89.25 lb Power: Solar
Similar to Explorer XII	Electron energy distribution—I Omnidirectional detector —I Angular detector—E Directional detector—I Ion-electron detector—E Magnetic field—E Solar cell damage—I	W. Brown U. Desai C. McIlwain W. Brown C. McIlwain L. Davis L. Cahill H. K. Gummel	BTL GSFC U. of California BTL U. of California GSFC U. of New Hampshire BTL	Good data received on artificial radiation belt. Weight: 100 lb Power: Solar
The spacecraft contained an active communications repeater to receive and retransmit communications between the U.S. and Europe, U.S. and South America, U.S. and Japan, and Europe and South America; and an experiment to assess radiation damage to solar cells, and to measure proton and electron energy.	Determine radiation damage to solar cells and semiconductor diodes—E Measure proton energy (2.5–25.0 MeV)—E Measure electron energy (1.25–2.0 MeV)—E Measure integral omnidirectional proton flux energy (35.0–300.0 MeV) —E Measure directional electron energy (0.5–1.2 MeV)—E Measure directional proton energy (15.0–60.0 MeV)—E	R. Waddel W. Brown W. Brown C. McIlwain C. McIlwain C. McIlwain	GSFC BTL BTL U. of California U. of California U. of California	Orbit achieved. TV, telephone, teletype, facsimile, and digital-data transmissions were made with very satisfactory results. Conducted more than 2,000 technical tests and 172 successful demonstrations. Weight: 172 lb Power: Solar

Designation	Objectives	Launch and orbit data					Project manager and project scientist
		Launch date/ silent date	Vehicle and launch site	Period, min.	Statute miles		
					Perigee	Apogee	
Relay I— Con.	and other communications. To measure the effects of the space environment on the system; to include radiation damage to solar cells and radiation flux density. To provide tests and demonstrations of low-altitude communications satellite.						
Syncom I 1963 4A A–25	To provide experience in using communications satellites in a 24-hour orbit. To flight-test a new, simple approach to satellite attitude and period control. To develop transportable ground facilities to be used in conjunction with communications satellites. To develop capability of launching satellites into 24-hour orbit using existing vehicles, plus apogee kick techniques and to test components' life at 24-hour-orbit altitude.	Feb. 14, 1963 Feb. 14, 1963	Delta ETR	24 hours	Near-synchronous orbit	22,300	R. J. Darcey

Satellite and Space Probe Projects (Cont.)

Experiment data				Remarks
Instrumentation summary	Experiment and discipline	Experimenter	Affiliation	
	Measure directional proton energy (1.0–8.0 MeV)—E	C. McIlwain	U. of California	
The 24-hour communications satellite consists of a spin-stabilized active repeater in a near-synchronous low-inclination orbit. The spacecraft is in the form of a cylinder 28 inches in diameter and 15 inches high. The repeater consists of a 7200-Mc receiver and an 1800-Mc transmitter with an output of 2 watts. In addition, the spacecraft contains a vernier velocity control system for orientation of spin axis and adjustment of the orbit.				Twenty seconds after firing apogee rocket, all satellite transmissions stopped. The satellite was sighted on Feb. 28, 1963, and later dates. It was traveling in a near-synchronous orbit eastward at about 2.8° per day. Weight: 78 lb Power: Solar

Goddard Space Flight Center

Designation	Objectives	Launch and orbit data						Project manager and project scientist
		Launch date/ silent date	Vehicle and launch site	Period, min.	Statute miles			
					Perigee	Apogee		
Explorer XVII Atmosphere Explorer 1963 9A S–6	To measure the density, composition, pressure, and temperature of the earth's atmosphere from 135 to 540 nautical miles and to determine the variations of these parameters with time of day, latitude, and in part, season.	Apr. 3, 1963 July 10, 1963	Delta ETR	96.4	158.1	598.5		N. W. Spencer
Telstar II 1963 13A (A project of AT&T) A–41	Joint AT&T–NASA investigation of wideband communications.	May 7, 1963	Delta ETR	221	575	6,559		C. P. Smith, Jr.
Tiros VII 1963 24A A–52	To launch into orbit a satellite capable of viewing cloud cover and the earth's surface and atmosphere by means of television cameras and radiation sensors. To acquire and process collected data from satellite and to control its attitude by magnetic means.	June 19, 1963	Delta ETR	97.4	385.02	401.14		Robert Rados
Syncom II 1963 31A A–26	To provide experience in using communications satellites in a 24-hour orbit.	July 26, 1963	Delta ETR	24 hours	22,300 near-synchronous orbit			R. J. Darcey

Satellite and Space Probe Projects (Cont.)

Experiment data				Remarks
Instrumentation summary	Experiment and discipline	Experimenter	Affiliation	
Primary detectors employed (two each) are: Double focusing magnetic sector mass spectrometer, hot-cathode total-pressure ionization gauges, and cold-cathode total-pressure ionization gauges. The remaining satellite instrumentation converts the outputs from six detectors to radio signals.	Two mass spectrometers —P Four vacuum (pressure) gauges—P Two electrostatic probes —I	C. Reber R. Horowitz G. Newton N. Spencer L. Brace	GSFC GSFC GSFC GSFC	Confirmed that the earth is surrounded by a belt of neutral helium at an altitude of from 150 to 600 miles. Weight: 405 lb Power: Silver-zinc batteries
The system provides for TV, radio, telephone, and data transmission via a satellite repeater system.	Included electron detector for energy range 0.75 to 2 MeV			Weight: 175 lb Power: Solar
Two vidicon camera systems with tape recorder for recording remote picture area, five-channel medium-resolution radiometer, electron temperature probe, and magnetic attitude coil.	Omnidirectional radiometer—P Scanning radiometer Electron temperature experiment—R Two TV camera systems	V. Suomi A. McCulloch N. Spencer	U. of Wisconsin GSFC GSFC	TV coverage extended to 65° N and 65° S latitudes. Launch date selected to provide maximum northern hemisphere coverage during 1963 hurricane season. Electron temperature probe malfunction 26 days after launch. First Tiros to have two operational camera systems and fully functioning IR subsystem 15 months after launch. Weight: 297 lb Power: Solar Inclination: 58° to equator
The 24-hour communications satellite consists of a spin-stabilized active repeater in a near-synchronous low-inclination				Orbit and attitude control of the spin-stabilized synchronous satellite achieved. Data telephone and facsimile transmission were excellent.

Designation	Objectives	Launch and orbit data					Project manager and project scientist
		Launch date/ silent date	Vehicle and launch site	Period, min.	Statute miles		
					Perigee	Apogee	
Syncom II— Con.	To flight-test a new, simple approach to satellite attitude and period control. To develop transportable ground facilities to be used in conjunction with communications satellites. To develop capability of launching satellites into 24-hour orbit using existing vehicles, plus apogee kick techniques and to test components' life at 24-hour orbit altitude.						
Explorer XVIII Interplanetary Monitoring Platform 1963 46A IMP–A	To study in detail the radiation environment of cislunar space and to monitor this region over a significant portion of a solar cycle. To study the quiescent properties of the interplanetary magnetic field and its dynamical relationships with particle fluxes from the sun. To develop a solar flare prediction capa-	Nov. 27, 1963 May 1965	Delta ETR	93 hours	122	121,605	Paul Butler Dr. F. B. McDonald

Satellite and Space Probe Projects (Cont.)

Experiment data				Remarks
Instrumentation summary	Experiment and discipline	Experimenter	Affiliation	
orbit. The spacecraft is in the form of a cylinder 28 inches in diameter and 15 inches high. The repeater consists of a 7,200-Mc receiver and an 1,800-Mc transmitter with an output of 2 watts. In addition, the spacecraft contains a vernier velocity-control system for orientation of spin axis and adjustment of the orbit.				Television video signals also were successfully transmitted, even though the satellite was not designed for this capability. Weight: 70 lb Power: Solar
To carry 10 experiments; essentially a combination of the successful GSFC Explorer X and XII satellites. It is spin-stabilized and powered by solar cells. The system is designed so that data can be received from apogee by the GSFC Minitrack stations.	Plasma: measure thermal ions and electrons 0.10 eV—I	G. P. Serbu R. Bourdeau	GSFC	All experiments and equipment operated satisfactorily except for thermal ion experiment which gave only 10 percent good data. Continued to provide significant data. First accurate measure of the interplanetary magnetic field, and the shock front. First satellite to survive a severe earth shadow of 7 hr 55 min. Electronics equipment estimated to have cooled to below −60° C. Weight: 137.5 lb Power: 38 watts solar
	Magnetic field experiment (fluxgate magnetometer)—E	N. F. Ness	GSFC	
	Measure solar and galactic protons and alpha particles—E	J. A. Simpson	U. of Chicago	
	Measure total ionization produced per unit time in a unit volume of standard density air—E	K. A. Anderson	U. of California	
	Measure flux of low-energy interplanetary plasma—E	H. S. Bridge	MIT	
	Measure solar and galactic protons, electrons, alpha particles, heavy primaries, and isotropy of solar proton events and of cosmic-ray modulation—E	F. McDonald G. Ludwig	GSFC	
	Magnetic field (rubidium-vapor magnetometer)—E	N. F. Ness	GSFC	

Designation	Objectives	Launch and orbit data					Project manager and project scientist
		Launch date/ silent date	Vehicle and launch site	Period, min.	Statute miles		
					Perigee	Apogee	
Explorer XVIII— Con.	bility for Apollo. To extend the knowledge of solar-terrestrial relationships. To further the development of simple, inexpensive, spin-stabilized spacecraft for interplanetary investigations.						
Tiros VIII 1963 54A A–53	To launch into orbit a satellite capable of viewing cloud cover and the earth's atmosphere by means of television cameras. To acquire and process collected data from satellite and to control its attitude by magnetic means.	Dec. 21, 1963	Delta ETR	99.35	435.01	468.30	Robert Rados

Satellite and Space Probe Projects (Cont.)

Experiment data				Remarks
Instrumentation summary	Experiment and discipline	Experimenter	Affiliation	
	Solar-wind proton con-centrations—E	John Wolfe	ARC	
One standard Tiros vidicon with a wide-angle lens camera system, and one automatic picture transmission camera system; magnetic at-titude coil.	One standard Tiros TV system One APT camera system	C. Hunter	GSFC	This satellite proved for the first time the feasi-bility of APT (automatic picture transmission), an inexpensive direct fac-simile readout. Weight: 265 lb Power: Solar

Appendix C
NASA Sounding
Rocket Flights

Notes

Numbering System

1. Aerobee-100
2. Arcon
3. Nike-Asp
4. Aerobee-150, 150A
5. Iris
6. Aerobee-300
7. Argo E–5
8. Argo D–4
9. Skylark
10. Nike-Cajun
11. Argo D–8
12. Special Projects
14. Nike-Apache
15. Arcas
16. Astrobee-1500
17. Aerobee-350
18. Nike-Tomahawk

Identifying Letters

The letters which follow each rocket number identify (1) the instrumenting agency, and (2) the experiment according to the following list:

Agency		*Experiment*	
G	Goddard	A	Aeronomy
N	Other NASA Centers	M	Meteorology
U	College or University	E	Energetic Particles and Fields
D	DOD	I	Ionospheric Physics
A	Other Government Agency	S	Solar Physics
C	Industrial Corporations	G	Galactic Astronomy
I	International	R	Radio Astronomy
		B	Biological
		P	Special Projects
		T	Test and Support

Firing Sites

ARG	Chamical, Argentina	IND	Thumba, India
ASC	Ascension Island	Italy	Sardinia, Italy
AUS	Woomera, Australia	NOR	Andöya, Norway
BRZ	Natal, Brazil	NZ	Karikari, New Zealand
EGL	Eglin Air Force Base, Florida	PB	Point Barrow, Alaska
FC	Fort Churchill, Canada	PMR	Pacific Missile Range

PAK	Karachi, Pakistan	WI	Wallops Island, Virginia
SWE	Kronogård, Sweden	WS	White Sands Missile Range,
SUR	Coronie, Surinam		New Mexico

Abbreviations

AFCRL	Air Force Cambridge Research Laboratories, Bedford, Mass.	U. Pitt.	University of Pittsburgh, Pittsburgh, Pa.
Ames	NASA, Ames Research Center, Moffett Field, Calif.	U. Wisc.	University of Wisconsin, Madison, Wis.
AS&E	American Science and Engineering, Inc., Cambridge, Mass.	Varian	Varian Associates, Palo Alto, Calif.
BRL	Ballistics Research Laboratories, Aberdeen, Md.	Harvard	Harvard College, Cambridge, Mass.
BuStds	National Bureau of Standards, Boulder, Colo.	JHU	Johns Hopkins University, Baltimore, Md.
CRPL	Central Radio Propagation Laboratories, National Bureau of Standards, Boulder, Colo.	JPL	Jet Propulsion Laboratory, Pasadena, Calif.
AIL	Airborne Instruments Laboratory, New York	LaRC	NASA, Langley Research Center, Hampton, Va.
DRTE	Canadian Defence Research Telecommunications Establishment, Ottawa, Canada	LeRC	NASA, Lewis Research Center, Cleveland, Ohio
GCA	Geophysics Corporation of America, Bedford, Mass.	Lockheed	Lockheed Missiles and Space Division, Palo Alto, Calif.
NRL	Naval Research Laboratory, Washington, D.C.	U. Minn.	University of Minnesota, Minneapolis, Minn.
U. Colo.	University of Colorado, Boulder, Colo.	NYU	New York University, New York, N.Y.
U. Ill.	University of Illinois, Urbana, Ill.	Penn State	Penn State University, University Park, Pa.
U. Mich.	University of Michigan, Ann Arbor, Mich.	Princeton	Princeton University, Princeton, N.J.
UNH	University of New Hampshire, Durham, N.H.	Rice	Rice University, Houston, Tex.
		SCAS	Southwest Center for Advanced Studies, Dallas, Tex.

NASA Sounding Rocket Flights

Aeronomy

NASA No.	Firing Date	Firing Site	Firing Performance[a]	Experimenter	NASA scientist and location	Experiment	Results[a]
	1960						
4.09 GA	Apr. 29	WI	S	Horowitz, GSFC	Horowitz, GSFC	Atmospheric Composition	S
10.03 GA	June 16	WI	P	Nordberg, GSFC	Nordberg, GSFC	Grenade	X
10.04 GA	July 9	WI	S	Nordberg, GSFC	Nordberg, GSFC	Grenade	S
10.01 GA	14	WI	S	Nordberg, GSFC	Nordberg, GSFC	Grenade	X
4.14 GA	Nov. 15	WI	S	Taylor, GSFC	Taylor, GSFC	Atmospheric Composition	S
10.06 GA	Dec. 14	WI	S	Nordberg, GSFC	Nordberg, GSFC	Grenade	S
	1961						
10.07 GA	Feb. 14	WI	S	Nordberg, GSFC	Nordberg, GSFC	Grenade	S
10.08 GA	17	WI	P	Nordberg, GSFC	Nordberg, GSFC	Grenade	S
10.33 GA	Apr. 5	WI	S	Nordberg, GSFC	Nordberg, GSFC	Grenade	P
10.34 GA	27	WI	X	Smith, GSFC	Smith, GSFC	Grenade	X
10.02 GA	May 5	WI	S	Smith, GSFC	Smith, GSFC	Grenade	S
10.28 GA	6	WI	S	Smith, GSFC	Smith, GSFC	Grenade	S
10.29 GA	9	WI	S	Smith, GSFC	Smith, GSFC	Grenade	P
10.30 GA	July 13	WI	S	Smith, GSFC	Smith, GSFC	Grenade	S
10.31 GA	14	WI	S	Smith, GSFC	Smith, GSFC	Grenade	S
10.32 GA	20	WI	S	Smith, GSFC	Smith, GSFC	Grenade	S
10.35 GA	21	WI	S	Smith, GSFC	Smith, GSFC	Grenade	X

[a] S—Successful
P—Partial success } Subject to interpretation.
X—Unsuccessful

NASA Sounding Rocket Flights (Cont.)

NASA No.	Firing Date	Firing Site	Firing Performance[a]	Experimenter	NASA scientist and location	Experiment	Results[a]
	1961			Aeronomy—Continued			
10.36 GA	Sept. 16	WI	P	Smith, GSFC	Smith, GSFC	Grenade	P
10.37 GA	17	WI	S	Smith, GSFC	Smith, GSFC	Grenade	X
1.08 GA	23	FC	S	Varian Associates	Martin, GSFC	Atmospheric Structure	S
1.09 GA	30	FC	S	Varian Associates	Martin, GSFC	Atmospheric Structure	S
8.23 GA	Oct. 10	WI	S	Taylor, GSFC	Taylor, GSFC	Ionosphere	S
1.10 GA	15	FC	S	Varian Associates	Martin, GSFC	Atmospheric Structure	S
1.07 GA	17	FC	S	Varian Associates	Martin, GSFC	Atmospheric Structure	S
1.11 GA	Nov. 2	FC	S	Varian Associates	Martin, GSFC	Atmospheric Structure	S
1.12 GA	5	FC	S	Varian Associates	Martin, GSFC	Atmospheric Structure	S
10.64 GA	Dec. 21	WI	S	U. Mich.	Spencer, GSFC	Atmospheric Structure	S
	1962						
10.38 GA	Mar. 2	WI	S	Smith, GSFC	Smith, GSFC	Grenade	S
10.39 GA	2	WI	S	Smith, GSFC	Smith, GSFC	Grenade	S
4.18 GA	19	WI	X	U. Mich.	Spencer, GSFC	Atmospheric Structure	X
10.40 GA	23	WI	S	Smith, GSFC	Smith, GSFC	Grenade	S
10.41 CA	28	WI	S	Smith, GSFC	Smith, GSFC	Grenade	S
10.42 GA	Apr. 17	WI	S	Smith, GSFC	Smith, GSFC	Grenade	S
5.04 GA	May 3	WI	P	Taylor, GSFC	Taylor, GSFC	Atmospheric Structure	S
10.43 GA	June 7	WI	S	Smith, GSFC	Smith, GSFC	Grenade	S
10.44 GA	8	WI	S	Smith, GSFC	Smith, GSFC	Grenade	S
10.55 GA	Nov. 16	FC	X	Smith, GSFC	Smith, GSFC	Grenade	X
6.06 GA	20	WI	S	U. Mich.	Brace, GSFC	Thermosphere Probe	S

	Date						
10.45 GA	Dec. 1	WI	S	Smith, GSFC	Smith, GSFC	Grenade	S
10.68 GA	1	FC	S	Smith, GSFC	Smith, GSFC	Grenade	X
10.46 GA	4	WI	S	Smith, GSFC	Smith, GSFC	Grenade	X
10.67 GA	4	FC	X	Smith, GSFC	Smith, GSFC	Grenade	S
10.47 GA	6	WI	S	Smith, GSFC	Smith, GSFC	Grenade	S
10.66 GA	6	FC	S	Smith, GSFC	Smith, GSFC	Grenade	S
	1963						
10.48 GA	Feb. 20	WI	S	Smith, GSFC	Smith, GSFC	Grenade	S
10.58 GA	20	FC	S	Smith, GSFC	Smith, GSFC	Grenade	S
10.53 GA	28	WI	S	Smith, GSFC	Smith, GSFC	Grenade	S
10.59 GA	28	FC	S	Smith, GSFC	Smith, GSFC	Grenade	S
10.54 GA	Mar. 9	WI	S	Smith, GSFC	Smith, GSFC	Grenade	S
10.60 GA	9	FC	S	Smith, GSFC	Smith, GSFC	Grenade	S
6.07 GA	Apr. 18	WI	S	U. Mich.	Brace, GSFC	Thermosphere Probe	S
10.55 GA	Dec. 7	WI	S	Smith, GSFC	Smith, GSFC	Grenade	S
	1961						
10.72 NA	Nov. 18	WI	S	LaRC	Hord, LaRC	Airglow	S
	1962						
10.79 NA	Apr. 5	WI	S	LeRC	Potter, LeRC	Ozone	S
1.13 NA	Sept. 6	WI	S	JPL	Dubin, HQ	UV Airglow	S
1.14 NA	Nov. 20	WI	X	JPL	Dubin, HQ	UV Airglow	X
	1963						
10.80 NA	Jan. 17	WI	S	LeRC	Potter, LeRC	Ozone	S
10.92 NA	Sept. 25	WI	S	LaRC	LaRC	Chemical Release	S

a S—Successful
P—Partial success } Subject to interpretation.
X—Unsuccessful

185

NASA Sounding Rocket Flights (Cont.)

NASA No.	Firing			Experimenter	NASA scientist and location	Experiment	Results[a]
	Date	Site	Performance[a]				
				Aeronomy—Continued			
1963							
10.93 NA	Sept. 25	WI	S	LaRC	LaRC	Chemical Release	S
14.102 NA	Oct. 9	WI	S	LeRC	Potter, LeRC	Chemical Release	S
14.103 NA	Oct. 10	WI	S	LeRC	Potter, LeRC	Chemical Release	S
4.85 NA	Nov. 18	WI	S	JPL	Dubin, HQ	Airglow	S
1960							
10.09 UA	Nov. 2	WI	S	U. Mich.	Dubin, HQ	Atmospheric Composition	X
10.10 UA	16	WI	S	U. Mich.	Dubin, HQ	Atmospheric Composition	X
1961							
10.50 UA	June 6	WI	S	U. Mich.	Dubin, HQ	Atmospheric Structure	S
10.56 UA	9	WI	S	U. Mich.	Dubin, HQ	Atmospheric Composition	X
10.57 UA	July 26	WI	S	U. Mich.	Dubin, HQ	Atmospheric Composition	X
1962							
10.90 UA	Feb. 20	WI	S	U. Mich.	Dubin, HQ	Atmospheric Composition	X
10.91 UA	May 18	WI	S	U. Mich.	Dubin, HQ	Atmospheric Composition	S
14.19 UA	June 6	WI	S	U. Mich.	Spencer, GSFC	Atmospheric Structure	S
14.20 UA	Dec. 1	WI	S	U. Mich.	Spencer, GSFC	Atmospheric Structure	S
4.74 UA	13	WI	X	JHU	Dubin, HQ	Airglow	X

No.	Date	Site		Agency	Experimenter	Experiment	
	1963						
4.73 UA	Jan. 29	WI	X	JHU	Dubin, HQ	Airglow	X
14.08 UA	Mar. 28	WI	S	U. Mich.	Dubin, HQ	Atmospheric Composition	S
14.09 UA	28	WI	S	U. Mich.	Dubin, HQ	Atmospheric Composition	X
4.98 UA	May 7	WI	S	JHU	Dubin, HQ	Airglow	S
4.75 UA	July 20	FC	X	JHU	Dubin, HQ	Airglow	X
10.75 UA	Aug. 2	WI	S	U. Mich.	Holtz, HQ	Atmospheric Density	S
4.76 UA	Nov. 12	WI	S	JHU	Dubin, HQ	Airglow	S
14.10 UA	26	WI	S	U. Mich.	Dubin, HQ	Atmospheric Composition	S
10.131 UA	26	WI	S	U. Mich.	Dubin, HQ	Atmospheric Density	S
14.21 UA	Dec. 7	WI	S	U. Mich.	Smith, GSFC	Atmospheric Structure	S
	1963						
14.140 DA	May 18	EGL	S	AFCRL	Dubin, HQ	Sodium Vapor	S
14.141 DA	18	EGL	S	AFCRL	Dubin, HQ	Sodium Vapor	S
10.130 DA	22	EGL	S	AFCRL	Dubin, HQ	Sodium Vapor	S
	1959						
3.13 CA	Aug. 17	WI	S	GCA	Dubin, HQ	Sodium Vapor	S
3.14 CA	19	WI	X	GCA	Dubin, HQ	Sodium Vapor	X
3.15 CA	Nov. 18	WI	S	GCA	Dubin, HQ	Sodium Vapor	X
3.16 CA	19	WI	S	GCA	Dubin, HQ	Sodium Vapor	X
3.17 CA	20	WI	S	GCA	Dubin, HQ	Sodium Vapor	X
	1960						
3.23 CA	May 24	WI	X	GCA	Dubin, HQ	Sodium Vapor	X
3.24 CA	25	WI	S	GCA	Dubin, HQ	Sodium Vapor	S
10.05 CA	Sept. 20	WI	S	Nordberg, GSFC	Nordberg, GSFC	Grenade	X

ᵃ S—Successful
P—Partial success ⎱ Subject to interpretation.
X—Unsuccessful ⎰

187

NASA Sounding Rocket Flights (Cont.)

NASA No.	Firing Date	Firing Site	Firing Performance[a]	Experimenter	NASA scientist and location	Experiment	Results[a]
				Aeronomy—Continued			
	1960						
8.04 CA	Nov. 10	WI	S	Lockheed	Dubin, HQ	Ionosphere	P
10.11 CA	Dec. 9	WI	X	GCA	Dubin, HQ	Sodium Vapor	X
10.12 CA	9	WI	S	GCA	Dubin, HQ	Sodium Vapor	S
8.05 CA	10	WI	S	GCA	Dubin, HQ	Sodium Vapor	S
	1961						
3.05 CA	Apr. 19	WI	S	GCA	Dubin, HQ	Sodium Vapor	S
3.06 CA	21	WI	S	GCA	Dubin, HQ	Sodium Vapor	S
3.07 CA	21	WI	X	GCA	Dubin, HQ	Sodium Vapor	X
3.08 CA	21	WI	S	GCA	Dubin, HQ	Sodium Vapor	S
8.06 CA	Sept. 13	WI	S	GCA	Smith, GSFC	Sodium Vapor	S
8.22 CA	13	WI	S	GCA	Smith, GSFC	Sodium Vapor	S
3.09 CA	16	WI	X	GCA	Smith, GSFC	Sodium Vapor	X
3.18 CA	16	WI	S	GCA	Smith, GSFC	Sodium Vapor	S
3.19 CA	17	WI	S	GCA	Smith, GSFC	Sodium Vapor	S
	1962						
10.100 CA	Mar. 1	WI	S	GCA	Smith, GSFC	Sodium Vapor	S
10.101 CA	2	WI	S	GCA	Smith, GSFC	Sodium Vapor	S
10.102 CA	23	WI	S	GCA	Smith, GSFC	Sodium Vapor	S
10.103 CA	27	WI	S	GCA	Smith, GSFC	Sodium Vapor	S
3.20 CA	Apr. 17	WI	S	GCA	Smith, GSFC	Sodium Vapor	S

ID	Date	Site		Organization	Experimenter	Experiment	
3.21 CA	June 7	WI	S	GCA	Smith, GSFC	Sodium Vapor	S
3.22 CA	7	WI	X	GCA	Smith, GSFC	Sodium Vapor	X
14.30 CA	Aug. 23	WI	P	Lockheed	Depew, GSFC	Atmospheric Structure	X
14.16 CA	Nov. 7	WI	S	GCA	Smith, GSFC	Sodium Vapor	S
14.17 CA	30	WI	S	GCA	Smith, GSFC	Sodium Vapor	S
14.18 CA	Dec. 5	WI	S	GCA	Smith, GSFC	Sodium Vapor	P
1963							
3.11 CA	Feb. 18	WI	X	GCA	Smith, GSFC	Sodium Vapor	X
14.35 CA	20	WI	S	GCA	Smith, GSFC	Sodium Vapor	S
14.39 CA	21	WI	S	GCA	Smith, GSFC	Sodium Vapor	S
14.110 CA	May 8	WI	S	Lockheed	Bourdeau, GSFC	Massenfilter	X
14.13 CA	22	FC	S	GCA	Dubin, HQ	Sodium Vapor	S
14.14 CA	22	FC	S	GCA	Dubin, HQ	Sodium Vapor	S
14.15 CA	23	FC	S	GCA	Dubin, HQ	Sodium Vapor	S
14.40 CA	24	WI	S	GCA	Dubin, HQ	Sodium Vapor	S
14.41 CA	24	WI	S	GCA	Dubin, HQ	Sodium Vapor	X
14.42 CA	25	WI	S	GCA	Dubin, HQ	Sodium Vapor	X
10.77 IA	May 16	PAK	S	Pakistan	Dubin, HQ	Sodium Vapor	S
14.137 IA	20	Italy	S	Italy	Dubin, HQ	Sodium Vapor	S
14.138 IA	21	Italy	S	Italy	Dubin, HQ	Sodium Vapor	S
14.139 IA	21	Italy	S	Italy	Dubin, HQ	Sodium Vapor	S
14.128 IA	Nov. 21	IND	S	India	Dubin, HQ	Sodium Vapor	P
1962							
Rehbar 1[b]	June 7	PAK	S	Pakistan	Dubin, HQ	Sodium Vapor	X
Rehbar 2[b]	11	PAK	S	Pakistan	Dubin, HQ	Sodium Vapor	X

[a] S—Successful
P—Partial success } Subject to interpretation.
X—Unsuccessful
[b] Nike-Cajun

189

NASA Sounding Rocket Flights (Cont.)

NASA No.	Date	Site	Performance[a]	Experimenter	NASA scientist and location	Experiment	Results[a]
	1960			Energetic Particles and Fields			
10.17 GE	June 6	FC	S	Fichtel, GSFC	Fichtel, GSFC	SBE	S
8.07 GE	30	WI	X	Heppner, GSFC	Heppner, GSFC	Magnetic Field	S
10.18 GE	July 22	FC	X	Fichtel, GSFC	Fichtel, GSFC	SBE	S
10.19 GE	Sept. 3	FC	S	Fichtel, GSFC	Fichtel, GSFC	SBE	S
10.20 GE	3	FC	S	Fichtel, GSFC	Fichtel, GSFC	SBE	S
11.01 GE	19	PMR	S	Naugle, GSFC	Naugle, GSFC	NERV 1	S
10.21 GE	27	FC	S	Fichtel, GSFC	Fichtel, GSFC	SBE	S
10.22 GE	Nov. 11	FC	S	Fichtel, GSFC	Fichtel, GSFC	SBE	P
10.23 GE	11	FC	S	Fichtel, GSFC	Fichtel, GSFC	SBE	S
10.24 GE	12	FC	S	Fichtel, GSFC	Fichtel, GSFC	SBE	S
10.15 GE	12	FC	S	Fichtel, GSFC	Fichtel, GSFC	SBE	S
10.16 GE	13	FC	S	Fichtel, GSFC	Fichtel, GSFC	SBE	S
10.13 GE	16	FC	S	Fichtel, GSFC	Fichtel, GSFC	SBE	S
10.14 GE	17	FC	S	Fichtel, GSFC	Fichtel, GSFC	SBE	S
10.26 GE	18	FC	S	Fichtel, GSFC	Fichtel, GSFC	SBE	S
10.27 GE	18	FC	S	Fichtel, GSFC	Fichtel, GSFC	SBE	S
8.08 GE	Dec. 12	WI	S	Heppner, GSFC	Heppner, GSFC	Magnetic Fields	S
	1961						
10.76 GE	Dec. 10	FC	S	Ogilvie-Fichtel, GSFC	Ogilvie-Fichtel, GSFC	Cosmic Ray	S

	1963						
4.91 GE	Sept. 4	FC	S	Fichtel, GSFC	Fichtel, GSFC	Heavy Cosmic Rays	S
	1960						
4.16 UE	Aug. 23	WI	S	NYU	Meredith, GSFC	Cosmic Ray	S
	1961						
14.03 UE	July 14	WI	S	UNH	Heppner, GSFC	Magnetic Field	S
14.04 UE	14	WI	S	UNH	Heppner, GSFC	Magnetic Field	S
14.05 UE	20	WI	S	UNH	Heppner, GSFC	Magnetic Field	S
	1963						
11.06 UE	Feb. 12	PMR	S	U. Minn.	Cline, GSFC	Electron Spect.	S
14.06 UE	Sept. 9	WI	S	UNH	Schardt, HQ	Electrojet	S
					Ionospheric Physics		
	1959						
4.08 GI	Sept. 11	FC	S	Jackson, GSFC	Jackson, GSFC	Ionosphere	S
4.07 GI	14	FC	S	Jackson, GSFC	Jackson, GSFC	Ionosphere	S
	1960						
1.01 GI	Nov. 23	FC	S	Whipple, GSFC	Whipple, GSFC.	Ionosphere	S
1.02 GI	27	FC	S	Whipple, GSFC	Whipple, GSFC	Ionosphere	S

[a] S—Successful
P—Partial success } Subject to interpretation.
X—Unsuccessful

NASA Sounding Rocket Flights (Cont.)

NASA No.	Firing Date	Firing Site	Firing Performance[a]	Experimenter	NASA scientist and location	Experiment	Results[a]
				Ionospheric Physics—Continued			
1961							
8.10 GI	Apr. 27	WI	S	Jackson, GSFC	Jackson, GSFC	Ionosphere	P
8.09 GI	June 13	WI	S	Jackson, GSFC	Jackson, GSFC	Ionosphere	P
10.74 GI	Dec. 21	WI	S	Kane, GSFC	Kane, GSFC	Ionosphere	S
1962							
10.110 GI	Apr. 26	WI	S	Serbu, GSFC	Serbu, GSFC	Electron Temperature	S
8.21 GI	May 3	WI	S	Serbu, GSFC	Serbu, GSFC	ELF Electron Trap	S
10.112 GI	16	WI	S	Serbu, GSFC	Serbu, GSFC	Electron Temperature	S
10.111 GI	17	WI	S	Serbu, GSFC	Serbu, GSFC	Electron Temperature	S
14.12 GI	June 15	WI	S	Kane, GSFC	Kane, GSFC	Ionosphere	S
K62–1[b]	Aug. 7	SWE	S	Sweden	Witt, Sweden	Air Sample	S
K62–3[b]	11	SWE	S	Sweden	Smith, GSFC	Air Sample	S
K62–4[b]	11	SWE	S	Sweden	Smith, GSFC	Air Sample	P
K62–5[b]	31	SWE	S	Sweden	Smith, GSFC	Air Sample	X
14.31 GI	Oct. 16	WI	S	Bauer, GSFC	Bauer, GSFC	Ionosphere	S
14.32 GI	Dec. 1	WI	S	Bauer, GSFC	Bauer, GSFC	Ionosphere	S
1963							
14.107 GI	Mar. 8	WI	S	Whipple, GSFC	Whipple, GSFC	Ionosphere	P
14.108 GI	Apr. 9	WI	S	Kane, GSFC	Kane, GSFC	D-Region	S
4.44 GI	23	WI	S	Bauer, GSFC	Bauer, GSFC	Electron Density	S
8.14 GI	July 2	WI	S	Bauer, GSFC	Bauer, GSFC	Ionosphere	S

No.	Date	Site	Status		Experiment	Status
6.08 GI	July 20	WI	S	Brace, GSFC · Brace, GSFC	Thermosphere Probe	S
K63-1[b]	July 27	SWE	S	Sweden · Smith, GSFC	Grenade	S
K63-2[b]	July 29	SWE	S	Sweden · Smith, GSFC	Grenade	S
K63-3[b]	Aug. 1	SWE	S	Sweden · Smith, GSFC	Grenade	S
K63-4[b]	Aug. 7	SWE	S	Sweden · Smith, GSFC	Heavy Cosmic Rays	S
4.65 GI	Sept. 25	WI	S	GSFC · Serbu, GSFC	Ionosphere	S
				Hirao, Japan		
4.64 GI	28	WI	S	GSFC · Serbu, GSFC	Ionosphere	S
				Hirao, Japan		
8.18 GI	29	WI	S	Bauer, GSFC · Bauer, GSFC	Ionosphere	
14.37 GI	Dec. 13	WI	P	Whipple, GSFC · Whipple, GSFC	Ionosphere	
1960						
6.01 UI	Mar. 16	FC	S	U. Mich. · Bourdeau, GSFC	Ionosphere	S
3.10 UI	17	FC	X	U. Mich. · Bourdeau, GSFC	Ionosphere	X
6.02 UI	June 15	FC	S	U. Mich. · Bourdeau, GSFC	Ionosphere	S
6.03 UI	Aug. 3	WI	S	U. Mich. · Bourdeau, GSFC	Ionosphere	S
1961						
6.04 UI	Mar. 26	WI	S	U. Mich. · Bourdeau, GSFC	Ionosphere	S
6.05 UI	Dec. 22	WI	S	U. Mich. · Wright, GSFC	Ionosphere	S
1963						
4.58 UI	Apr. 3	WI	S	Stanford · Bourdeau, GSFC	Ionosphere	S
4.59 UI	July 10	WI	S	Stanford · Bourdeau, GSFC	Ionosphere	S

[a] S—Successful
P—Partial success ⎫ Subject to interpretation
X—Unsuccessful ⎭

[b] Nike-Cajun

NASA Sounding Rocket Flights (Cont.)

NASA No.	Firing Date	Firing Site	Firing Performance[a]	Experimenter	NASA scientist and location	Experiment	Results[a]
				Ionospheric Physics—Continued			
14.36 DI	*1963* Oct. 7	FC	S	BRL	Bourdeau, GSFC	Ionosphere	P
8.15 AI	*1961* June 24	WI	S	CRPL/AIL	Jackson, GSFC	Ionosphere	S
8.17 AI	Oct. 14	WI	S	Jackson, GSFC	Jackson, GSFC	Ionosphere	S
8.16 AI	*1962* Feb. 7	WI	S	Jackson, GSFC	Jackson, GSFC	Ionosphere	X
3.12 CI	*1960* Aug. 22	WI	X	GCA	Bourdeau, GSFC	Langmuir Probe	X
10.25 CI	Dec. 8	WI	S	GCA	Bourdeau, GSFC	Langmuir Probe	S
10.51 CI	*1961* Aug. 18	WI	S	GCA	Bourdeau, GSFC	Langmuir Probe	S
10.52 CI	Oct. 27	WI	S	GCA	Bourdeau, GSFC	Langmuir Probe	S
10.99 CI	*1962* Nov. 7	WI	S	GCA	Bourdeau, GSFC	Ionosphere	S

	Date						
10.108 CI	30	WI	S	GCA	Bourdeau, GSFC	Ionosphere	S
10.109 CI	Dec. 5	WI	S	GCA	Bourdeau, GSFC	Ionosphere	S
1963							
14.86 CI	Feb. 27	WI	S	GCA	Bourdeau, GSFC	Ionosphere	S
14.87 CI	Mar. 28	WI	P	GCA	Bourdeau, GSFC	Ionosphere	S
14.88 CI	July 14	FC	P	GCA	Bourdeau, GSFC	Ionosphere	P
14.89 CI	20	FC	X	GCA	Bourdeau, GSFC	Eclipse Ionosphere	X
14.90 CI	20	FC	X	GCA	Bourdeau, GSFC	Eclipse Ionosphere	X
14.91 CI	20	FC	S	GCA	Bourdeau, GSFC	Eclipse Ionosphere	S
14.92 CI	20	FC	S	GCA	Bourdeau, GSFC	Eclipse Ionosphere	S
14.93 CI	20	FC	S	GCA	Bourdeau, GSFC	Eclipse Ionosphere	S
14.94 CI	20	FC	S	GCA	Bourdeau, GSFC	Eclipse Ionosphere	S
1959							
4.02 II	Sep. 17	FC	S	DRTE	Jackson, GSFC	Ionosphere	S
4.03 II	20	FC	P	DRTE	Jackson, GSFC	Ionosphere	X
1961							
8.13 II	June 15	WI	S	DRTE	Jackson, GSFC	Antenna Test	S
1962							
4.79 II	Nov. 16	WI	X	Australia	Cartwright, Australia	Ionosphere	X
4.80 II	Dec. 11	WI	X	Australia	Cartwright, Australia	Ionosphere	X
Ferdinand III[b]	11	NOR	S	Norway	Kane, GSFC	Ionosphere	S
Ferdinand II[b]	14	NOR	S	Norway	Kane, GSFC	NASA T/M only	S

[a] S—Successful
P—Partial success } Subject to interpretation.
X—Unsuccessful
[b] Nike-Cajun

195

NASA Sounding Rocket Flights (Cont.)

NASA No.	Firing Date	Firing Site	Firing Performance[a]	Experimenter	NASA scientist and location	Experiment	Results[a]
	1963			Ionospheric Physics—Continued			
4.96 II	Apr. 12	WI	S	Australia	Cartwright, Australia	VLF	S
4.97 II	May 9	WI	S	Australia	Cartwright, Australia	VLF	S
Ferdinand V[b]	Sept. 8	NOR	S	Norway	Kane, GSFC	Ionosphere	X
Ferdinand IV[c]	11	NOR	S	Norway	Kane, GSFC	Ionosphere	S
4.93 II	Oct. 17	WI	S	France	Shea, GSFC	Ionosphere	S
4.94 II	31	WI	S	France	Shea, GSFC	Ionosphere	S
				Solar Physics			
	1960						
3.01 GS	Mar. 1	WI	S	Hallam, GSFC	Hallam, GSFC	Solar Study	X
3.02 GS	3	WI	S	Hallam, GSFC	Hallam, GSFC	Solar Study	X
3.03 GS	Apr. 27	WI	X	Hallam, GSFC	Hallam, GSFC	Solar Study	X
3.04 GS	May 25	WI	X	Hallam, GSFC	Hallam, GSFC	Solar Study	X
	1961						
4.25 GS	Sept. 30	WI	S	Behring, GSFC	Behring, GSFC	Solar Studies	S
	1963						
4.77 GS	July 20	WI	S	Hallam, GSFC	Hallam-Wolff, GSFC	Solar Studies	X
4.78 GS	Oct. 1	WI	S	Hallam, GSFC	Hallam, GSFC	Solar Studies	P

4.33 GS	15 *1962*	WI	S	Muney, GSFC	Muney, GSFC	Solar Studies	S
4.23 US	July 24	WI	S	U. Colo.	Lindsay, GSFC	Sunfollower	P
4.21 US	Nov. 27	WI	S	Harvard	Lindsay, GSFC	Solar	X
	1963						
4.22 US	Sept. 6	WI	S	Harvard	Lindsay, GSFC	Solar Studies	S
	1963						
4.61 AS	June 20	WI	S	NRL	Packer, NRL	Coronagraph	P
4.62 AS	28	WI	S	NRL	Packer, NRL	Coronagraph	P

Galactic Astronomy

	1960						
4.40 GG	Apr. 27	WI	P	Kupperian, GSFC	Kupperian, GSFC	Stellar Fluxes	P
4.05 GG	May 27	WI	S	Boggess, GSFC	Boggess, GSFC	Stellar Fluxes	P
4.06 GG	June 24	WI	S	Boggess, GSFC	Boggess, GSFC	Stellar Fluxes	S
4.11 GG	Nov. 22	WI	S	Stecher, GSFC	Stecher, GSFC	Stellar Spectra	S
	1961						
4.34 GG	Mar. 31	WI	P	Boggess, GSFC	Boggess, GSFC	Stellar Fluxes	P
9.01 GG	Sept. 18	AUS	S	Boggess, GSFC	Boggess, GSFC	Stellar Photo	S
9.02 GG	Oct. 4	AUS	S	Boggess, GSFC	Boggess, GSFC	Stellar Photo	S

[a] S—Successful
P—Partial success } Subject to interpretation.
X—Unsuccessful
[c] Nike-Apache

197

NASA Sounding Rocket Flights (Cont.)

NASA No.	Firing			Experimenter	NASA scientist and location	Experiment	Results[a]
	Date	Site	Performance[a]				
				Galactic Astronomy—Continued			
	1961						
9.03 GG	Nov. 1	AUS	S	Boggess, GSFC	Boggess, GSFC	Stellar Photo	P
9.04 GG	20	AUS	S	Boggess, GSFC	Boggess, GSFC	Stellar Photo	S
	1962						
4.35 GG	Feb. 7	WI	X	Stecher, GSFC	Stecher, GSFC	Stellar Spectra	X
4.36 GG	Sept. 22	WI	S	Stecher, GSFC	Stecher, GSFC	Stellar Photo	S
	1963						
4.30 GG	Mar. 28	WI	S	Boggess, GSFC	Boggess, GSFC	Stellar Spectra	S
4.37 GG	July 19	WI	S	Stecher, GSFC	Stecher, GSFC	Stellar Spectra	S
4.29 GG	23	WI	S	Stecher, GSFC	Stecher, GSFC	Stellar Spectra	S
4.31 GG	Oct. 10	WI	X	Boggess, GSFC	Boggess, GSFC	Stellar Spectra	X
	1962						
4.54 UG	Oct. 30	WI	S	U. Wisc.	Kupperian, GSFC	Stellar Studies	S
	1962						
4.69 CG	Sept. 30	WI	S	Lockheed	Dubin, HQ	Night Sky Mapping	S

	Date		a	Lockheed	Depew, GSFC	Stellar Spectra	a
4.70 CG	*1963* Mar. 16	WI	S				S
					Biological		
11.04 GB	*1961* Nov. 15	Pt. A	S	Ames	Smith, HQ	BIOS 1	X
11.05 GB	18	Pt. A	P	Ames	Smith, HQ	BIOS 1	X
	1960				Special Projects		
1.03 GP	Sept. 15	FC	S	Baumann, GSFC	Baumann, GSFC	AMPP	S
1.05 GP	24	FC	S	Baumann, GSFC	Baumann, GSFC	AMPP	P
4.43 GP	Oct. 5	FC	S	NRL	Baumann, GSFC	AMPP	S
	1961						
1.04 GP	May 17	FC	S	Baumann, GSFC	Baumann, GSFC	AMPP	P
1.06 GP	19	FC	S	Baumann, GSFC	Baumann, GSFC	AMPP	S
	1961						
4.38 NP	Feb. 5	WI	S	LeRC	Gold, LeRC	Hydrogen Zerog	P
4.39 NP	Apr. 21	WI	S	LeRC	Gold, LeRC	Hydrogen Zerog	S
4.42 NP	Aug. 12	WI	S	LeRC	Plohr, LeRC	Hydrogen Zerog	P
4.40 NP	Oct. 18	WI	S	LeRC	Regetz, LeRC	Hydrogen Zerog	S

ª S—Successful
P—Partial success ⎫ Subject to interpretation.
X—Unsuccessful ⎭

199

NASA Sounding Rocket Flights (Cont.)

NASA No.	Firing			Experimenter	NASA scientist and location	Experiment	Results[a]
	Date	Site	Performance[a]				
				Special Projects—Continued			
1962							
4.41 NP	Feb. 17	WI	S	LeRC	Dillon, LeRC	Hydrogen Zerog	S
4.46 NP	May 8	WI	P	JPL	Brown, JPL	Radar	X
4.26 NP	June 20	WI	S	LeRC	Flagge, LeRC	Hydrogen Zerog	P
4.47 NP	July 10	WI	S	JPL	Brown, JPL	Radar	X
4.27 NP	Nov. 18	WI	S	LeRC	Corpas, LeRC	Hydrogen Zerog	S
1963							
4.66 NP	May 14	WI	S	LaRC	Kinard, LaRC	Paraglider	X
4.28 NP	June 19	WI	S	LeRC	Corpas, LeRC	Hydrogen Zerog	P
4.32 NP	Sept. 11	WI	S	LeRC	Corpas, LeRC	Hydrogen Zerog	S
1962							
4.71 UP	June 29	WI	S	JHU	Depew, GSFC	Airglow	S
4.72 UP	29	WI	S	JHU	Depew, GSFC	Airglow	S
				Test and Support			
1959							
2.01 GT	May 14	WI	X	Medrow, GSFC	Medrow, GSFC	Rocket Test	S
2.02 GT	15	WI	X	Medrow, GSFC	Medrow, GSFC	Rocket Test	S

ID	Date		Result			Test	Result
2.03 GT	Aug. 15	WI	X	Medrow, GSFC	Medrow, GSFC	Rocket Test	X
2.04 GT	Aug. 7	WI	X	Medrow, GSFC	Medrow, GSFC	Rocket Test	X
2.05 GT	Aug. 7	WI	X	Medrow, GSFC	Medrow, GSFC	Rocket Test	X
2.06 GT	Aug. 7	WI	X	Medrow, GSFC	Medrow, GSFC	Rocket Test	S
8.01 GT	Dec. 22	WI	S	GSFC/NRL/DRTE	Winkler, GSFC	X248 Vibration Test	S
	1960						
8.02 GT	Jan. 26	WI	S	GSFC/NRL/DRTE	Winkler, GSFC	X248 Vibration Test	S
4.01 GT	Feb. 16	WI	X	Medrow, GSFC	Medrow, GSFC	Rocket Test	X
4.12 GT	Mar. 25	WI	S	Medrow, GSFC	Medrow, GSFC	Rocket Test	S
4.10 GT	Apr. 23	WI	S	Medrow, GSFC	Medrow, GSFC	Rocket Test	S
5.01 GT	July 22	WI	S	Sorgnit, GSFC	Sorgnit, GSFC	Rocket Test	S
3.28 GT	Aug. 9	WI	S	Sorgnit, GSFC	Sorgnit, GSFC	Rocket Test	S
5.02 GT	Oct. 18	WI	S	Sorgnit, GSFC	Sorgnit, GSFC	Rocket Test	S
3.29 GT	Nov. 3	WI	S	Sorgnit, GSFC	Sorgnit, GSFC	Rocket Test	S
	1961						
3.36 GT	Jan. 17	WI	S	Sorgnit, GSFC	Sorgnit, GSFC	Rocket Test	S
5.03 GT	Jan. 19	WI	X	Sorgnit, GSFC	Sorgnit, GSFC	Rocket Test	P
10.49 GT	Mar. 15	WI	S	Sorgnit, GSFC	Sorgnit, GSFC	Cajun Fin Test	S
4.19 GT	Apr. 14	WI	S	Russell, GSFC	Russell, GSFC	Attitude Control	P
12.01 GT	May 2	WI	S	U. Mich.	Spencer, GSFC	Cone Test	S
14.01 GT	May 25	WI	S	Sorgnit, GSFC	Sorgnit, GSFC	Rocket Test	S
4.20 GT	June 26	WI	S	Russell, GSFC	Russell, GSFC	Attitude Control	P
14.02 GT	Aug. 16	WI	S	Sorgnit, GSFC	Sorgnit, GSFC	Rocket Test	S
	1962						
4.68 GT	Jan. 13	WI	S	Russell, GSFC	Russell, GSFC	Attitude Control	S
10.69 GT	Mar. 1	WI	X	Donn, GSFC	Donn, GSFC	Water Launch	S

[a] S—Successful
P—Partial success } Subject to interpretation
X—Unsuccessful

NASA Sounding Rocket Flights (Cont.)

NASA No.	Firing			Experimenter	NASA scientist and location	Experiment	Results[a]
	Date	Site	Performance[a]				
				Test and Support—Continued			
1962							
10.70 GT	Mar. 2	WI	S	Donn, GSFC	Donn, GSFC	Water Launch	S
4.48 GT	May 25	WI	S	Pressly, GSFC	Pressly, GSFC	Sea Recovery	S
4.60 GT	Aug. 8	WI	P	Russell, GSFC	Russell, GSFC	Attitude Control	P
1963							
16.01 GT	Apr. 8	WI	X	Sorgnit, GSFC	Sorgnit, GSFC	ACS Test	X
4.87 GT	June 17	WI	S	Russell, GSFC	Russell, GSFC	Attitude Control	S
14.111 GT	Oct. 31	WI	S	Williams, GSFC	Williams, GSFC	Vibration Test	S

[a] S—Successful
P—Partial success } Subject to interpretation.
X—Unsuccessful

Appendix D

A Chronology of Events Related to the Goddard Space Flight Center

THE FOLLOWING CHRONOLOGY is parallel and supplementary to the text. Events considered important for the achievements and early history of Goddard Space Flight Center and its missions have been included.

1915

April 15: The Secretary of War called the first meeting of the National Advisory Committee for Aeronautics (NACA) in his office. Brig. Gen. George P. Scriven, Chief Signal Officer, was elected temporary Chairman, and Dr. Charles D. Walcott, Secretary of the Smithsonian Institution, was elected first Chairman of the important NACA Executive Committee.

1918

November 6–7: Robert H. Goddard fired several rocket devices before representatives of the Signal Corps, Air Service, Army Ordnance, and others at Aberdeen Proving Ground, Md.

1919

May 26: Date of Dr. Robert H. Goddard's progress report to the Smithsonian Institution entitled "A Method of Reaching Extreme Altitudes." It was published by the Smithsonian in January 1920.

1923

November 1: Robert H. Goddard successfully operated a liquid oxygen and gasoline rocket motor on a testing frame, both fuel components being supplied by pumps installed on the rocket.

1926

March 16: Robert H. Goddard launched the world's first liquid-fueled rocket at Auburn, Mass., which traveled 184 feet in 2½ seconds. This event was the "Kitty Hawk" of rocketry.

1929

July 17: A liquid-fueled, 11-foot rocket, fired by Robert Goddard at Auburn, Mass., carried a small camera, thermometer, and a barometer which were recovered intact after the flight. Much "moon rocket" publicity was made of this flight.

1930

December 30: Robert H. Goddard fired 11-foot liquid-fueled rocket to a height of 2,000 feet and a speed of almost 500 mph near Roswell, N.Mex.

1932

April 19: First flight of Goddard rocket with gyroscopically controlled vanes for automatically stabilized flight, near Roswell, N.Mex.

1935

March 28: Robert Goddard launched the first rocket equipped with gyroscopic controls, which attained a height of 4,800 feet, a horizontal distance of 13,000 feet, and a speed of 550 mph, near Roswell, N.Mex.

1936

March 16: Robert H. Goddard's classic report on "Liquid Propellant Rocket Development," reviewing his liquid-fuel rocket research and flight testing since 1919, was published by the Smithsonian Institution.

1940

May 28: Robert H. Goddard offered all his research data, patents, and facilities for use by the military services at a meeting arranged by Harry Guggenheim with representatives of Army Ordnance, Army Air Corps, and Navy Bureau of Aeronautics. Nothing resulted from this except an expression of possible use of rockets in jet-assisted takeoffs of aircraft.

1943

During September: Rocket Development Branch was created in Army Ordnance to direct and coordinate development of rockets.

1945

May 8: At time of Germany's surrender, more than 20,000 V-weapons (V-1's and V-2's) had been fired. Although figures vary, best estimate is that 1,115 V-2 ballistic rockets had been fired against England and 1,675 against continental targets. Great disparity between production figures and operational missions was caused by series production and development testing being performed concurrently, there being as many as 12 major modifications in basic design features.

August 10: Dr. Robert H. Goddard, American rocket pioneer, died.

December 17: Rocket Sonde Research Branch was constituted in Naval Research Laboratory to conduct scientific exploration of the upper atmosphere.

1946

March 22: First American rocket to escape earth's atmosphere, the JPL-Ordnance Wac, reached 50-mile height after launch from WSPG.

May 17: Original design and development of Aerobee sounding rocket began when contract was given to Aerojet Engineering Corp.

June 6: Joint Army-Navy Research and Development Board was created for purpose of coordinating all activities of joint interest in fields of aeronautics, atomic energy, electronics, geographical exploration, geophysical sciences, and guided missiles.

September 25: First successful firing of Applied Physics Laboratory Aerobee research rocket at White Sands Proving Ground, N.Mex.

During September: After completing studies, Project RAND reported that earth satellites were technically feasible.

November 14: First complete Aerobee rocket was fired to a height of 190,000 feet from White Sands Proving Ground, N.Mex.

1948

October 19: Photographs of the earth's surface, taken from altitudes between 60 and 70 miles by cameras installed in rockets, were released by the Navy.

1949

May 11: President Harry S Truman signed a bill providing a 5,000-mile guided-missile test range, subsequently established at Cape Canaveral, Fla.

1950

June 13: Department of Defense assigned range responsibilities to the armed services: Army: White Sands (N.Mex.) Proving Ground and nearby Holloman AFB at Alamogordo; Navy: Point Mugu, Calif.; Air Force: Long-Range Proving Ground at Banana River, Fla. (later called Cape Canaveral).

1954

March 17: President Dwight D. Eisenhower signed Executive Order 10521 on the "Administration of Scientific Research by Federal Agencies," which gave the National Science Foundation major responsibility in pure scientific research.

During April: Bell Laboratories announced invention of the silicon solar battery.

August 26: The Supplemental Appropriations Act, 1955, appropriated $2 million to the National Science Foundation to support the U.S. IGY program sponsored and coordinated by the National Academy of Sciences.

During October: NRL Aerobee fired at White Sands took photographs at 100-mile altitude, first picture taken of complete hurricane, off the Texas gulf coast.

1955

During March: The Navy proposed a program for the launch of an elementary uninstrumented satellite in 2 or 3 years. This program, jointly developed by the Office of Naval Research and the Army, was known as Project Orbiter. It called for the use of the Redstone booster and Loki rockets (small solid-propellant rockets).

April 26: Moscow Radio reported U.S.S.R. planned to explore the moon with a tank remotely controlled by radio, foresaw trips by man in 1 to 2 years and reported formation of scientific team to devise satellite able to circle earth.

July 20: President Eisenhower endorsed IGY earth satellite proposal, the White House announced: "The President has approved plans by this country for going ahead with the launching of small, unmanned, earth-circling satellites as part of the U.S. participation in the International Geophysical Year which takes place between July 1957 and December 1958." Scientific responsibility was assumed by the National Academy of Sciences, fiscal responsibility by the National Science Foundation, and responsibility for logistic and technical support by the Department of Defense.

July 30: U.S.S.R. announced that it planned to launch an earth satellite in connection with IGY.

September 9: Project Vanguard was born when the Department of Defense wrote a letter to the Secretary of the Navy authorizing him to proceed with the Naval Research Laboratory proposal for launch of at least one U.S. satellite in the IGY, which was to end in December 1958.

October 2: National Academy of Sciences' IGY committee established Technical Panel for the Earth Satellite Program, with Richard W. Porter as Chairman, to plan the scientific aspects of the program, including the selection of experiments, the establishment of optical tracking stations, and the handling of international and interdisciplinary relations.

During November: Naval Research Laboratory transmitted transcontinental communications from Washington, D.C., to San Diego, Calif., by reflecting teletype messages off the moon.

1956

Spring: A plan was developed at NRL for seven test vehicles and six satellite-launching vehicles in Project Vanguard.

September 10–15: Scientists from 40 nations, including the U.S. and U.S.S.R., at a meeting in Barcelona of the Special Committee for the IGY (CSAGI), approved resolutions calling for, among other things, countries having satellite programs to use tracking and telemetering radio systems compatible with those announced at the current CSAGI meeting, and to release technical information on tracking equipment and scheduling and planning information essential to preparation for and execution of optical and radio observations.

December 8: NRL Test Vehicle 0 (TV-0), a Viking rocket carrying no Vanguard components, was successfully fired in a test of range facilities, telemetry, and instrumentation.

1957

April 11: U.S.-IGY scientific satellite equipment, including a radio transmitter and instruments for measuring temperature, pressure, cosmic rays, and meteoric dust encounters, was tested above earth for the first time, as a rocket containing this equipment was fired by the Navy to a 126-mile altitude.

During April: Upper Atmosphere Rocket Research Panel was renamed the Rocket and Satellite Research Panel. Its chairman was James A. Van Allen of the State University of Iowa.

May 1: NRL TV-1, with a Viking first stage, launched a Vanguard third stage in a successful test of the control system and of the

1957 Continued

third-stage separation, spin-up, ignition, and propulsion.

October 4: Sputnik I, the first manmade earth satellite, was launched by the U.S.S.R. It remained in orbit until January 4, 1958.

October 14: The American Rocket Society presented to President Dwight D. Eisenhower a program for outer space research which proposed establishment of an Astronautical Research and Development Agency similar to NACA and AEC, with responsibility for all space projects except those directly related to military defense.

October 23: The launch of NRL TV–2 was the first successful launch of the complete Vanguard configuration—a successful test of the first-stage engine, control system, and vehicle structure; second and third stages were dummies. A 109-mile altitude was reached at 4,250 mph.

During October: Project Vanguard worldwide tracking system became operational.

November 21: The National Advisory Committee for Aeronautics (NACA) authorized establishment of a special committee on space technology, headed by H. Guyford Stever.

December 4: The American Rocket Society's proposal for an Astronautical Research and Development Agency, which had been presented to President Eisenhower on October 14, 1957, was announced.

December 6: An attempt to launch NRL TV–3, the first test of the complete Vanguard vehicle and control system, failed when the first engine lost thrust after 2 seconds and the vehicle burned on the pad. This was the first Vanguard vehicle with three live stages and orbit capability.

1958

January 4: The American Rocket Society and the Rocket and Satellite Research Panel issued a summary of their proposals for a National Space Establishment. Preferably independent of DOD, but in any event not under one of the military services, this establishment would be responsible for the "broad cultural, scientific, and commercial objectives" of outer space research.

January 9: In his State of the Union message,

President Eisenhower reported: "In recognition of the need for single control in some of our most advanced development projects, the Secretary of Defense has already decided to concentrate into one organization all antimissile and satellite technology undertaken within the Department of Defense."

January 16: NACA adopted a resolution recommending that the national space program could be most effectively implemented by the cooperative effort of DOD, the National Academy of Sciences, the National Science Foundation, and NACA, together with universities, research institutions, and industrial companies of the Nation. Military development and operation of space vehicles would be the responsibility of DOD, and research and scientific space operations the responsibility of NACA.

January 31: Explorer I, the first U.S. satellite, was launched by an Army Ballistic Missile Agency-Jet Propulsion Laboratory team on a modified Jupiter C, with the U.S.-IGY scientific experiment of James A. Van Allen which would discover the radiation belt region around the earth.

February 5: NRL TV–3 backup was a repeat of the TV–3 launch attempt on Dec. 6, 1957. It failed when a control malfunctioned after 57 seconds of flight; the vehicle broke up at about 20,000 feet.

March 17: The second U.S.-IGY satellite, *Vanguard I,* was launched into orbit with a life expectancy of perhaps 1,000 years. A highly successful scientific satellite, its data proved the earth to be slightly pear shaped. Operating on solar-powered batteries, it transmitted for more than 6 years.

March 26: The third U.S.-IGY satellite, *Explorer III,* another joint ABMA-JPL project, was successfully launched by an Army Juno II rocket. It yielded valuable data on the radiation belt region, micrometeoroid impacts, and temperatures before reentering on June 27.

April 2: In a message to Congress, President Eisenhower proposed the establishment of a national aeronautics and space agency into which NACA would be absorbed. This agency was to have responsibility for civilian space science and aeronautical research. It would conduct research in

Explorer I, the first U.S. satellite, launched January 31, 1958.

these fields in its own facilities or by contract and would also perform military research required by the military departments. Interim projects pertaining to the civilian program which were under the direction of the Advanced Research Projects Agency (ARPA) would be transferred to this civilian space agency.

April 14: A proposal for a National Aeronautics and Space Agency, drafted by the Bureau of the Budget, was submitted to the Congress by the President.

April 28: Project Vanguard's TV-5 failed to put its 21.5-pound spacecraft into orbit when the control system release failed and the third stage was not ignited.

May 1: Scientific findings from the two Explorer satellites (I and III) disclosed an unexpected band of high-intensity radiation extending from 600 miles above the earth to possibly 8,000 miles.

—Responsibility for the Project Vanguard portion of the U.S.-IGY scientific satellite program was transferred within DOD from the Navy to ARPA.

May 27: The first Vanguard satellite launch vehicle (NRL SLV-1) generally was successful in its launch with exception of premature second-stage burnout, which prevented achievement of satisfactory orbit.

June 26: The NRL Vanguard SLV-2 launch failed when the second stage cut off prematurely because of low chamber pressure, terminating the flight.

July 26: Explorer IV, under the project direction of the DOD's ARPA, was launched for the purpose of studying radiation belts detected by *Explorer I* and *Explorer III* and for measurement of artificial radiation created by DOD nuclear experiments.

July 29: President Eisenhower signed the National Aeronautics and Space Act of 1958.

Summer 1958: At Langley, Edmond C. Buckley unofficially formed a network study group for the embryonic manned satellite program (later to become Project Mercury). Key technical personnel were: George B. Graves, Jr. (network arrangement); Robert L. Kenimer (tracking); James H. Schrader (telemetry and capsule communication); William J. Boyer (ground communication); Eugene L. Davis, Jr. (computing); Howard C. Kyle (control center).

August 1: U.S. Senator J. Glenn Beall, Maryland, announced that the new "outer space agency" would establish its laboratory and plant in Maryland. The location at Greenbelt, Md., was considered as "ideal" for the new agency. The Greenbelt laboratory was to employ 650 technicians, mostly electronic engineers and some chemists, the announcement stated. Construction on the plant was expected to start immediately in view of the fact that legislation authorizing appropri-

1958 Continued

ations of $47,800,000 for construction of the "space projects center" (S4208) had passed the Senate and was expected to clear the House of Representatives shortly.

August 14: Public Law 85–657 was approved, authorizing appropriations to NASA for construction and other purposes and specifically for a "space projects center in the vicinity of Washington, D.C.": a space projects building; research projects laboratory; posts and appurtenances; utilities; equipment and instrumentation, $3,750,000.

August 19: T. Keith Glennan was sworn in as Administrator and Hugh L. Dryden as Deputy Administrator. Forty days later, October 1, 1958, NASA was declared ready to function.

August 21: NACA held its final meeting and invited T. Keith Glennan, newly appointed Administrator of NASA, to attend.

September 24: First meeting of the senior staff of the National Aeronautics and Space Administration (NASA) was held, with T. Keith Glennan, Administrator, and Hugh L. Dryden, Deputy Administrator.

September 26: The third Vanguard satellite launch vehicle (SLV–3) reached an altitude of 265 miles, and was believed to have made one orbit and to have been destroyed 9,200 miles downrange over Central Africa on reentry into the atmosphere.

October 1: First official day of NASA. By executive order of the President, DOD responsibilities for the remaining U.S.-IGY satellite and space probe projects were transferred to NASA; included were Project Vanguard and the four lunar probes and three satellite IGY projects which had previously been assigned by ARPA to the Air Force Ballistic Missile Division and the Army Ballistic Missile Agency (ABMA). Also transferred were a number of engine development research programs.

October 21: Three weeks after NASA officially began operating, prospective contractors were invited to a briefing at NASA Hq. on development of a 1.5-million-pound-thrust F–1 engine for Saturn V.

November 7: A bidders' conference was held by NASA on a manned-satellite capsule for Project Mercury.

November 17: Senator Lyndon B. Johnson presented U.S. proposal for the international control of outer space before the United Nations in New York.

December 3: The President transferred the functions and facilities of the Jet Propulsion Laboratory (JPL) of the California Institute of Technology, Pasadena, Calif., from the Army to NASA.

December 3: NASA and the Army reached an agreement whereby the Army Ordnance Missile Command (AOMC), Huntsville, Ala., would be responsive to NASA requirements.

December 18: Project Score, the fifth U.S.-IGY satellite—under the project direction of ARPA—was launched at 12:45 a.m. from AMR by a Juno II rocket.

December 19: President Eisenhower's Christmas message was beamed from the Score satellite in orbit—the first voice transmitted from a satellite to earth.

December 31: IGY had been scheduled to end on this date; but in October 1958 the International Council of Scientific Unions, meeting in Washington, approved extension of operation through 1959 (IGC–59) and also approved establishment of the Committee on Space Research (COSPAR) to continue international cooperation in the scientific exploration of space.

1959

January 8: NASA requested eight Redstone launch vehicles from the Army to be used in Project Mercury development.

January 15: In General Notice No. 1 signed by T. E. Jenkins, Administrative Officer, it was announced that "four divisions (Construction Division, Space Sciences Division, Theoretical Division, Vanguard Division) have been designated as comprising the Beltsville Space Center of the National Aeronautics and Space Administration. . . ."

February 17: Vanguard II was successfully launched. It was a 21.5-pound satellite with infrared sensors for cloud-cover measurement.

February 28: Discoverer I, a 1,450-pound USAF satellite, was successfully launched into first near-polar orbit by a Thor-Hustler booster from PMR; stabilization difficulties hampered tracking acquisition.

March 3: Pioneer IV, the fourth U.S.-IGY space probe, a joint AMBA-JPL project under direction of NASA, was launched by a Juno II rocket from AMR and achieved an earth-moon trajectory, passing within 37,000 miles of the moon before going into a permanent solar orbit. Radio contact was maintained to a record distance of 406,620 miles.

March 11: NASA granted $350,000 to the National Academy of Sciences-National Research Council for a program of research appointments in theoretical and experimental physics to stimulate basic research in the space sciences.

March 24: NASA announced that Wallops Island, Va., had made 3,300 rocket firings since 1945.

April 10: The first construction contract for the Beltsville Space Center was awarded.

April 13: Vanguard's SLV–5 launch failed when the second stage did not operate properly and the vehicle tumbled. The 23.3-pound payload included a 13-inch ball with a magnetometer attached for mapping the earth's magnetic field and a 30-inch inflatable sphere to measure atmospheric drag.

—*Discoverer II* was successfully placed into a polar orbit by a Thor-Agena A booster but capsule ejection malfunctioned, causing it to impact in the vicinity of the Spitsbergen Islands (Arctic Ocean) on Apr. 14 instead of in the vicinity of Hawaii. It was the first vehicle known to have been placed in a polar orbit and was the first attempt to recover an object from orbit.

April 15: A NASA-DOD joint working group discussed procedures for search and recovery aspects of Project Mercury involving Army, Navy, and Air Force units.

April 20: NASA announced acceptance of proposals by the Canadian Defence Research Telecommunications Establishment for continuing joint rocket and satellite ionospheric experiments of a nonmilitary nature.

April 24: Construction began at Goddard Space Flight Center on Buildings 1 and 2, the Space Projects Building, and Research Projects Laboratory, respectively.

April 28: NASA announced the signing of a $24-million contract with Douglas Aircraft Company, Inc., for a three-stage Thor-Vanguard launching rocket called "Delta."

During April: The Tiros meteorological satellite program was transferred from DOD to NASA.

May 1: NASA Administrator Glennan announced that the Beltsville Space Center was renamed "Goddard Space Flight Center," in commemoration of Dr. Robert H. Goddard, the American pioneer in rocket research. John W. Townsend, Jr., was named Assistant Director for Space Science and Satellite Applications; John T. Mengel was named Assistant Director for Tracking and Data Systems; and Dr. Robert R. Gilruth was named Assistant Director for Manned Satellites. The three Assistant Directors reported to the Director of Flight Development, NASA Hq. The announcement also stated that Dr. Michael J. Vaccaro would head the Office of Business Administration.

June 1: The Smithsonian Optical Tracking Station at Woomera, Australia, successfully photographed *Vanguard I* at the apogee of its orbit, nearly 2,500 miles from the earth. This feat has been compared with taking a picture of a golf ball 600 miles away.

July 7: A four-stage rocket with an Air Research and Development Command payload was fired from Wallops Island to an altitude of 750 miles. This was the first in a series of launchings to measure natural radiation surrounding the earth.

July 20: NASA selected the Western Electric Company to build its worldwide network of tracking and ground instrument stations to be used in Project Mercury.

During August: A conference of the International Telecommunication Union at Geneva, Switzerland, allocated radio frequency bands for space and earth-space use.

August 7: Explorer VI was launched. All experiments performed; it provided the first complete televised cloud-cover pictures. A better map of the Van Allen radiation belt region was obtained. This was the first scientific satellite under the project direction of the Goddard Space Flight Center.

August 14: While *Explorer VI* was passing

Above, Building 1 under construction; below, Building 2 under construction.

1959 Continued

over Mexico at an altitude of about 17,000 miles, it successfully transmitted a crude picture of a sunlit, crescent-shaped portion of the North Central Pacific Ocean. The area of the earth photographed was 20,000 square miles.

August 17: The first of the Nike-Asp sounding rockets, which were to provide geophysical information on wind activity between 50 and 150 miles high, was launched successfully from Wallops Island.

September 1: Dr. Harry J. Goett was appointed Director of GSFC. Dr. Goett came from the NASA Ames Research Center, Moffett Field, Calif., where he had been Chief of the Full Scale and Flight Research Division since 1948.

September 16: Goddard's Building 2, the Research Projects Laboratory, was fully occupied.

September 18: Vanguard III was successfully launched. It had a 50-pound payload which measured the earth's magnetic field, solar x-rays, and space environmental conditions. This vehicle was SLV–7, the TV–4 backup vehicle, and had a more powerful third stage than previous Vanguards.

September 21: Construction began on Building 3, the Central Flight Control and Range Operations Building, at GSFC.

October 13: Explorer VII, the seventh and last U.S.-IGY earth satellite, under the direction of NASA with the Army as executive agent, was launched into an earth orbit by a modified Army Juno II booster.

October 28: A 100-foot-diameter inflatable sphere for Project Echo was launched on a suborbital test flight from Wallops Island to an altitude of 250 miles by the first Sergeant-Delta rocket. It was an aluminum-coated Mylar-plastic sphere; when in orbit, such a sphere would be used as a passive electronic reflector.

December 11: The transmitters of *Vanguard III,* launched Sept. 18, became silent after providing tracking signals and scientific data for 85 days. The satellite was expected to remain in orbit 40 years.

December 17: T. Keith Glennan, NASA Administrator, offered the services of the U.S. worldwide tracking network in support of any manned space flight the U.S.S.R. might plan to undertake, in a speech before the Institute of World Affairs in Pasadena, Calif.

December 22: In a Canadian-U.S. cooperative project, NASA launched a four-stage Javelin sounding rocket from Wallops Island to measure the intensity of galactic radio noise.

December 31: Approximately 300 research rockets were launched during the 30-month IGY and IGC-59 periods; 221 of these had been launched during IGY.

1960

February 27: A 100-foot-diameter inflatable sphere for Project Echo was launched on the third suborbital test from Wallops Island.

March 11: Pioneer V space probe was successfully launched by Thor-Able on a historic flight that measured radiation and magnetic fields in space and that communicated over great distances.

March 24: Pioneer V radio signals were received 2,000,000 miles from earth, more than 4 times the distance radio signals had previously been transmitted from a satellite.

April 1: Tiros I, a weather observation satellite, was launched into orbit by a Thor-Able and took pictures of the earth's cloud cover on a global scale from about 450 miles above the surface.

— Fourth suborbital test of the 100-foot-diameter Echo sphere was launched from Wallops Island to an altitude of 235 miles.

April 23: NASA fired the first of five Aerobee-Hi sounding rockets from Wallops Island in a program to measure ultraviolet radiation.

May 8: A 150-MW transmitter on *Pioneer V,* commanded at 5:04 a.m. EDT, worked satisfactorily at 8,001,000 miles from the earth.

May 19: Tiros I spotted a tornado storm system in the vicinity of Wichita Falls, Tex.

May 23: Construction began on Building 4, the Boiler House and Electric Substation, at GSFC; it would house service shops, a central powerplant, a refrigeration plant, and office areas.

May 31: NASA launched a Project Echo 100-foot inflatable sphere to an altitude of 210 miles to test a payload configuration carrying two beacon transmitters.

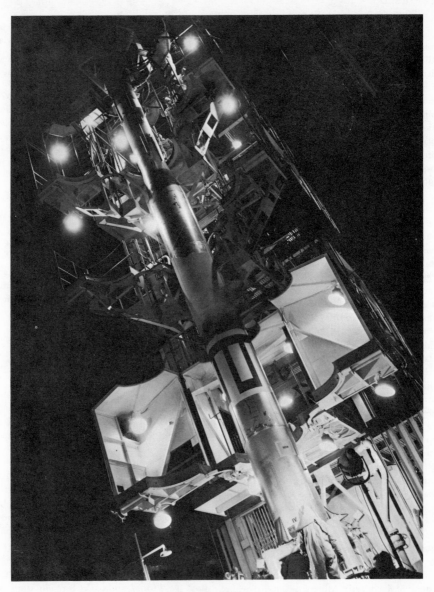

Vanguard vehicle in a gantry.

1960 Continued

June 26: A 6-minute message was received by the Jodrell Bank tracking station, England, from *Pioneer V,* the last communication received from this spacecraft, then 22.5 million miles from the earth, moving at a relative velocity of 21,000 mph.

June 28: The Smithsonian Institution posthumously awarded its highest honor, the Langley Medal, to Robert H. Goddard.
—Building 1, the Space Projects Building at GSFC, was fully occupied.

July 1: The first complete Scout rocket vehicle was launched from Wallops Island, but the fourth-stage separation and firing were not accomplished.

July 21: A Nike-Cajun sounding rocket was fired from Fort Churchill, Manitoba, Canada, containing an instrumental payload to measure data on energetic particles during a period of low solar activity.

August 12: Echo I, the first passive communications satellite, was successfully launched into orbit; it reflected a radio message from President Eisenhower across the nation, thus demonstrating the feasibility of global radio communications via satellites. *Echo I,* visible to skywatchers, provided reflection for numerous long-range radio transmissions by private and Government research agencies.

August 24: Echo I first went into the earth's shadow, with its two tracking beacons still operating. Since going into orbit on August 12, it had bounced back hundreds of telephonic experiments and transmissions.

October 4: The second complete NASA Scout rocket was fired successfully from Wallops Island to its predicted 3,500-mile altitude and 5,800-mile impact range.

October 12: NASA Administrator Glennan announced that communications satellites developed by private companies would be launched by NASA at cost to assist private industry in developing a communications network.

November 3: Explorer VIII was launched. Measurements were taken of the electron density, temperature, ion density and com-position, and charge on the satellite in the upper atmosphere.

November 19: Construction began on Building 6, the Space Sciences Laboratory, at GSFC.

November 22: An Aerobee-Hi was fired to a 105-mile altitude from Wallops Island, with four stellar spectrometers developed for an experiment by the University of Rochester's Institute of Optics.

November 23: Tiros II was launched by Thor-Delta booster from AMR—the fourteenth successful U.S. satellite launched in 1960.

November 26: Construction began on Building 5, the Instrument Construction and Installation Laboratory, at GSFC.

— Patent awarded to Stephen Paull, GSFC's Spacecraft Technology Division, for a Variable Frequency Multivibrator Subcarrier Oscillator for Telemeter System.

1961

January 29: The Goddard Institute for Space Studies was established in New York City.

January 31: A contract was awarded for construction of Buildings 7 and 10, the Payload Testing Facility and Environmental Testing Laboratory at GSFC.

— Experiments with *Echo I* were discontinued except for occasional checks, having provided innumerable communications since launch on August 12, 1960.

February 5: The orientation of *Tiros II* made it impossible to obtain Northern Hemi-

Architect's drawing of Buildings 7 and 10.

1961 Continued

sphere pictures, and malfunctions made remote picture taking undesirable; use of the satellite's cameras was suspended until orbit precession again made Northern Hemisphere pictures possible.

February 10: A voice message was sent from Washington to Woomera, Australia, by way of the moon. NASA Deputy Administrator Hugh L. Dryden spoke on telephone to Goldstone, Calif., which "bounced" it off the moon to the deep space instrumentation station at Woomera. The operation was held as part of the official opening ceremony of the Deep Space Instrumentation Facility site in Australia.

Antenna at Goldstone, California.

February 15: James E. Webb was sworn in as second NASA Administrator.

February 16: Explorer IX, a 12-foot inflatable sphere of Mylar and aluminum, painted with white "polka dots," was placed in orbit by a four-stage Scout booster from Wallops Island. This was the first satellite launching from Wallops and the first satellite boosted by a solid-fuel rocket.

— France and NASA agreed to establish a joint program to test NASA communications satellites in Projects Relay and Rebound, to be launched by NASA in 1962 and 1963.

February 17: Explorer IX was located in orbit, by visual and photographic means, after failure of its radio beacon delayed orbit confirmation.

February 23: NASA Administrator James E. Webb and Deputy Secretary of Defense Roswell L. Gilpatric signed a letter of understanding confirming the national launch vehicle program—the integrated development and procurement of space boosters by DOD and NASA. Neither DOD nor NASA would initiate the development of a launch vehicle or booster for use in space without the written acknowledgment of the other agency.

— *Tiros II* completed 3 months in orbit, continuing useful observations beyond the original estimate of useful life.

February 27: A memorandum of understanding between the Federal Communications Commission and NASA delineating and coordinating civil communication space activities was signed. It stated that "earliest practicable realization of a commercially operable communications satellite system is a national objective."

During February: Dr. Joseph W. Siry, Head of GSFC's Theory and Analysis Office, received the Arthur S. Flemming award "For accomplishments in the field of orbit determination and prediction."

March 1: The installation of computer equipment was completed in Building 3 at GSFC.

March 6: Direct-mode pictures by the *Tiros II* camera were resumed after a month of inoperation. The quality of the pictures showed slight improvement, supporting the theory that foreign matter might have been deposited on the lens and was gradually evaporating.

March 16: The Goddard Space Flight Center was officially dedicated at Greenbelt, Md.; the dedication address was delivered by Dr. Detlev Bronk, President of the National Academy of Sciences. It was the 35th anniversary of Dr. Goddard's successful launching of the world's first liquid-fuel rocket. Mrs. Goddard accepted the Congressional Medal honoring her husband.

March 23: Tiros II had completed 4 months in orbit and continued to provide useful cloud pictures and radiation data. A signal from *Tiros II* was used on orbit 1763 to trigger dynamite to break ground for new RCA Space Environment Center at Princeton, N.J.

March 25: Explorer X, on a Thor-Delta, launched into a highly elliptical orbit (apogee 186,000 miles, perigee 100 miles) with instruments to transmit data on the nature of the magnetic field and charged particles in the region of space where the earth's magnetic field merges with that of interplanetary space.

March 27: Its instruments recording a magnetic impulse, *Explorer X* became the first satellite to measure the shock wave generated by a solar flare.

March 28: GSFC scientists reported that *Explorer X* had encountered magnetic fields considerably stronger than expected in its elongated orbit which carried it 186,000 miles from the earth (almost halfway to the moon).

March 31: All stations in the Goddard-managed worldwide Mercury tracking network became operational.

April 19: Preliminary data from *Explorer X* indicated that solar wind blows the sun's magnetic field past the orbit of the earth.

April 27: Explorer XI was launched. It detected directional gamma rays from space.

May 1: Tiros operations at Belmar, N.J., were terminated to begin the move of equipment to Wallops Island.

May 18: The first test inflation of a 135-foot rigidized inflatable balloon (*Echo II* series) in a dirigible hangar was conducted by NASA Langley Research Center and G. T. Schjeldahl Co. at Weeksville, N.C.

— The GSFC Institute for Space Studies in New York announced that its first major project, a 2-month seminar on the origin of the solar system, would be held in the fall of 1961.

May 22: Construction began on Building 7, the Payload Testing Facility, at GSFC.

May 24: FCC endorsed the ultimate creation of a commercial satellite system to be owned jointly by international telegraph and telephone companies and announced a meeting for June 5 to explore "plans and procedures looking toward early establishment of an operable commercial communications satellite system."

May 25: In his second State of the Union message President Kennedy set forth an accelerated space program based upon the long-range national goals of landing a man on the moon and returning him safely to earth, "before this decade is out"; early development of the Rover, a nuclear rocket; speed-up of the use of earth satellites for worldwide communications; and providing "at the earliest possible time a satellite system for worldwide weather observation."

— An additional $549 million was requested for NASA over the new administration's March budget requests; $62 million was requested for DOD for starting development of a solid-propellant booster of the Nova class. (Nova would be capable of placing 100,000 pounds on the moon; its first stage would have six 1,500,000-pound-thrust engines.)

June 8: NASA announced accelerated recruiting of qualified scientists and engineers at its field centers to fill anticipated manpower requirements in the expanded space exploration program. During 1960 NASA had interviewed 3,000 persons on 100 college campuses.

— Astronomers of Lick Observatory positioned a 36-inch refractor telescope to intersect the path of *Echo I* at its predicted point of maximum elevation. The prediction of GSFC was confirmed at the exact time and within 10 minutes of arc.

June 9: A NASA press conference revealed that data from *Vanguard III* (November 15 to 17, 1960) and *Explorer VIII* (also during November 1960) indicated that high-velocity clouds of micrometeoroids moved near the earth, perhaps in a meteor stream around the sun. These new data had just been discovered from completed analysis.

June 14: The Argentine Comisión Nacional de Investigaciones Espaciales and NASA signed a memorandum of understanding for a cooperative space science research program using sounding rockets.

— A four-stage Javelin fired to 560-mile altitude from Wallops Island tested the extension of two 75-foot antenna arms on radio command, a test flight in the Canadian-U.S. Alouette satellite program.

June 15: President Kennedy directed the Na-

Dr. Robert Jastrow addresses the Conference on Origins of the Solar System held shortly after the Institute for Space Studies began operation in New York.

1961 Continued

tional Aeronautics and Space Council to undertake a full study of the Nation's communications satellite policy; he stated that leadership in science and technology should be exercised to achieve worldwide communications through the use of satellites at the earliest practicable date. Although no commitments as to an operational system should be made, the Government would "conduct and encourage research and development to advance the state of the art and to give maximum assurance of rapid and continuing scientific and technological progress."

During June: NASA entered a letter contract with RCA for four Tiros satellites.

July 9: The National Science Foundation released a forecast of the Nation's scientific needs for the next decade, which predicted that the United States would need nearly twice as many scientists in 1970 (168,000) as in 1961 (87,000).

July 12: Tiros III weather satellite was successfully launched into a near-circular orbit by the Thor-Delta booster from Cape Canaveral.

July 13 to 14: Two Nike-Cajun rockets launched Univ. of N.H.-GSFC payloads from Wallops Island.

July 19: Tiros II photographed tropical storm Liza in the Pacific Ocean, pinpointing its location for meteorologists.

July 23: NASA Administrator Webb, in congressional testimony, pointed out that the Tiros cloud-cover program was known to the entire world, involved no surveillance, and promised great benefits to all nations. He said data from the Tiros satellites had been made available to all, including the Soviet Union.

July 28: NASA and AT&T signed a cooperative agreement for the development and testing of two, possibly four, active communications satellites during 1962. AT&T would design and build the TSX satellites at its own expense and would reimburse NASA for the cost of the launchings by Thor-Delta vehicles at Cape Canaveral.

July 31: NASA awarded a contract to the Univ. of Michigan to continue to provide research instrumentation for measurement of temperatures and winds at altitudes up to 150 kilometers with Nike-Cajun and other sounding rockets.

August 8: Over 100 foreign weather services were invited by NASA and the U.S. Weather Bureau to participate in the *Tiros III* experiment for a 9-week period beginning today. The program provided cooperating services with an opportunity to conduct special meteorological observations synchronized with passes of the satellite.

August 11: NASA announced negotiation of a contract with Hughes Aircraft Co. for con-

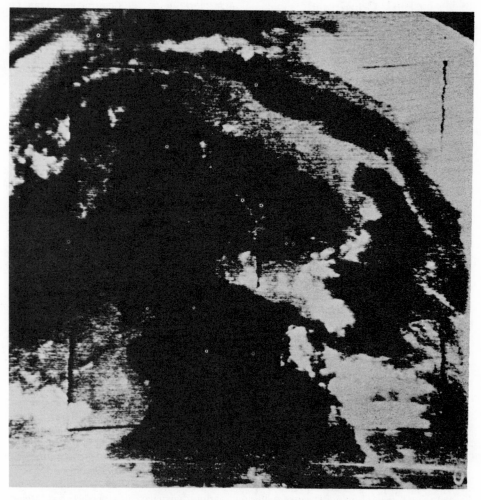

Italy and the Mediterranean as seen from a Tiros satellite.

struction of three experimental synchronous communications satellites (Syncom).

August 12: Echo I completed its first year in orbit, still clearly visible to the naked eye, after traveling 4,480 orbits and 138 million miles. *Echo I* had provided the basis for over 150 communications experiments, recent ones indicating only a 40 percent reduction in transmission reflection, caused by the changed shape. It also provided significant data on atmospheric drag and solar pressure.

— Aerobee 150A, with a liquid-hydrogen experiment, was fired from Wallops Island.

August 15: Explorer XII was placed into a highly eccentric orbit by a Thor-Delta booster from AMR; would provide detailed evaluation of the behavior of energetic particles between a 180- and 47,800-mile altitude. Under GSFC management, this "windmill" satellite carried six experiments developed by Ames Research Center, State Univ. of Iowa, Univ. of N.H., and GSFC. Several days were required to

217

1961 Continued

confirm the orbit. All instrumentation operated normally.

August 17: NASA announced that *Explorer XII* had successfully completed its first orbit and was sending data on magnetic fields and solar radiation from an apogee near 54,000 miles and a perigee within 170 miles of the earth.

August 21: NASA held a news conference on *Explorer XII,* at which the great amount of continuous coverage of interrelated data in its eccentric orbit was pointed out.

August 25: Explorer XIII was placed into orbit by the Scout rocket from Wallops Island; it was a micrometeoroid counting satellite developed by the Langley Research Center with GSFC participation.

August 29: NASA announced Explorer *XIII* had reentered the atmosphere. Transmitting data on micrometeoroids, the spacecraft was last heard from on August 27 by the Minitrack facility at Antofagasta, Chile.

During August: With the successful launch of *Explorer XII* on August 15, the Delta launch vehicles had successfully launched five satellites in six attempts, the only failure being the first attempt. Delta's high reliability record began with *Echo I* on August 12, 1960, and included *Tiros II* and *Tiros III* and *Explorer X* and *Explorer XII*. Built by prime contractor Douglas Aircraft, the NASA Delta launch vehicle consisted of a Thor first stage (Rocketdyne MB-3 liquid-fuel engine), Aerojet-General second stage (AJ-10-118, an improved Vanguard second stage), and an Allegany Ballistics Laboratory third stage (X-248 rocket is a spin-stabilized version of the Vanguard third stage).

September 13: Two experiments to measure atmospheric winds, temperature, and density in relatively high altitudes were conducted from Wallops Island in two four-stage Argo D-4 rocket launches. Sodium clouds were released at near 120 miles and again at 228 miles in the first launch, and at 118 and 230 miles in the second launch. French scientists participated by using special optical instruments to observe the brilliant orange and yellow clouds which stirred a rash of public inquiries from hundreds of miles.

September 16 to 29: Construction began on Building 8, the Satellite Systems Laboratory, at GSFC.

—A pair of spin-up rockets on *Tiros II* were fired after more than 10 months in orbit.

During September: Congress appropriated funds to the U.S. Weather Bureau for implementation of the National Operational Meteorological Satellite System. To phase in as early as technology warranted and to continue expanding the operational capability through the early Nimbus (advanced weather satellite) launchings by NASA, the system was planned to be fully operational by 1966, when the Nimbus system would become operational. The system would include data acquisition stations in northern latitudes, communications for transmitting the data, and a National Meteorological Center to receive, process, analyze, and disseminate the derived information over domestic and international weather circuits.

October 11: The final report of the House Committee on Science and Astronautics relating to their hearings on "Commercial Applications of Space Communications Systems" was released, having among its conclusions:

(1) Because of the worldwide interest and potential usefulness of a space communications system, the U.S. Government must "retain maximum flexibility regarding the central question of ownership and operation of the system."

(2) NASA would not only evaluate the various commercial proposals but would "conduct all space launches and retain direct control over all launching equipment, facilities, and personnel."

(3) Research and development of military space communications systems should continue to be conducted by DOD, but all research and development in space communications "should be conducted under the general supervision of NASA in accordance with its statutory mandate to plan, direct, and conduct aeronautical and space activities" as well as evaluate the technical merits of proposed systems.

October 13: The Ad Hoc Carrier Committee established by FCC to make an industry proposal on the development and operation of commercial communications satellites recommended a nonprofit corporation be formed, to be owned by companies engaged in international communications, with the U.S. Government having one more representative on the board of directors than any single company. Western Union filed a minority statement proposing a public stock company arrangement to prevent dominance of the corporation by any one company.

— After its second year, *Explorer VII* was still transmitting, although the predicted lifetime of its transmitters had been only one year.

October 14: An Argo D–4 launched from Wallops Island carried a Canadian-U.S. topside sounding satellite payload to 560-mile altitude.

October 19: P–21, the Electron Density Profile Probe, was launched, with good data received. Electron density measurements were obtained to about 1,500 miles.

— Construction began on Building 10, the Environmental Testing Laboratory, at GSFC.

October 23: NASA announced it had ordered 14 additional Delta launch vehicles for Relay, Syncom, Telstar, and Tiros satellites.

October 27: GSFC and the Geophysics Corp. of America launched a Nike-Cajun rocket from Wallops Island with a 60-pound payload that reached a 90-mile altitude in a study of electron density and temperature in the upper level of the atmosphere.

October 29: NASA announced that the first Mercury-Scout launch to verify the readiness of the worldwide Mercury tracking network would take place at AMR.

November 23: *Tiros II* had completed its first year in orbit, still transmitting cloud-cover photographs of usable quality, although it had been expected to have a useful lifetime of only 3 months. *Tiros II* had completed 5,354 orbits and had transmitted over 36,000 photographs.

November 27: Sen. Robert Kerr announced that he would introduce legislation to authorize private ownership in the U.S. portion of the proposed worldwide communications satellite system. His bill would create

the "Satellite Communications Corporation," which the participating firms would buy into.

December 18: NASA announced that the first station in a network of data-gathering stations for use with second-generation (advanced) satellites had been completed near Fairbanks, Alaska. The site for the second of the $5 million installations (each had a high-gain antenna 85 feet in diameter) was announced to be Rosman, N.C., 40 miles southwest of Asheville.

During December: The West German Post Office indicated it would construct near Munich by late 1963 or early 1964, a ground station capable of handling up to 600 phone calls simultaneously for operations with Telstar and Relay satellites.

1962

January 18: GSFC selected Rohr Aircraft Corp. to negotiate the manufacture and erection of three 85-foot-diameter parabolic antenna systems at Pisgah National Forest (Rosman, N.C.) ; Fairbanks, Alaska; and an undetermined location in eastern Canada.

January 19: At a NASA press conference, scientists described preliminary scientific results obtained by *Explorer XII*, based on a study of 10 percent of the data. It appeared that instead of the two radiation belts (previously called the inner and outer Van Allen belts) there was one magnetosphere extending roughly from 400 miles above the earth to 30,000 to 40,000 miles out.

January 23: GSFC announced the selection of Motorola, Inc., Military Electronics Division, of Scottsdale, Ariz., as contractor for research and development on the Goddard range and range-rate tracking system. Intended for tracking satellites in near-space and cislunar space, the system would measure spacecraft position to within a few feet and velocity to within fractions of a foot per second, by measuring carrier and sidetone modulations.

— Dr. Sigmund Fritz of the U.S. Weather Bureau reported that *Tiros III* had spotted fifty tropical storms during the summer of 1961.

January 25: *Explorer X* detected a "shadow" on the side of the earth away from the sun;

Rosman tracking facility.

1962 Continued

this shadow was marked by an absence of the solar wind, a belt of plasma moving out from the sun at about 200 miles per second but deflected around the earth by the earth's magnetic field and creating a cone-shaped "shadow" some 100,000 miles across at its larger end. The *Explorer X* findings were reported to the annual meeting of the American Physical Society in New York by Dr. Bruno Rossi of MIT.

— "Satellite Communications Corporation" bills were introduced by Sen. Robert Kerr (S. 2650) and by Rep. George Miller H.R. 9696), which would amend the NASA Act by adding a new section declaring that it is "the policy of the United States to provide leadership in the establishment of a worldwide communications system involving the use of space satellites." The section would create a "Satellite Communications Corporation" which would be privately owned and managed, and which would develop and operate a communications satellite system.

January 31: Explorer I had completed its

fourth year in orbit and had a life expectancy of several more years.

During January: The Nimbus meteorological satellite underwent a rigorous test program at General Electric's Missile and Space Vehicle Center, Valley Forge, Pa.

— NASA awarded a contract to the Kollsman Instrument Division for a 38-inch-diameter primary mirror in the space telescope to be used in the Orbiting Astronomical Observatory (OAO).

February 8: Tiros IV was launched by a three-stage Thor-Delta rocket from Cape Canaveral into a near-circular orbit with an apogee of 525 miles and a perigee of 471 miles. It featured the same basic types of equipment as previous Tiros satellites, including cameras for cloud-cover photography and infrared sensors to measure temperatures at various levels in the atmosphere. The principal innovation was a camera with new type of wide-angle lens covering an area 450 miles on a side, which was expected to provide minimum distortion. The quality of *Tiros IV* pictures was good.

February 16: Explorer IX was launched. The

balloon and fourth stage orbited. **Transmitter** on the balloon failed to function properly, so the satellite required optical tracking.

February 25: Soviet scientists claimed to have discovered the third radiation belt around the earth and published such findings 2 years before the findings of *Explorer XII* were made public by NASA on January 19, 1962.

February 28: James S. Albus, an engineer at GSFC, was awarded $1,000 for his invention of a digital solar aspect sensor.

The digital solar aspect sensor.

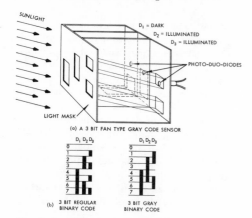

(a) A 3 BIT FAN TYPE GRAY CODE SENSOR

(b) 3 BIT REGULAR BINARY CODE   3 BIT GRAY BINARY CODE

March 7: OSO I (Orbiting Solar Observatory I) was successfully launched into orbit from Cape Canaveral, marking the seventh straight success for the Thor-Delta booster.

March 8: The tracking network that operated during John Glenn's orbital Mercury flight (MA–6) would be sufficient to handle the 18-orbit manned flights to follow, according to Edmond C. Buckley, NASA's Director of Tracking and Data Acquisition, in testimony before a subcommittee of the House Committee on Science and Astronautics.

March 11: NASA announced that *Echo I,* the 100-foot balloon-type passive communications satellite launched on August 12, 1960, had recently become increasingly difficult to see. The sphere now presented only one-half to one-fourth its original size; this was due either to shrinkage or distortion during its 1½ years in orbit.

March 14: A press conference of Smithsonian Astrophysical Observatory and NASA scientists reported that *Explorer IX,* launched on February 16, 1961, had provided new and refined information on the density of the upper atmosphere. *Explorer IX,* a 12-foot aluminum-foil sphere painted with white "polka dots," was expected to have an orbital life of 2 more years. As it spiraled down into denser atmosphere, it was expected to provide much more information on density at altitudes down to 100 miles.

March 16: First anniversary of the dedication of NASA's Goddard Space Flight Center. During this year, seven Goddard satellites were orbited and the Center successfully operated the new 18-station world tracking network for the first manned orbital flight; began expansion of the 13-station scientific satellite tracking and data network; saw some 70 of its sounding rocket payloads launched from Wallops Island; established the Institute for Space Studies in New York; and added three buildings and 700 persons to its staff.

March 27: NASA fired a Nike-Cajun rocket from Wallops Island, releasing a sodium vapor cloud between 25- and 74-mile altitude. Rays of the setting sun colored the sodium cloud red (instead of sodium vapor's normal yellow).

March 28: The Senate Aeronautical and Space Sciences Committee unanimously approved a bill for ownership and operation of the Nation's commercial communications satellites.

March 29: A four-stage NASA Scout rocket carried the P–21A probe payload 3,910 miles into space and 4,370 miles downrange from Wallops Island.

During March: NASA completed work on its first major launching facility on the West Coast, a Thor-Agena pad at Vandenberg AFB, Calif. A used gantry was shipped from Marshall Space Flight Center and installed at a $1 million saving over cost of new construction. This pad would be used for NASA polar-orbit launches, such as for *Echo II,* Nimbus, and POGO (Polar Orbiting Geophysical Observatory).

During March: William G. Stroud, Chief of GSFC's Aeronomy & Meteorology Division, was awarded the Astronautics Engineer

1962 Continued

Achievement Award "For his personal contribution to the technology of meteorological satellites which are now culminating in rapid development of an operational system." Bernard Sisco, Deputy Assistant Director for Administration at GSFC, was awarded the Distinguished Service Award of Prince Georges County Junior Chamber of Commerce, "In recognition of his contributions to the general community welfare during the year."

April 1: Beginning of the third year of successful weather satellite operation by Tiros satellites; *Tiros I,* launched on Apr. 1, 1960, performed beyond all expectations, operated for 78 days, transmitted almost 23,000 cloud photos, of which some 19,000 were useful to meteorologists. *Tiros II,* launched Nov. 23, 1960, had transmitted more than 33,000 photos and one year after launch was still occasionally taking useful photos. *Tiros III,* launched July 12, 1961, took 24,000 cloud photos and was most spectacular as a "hurricane hunter." *Tiros IV,* launched Feb. 8, 1962, had averaged 250 operationally useful photos per day.

April 2: OSO I, launched Mar. 7, 1962, was reported by NASA to be performing well. As of this date, 360 telemetry data tapes had been recorded from 403 orbits. About one year would be required for complete analysis of the data.

April 11: NASA Administrator James E. Webb, testifying before the Senate Commitee on Commerce, supported the President's bill setting up a communications satellite corporation and approved of the Senate amendments, but noted his reservations on the one that would direct the FCC to encourage communications common carriers to build and own their own ground stations.

April 13: NASA Administrator James E. Webb, addressing the National Conference of the American Society for Public Administration in Detroit, said: "No new department or agency in the recent history of the Executive Branch of the Federal Government was created through the transfer of as many units from other departments and agencies as in the case of NASA. Three and one-half years ago, NASA did not exist. Today

NASA comprises approximately 20,500 employees, ten major field centers, and an annual budget approaching the $2 billion mark."

April 15: U.S. Weather Bureau began daily international transmissions of cloud maps based on photos taken by *Tiros IV.*

April 17: NASA launched a Nike-Cajun sounding rocket from Wallops Island which detonated 12 grenades at altitudes from 25 to 57 miles.

April 24: The first transmission of TV pictures in space was made via orbiting *Echo I.* Signals were beamed from MIT's Lincoln Laboratory, Camp Parks, Calif., bounced off *Echo I,* and received at Millstone Hill near Westford, Mass.

April 26: Ariel I, the first international satellite (a joint U.K.-U.S. effort), was launched into orbit from Cape Canaveral by a Thor-Delta booster. The 136-pound spacecraft was built by GSFC and carried six British experiments to make integrated measurements in the ionosphere.

— Japan and the U.S. launched their first joint sounding rocket from Wallops Island. NASA provided the Nike-Cajun rocket, launch facilities, data acquisition, and a Langmuir probe to measure electron temperature. Japan furnished other instrumentation. The altitude of the flight was 75.6 miles.

— NASA graduated its first group of Project Mercury tracking personnel from the new course conducted at the Wallops Island training facilities; the seven graduates were personnel from firms having contracts with DOD and NASA.

During April: Tiros IV continued in operation and, to a great extent, provided excellent data. Over 20,000 pictures had been received. A total of 217 nephanalyses had been prepared up to March 26, and 199 had been transmitted over national and international weather circuits. *Tiros II* was turned on late in April by an unknown spurious source. An engineering investigation was run in early May before turning it off again. An analysis of the data indicated that some usable IR data were obtained.

— Robert W. Hutchison, GSFC's Personnel Director, was awarded the Federal Civil

Dr. Kunio Hirao and Toshio Muraoka at the launch of the first U.S.-Japanese sounding rocket experiment in the joint program.

Servant of the Year-State of Maryland, "In recognition of outstanding achievements in contributing to the rapid growth and establishment of Goddard Space Flight Center."

May 2: NASA scientists reported to the COSPAR session that data from *Explorer IX* indicated that the upper atmosphere was heated by sunspot activity.

May 3: Two GSFC scientific sounding rockets were launched from Wallops Island. An Iris research rocket launched with test instrumentation did not achieve its programed altitude and landed 175 statute miles downrange.

— House of Representatives passed the Communications Satellite Act of 1962 by a vote of 354 to 9.

May 17: The second and third joint Japan-U.S. space probes were successfully launched from Wallops Island; the second Nike-Cajun reached a 76-mile altitude and the third, and last—a night shot—reached an 80-mile altitude. The first of a series of 80 rocket probes to determine wind patterns over Cape Canaveral was initiated with the launch of a single-stage Nike to 80,000 feet, where it released a white smoke screen for photographic study.

May 18: Geophysics Corp. of America reported receipt of a Weather Bureau contract to study and explain the formation of vast bands of cloud patterns in the upper atmosphere, a phenomenon first revealed in photographs relayed by *Tiros I.*

May 20: Building 5 at GSFC was completed.

May 22: *OSO I,* launched March 7, 1962, experienced telemetry failure; it had provided 1,000 hours of data from its solar-pointed experiments.

May 29: NASA announced that *Ariel I,* the U.K.-U.S. ionosphere satellite launched on April 26, was functioning well except for one experiment, the solar ultraviolet detector.

During May: Checkout was completed for the Alaska Data Acquisition Facility near Fairbanks, and the Univ. of Alaska assumed responsibility. Part of the GSFC system, the Alaskan facility was an 85-foot dish; its associated electronics system would be used on tracking and data acquisition of the polar-orbiting Nimbus, EGO (Eccentric Geophysical Observatory), and POGO (Polar-Orbiting Geophysical Observatory) satellites.

June 6: Three sounding rockets were launched from Wallops Island. The first, a Nike-Apache, launched at 7:40 p.m. (EDT) with a 70-pound payload containing a pitot-static

1962 Continued

probe, reached a 78-mile altitude. The second, a Nike-Cajun, launched at 8:05 p.m., consisted of 11 explosive charges and a balloon, released between 25 and 64 miles altitude. The third, a Nike-Asp, was launched at 8:56 p.m. and released sodium vapor clouds to measure atmospheric winds and diffusion, at about 20 miles and extending to a peak altitude of about 100 miles.

June 7: A Nike-Cajun vehicle with an experiment to measure winds and temperatures in the upper atmosphere was launched from Wallops Island. In the night flight, 12 special explosive charges were ejected and detonated at intervals from about 25 up to 58 miles altitude.

— NASA announced selection of Bendix Corp.'s Radio Division, Towson, Md., for a contract to operate five of NASA's worldwide Project Mercury tracking and communications stations.

June 14: *Tiros IV* was no longer transmitting pictures usable for global weather forecasting, although it was still taking "direct" pictures on command which were suitable for limited U.S. weather analysis.

June 15: A two-stage Nike-Apache sounding rocket was launched from Wallops Island with a 95-pound payload to a 89-mile altitude with a GSFC experiment to measure electron density and electron collision frequency in the ionosphere under undisturbed conditions.

— NASA launched the first two of six tests on the performance of the Canadian Black Brant sounding rocket. The first carried a payload to 58 miles above Wallops Island, the second reached 62 miles.

— In preparation for the 1962 hurricane season, the Weather Bureau arranged to transmit satellite cloud photographs by photofacsimile to warning centers in San Juan, New Orleans, and Miami, where they would be used in forecasting and tracking tropical storms.

June 18: NASA selected Hughes Aircraft Co. for negotiation of a $2.5 million, 6-month study contract on an Advanced Syncom (synchronous communications) satellite. The contract covered satellite subsystems which would require long lead-time de-

velopmental and feasibility work. This second-generation Syncom would be a 500-pound, spin-stabilized satellite capable of relaying hundreds of telephone calls or carrying several TV channels. (The first-generation Syncom, for which Hughes was prime contractor, was limited to single telephone channel relay.) The Syncom project was under the technical direction of GSFC.

June 19: *Tiros V* was launched into orbit by a Thor-Delta booster from Cape Canaveral. A faulty guidance system placed it into an elliptical orbit (apogee, 604 miles; perigee, 367 miles; period, 100.5 minutes) instead of a 400-mile circular orbit.

June 20: An Aerobee 150A was launched from Wallops Island with a 271-pound payload boosted to 97-mile altitude; it carried a camera to study the behavior of liquid hydrogen under conditions of symmetrical heating and zero gravity.

June 24: *OSO I* began transmitting real-time data on solar observations after 5 weeks of intermittent transmittal.

July 1: *OSO I* was transmitting continuous signals, and 20 percent of real-time data was being acquired from each 95-minute orbit.

July 3: *Ariel I* discovery of a new ion belt at an altitude of 450 to 500 miles was announced at the International Conference on the Ionosphere, London, by Prof. James Sayers of Birmingham University.

July 9: *Tiros V* stopped transmitting pictures from the Tegea-lens, medium-angle camera. The Tegea camera system transmitted 4,701 pictures of which 70 percent were considered of excellent quality. The wide-angle Elgeet-lens camera, which still functioned, had transmitted 5,100 pictures to date, some of which aided in the analysis of Typhoon Joan over the western Pacific.

July 10: *Telstar I*, the first privately financed satellite, was launched by a Goddard launch team, from AMR on a Delta booster. The satellite was funded by AT&T and launched under a NASA-AT&T agreement of July 27, 1961. *Telstar I* made the world's first commercial transmission of live TV via satellite and the first transatlantic TV transmission on the same day it was launched. In one test, pictures were telecast from Andover, Me., to *Telstar I*, then returned and placed

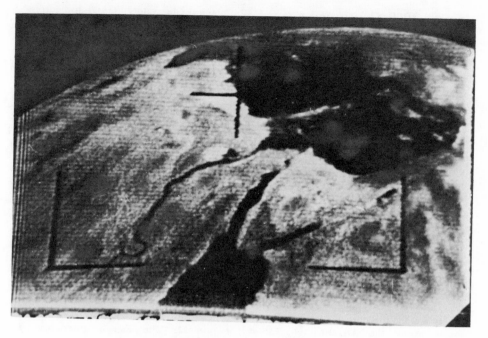

The Nile delta as seen from a Tiros satellite.

A picture transmitted by comsat *Telstar I.*

1962 Continued

on all three major TV networks in the U.S.

July 18: NASA launched a rigidized Echo-type balloon on a Thor booster to 922 miles in an inflation test. Nicknamed "Big Shot," the 135-foot balloon was inflated successfully and was visible for 10 minutes from Cape Canaveral. A movie film capsule parachuted into the sea, northeast of San Salvador, was recovered by three "pararescue" men of the Air Rescue Service. This was the largest man-made object sent into space, the previous record being held by the 100-foot *Echo. I.*

July 20: The Weather Bureau transmitted *Tiros V* photographs to Australia from Suitland, Md., the first time Tiros photographs had been transmitted abroad for current weather analysis by a foreign country. The photographs were of cloud formations west of Australia.

July 23: *Telstar I* relayed two 20-minute live TV shows, the first formal exchange of programs across the Atlantic via *Telstar I.* The United States Information Agency reported that U.S.S.R. had been invited to participate in the *Telstar I* broadcasts but had never answered the invitation.

July 24: Three major TV networks in the U.S. telecast separate 5-minute newscasts via *Telstar I,* each featuring their respective Paris news correspondents.

July 27: GSFC awarded a contract to IBM's Federal Systems Division for computer support services of Mercury flights, nonrendezvous Gemini flights (orbital flights of two men in one capsule), and the unmanned lunar flights scheduled as part of Project Apollo.

July 31: Former President Dwight D. Eisenhower spoke on the people-to-people benefits to be gained by live international communications in a broadcast televised to the U.S. via *Telstar I* from Stockholm, Sweden.

August 3: It was announced that the Advanced Syncom Satellite, being developed for NASA by the Hughes Aircraft Co., probably would carry four radio signal repeaters and would provide up to 300 two-way telephone channels or one TV channel.

August 7: General Electric announced that the control system for the first Orbiting Astronomical Observatory (OAO) had successfully completed its first simulated space flight.

August 8: NASA launched an Aerobee 150A sounding rocket from Wallops Island. Its 256-pound payload rose to 92-mile altitude and traveled a 60-mile distance downrange.

August 12: Five NASA representatives, led by Ozro M. Covington of GSFC, arrived in Australia to inspect proposed sites for new tracking stations.

August 15: NASA announced that GSFC had awarded three 3-month study contracts on the design of an Advanced OSO, to be launched into polar orbit during 1965. The Advanced OSO would aid development of a method of predicting flares.

August 16: Construction began on Building 11, the Applied Sciences Laboratory, at GSFC.

August 19: NASA launched a Scout vehicle from Wallops Island in an experiment to make direct measurements of radiative heating during atmospheric entry.

August 22: The French government announced its first satellite, weighing 150 pounds, would be launched in March 1966 and would be followed by others three and four times as large. GSFC was to assist in the training of the project staff.

August 27: GSFC announced it was training Italian scientists and engineers for the launching of Italy's first satellite. The 165-pound satellite would be launched by 1965 from a platform in the Indian Ocean off the eastern coast of Africa.

September 5: An agreement establishing the Italy-U.S. cooperative space program, signed in May, was confirmed in Rome by Italian Foreign Minister Attilio Piccioni and U.S. Vice President Lyndon B. Johnson. The Memorandum of Understanding between the Italian Space Commission and NASA provided a three-phase program, expected to culminate in the launching of a scientific satellite into equatorial orbit. Generally, NASA would provide Scout rockets and personnel training; Italians would launch the vehicle with its Italian payload and would be responsible for data acquisition as well as for a towable launch platform located in equatorial waters. Subsequently the satellites in this series were named "San Marco."

September 6: ITT announced plans for a NASA Project Relay satellite communication experiment to link North America and South America.

September 15: Signals from *Ariel I* were received again. The satellite had stopped transmitting after radiation from a U.S. high-altitude nuclear test damaged the satellite's solar cells. Although resumed transmission was not continuous, it did demonstrate *Ariel I*'s regained capability to return scientific data from space.

—NASA announced that the sixth Tiros weather satellite would be launched into orbit from Cape Canaveral on Sept. 18, at the earliest. The launch date was moved 2 months ahead to provide backup for *Tiros V* cloud-cover photography during the last half of current hurricane season and to provide weather forecasting support for Astronaut Walter M. Schirra's orbital space flight Sept. 28. The wide-angle TV camera in *Tiros V* continued to operate, but its medium-angle Tegea lens had stopped functioning on July 2 because of "random electrical failure in the camera's system."

September 18: Tiros VI was placed in orbit by a three-stage Delta vehicle from Cape Canaveral.

September 22: An Aerobee 150A was launched from Wallops Island; the rocket reached a 177-mile altitude in an experiment to measure the absolute intensity of the spectrum of stars with 50A resolution and to measure ultraviolet fluxes.

September 28: NASA announced plans to launch two Project Echo balloons during October. To be filled with helium while on the ground near the White Sands Missile Range, N. Mex., one balloon would be like *Echo I*, measuring 100 feet in diameter and the other would be an Advanced Echo type measuring 135 feet in diameter.

September 29: Alouette I, the Swept Frequency Topside Sounder, was placed in polar orbit by a Thor-Agena B from Vandenberg AFB. It was a Canadian Defence Research Board project.

September 30: NASA launched an Aerobee sounding rocket from Wallops Island. The 259-pound instrumented payload reached a 106-mile altitude in a test to map sources of photons of specific wavelengths in the nighttime sky.

October 2: Explorer XIV, an Energetic Particles Satellite, was launched. It was to study trapped corpuscular radiation, solar particles, cosmic radiation, and solar winds.

October 16: A Nike-Apache two-stage sounding rocket carried a 65-pound instrumented payload to 103 miles above Wallops Island.

October 20: An *Echo I*-type balloon launched from the White Sands Missile Range ruptured at a 21-mile altitude and fell back to earth 91 minutes after launch. The 100-foot-diameter balloon was to have reached 24 miles in structural test.

October 21: NASA announced that Swedish and U.S. experimenters were studying samplings of noctilucent clouds obtained in four Nike-Cajun sounding rocket flights during August. Preliminary analysis indicated that samples taken when noctilucent clouds were observed contained significantly more particles than when noctilucent clouds were not visible. Analysis of the origin and structure of the particles might take up to a year. Participants would include scientists from the Univ. of Stockholm Institute of Meteorology, Kiruna (Sweden) Geophysical Observatory, GSFC, and USAF Cambridge Research Laboratories.

October 22: Construction was begun on Building 12, the Tracking and Telemetry Laboratory, at GSFC.

October 27: Explorer XV was placed in orbit by a Thor-Delta vehicle launched from Cape Canaveral.

October 29: An Aerobee sounding rocket launched from Wallops Island carried a 230-pound payload to 116 miles. It landed in the Atlantic Ocean 59 miles from the launch site.

—NASA officials said that five experiments aboard *Explorer XV* were working well but that two others had been adversely affected by the satellite's excessive spin rate.

October 31: Explorer XIV had transmitted 589 hours of data to GSFC, which had released about 240 hours of data to the various experimenters.

During October: Patents were awarded to the following GSFC employees: Harold J. Peake, Space Technology Division, for a Data Con-

227

1962 Continued

version Unit; William A. Leavy, Aeronomy and Meteorology Division, for a Switching Mechanism; and Stephen Paull, Spacecraft Technology Division for a V/F Magnetic Multivibrator.

—Robert E. Bourdeau, Head of the Ionospheres Branch, Space Sciences Division, was awarded the NASA Medal for Exceptional Scientific Achievement, for: "Major scientific advances in the study of the ionosphere and significant progress in the understanding of the plasma sheath about satellites."

—Dr. John C. Lindsay, Associate Chief, GSFC's Space Sciences Division, was awarded the NASA Medal for Exceptional Scientific Achievement, "For the achievement of a major scientific advance in the study of the Sun and for significant technological progress in highly precise satellite attitude control."

—Dr. John W. Townsend, Jr., Assistant Director, GSFC's Space Science and Satellite Applications Directorate, was awarded the NASA Medal for Outstanding Leadership, "For outstanding and dynamic leadership in planning, developing, and directing a complex scientific organization whose notable achievements have significantly contributed to the preeminent position of this country in the space sciences, the development of space technology, and the practical application of such research and development."

—The Directorate for Tracking and Data Systems received the NASA Group Achievement Award, "For superior technical and administrative leadership and outstanding results in the operation of the global manned spacecraft tracking network."

November 1: NASA reported that *Explorer XV* radiation satellite was spinning at the rate of 73 rpm instead of a desired 10 rpm because of failure of the despin weights to deploy. Preliminary data indicated most experiments were functioning and that data received were of good quality.

November 5: GSFC announced the award of contracts totaling $12 million for tracking-network modifications in preparation for lengthy manned space flights.

November 7: NASA launched two experimental Nike-Apache rockets into the upper at-

mosphere within ½ hour of each other, to obtain a comparison of electron density and wind profiles measured at about the same time.

November 8: GSFC announced it would conduct experiments using a laser in tracking the S-66 ionosphere beacon satellite, to be launched into a polar orbit early next year.

November 9: NASA reported Canadian *Alouette I* topside-sounder satellite was performing as expected. Launched Sept. 28, it was considered "a very successful experiment since it is producing not only ionospheric data but also information about the earth's magnetic field. . . . Operation of the satellite continues to be normal. . . ."

November 12: It was reported that TAVE (Thor-Agena Vibration Experiment), flown with the Thor-Agena launching *Alouette I*, measured low-frequency vibrations to the Agena stage and measured spacecraft interfaces during the Thor boost phase.

November 14: In a news conference at MIT, Dr. James A. Van Allen predicted the radiation caused by the U.S. atmospheric nuclear test in July should be "undetectable" by July 1963. Dr. Van Allen reported that signals from *Injun, Telstar I, Explorer XIV,* and *Explorer XV* showed that the electronic stream had disappeared within a few days of the U.S. explosion and that the electrons at a 600-mile altitude were now undetectable. Electrons at a 900-mile altitude were still creating radio-astronomy interference, he acknowledged, but this should be gone by next July.

November 16: A Nike-Cajun sounding rocket was launched from Fort Churchill, Canada, under direction of GSFC. The second stage failed to ignite, so the rocket reached an altitude of only about 9.5 miles.

November 30: Franco-American scientific sounding rocket launchings were coordinated when two U.S. launchings were made from Wallops Island while France launched one from Algeria (and failed to launch one from France). The first U.S. rocket (a Nike-Cajun), fired at 5:57 a.m., carried a Langmuir probe to determine electron density and the temperature of the E layer of the ionosphere (50- to 100-mile altitude); the second (a Nike-Apache), launched at

6:15 a.m., released a sodium vapor cloud to a 106-mile altitude, which spread over 100 miles of the Eastern seaboard.

December 1: The medium-angle camera on *Tiros VI* stopped transmitting pictures during orbit 1,074, but the wide-angle camera was still sending pictures of "excellent quality."

December 4: GSFC launched two Nike-Cajun sounding rockets, one from Wallops Island, and one from Fort Churchill, Canada, for the purpose of comparing data on winds and temperatures in the upper atmosphere.

December 13: Relay I was launched. Its purpose was to investigate wideband communications between ground stations at a low altitude.

December 15: The power supply on *Relay I* remained too low to operate the satellite's instrumentation properly.

December 16: Explorer XVI was launched into orbit by a four-stage Scout vehicle from Wallops Island and it began measuring micrometeoroids in space.

—The *Relay I* 136-Mc beacon was detected by tracking stations at Santiago, Johannesburg, and Woomera, indicating the beacon had spontaneously turned itself on.

December 17: Although the *Relay I* power supply remained low, the Nutley, N.J., ground station was able to obtain about 10 minutes of usable telemetry data.

December 19: U.S. Weather Bureau announced the development of an infrared spectrometer, to be flight-tested in new balloons during the next 6 months. The 100-pound "flying thermometer" was planned for use in Nimbus weather satellites.

December 21: Canada and the U.S. announced a cooperative venture to build a data acquisition station for the Nimbus meteorological satellite program at Ingomish, Nova Scotia.

December 31: Goddard Space Flight Center had over 2,850 people employed or committed for employment.

1963

January 3: Both U.S. communications satellites, *Telstar I* and *Relay I*, came to life. *Telstar,* silent since Nov. 23, respond-

Aerobee sounding rocket fired from Wallops Island, Va.

ed to signals sent by Bell Telephone Laboratories; later in the day, *Relay,* silent since first being orbited Dec. 13, responded twice to television test patterns sent from New Jersey and Maine.

1963 Continued

January 5: Relay I communications satellite made two successful intercontinental television test transmissions between Andover, Me., and Goonhilly Downs, England, one for 23 minutes and the other for 1 hour; teletype tests were also successfully made from Nutley, N.J., to Fucino, Italy. NASA said *Relay I*'s power difficulty had apparently corrected itself, but "project officials have experienced difficulties with *Relay I* responding properly to commands. Tests during the past 3 years were possible by employing special operational procedures and altering command sequences to the satellite. Experiments will continue to evaluate communications and command systems."

January 7: U.K. sent television signals across the Atlantic for first time via *Relay I* communications satellite. Signals sent from Goonhilly Downs to Nutley, N.J., were described as "very good" and "extremely clear"; they were also clearly received at ground station of Italian space communications agency Telespazio in Fucino.

January 8: NASA reported *Relay I* communications satellite's low battery voltage had been result of faulty voltage regulator in one of its twin transponders. Continued tests by RCA and NASA engineers pinpointed the difficulty; the regulator failed to function properly when it became too hot or too cold. Engineers would attempt live television transmission via *Relay I* by sending special command signals to the satellite and concentrating on the remaining good transponder. *Relay I* communications satellite transmitted its first transatlantic television programs, sending British and French viewers clear pictures of ceremonial unveiling of "Mona Lisa" in its visit to Washington and 10 minutes of network program "Today."

January 10: Explorer XIV energetic particles satellite developed radio transmission difficulty, not correctable by remote control. Exact cause of difficulty, apparently in one of the binary counters of satellite's encoder system, was not determined.

—French Scientific Research Minister Gas-

The unveiling of "Mona Lisa" at National Gallery, Washington, D.C. (transmitted picture seen in Europe). Left to right, President John F. Kennedy, Madame Malraux, French Minister of Cultural Affairs André Malraux, Mrs. Kennedy, and Vice President Lyndon B. Johnson.

ton Palewski told French National Assembly a satellite launching site would be established in Eastern Pyrenees Department near the Spanish border. France's first satellite was scheduled for launching in 1965; other European satellites might also be launched from the site.

January 13: GSFC announced its sodium-vapor cloud experiments during past 2 years had shown wind behavior 44–50 miles above earth became erratic and unpredictable. Below that altitude winds generally follow global pattern, regularly reversing with the seasons. Region between 56- and 68-mile altitude is characterized by "remarkable wind sheers"—within altitude span of less than 3 miles, wind speed was observed to increase swiftly by more than 250 mph and even to reverse direction. Immediately above this band of maximum wind velocity, wind diminishes almost to zero. Above 70 miles, research indicated region of strong but more uniform winds, with velocities of about 200 mph. GSFC experiments, launched on sounding rockets from Wallops Station, did not extend beyond 105-mile altitude.

—NASA announced that it would procure Atlas-Agena B vehicles directly from contractors. NASA already had used seven of the vehicles—five for Ranger and two for Mariner—and was planning to use 20 Atlas-Agena B's over the next 3 years—in Gemini rendezvous flights, OGO, OAO, Ranger, and Mariner R. Prime vehicle contractors were General Dynamics Astronautics for Atlas stage and Lockheed for Agena; USAF had vehicle integration responsibility.

—NASA announced signing of Memorandum of Understanding with India's Department of Atomic Energy providing for cooperative U.S.-India space program. Joint scientific experiments to explore equatorial electrojet and upper-atmosphere winds from geomagnetic equator would be launched from Thumba, India, during 1963.

January 15: Explorer XIV energetic particles satellite transmitted 38 seconds of complete data, and Goddard officials were hopeful the satellite might eventually resume normal operations. *Explorer XIV* developed transmission difficulty Jan. 10, after 100 days of nearly continuous transmission. Project Manager Paul G. Marcotte reported *Explorer XIV* received less than 10 percent degradation from space radiation since its launch Oct. 2.

January 17: Relay I satellite transmitted 12-minute Voice of America program as well as AP and UPI news dispatches from Nutley, N.J., to Rio de Janeiro and back. Transmissions were reported perfect, even though ordinary high-frequency radio communication with Rio was not possible because of atmospheric conditions.

January 18: President John F. Kennedy and Dr. Hugh L. Dryden sent teletype and recorded voice messages, respectively, to Italy by way of the *Relay I* satellite.

January 29: Explorer XIV, silent since January 10, resumed normal transmission.

—NASA Director of Communications Systems Leonard Jaffe announced NASA would attempt to launch Syncom communications satellite into synchronous orbit with Delta vehicle no earlier than Feb. 6. Syncom launch was postponed "to insure that the [command and control] equipment is completely checked out" aboard USNS *Kingsport,* stationed in Lagos Harbor, and on the launch vehicle at Cape Canaveral.

January 30: The GSFC Spacecraft Systems Branch, Spacecraft Systems and Projects Division, was reorganized and the Spacecraft Projects Office established. The GSFC Constructions Inspection Service was reorganized and retitled the Construction and Renovation Section.

January 31: Representatives of Canadian Defence Research Board and NASA met for preliminary exploration of scientific and technical aspects involved in proposed joint ionospheric research program. Extension of joint Alouette Topside Sounder program would involve design and construction of four satellites in Canada, with first launching proposed for late 1964.

— Ceremonies at Goddard Space Flight Center celebrating the fifth anniversary of *Explorer I* and the GSFC tracking network used for tracking the satellite featured talks by Secretary of State Dean Rusk, NASA Administrator James E. Webb, Astronaut Walter M. Schirra, Jr., Goddard Director

1963 Continued

Harry J. Goett, and Dr. Edward C. Welsh, Executive Secretary of the National Aeronautics and Space Council. Radio transmissions from *Vanguard I*, second U.S. satellite and oldest still transmitting, were piped into Goddard auditorium. Highlighting ceremony was presentation of scrolls of appreciation to ambassadors of 16 nations that have cooperated with U.S. in establishing the tracking networks.

—Contract award was made to the Industrial Engineering Corporation for the construction of an Optical Tracking Observation Building and Ground Plane Test Facilities at Goddard. The construction starting date was Feb. 6, 1963.

During January: In *International Geophysics Bulletin*, NASA proposed contributions to IQSY (1964–65) were outlined. Prominently among them: sounding rockets; ionosphere explorers and monitors; atmospheric structure OSO, EGO, and POGO satellites; IMP, Pioneer, Mariner, and Surveyor probes.

February 1: NASA announced its first contract to study overall systems requirements for Synchronous Meteorological Satellite (SMS) had been awarded to Republic Aviation Corp. Administered by GSFC, contract called for 4-month study to determine "technical systems needed for 24-hour surveillance of the earth's cloud cover, and to identify the major scientific and engineering advances required for the ground stations."

February 4: On effects of artificial radiation on spacecraft solar cells, a joint AEC-DOD-NASA report said: "Improved types of solar cells (employing n-on-p silicon junctions) which are considerably more radiation resistant, are available and were employed on Telstar. With respect to manned missions in space, the shielding provided by normal capsule design effects a considerable reduction in the radiation exposure, and the artificial belt is not regarded as placing any significant restrictions on the conduct of current manned space flights. . . ."

— Sen. Leverett Saltonstall (R. Mass.) introduced in the Senate a bill (S. 656) "to promote public knowledge of progress and achievement in astronautics and related sciences through the designation of a special day (March 16) in honor of Dr. Robert

Astronaut Walter M. Schirra, Jr., addressing the Fifth Anniversary of Space Tracking ceremonies at Goddard Space Flight Center.

Hutchings Goddard, the father of modern rockets, missiles, and astronautics. . . ." On March 16, 1926, Dr. Goddard first successfully launched a liquid-fuel rocket.

February 6: Goddard Space Flight Center was host to an optical conference. Approximately 70 persons representing NASA's field centers and installations attended the first intra-agency technical conference on optical communications and tracking.

February 13: Proposal to establish international tracking system using lasers to track the S–66 satellite was made at Third International Congress of Quantum Electronics, Paris, by Richard Barnes of NASA Office of International Programs. Under the proposal, each country would establish and control its own stations, with U.S. furnishing the necessary information on the satellite. Laser system was expected to provide faster and more precise tracking than existing radio and radar systems; used with S–66 satellite, to be launched this spring, it should enable scientists to determine the profile of the ionosphere.

— *Explorer XVI* meteoroid detector satellite recorded 16 punctures by meteoroids during its first 29 days in orbit, NASA reported. Other spacecraft had reported hits by cosmic debris, but this was first time actual punctures were recorded. If *Explorer XVI* continued to report meteoroid data for a full year as expected, it should enable scientists to determine whether meteoroids are hazardous to a spacecraft. The satellite exposed 25 square feet of surface to meteoroid impacts, not large enough to provide good statistical data on larger and rarer particles in space. (On Feb. 5, NASA had announced plans to orbit two meteoroid-detector satellites, each with exposure surface of more than 2,000 square feet.)

February 14: NASA *Syncom I* synchronous-orbit communications satellite was launched into orbit by Thor-Delta vehicle from AMR, entered a highly elliptical orbit. About 5 hours later, apogee-kick motor was fired for about 20 seconds in maneuver designed to place the satellite into near-synchronous, 24-hour orbit 22,300 miles above the earth. At about the time the apogee-kick motor completed its burn,

ground stations lost contact with the satellite and could not confirm a synchronous orbit. Attempts to make contact with Syncom were continued.

— A contract was let to the Norair Construction Co. for GSFC's Building No. 16, Development Operations Building. The starting date was Feb. 21, 1963, with a scheduled completion date of Mar. 15, 1964. Partial occupancy in the warehouse portion was estimated for Dec. 1963.

February 15: U.S. worldwide tracking network was not able to locate *Syncom I* communications satellite; radio contact with the satellite was lost Feb. 14, seconds after onboard rocket had fired to transfer *Syncom* from its highly elliptical orbit into near-synchronous orbit.

February 18: Attempted launch of sodium-vapor cloud experiment from NASA Wallops Station was not successful because second stage of Nike-Asp launch vehicle failed to perform properly. A series of rocket grenade and sodium release experiments from Wallops Island and Fort Churchill began on this date and were continued through Mar. 8.

February 19: Dr. Hugh L. Dryden, NASA Deputy Administrator, testified before Communications Subcommittee of Senate Commerce Committee that experiences of both Telstar and Relay communications satellites were being "used continuously to review projects such as Syncom . . . in an attempt to achieve the 24-hour synchronous orbit, as well as all of our other satellite projects. I should like to add, finally, that the experience of Telstar and Relay to date have merely reinforced the opinion which I gave before this committee last year, that considerable research and development have yet to be performed before economic operational systems can be established . . ."

February 20: Following a period of hesitant response by the command decoders on *Telstar I,* due to radiation effects, the spacecraft was inadvertently turned off.

February 23: William Schindler, Goddard manager of the Delta launch vehicle program, was one of 21 engineers and scientists to receive a National Capital Award at the Engineers, Scientists and Architects Day

1963 Continued

awards luncheon. The D.C. Council of Engineering and Architectural Society and the Washington Academy of Sciences honors the men and professions of engineering, science, and architecture each year.

February 25: On communications satellites, Dr. Robert C. Seamans, Jr., NASA Associate Administrator, said: "We re-examined our Communication Satellite program quite carefully in the light of the creation of the Communication Satellite Corporation and the reoriented activities of the DOD following the cancellation of the Advent project. From this programmatic re-examination we have concluded that principal NASA effort should be focused on the research and development problems associated with the synchronous altitude class of communication satellite. We have, therefore, dropped the low altitude multiple passive satellite project, Rebound, and advanced intermediate active satellite projects from hardware development consideration at this time. As a result of these decisions, we reduced our communication satellite program by $35.2 million. . . ."

— 28-nation U.N. Committee on Peaceful Uses of Outer Space approved Indian progress report on plans to sponsor an international rocket base at Quilon for launchings in space above the equatorial regions. Italian delegate reported that the San Marco floating launching facilities would be completed in time for use in the International Quiet Sun Year.

February 28: NASA Director of Meteorological Systems Morris Tepper told House Committee on Science and Astronautics that *Tiros V* and *Tiros VI* (launched in June and September 1962, respectively) were still providing good data. Tiros data "continue to be used by the Weather Bureau for weather analysis and forecasting, storm tracking, hurricane reconnaissance, etc. The Meteorological Soundings project has continued throughout the year as planned. The project at Goddard Space Flight Center, which utilizes the larger meteorological sounding rockets, continues as it has in past years with excellent results. In addition, we have initiated at the Langley Research Center a project which will develop and utilize the smaller meteorological sounding rockets. We expect to have this well underway by the end of the fiscal year. . . ."

— Harvard College Observatory reported that astronomers at Boyden Observatory at Bloemfontein, South Africa, had photographed the *Syncom I* satellite, missing since Feb. 14. The Observatory's photographs indicated *Syncom* probably was in orbit about 22,000 miles high.

— GSFC plans for second-generation OSO satellite—known as Advanced Orbiting Solar Observatory, or Helios—were outlined at Philadelphia technical meeting by Goddard's AOSO Project Manager A. J. Cervenka. AOSO would be designed to have a pointing accuracy of 5 seconds of arc and 70 percent overall systems reliability, Cervenka said.

March 1: At Cape Canaveral, Fla., the team behind NASA's most reliable booster—the Delta—was honored for a success story unique to America's space program. NASA's Group Achievement Award was presented to Goddard's Delta Project Group, which managed the project for NASA. The Delta was used 16 times and was successful the last 15 times.

— U.S. Weather Bureau announced it was purchasing 11 ground stations capable of receiving cloud pictures directly from Nimbus meteorological satellites, to be launched by NASA.

March 2: Boyden Observatory near Bloemfontein, South Africa, had confirmed location of *Syncom I* communications satellite, Harvard University Observatory Director Donald H. Menzel announced. *Syncom I* was tumbling end over end in its orbital path about 19,000 miles high. Boyden's unconfirmed photographs of the satellite, missing since Feb. 14, were reported Feb. 28, and NASA had requested that the findings be confirmed by further observation. "Since then it has cleared and we obtained two good plates showing images in the expected position. With this final confirmation, we have no doubt whatever of the location of the satellite. It behaved approximately as expected."

March 4: U.S. plans for International Year of

Delta Day ceremony, March 1, 1963, at Cape Canaveral. Standing are, left to right, William Schindler, Delta Project Manager, and Dr. Harry J. Goett.

the Quiet Sun (IQSY), 1964-65, were announced by National Academy of Sciences-National Research Council (NAS-NRC), charged by President Kennedy in 1962 to correlate IQSY contribution of Federal agencies. Many IGY observations would be repeated and special experiments made possible by recent scientific advances would be added. IQSY would concentrate more intensively than IGY on the upper atmosphere and space phenomena directly affected by both the large periodic bursts of charged particles and associated magnetic fields escaping from the sun, and the continuous background activity known as "solar wind."

— Dr. Hugh L. Dryden, NASA Deputy Administrator, testifying on NASA's international programs before House Committee on Science and Astronautics, said that the "first substantial fruits of these programs were realized in 1962 and further significant programs were laid down for future years. During 1962, ". . . the first two international satellites, Ariel and Alouette, were successfully placed in orbit, . . . launchings of sounding rockets bearing scientific payloads were carried out in cooperation with eight countries, . . . 37 countries engaged in special projects in support of our weather and communications satellite programs, . . . foreign participation continued to grow in the operation of our global tracking and data acquisition network overseas, . . . and, a new NASA international fellowship program was successfully established in our own universities."

March 5: NASA announced agreement with Australia for establishment of deep space tracking facility about 11 miles southwest of

1963 Continued

Canberra; a manned flight and scientific satellite tracking station at Carnarvon; and a small mobile station at Darwin serving the Syncom communications satellite.

March 7: OSO I solar observatory satellite completed its first year in orbit, exceeding its estimated operating life by 6 months. Eleven of its 13 scientific experiments were still operating and were providing extensive data on behavior and composition of the sun. Preliminary results from *OSO I* would be presented at a symposium Mar. 14.

March 11: U.S.-U.S.S.R. negotiations began in Rome on technical details of a 3-year agreement signed at Geneva in June 1962, for exchange of data to be gained from satellite launchings. Dr. Hugh L. Dryden, Deputy Administrator of NASA, headed U.S. scientific delegation, and Prof. Anatoly A. Blagonravov of the Soviet Academy of Sciences headed the Russian delegation. Joint space research program would include coordination on meteorology, communications studies, and charting of the earth's magnetic field.

— *Relay I* communications satellite was turned off because of severe drain on the onboard power supply, a difficulty similar to that encountered during first week after launch. Power drain was encountered Mar. 9 after *Relay I*'s orbit had been in earth's shadow for 5 weeks and spacecraft temperatures were low.

— NASA and French National Center for Space Studies (CNES) jointly announced signing of Memorandum of Understanding for a cooperative U.S.-France program to investigate propagation of VLF electromagnetic waves. First phase of the program would consist of two electromagnetic-field experiments with French-instrumented payloads to be launched from NASA Wallops Station. Second phase, to be implemented upon mutual consent after Phase I had proved the experiments to be scientifically and technically feasible, would consist of orbiting of scientific satellite, designed and built by France, with a Scout vehicle.

March 13: Relay I communications satellite, its power supply voltage and temperature returned to normal, responded to command signals turning on its telemetry transmitter and encoder. NASA planned to resume normal experimental operations with the satellite Mar. 14. *Relay I* had been turned off because of severe power drain encountered Mar. 9.

March 13 to 15: The Goddard Scientific Satellite Symposium was held at the Interior Department Auditorium in Washington, D.C. The program covered presentations on *Alouette I* (S–27), *Ariel I* (UK–1), *OSO I* (S–16), and *Explorers XII* (S–3), *XIV* (S–3a), and *XV* (S–3b). Data from *Alouette I* showed that ionosphere is usually rough in high latitudes and that electron temperature of ionosphere increases with latitude. This evidence indicated Van Allen radiation belts, which extend to lower altitudes at higher latitudes, possibly are secondary heat source for ionosphere. Where ionospheric and radiation particles collide, ionospheric temperatures rise and F layers of ionosphere spread apart, causing radio waves to scatter. Results from *Ariel I* confirmed the ionospheric temperature relationship with latitude as detected by *Alouette I*. Solar x-ray detectors found solar flares are made up of two phases: (1) heating of sun's corona above sunspot, increasing x-ray flux by factor of 10; and (2) quiet period marked by flux leveling off at accelerated level, followed by streams of electrons pushed into chromosphere, causing x-ray emissions at 500 times greater than normal.

March 14: Dr. John Lindsay and William White, of Goddard Space Flight Center, reported that the *OSO I* satellite had found tentative evidence that solar flares may be preceded by series of microflares whose sequence and pattern may be predictable. *OSO I* reported at least four of these series during a year in orbit.

March 15: Dr. James A. Van Allen said that artificial radition belt caused by U.S. high-altitude nuclear test last July may last for 10 years. At GSFC's Scientific Satellite Symposium, Dr. Van Allen said data from *Injun III* and *Explorer XIV* satellites showed intensity at center of artificial belt had decreased only by a factor of two.

— Data from *Explorer XII* confirmed existence of low-energy proton current ringing earth in east-to-west direction, perpendicular to perpetual north-south spiraling motion along geomagnetic field lines.

— A contract was awarded to the Industrial Engineering Corp. for the construction of a Magnetic Range Control and Test Building and a Magnetic Instrument Test Laboratory at GSFC. The starting date was Apr. 3, 1963, with an estimated completion date of Oct. 1963.

March 19: Goddard Space Flight Center, in cooperation with NBC and RCA, accomplished first known transmission of television in color via *Relay I* communications satellite. Fifteen-minute sequence of movie "Kidnapped" was relayed by *Relay I* from 4,000-mile orbit, and was scheduled to be shown on Walt Disney's TV program on Mar. 24.

March 22: NASA announced *Relay I* communications satellite had achieved all its missions. Performance of *Relay I* included 500 communications tests and demonstrations in 660 orbits between Dec. 13, 1962–Mar. 11, 1964. Although all planned demonstrations were completed, more would be continued while the satellite remained in operation.

— Sixth Annual Robert H. Goddard Memorial Dinner, sponsored by the National Rocket Club, Washington, D.C. In an address, Vice President Lyndon B. Johnson paid tribute to the "father of modern rocketry." He said that those today who "understand the stakes of space" must help "the public to understand these stakes." He urged that communications barriers among scientists, engineers, and politicians be abolished so that public support for public policy can be obtained. "Unless and until this is done," said the Chairman of the National Aeronautics and Space Council, "the technological community cannot justifiably be impatient

Pictures of Italian Premier Fanfani's Chicago trip were transmitted to Europe via *Relay I*. This is a print from the television monitor in New Jersey.

1963 Continued

with those who are chosen to represent and express the public's own will."

—At GSFC Colloquium, Dr. John A. O'Keefe discussed the origin and evolution of the moon, submitting his theory that billions of years ago the moon separated from the still "undifferentiated earth," thereafter was subjected to volcanic eruptions, meteoroid bombardment, eventual cooling, and transformation into a hard cinder-like material. The volcanic dust produced the comparatively smooth lunar maria. If theory is correct, O'Keefe said, the original dust has long since become firm and constitutes "no hazard" for landings of space vehicles. O'Keefe supported his theory with available evidence on tektites.

March 25: Three major U.S. television networks each broadcast 7-minute programs from Paris to New York via *Relay I* communications satellite.

March 26: Dr. Fred S. Singer, Director of National Satellite Weather Center, told House Committee on Science and Astronautics' Subcommittee on Applications and Tracking and Data Acquisition that reports from Tiros weather satellites were being used by Soviet scientists in their weather research. Launching of a weather satellite "is probably an immediate Soviet objective."

March 28: Nike-Apache sounding rocket launched from NASA Wallops Station carried 65-pound instrumented payload to altitude of 100 miles, an experiment to measure electron density profile, electron temperatures, and solar radiation in the ionosphere. Secondary objective of the flight was to check out hardware to be flown from Ft. Churchill, Canada, during solar eclipse in July.

March 29: P–21A was launched from Wallops Island at 2:27 a.m. EST. Preliminary results showed that the ion trap was providing very good data.

During March: Canadian Government authorized four additional satellites for ionospheric research in joint U.S.-Canadian space program. Seven successful sounding rocket experiments were concluded.

April 3: NASA launched *Explorer XVII* (S–6) atmospheric structure satellite from Cape Canaveral, using Thor-Delta launch vehicle (its 16th consecutive success in 17 attempts). Under project management of NASA Goddard Space Flight Center, *Explorer XVII* was first scientific earth satellite to use new GSFC pulse-code-modulation telemetry system, a solid-state system providing output power of 500 milliwatts and capable of supplying 40 separate channels of information in digital form. Useful lifetime of the satellite was estimated at 2 to 3 months.

— Aerobee 150A rocket launched from NASA Wallops Station carried instrumented payload to 147-mile altitude in experiment to flight-test components of equipment for EOGO satellite and to measure propagation of VLF signals through ionosphere. Flight was joint project of Stanford Research Institute and GSFC.

April 7: The six winners of the third annual Federal Women's Award included Eleanor C. Pressly, Head of Vehicles Section, Spacecraft Integration and Sounding Rocket Division, NASA Goddard Space Flight Center. Miss Pressly was cited for her pioneer work in sounding rocket development and her "demonstrated organizational ability in scheduling and coordinating launchings of sounding rocket vehicles in support of upper atmospheric research." She developed the Aerobee Jr. sounding rocket, co-developed Aerobee-Hi 150, and directed improvement of Aerobee-Hi 150 A—all used extensively in IGY.

April 8: Attempt to launch two-stage Astrobee 1500 sounding rocket from NASA Wallops Station failed with first stage of the vehicle failing to perform properly. This was NASA's first attempt to launch the Astrobee; purpose of test was to evaluate the rocket's performance as a NASA test vehicle.

April 9: Televised White House ceremony, with President John F. Kennedy signing bill making Sir Winston Churchill an honorary citizen of the U.S., was transmitted to U.K. and continent via *Relay I* communications satellite. Broadcast was viewed by millions of Britons and Sir Winston himself, and both audio and visual reception were considered perfect.

— In its first few days of operation, *Ex-*

plorer XVII satellite had obtained data that more than tripled all previous direct measurements of the neutral gases in earth's upper atmosphere, it was announced. New communications system, utilizing special data readout station at GSFC, was providing scientific and technical data from the satellite within minutes of its transmission.

April 17: Five New Jersey newspapermen held first press conference through space, using *Relay I* communications satellite in 25-minute broadcast to Rio de Janeiro, Brazil. Photo of newsmen sent via *Relay I* during conference was of good quality, Rio officials said.

April 18: NASA launched 85-pound scientific payload to 208-mile altitude at exact moment *Explorer XVII* atmospheric structure satellite passed over the Wallops Island, Va., launch site, an unusual "first" in NASA sounding rocket program. Carried on an Aerobee 300A sounding rocket, experiment obtained temperature data on electron and neutral particles and measured ion and neutral particle densities. Data from this experiment would be compared with similar

data obtained from *Explorer XVII* as it passed over Wallops Island at 198-mile altitude during its 236th orbit of earth. Preliminary evaluation by GSFC scientists revealed data were of excellent quality. Data from *Explorer XVII* indicated the earth is surrounded by belt of neutral helium atoms, GSFC scientists said at American Geophysical Union meeting. Based on preliminary data received one day after launch, Goddard scientists said *Explorer XVII* atmospheric structure satellite had sent back more than 8 hours of scientific information on physics and chemistry of tenuous gases making up the earth's atmosphere.

— The 3-year milestone in the Tiros success story was officially recognized when the Tiros team received NASA's group achievement award in special ceremonies. Six-out-of-six successful Tiros launches had created an unmatched series of successes for this spacecraft. More than 220,000 cloud-cover pictures had been transmitted back to earth.

— A contract was awarded to Jack Bays, Inc., for the construction of an Anechoic Chamber at Goddard. The starting date

Relay engineers monitor program awarding U.S. citizenship to former Prime Minister Sir Winston Churchill. Segment above shows address by President John F. Kennedy, speaking at the White House ceremony, April 9, 1963.

1963 Continued

was May 10, 1963, with a scheduled completion date of Oct. 1963.

April 20: Preliminary test of instrumentation to be used in joint Italian-U.S. San Marco project was made by two-stage Shotput sounding rocket from Wallops Station; the rocket carried 180-pound instrumented payload to 265-mile altitude. Flight was first in three-phase project being conducted by Italian Commission for Space Research and NASA, to be followed by further tests of San Marco instrumentation with launching of Shotput vehicle from towable platform in Indian Ocean and to be culminated in launching of scientific satellite into equatorial orbit from the platform. Basic objective of San Marco project was to obtain high-altitude measurements of atmospheric and ionospheric characteristics in equatorial region. GSFC assisted in testing the spacecraft.

April 25: Relay I communications satellite was used to transmit electroencephalograms ("brain waves") from Bristol, England, to Minneapolis, Minn., in demonstration experiment conducted in connection with meeting of National Academy of Neurology in Minneapolis.

During April: NASA awarded 4-month study contracts for a synchronous meteorological satellite to Radio Corp. of America and Hughes Aircraft.

May 1: A contract was awarded to the Norair Construction Co. for the construction of GSFC's Building No. 14, Spacecraft Operations Building. The starting date was May 11 with a scheduled completion date of May 15, 1964.

May 3: The Documentation Branch was established in the GSFC Technical Information Division to provide support in writing and publishing documents.

— The Telescopic Systems Section was established in the Astrophysics Branch of the Space Sciences Division at GSFC. The former Detector Section in the Astrophysics Branch was retitled as the Planetary Optics Section.

May 7: Telstar II communications satellite placed in elliptical orbit (6,717-mile apogee, 604-mile perigee, 225.3-mile period, 42.7° inclination to equator). Thor-Delta vehicle launched from Cape Canaveral boosted the satellite into orbit for its 17th straight success, an unmatched record for U.S. satellite-launching vehicles.

May 9: Sen. Margaret Chase Smith (R.-Me.) and NASA Administrator James E. Webb were co-hosts at Senate luncheon for three women accorded national recognition for space age accomplishments—Marcia S. Miner, student at American Univ. and winner of National Rocket Club's 1963 Goddard Memorial Scholarship Award; Dr. Nancy C. Roman, Chief of Astronomy and Solar Physics in NASA Geophysics and Astronomy Program and 1962 winner of Federal Women's Award; and Eleanor C. Pressly, Head of Vehicles Section, Sounding Rocket Branch, in NASA Goddard Space Flight Center's Spacecraft Integration and Sounding Rocket Division, and 1963 winner of Federal Women's Award.

May 16: L. Gordon Cooper completed 22 earth orbits in 34-hour MA–9 space flight. The Goddard-operated Mercury tracking network with 19 stations functioned perfectly, providing "real-time" tracking throughout the entire mission. Final project Mercury flight.

— The launch of two Nike-Cajuns at Wallops Island on this date successfully concluded the series of three cooperative U.S.-Japanese ionospheric experiments. Much useful information was obtained.

May 20: Two-stage sounding rocket instrumented to observe ionosphere was successfully launched to 215-mile altitude by Japanese scientists near Kagoshima, Japan.

May 23: Sodium-vapor experiment to measure high-altitude winds and diffusion rates was launched on Nike-Apache sounding rocket from Wallops Island, Va. Sodium vapor trail, ejected from 27- to 127-mile altitudes, was visible for several hundred miles from launch site.

May 28: GSFC Procurement and Supply Division, Office of Administration, was reorganized and retitled Procurement Division. The former Management Services Division, Office of Administration, was reorganized and retitled Management Services and Supply Division.

May 31: As of this date, Goddard Space Flight Center had on board 38 employees in excepted positions, 2,833 employees in Classification Act positions, and 250 Wage Board employees. In addition, 14 military personnel were assigned to the Center.

During May: Six successful sounding rocket projects were carried out. These included aeronomy, ionospheric physics, and test and support experiments.

June 3 to 11: On June 5, Goddard Space Flight Center offered world scientists the design of small rocket payload and ground telemetry station suitable for ionospheric research. GSFC scientists Siegfried J. Bauer and John E. Jackson said payload's "versatility, simplicity and relatively low cost should make it an ideal tool for the investigation of the many problems of the ionosphere by the international scientific community, especially during the IQSY (International Year of the Quiet Sun).

June 7 to 16: Goddard satellites were exhibited at the Paris International Air Show. French President Charles de Gaulle spent some time at the display and expressed deep interest in it. In the United States pavilion at the show was the most complete presentation of present and future space programs ever assembled under one roof. It included a prototype of *OSO I.*

June 14: Goddard Space Flight Center announced series of sounding rocket tests had confirmed association of Sporadic-E disturbances with presence of wind shears in altitude regions measured Nov. 7, Nov. 30, and Dec. 5, 1962. Under NASA contract, Geophysics Corp. of America scientists measured velocity of wind movements (using Nike-Apache rockets with sodium vapor trails) and ionospheric phenomena (using Nike-Cajun with Langmuir probe electrical equipment) at nearly the same time. Experiments confirmed theory of Australian scientist J. D. Whitehead that action of upper atmosphere wind pulls electrons from above and below into thin cloud-like layers, causing Sporadic-E layers that often interfere with radio signals being reflected off higher F layer of ionosphere.

June 19: Tiros VII (A–52) meteorological satellite placed in orbit with Thor-Delta launch vehicle launched from Cape Canaveral. On satellite's first orbit, command and data acquisition station at Wallops Island, Va., obtained direct pictures from Camera 2 showing cloud vortex over Newfoundland and set Camera 1 to read out pictures on next orbit. First pictures were transmitted within one hour to Cape Canaveral, Fla.; GSFC; and National Weather Satellite Center, Suitland, Md. In addition to two wide-angle TV cameras, *Tiros VII* carried infrared sensors and electron temperature probe. Orbiting marked 18th straight successful satellite orbiting by Thor-Delta launch vehicles.

June 21: U.S. television audiences witnessed first public appearance of Pope Paul VI via Relay communications satellite.

June 29: The University Building at Adelphi, Maryland, leased by GSFC, was partially occupied by the Space Flight Support Division, Office of Tracking and Data Systems.

July 2: A 50-pound payload of ionosphere measuring instruments was launched with Argo D–4 sounding rocket from Wallops Station, Va., into orbital path of *Alouette I* satellite. Preliminary data indicated measurements were made in upper ionosphere within 2 minutes of soundings taken from *Alouette I.* Payload reached peak altitude of 590 miles. Purpose of experiment was to obtain measurements of ion and electron temperatures and densities; data from payload instruments would be compared with similar data transmitted simultaneously by *Alouette I.*

July 3: With President John F. Kennedy's return to Washington from Europe, NASA communications satellite *Relay I* marked end of its busiest programing period. *Relay I* was "booked solid" during past weeks to cover the President's trip, death of Pope John XXIII, and election of Pope Paul VI. During its 6 months of operation, *Relay I* had been used for 85 public communications demonstrations, including transmission of television, voice, radiophoto, and teletype.

July 9: A 164-pound payload sent to 127-mile altitude with Aerobee 150A sounding rocket from NASA Wallops Station in experiment to obtain nighttime electromagnetic noise and

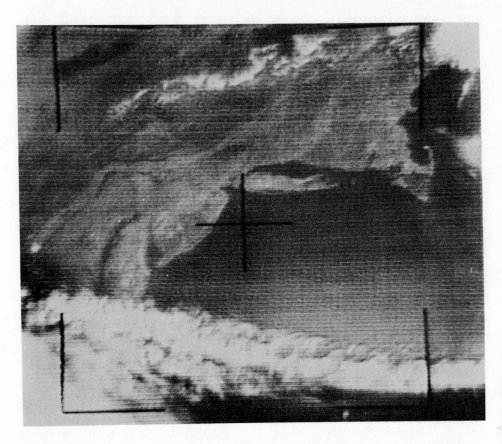

Tiros VII photograph showing cloud-free view of U.S. eastern seaboard from well above Cape Cod to below Chesapeake Bay, June 23, 1963.

1963 Continued

propagation data. Included in payload were three sweeping receivers and a broad-band receiver of the type to be included in EOGO satellite (Eccentric Orbiting Geophysical Observatory) next year. Preliminary telemetry evaluation indicated all experiment objectives were met.

July 19: The former GSFC Communications Branch Spacecraft Systems and Projects Division of the Office of Space Science and Satellite Applications was reorganized and retitled as the Communications Satellite Research Branch. A new branch was established in the Spacecraft Systems and Projects Division and titled Communications Satellite Branch.

July 20: Eclipse of the sun was visible across Canada and northeastern U.S. NASA joined other scientists and astronomers in scientific studies during the eclipse, with emphasis on ionosphere and on sun's corona.

— At Churchill Research Range, USAF OAR facility located at Ft. Churchill, Canada, six Nike-Apache sounding rockets equipped with instruments to measure electron density, electron temperature, and solar radiation in ultraviolet and x-ray regions, were launched for GSFC; Aerobee 150 sounding rocket equipped with spectrophotometric instruments to measure absolute intensity of spectral features in ultraviolet region was launched for Johns Hopkins University; and Canadian Black Brant sounding rocket with instruments to measure variations in D and E layers of ionosphere was launched for USAF Cambridge Research Laboratories. GSFC and AFCRL scientists said preliminary results indicated collected data confirmed previous predictions of composition of the ionosphere.

— At Pleasant Pond, Me., Luc Secretan and Francois V. Dossin of GSFC photographed eclipse with specially made instrument for photographing stars and comets near the sun.

July 26: Syncom II communications satellite was launched into orbit with Thor-Delta launch vehicle from AMR, entering elliptical orbit (140-mile perigee, 22,548-mile apogee). Five hours 33 minutes after launching,

Luc Secretan and Francois V. Dossin with their special instrument that photographed the eclipse of the sun at Pleasant Pond, Me., July 20, 1963.

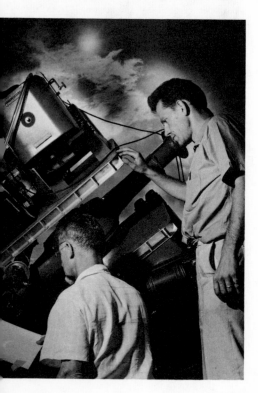

apogee kick motor on board fired for 21 seconds, placing *Syncom II* in orbital path ranging from 22,300-mile to 22,548-mile altitude and adjusting its speed to near-synchronous 6,800 mph. Traveling in slightly lower than synchronous orbit and at less than synchronous speed, satellite began drifting eastward at rate of 7.5° per day. Ground signals would attempt to reverse drifting so that satellite would attain synchronous position over Brazil.

— A contract was let to Kalmia Construction Co., Inc., Silver Spring, Md., to alter Goddard's Data Acquisition and Communications Center building for the installation of a microwave antenna. The contract called for a supporting structure, an equipment room, and a cooling tower enclosure for the antenna.

August 2: Sweden successfully launched U.S. Army Nike-Cajun rocket from Kronogård rocket range in test to explore "bright night clouds."

— Schedule of funding for the Goddard Space Flight Center for FY 1964 and previous years was released:

	Inception through FY 1963	FY 1964 Program
	(thousands of dollars)	
Construction of facilities:		
On-site:		
Buildings _____	$35,123.5	
Equipment _____	25,614.3	
Total on-site authorized __	60,737.8	$20,932.0
Portion Completed and occupied _____	37,091.0	
Off-site:		
All sites _____	44,610.2	
Transfer to NASA from Vanguard Project _____	13,000.0	
Total off-site authorized __	57,610.2	111,600.0
Portion completed and operational (includes Vanguard transfer)	40,821.2	
Research, development, and operations:		
Direct allotments ___		492,286.0

1963 Continued

Anticipated reimbursements _____	56,350.5
Total R, D, and O _____	548,636.5
Total GSFC FY 1964 Program	681,168.5

On-board personnel—8/2/63, 3,629 (including 332 summer employees).

— The second San Marco suborbital flight unit was successfully launched from Wallops Island to an altitude of 155 nautical miles and a surface distance of 560 nautical miles. GSFC was assisting in testing this Italian space project.

August 4: First public demonstration of communications exchange via synchronous satellite, when two U.S. wire services and Nigerian newsmen exchanged news stories via *Syncom II* communications satellite, hovering 22,823 miles over Western Africa. Photographs of President Kennedy and Nigerian Governor General Dr. Nnamdi Azikiwe also were exchanged. Transmissions were made from NASA station at Lakehurst, N.J., and USNS *Kingsport* communications ship in Lagos Harbor, Nigeria.

August 5: NASA announced *Syncom II* communications satellite, now drifting westward over Atlantic Ocean at 22,800-mile altitude, would be stopped when it reached desired position at 55° west longitude. At this location *Syncom II* would be lowered into precise synchronous orbit, so it would appear to trace elongated figure-eight pattern along 55° meridian to points 33° north and south to the equator.

August 6: Tracking and data acquisition operations ceased for *OSO I* (Orbiting Solar Observatory), launched March 7, 1962.

August 8: With launching of Nike-Cajun sounding rocket from Kronogård Range, Sweden and U.S. completed series of sounding rocket experiments to study noctilucent clouds near Arctic Circle. Sponsored by NASA and Swedish Committee for Space Research, program included launchings of Arcas rockets with payloads to measure winds and Nike-Cajun rockets with payloads to make direct cloud samplings during 1961 and 1962. Four Nike-Cajun rockets with rocket grenade payloads were successfully launched during summer 1963, these experiments measuring upper atmosphere temperatures, wind pressure and density, and measuring changes in size of artificial cloud particles created by smoke puffs from the payloads. Experimenters were scientists from Institute of Meteorology, University of Stockholm; GSFC had responsibility for U.S. coordination in the project.

August 9: Voice and teletype messages exchanged via *Syncom II* communications satellite between ground station at Paso Robles, Calif., and communications ship,

On August 4 this picture of Nigerian Governor General Nnamdi Azikiwe was transmitted via *Syncom II* satellite.

Kingsport, in Lagos Harbor, Nigeria. The test spanned 7,700 miles, greatest surface distance ever spanned between two points on earth via a communications satellite.

— The *Explorer XIV* encoder hung up in a 4-channel (8, 9, 10, and 11) mode of operations. It had completed 310 days of operation with only 15 days of major malfunction.

— The transition of the *Relay I* spacecraft into 100 percent sunlight occurred. Some anomalies were observed but no significant difficulties occurred.

August 11: Tiros VI and VII meteorological satellites observed Hurricane Arlene approximately 600 miles northeast of Bermuda, Typhoon Bess approximately 100 miles west of Japan, and Typhoon Carmen approximately 500 miles east of the Philippine Islands.

August 12: The Program Support Division was established in the Office of Administration. Functions of the Financial Management Analysis Branch were transferred to the Procurement Division. The Business Data Procurement Branch was reconstructed and redesignated as the Business Data Branch. The Reports and Statistics Branch and the Systems Review Branch were established in the Financial Management Division.

August 15: Syncom II communications satellite was successfully maneuvered into synchronous position 55° west longitude, over Brazil and South Atlantic Ocean. The maneuvers were directed by engineers at GSFC, and actual command was executed from ground station at Lakehurst, N.J. *Syncom II* was now stationed about 22,300-mile altitude and traveling at speed of about 6,800 mph, matching earth's rotation speed of 1,040 mph at the equator to keep it on station. It was hovering in figure-eight pattern 33° north and south of equator. NASA Administrator James E. Webb called completion of the positioning maneuvers the culmination of "one of the outstanding feats in the history of space flight."

August 21: The GSFC Sounding Rocket Branch reported that 61 rockets had been fired this year to date. Of this total eight were in the Meteorology Program.

August 23: U.S.-Canada agreement for cooperative testing of communications satellites launched by NASA was announced by NASA and Canada's Department of Transport. Each cooperating national agency would provide a ground station to receive and transmit television and multichannel telephone and telegraphic signals via communications satellites, according to Memorandum of Understanding signed in April and made operative by exchange of notes today.

— *Syncom II* communications satellite relayed its first live telephone conversations, a transmission between President John F. Kennedy and Nigerian Prime Minister Sir Abubaker Tafawa Balewa and other messages between U.S., Nigerian, and U.N. officials. Arranged by USIA, the demonstration program originated from the White House and Voice of America studios in Washington and from ground station aboard USNS *Kingsport* in Lagos Harbor, Nigeria.

September 3: The Alaska Data Acquisition Facility near Anchorage began limited operations by interrogating *Tiros VI* for two orbits. Performance was satisfactory except for some interference on 235 Mc from the command transmission.

— GSFC announced Belgian astrophysicist Dr. Francois V. Dossin, working at GSFC on National Academy of Sciences fellowship, discovered faint comet about 5° from sun during July 20 solar eclipse. Dr. Dossin made seven camera-plate exposures of comet from Pleasant Pond, Me., during 60 seconds of total eclipse. He used blue-green filter to bring out the light of carbon molecules in the comet. Microscopic examination of developed plates showed a diffuse image emitting the light of molecular carbon.

September 4: An Aerobee sounding rocket containing the low energy cosmic ray heavy nuclei experiment was launched from Fort Churchill. Experiment and performance reported good.

— Aerobee 150 sounding rocket launched from Ft. Churchill, Canada, with nuclear emulsion payload to study very-low-energy cosmic ray heavy nuclei. Payload reached 150-mile altitude, was recovered from an inland lake approximately 90 miles from

1963 Continued

launch site. Instrumentation and nuclear emulsions were in excellent condition.

— Construction work on the penthouse on Building 3 to house the AT&T equipment was begun.

— The former Fields and Particles Branch, Space Sciences Division, was reorganized and retitled the Energetic Particles Branch. A new Branch, the Fields and Plasmas Branch, was established in the Space Sciences Division.

September 5: Syncom II communications satellite achieved perfect synchronous orbit.

September 10: The German Transportable Ground Station began to receive *Relay I* pointing data and operational traffic.

September 13: Syncom I and Relay I linked Rio de Janeiro and Lagos, Nigeria, in 20-minute voice conversation, first operation employing both communications satellites in single communications circuit and world's first three-continent telephone conversation. Signal began from USNS *Kingsport* in Lagos Harbor, then to *Syncom I*, which sent it to Lakehurst, N.J., ground station, then to *Relay I* overhead which sent it to Rio de Janeiro ground station. GSFC engineers monitoring the conversation declared quality of transmission to be good.

September 14: U.S.-Scandinavia approval of Memorandum of Understanding for testing of NASA-launched experimental communications satellites was announced by NASA and Scandinavian Committee for Satellite Telecommunication. Vice President Lyndon B. Johnson, on official tour of Scandinavia, received in Copenhagen the Danish Government's note of approval, making the Memorandum effective; Norway had approved Memorandum in note dated September 11 and Sweden, in note dated July 25. Under agreement, Scandinavian Committee would provide ground station to receive multichannel telephone or telegraph signals transmitted from U.S. via orbiting communications satellite.

September 15: Third command and data acquisition station in Tiros meteorological satellite CDA system became operational, the Fairbanks, Alaska, station joining those at Wallops Island, Va., and Pt. Mugu, Calif. CDA stations receive cloud-cover photographs and other data from orbiting Tiros satellites, and relay them to Weather Bureau's National Weather Satellite Center, Suitland, Md., for analysis.

September 17: Opening of U.N. General Assembly transmitted via *Relay I* and *Syncom II* to Europe and Africa.

September 18: First anniversary of orbiting of *Tiros VI* meteorological satellite, its year-long operational lifetime setting new record for weather satellites. On July 31, 1963, *Tiros VI* discovered first hurricane (Arlene) of 1963 season in tropical Atlantic; altogether, *Tiros VI* photographed two hurricanes in Atlantic, two tropical storms in eastern Pacific, eight typhoons in central and western Pacific, as well as sandstorms in Saudi Arabia and ice conditions in southern and northern hemispheres. Along with *Tiros V* it supported Mercury space flights of Astronauts Schirra and Cooper. National Weather Satellite Center issued about 600 weather advisories around the world based on some of the 63,000 cloud-cover pictures from *Tiros VI*.

— Goddard Space Flight Center selected two companies for negotiation of contracts pertaining to Nimbus weather satellite. $252,000 contract to General Electric Company called for development of operating procedures for Nimbus control center as well as training of personnel to operate the center. $165,000 contract to RCA Electron Tube and Semiconductor Division required contractor to furnish solar cells for Nimbus satellites and Nimbus operational system.

September 19: The following offices were established in the GSFC Tracking and Data Systems Directorate: the Systems Analysis Office, the Manned Flight Support Office, The Project Resources Office, and the Directorate Support Office. At the Division level, parts of the Tracking Systems Division and the Space Data Acquisition Division were merged and named Advanced Development Division. The Data Systems Division was expanded with the addition of telemetry and data processing from the Space Data Acquisition Division and the Operations and Support Division and retitled the Network Engineering and Operations Division.

The former Manned Space Flight Support Division was renamed Manned Flight Operations Division.

— *Syncom II* 24-hour communications satellite used to relay oceanographic data from research vessel *Geronimo* in Gulf of Guinea off Africa to National Oceanographic Data Center in Washington, which compared the data with its records and sent back to the *Geronimo* the deviations to correct errors. Demonstration via *Syncom II* was performed to determine practicability of providing research ships quickly with information to correct errors. Line of transmission: from *Geronimo* to *Kingsport* in Lagos Harbor, to *Syncom II* some 22,300 miles above Atlantic Ocean, to ground station at Lakehurst, N.J., along ground lines to NODC, and return.

September 20: President John F. Kennedy's speech to the United Nations General Assembly was transmitted to the USNS *Kingsport* via Syncom for further broadcast over the Voice of America network in Nigeria.

September 21: Tiros VII meteorological satellite discovered Hurricane Debra, fourth hurricane of season, headed north in Atlantic southeast of Bermuda.

September 23: Syncom II communications satellite relayed transmission of speech and teletype between Fort Dix, N.J., and moving USNS *Kingsport* about 40 miles west of Lagos, Nigeria. This was first such transmission via a communications satellite to a moving ship at sea. This was first in series of experiments designed to test shipboard equipment and reception in fringe areas.

September 25: Two similar experiments (one built by U.S., the other by Japan), were launched aboard an Aerobee 150 sounding rocket from Wallops Island. The purpose of the experiments was to make simultaneous measurements in the ionosphere by different methods and then to compare the data obtained. Instruments were supplied by GSFC and the Radio Research Laboratory, Tokyo, Japan. The Japanese scientists' radio-frequency resonance probe was designed to make it possible to measure electron density and temperature simultaneously with one instrument and to process

the data faster. The Aerobee reached a peak altitude of 139 statute miles; it impacted in the Atlantic Ocean 80 miles from launch site after 8 minutes of flight. Preliminary data indicated that the experiment succeeded.

September 26: Hurricane Edith was observed between Hispaniola and Puerto Rico by *Tiros VII.* Hurricane Flora was also picked up by this satellite.

— Operations with the *Relay I* satellite continued with successful completion of all scheduled experiments. The spacecraft operations as of this date, for 2,227 orbit revolutions, were: 1,107 wideband experiments; 519 narrowband experiments; 99 demonstrations (TV and narrowband). The transponder had been operated for 225 hours over a period of 560 operations.

— NASA announced first television experiments via *Syncom II* communications satellite had been conducted. Test pattern signals sent Sept. 23 were followed by TV pictures Sept. 24 and 25; because of band-width limitations, no audio was sent. Officials said transmissions were of good quality. Transmissions originated at Fort Dix, N.J., ground station, were sent to *Syncom II* 22,300 miles above the earth, and retransmitted to AT&T ground station at Andover, Me.

September 27: Explorer XIV satellite progress report indicated no usable scientific data had been obtained from the scientific satellite since mid-August. In its 10 months of operation since launch into highly elliptical orbit Oct. 2, 1962, *Explorer XIV* sent back more than 6,500 hours of data from the six onboard scientific experiments to chart boundaries of earth's magnetosphere, measure particle population and energies of electrons and protons, and determine how magnetic fields influence these particles. There had been 3,700 hours of data processed through computers and scientific analysis was continuing.

September 28: Aerobee 150A sounding rocket launched from NASA Wallops Station with U.S.-Japanese experiment to measure electron temperatures and densities in the ionosphere by two different methods; Langmuir probe, supplied by NASA Goddard Space Flight Center, and radio-frequency

1963 Continued

resonance probe, developed by Radio Research Laboratory, Tokyo. A 185-pound payload reached 141-mile altitude and transmitted approximately 8 minutes of telemetry before impacting in Atlantic Ocean about 71 miles from launch site. Data obtained from the daytime experiment were compared with data from similar experiment conducted at night, 3 days earlier.

September 29: An Argo D-4 was launched. Based on plotting board information, it achieved an altitude of 1,038 kilometers. Telemetry signals were received for 12 minutes and all experiments functioned normally.

— At the end of the first year of operation of *Alouette I,* all four experiments were performing very well and continued to provide good data. No problems had been encountered in commanding the satellite or in recording of the telemetry transmissions.

October 1: NASA marked its fifth anniversary, with a salute to 23 individuals whose outstanding personal efforts have contributed significantly to the nation's civilian space program. Among cash awards was a $1,500 award to Jesse M. Madley and Xopher W. Mayer at GSFC for the invention of a structural spacer.

October 1 to 3: Youth Science Congress, sponsored by NASA and the National Science Teachers Association, was held at GSFC. Feature event was presentation of 25 award-winning research papers of high school students from Washington, D.C., Maryland, Delaware, Pennsylvania, and New Jersey.

October 8: Explorer XIV energetic particles satellite had ceased useful transmission after almost 10 months of successful operation. Scientists at GSFC said trouble began in August when the satellite's transmitter failed to modulate—translate instrument signals into telemetry code—properly. Intermittent modulation had occurred since then, but little useful data had been received. The satellite signal was still useful for position reference. Some 6,500 hours of data were received from the satellite. While not all the data had been analyzed, Dr. L. Cahill, Univ. of New Hampshire, said a number of new insights had already emerged, among them being: earth's magnetosphere, as shown by mapping charged particles, flared away from the earth in an ogival—pointed arch—shape; confirmation that the vector

The Rosman, N.C., tracking facility.

magnetic field changes gently from a dipole configuration to a radial field at increasing distance on the night side of the earth near the equatorial plane; and further evidence probably supporting *Explorer VI's* finding of a ring current flow on the night side of the earth.

October 9: As of this date, the *Relay I* satellite had continued with successful completion of a majority of the scheduled experiments. Its operations covered 2,334 orbit revolutions with 1,132 wideband experiments; 54 narrowband experiments; 99 demonstrations (TV and narrowband). The transponder had been operated for 234 hours over a period of 582 operations.

October 11: Syncom II operation in orbit remained satisfactory. The N_2 system and H_2O_2 system pressures remained the same. There was no perceptible change in these parameters for the last several weeks. The satellite spin speed continued to decrease.

—*Tiros VI* acquired its last usable pictures, after 338 days of useful life.

October 17: The *Relay I* spacecraft operations as of Oct. 17, for 2,389 orbit revolutions, were as follows: 1,151 wideband experiments; 553 narrowband experiments; 100 demonstrations (TV and narrowband). The transponder had been operated for 239 hours over a period of 593 operations.

October 22: GSFC began negotiations with Republic Aviation Corp. for Phase I contract for Advanced Orbiting Solar Observatory (AOSO). AOSO would be launched into a 300-mile near-polar orbit for observations of x-rays, gamma rays, and ultraviolet emissions of the sun. Phase I calls for one-year development of systems engineering and detailed design of the satellite.

October 26: The Rosman, N.C., tracking and data acquisition facility was dedicated. A key station in NASA's Satellite Tracking and Data Acquisition Network (STADAN), the 85-foot-diameter parabolic antenna at Rosman would be used to track and receive the large flow of telemetered data from the large orbiting observatories and would relay the data to GSFC for processing and analysis.

October 30: Symposium on the Physics of Solar Flares was held at GSFC, sponsored by NASA and the American Astronomical Society.

— *Syncom II* operation in orbit remained satisfactory. The orbital elements were:

Epoch 22 October 1963 _ 0200.00 hours UT
Semi-major axis _____ 26,204.11 miles
Eccentricity _____ 0.00026
Inclination _____ 32.993°
R.A. of ascending node _ 316.603°
Height of perigee _____ 22,233.97 miles
Height of apogee _____ 22,247.58 miles
Anomalistic period _____ 1,436.3957 min.

All telemetry indicated that the 10 instruments aboard the 128-pound satellite were functioning normally.

October 31: A second Aerobee-Hi research rocket in the NASA-French joint program investigating propagation of very-low-frequency waves in the ionosphere was launched from Wallops Station. The 193-pound payload went to an altitude of 115 miles and yielded 7 minutes of telemetry data before impact. The first experiment in this series was conducted on October 17, 1963.

November 1: GSFC awarded contract to Yale Univ. to design and develop a worldwide radio monitoring network for study of planet Jupiter. Four stations would comprise the global network, located at approximately every 90° longitude around the earth—one at GSFC in Greenbelt, Md., and the other three at U.S. satellite tracking stations at Hartesbeesthoek, South Africa; Carnarvon, Australia; and South Point, Hawaii. Primary duty of the stations would be to maintain a 24-hour radio monitor of the mysterious low-frequency radio noises sporadically emitted from the planet. The data should provide information on Jupiter's magnetosphere, the interplanetary medium, and the earth's ionosphere.

November 7: French VLF project: The second Aerobee in the French VLF program launched from Wallops Island Oct. 31, was successful. The experimenter, Dr. Owen Story, indicated in a preliminary appraisal that the data were of excellent quality. The monitoring circuit operated as anticipated. Both firings occurred during periods of ionospheric disturbances due to solar

Artist's conception of Relay mission received in Japan.

1963 Continued

flare activity. This was expected to complicate reduction of the data.

November 8: West Germany joined the list of nations participating in satellite communications with the opening of its narrowband station at Raisting, near Munich. A wideband station to permit television transmission was under construction. Raisting became the seventh station in the satellite communications network. Other narrowband stations were at Nutley, N.J., Rio de Janeiro, Brazil; Fucino, Italy. Wideband stations were at Andover, Me.; Goonhilly Downs, U.K.; and Pleumeur-Bodou, France.

November 21: GSFC announced that with a $2 million contract, under final negotiation, Sperry Rand Corp.'s Univac Div. would deliver 11 Model 1218 computer systems to manned space flight tracking stations for operation by July 1964. These computers would automatically summarize telemetry from the spacecraft, provide summaries for display in the Mission Control Center so that the controllers can select and examine certain data on a "real-time" basis, and prepare the telemetry data for final processing in the more elaborate computers at GSFC and MSC. During the Mercury program, controllers at the tracking stations had to select data manually. The computers would be located at Cape Canaveral; Bermuda; Canary Islands; Corpus Christi, Tex.; Guaymas, Mexico; Carnarvon, Australia; Wallops Island, Va.; Greenbelt, Md.; and on two ships used in manned space flight tracking, the *Rose Knot Victory* and the *Coastal Sentry Quebec.*

—First rocket to be launched from India was achieved as the result of the coordinated efforts of France, India, and the U.S. The Nike-Apache was launched from

Thumba, the site near the southern tip of India that would become an international rocket launching facility. The Thumba site is located at the earth's magnetic equator, making possible the investigation of important phenomena which could be studied to a greater advantage from this region.

November 22: The first live American television transmission across the Pacific by means of *Relay I* communications satellite was received clearly in Tokyo. Pictures transmitted by the Mojave ground station in California and received at the new Space Communications Laboratory in Ibaraki Prefecture, north of Tokyo, were clear and distinct. The sound transmission was excellent. The transmission was received live from 5:16 a.m. to 5:46 a.m. Viewers in Tokyo saw and heard taped messages from Ryuji Takeuchi, Japanese Ambassador to Washington, and James E. Webb, Administrator of the National Aeronautics and Space Administration. A message of greeting from President John F. Kennedy to the Japanese people, which was to have been the highlight of the program, was deleted when news of the President's death was received shortly before the transmission. In place of the taped 2½-minute appearance of the President, viewers saw brief panoramic views of the Mojave transmitting station and the surrounding desert area. ABC and NBC shared in producing the program.

—A solar array characteristics test was run on the orbiting *Syncom II* synchronous-orbit communications satellite. The test found a power loss of 20 percent from the effects of solar radiation on the solar cells during 4 months in orbit. The test confirmed the desirability of changing the next Syncom satellite.

November 25: President John F. Kennedy was buried in Arlington National Cemetery in a state funeral attended by the largest gathering of foreign dignitaries ever to visit Washington. *Relay I* communications satellite enabled all of Europe, including the U.S.S.R., to view events of the tragic weekend and the funeral ceremonies. The satellite also provided transmission across the Pacific to Japan, where an estimated 95 million persons viewed the ceremonies.

November 27: Explorer XVIII, first of a series of Interplanetary Monitoring Platforms (IMP) to map magnetic fields of space and the effects of solar winds and cosmic rays on the earth's atmosphere, was launched.

—GSFC's Field Projects Branch launched their first Atlas-Centaur. The booster, a new experimental hydrogen fuel 2d-stage rocket for deep space work, was launched from pad 36–A, Cape Kennedy, atop an Atlas 1st stage.

November 29: GSFC announced negotiations with Northrop Electronics for design and construction of a test device to simulate the launch phase of space flight. Final negotiations are expected to lead to a contract estimated at $1,800,000. Called a Launch Phase Simulator (LPS), the device would test unmanned space-flight units and components under the separate or combined conditions of acceleration, vibration, noise, and vacuum. It is designed to duplicate, as nearly as possible, the environmental conditions typical of current launch vehicles.

December 2: House Joint Resolution 787 was submitted to Congress providing for the erection of a memorial statue to the late Dr. Robert H. Goddard, the father of American rocketry.

—Nike-Cajun was launched from Wallops for the "falling sphere" experiment and consisted of ejecting three balloons which were tracked by radar. Data correlation between these two experiments was studied.

December 9: 350 representatives of 55 aerospace firms were briefed on GSFC's requirements for a new "Unified S-Band" method for tracking and communications for Apollo lunar missions.

December 11: On Dec. 11 and Dec. 13 the GSFC Data Operations Branch supported SA–5 network simulations. The nominal SA–5 launch and orbital phase were simulated in real-time using data tapes from the sites. These tapes were generated using the SA–5 nominal insertion conditions. The real-time computing program which reflects the operational Apollo launch and near-earth orbit determination program worked well. This was the first time the three networks, SAO, STADAN, and Manned Flight Networks, were simultaneously controlled from

View of the Space Communications Laboratory, Ibaraki, Japan.

1963 Continued

Goddard. The first simulation served as a training session for the development of standard operating procedures to control all three networks. The second simulation ran very smoothly.

December 18: The final static inflation test with *Echo II* balloon No. 16 was successfully conducted by NASA at Lakehurst, N.J. The balloon burst at a nominal skin stress level of 23,000 psi. Visual inspection of the inflated balloon indicated an improved balloon surface. This balloon was fabricated using the GSFC-developed gore cutting and sealing technique as well as preshrunk material. The balloon was pressurized to 3,400 psi nominal skin stress; relaxed to approximately 500 psi; pressurized to 7,400 psi, relaxed and then inflated to the burst pressure of 23,000 psi nominal skin stress. RF measurements at L-band and C-band were obtained for each of the test pressure levels.

—*Relay I* operations as of this date for 2,800 orbit revolutions were: 1,330 wideband experiments; 720 narrowband experiments; 157 demonstrations (TV and narrowband). The transponder had been operated for 288

Antenna at the Space Communications Laboratory, Ibaraki, Japan.

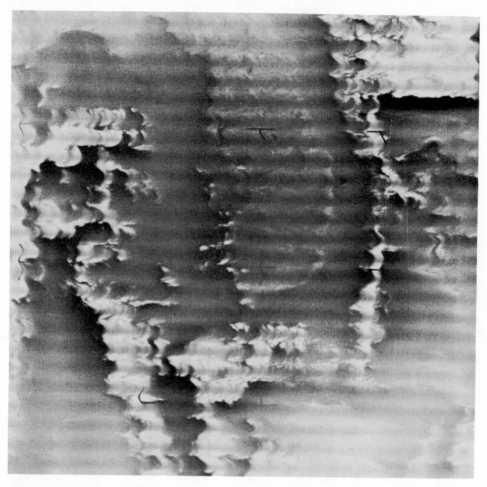

Tiros VIII: The experimental Automatic Picture Transmission camera beamed this photo from more than 400 miles in space to GSFC at 12:30 EST, December 21, 1963. Florida and the Gulf of Mexico are shown.

hours over a period of 720 operations. Since Oct. 1, 1963, 80 hours of radiation data had been taken by *Relay I*.

December 19: All major components of the Univac 490 communications switching system had been installed at the GSFC communications complex. Items remaining to be installed consisted of the Communications Line Terminations (CLT's) and two tape decks for the second system and system transfer switches.

December 21: Tiros VIII was launched at AMR. The satellite contained the first Automatic Picture Transmission camera, permitting rather "inexpensive" readouts at ground receiving stations. The APT system was developed for Nimbus, the advanced meteorological weather satellite.

December 30: Aviation Week and Space Technology magazine gave "Laurels for 1963 to Harry Goett, Jack Townsend, and Bob Gray of NASA's Goddard Space Flight Center for

1963 Continued

their excellent record (100 percent on eight launched in 1963) of successful satellite launchings and operations. This is the second consecutive year that all of Goddard's satellites were successful. . . ."

During December: The Italian Space Commission advised that it planned to ship the San Marco flight spacecraft to Goddard for the following tests: Minitrack compatibility tests at Blossom Point and dynamic balance procedures at the Center's test facilities. The spacecraft was then to be shipped to the Langley Center for mating checks with the vehicle.

—*Ariel I* radiated normal modulation for a 3-month period, Aug. 14 through Nov. 17. During this time, the percentage of sunlight varied between 75 and 63 percent. Good data were obtained for housekeeping and the electron temperature experiment. From Nov. 17, 1963, through Dec. 6, 1963, the percentage of sunlight was above 76 percent and abnormal modulation (an intermittent 312-cps signal) prevailed.

Appendix E

Reports of Procurement Actions 1960-1963

SUMMARY REPORT OF PROCUREMENT ACTIONS

For January 1, 1960, thru June 30, 1960

FROM: Goddard Space Flight Center*

TO: NASA Headquarters

NUMBER AND DOLLAR VALUE OF CONTRACT TRANSACTIONS

ACTIONS OVER $2500	Govt. Agency		Small business		Big business		Educational et al	
	No.	$ Value	No.	$ value	No.	$ value	No.	$ value
1. RESEARCH & DEVELOPMENT								
a. Negotiated			50	1,502,222	69	18,675,289	2	920,787
b. Interdepartmental	102	29,067,246						
Total	102	29,067,246	50	1,502,222	69	18,675,289	2	920,787
2. CONSTRUCTION								
a. Advertised			7	482,618	4	1,558,743		
b. Negotiated			11	199,950	4	94,551		
c. Interdepartmental	9	2,103,340						
Total	9	2,103,340	18	382,568	8	1,653,294	-	-
3. SUPPLY								
a. Advertised			9	202,392	7	54,839		
b. Negotiated			17	295,136	20	473,460		
c. Interdepartmental	67	4,585,142						
d. GSA schedule			4	19,486	11	60,844		
Total	67	4,585,142	30	517,014	38	589,143		
4. TOTAL ACTIONS OVER $2500	178	36,147,504	94	2,401,804	115	20,917,726	2	920,787
5. ALL ACTIONS NOT EXCEEDING $2500	75	40,311	856	343,607	450	259,956		

NASA Form 274 rev.   *This Report includes Space Task Group, Langley
(Jan. 1959)

YEARLY REPORT OF PROCUREMENT ACTIONS

NASA Installation GODDARD SPACE FLIGHT CENTER   FISCAL YEAR 1961

PART A: PROCUREMENT ACTIONS BY NASA APPROPRIATION

Category	Total		Research & Development		Construction & Equipment		Salaries & Expenses	
(a)	No. (b)	$ Value (c)	No. (d)	$ Value (e)	No. (f)	$ Value (g)	No. (h)	$ Value (i)
1. TOTAL	10723	188,420,999	10426	165,376,920	248	21,921,420	51	1,122,659
2. INTERGOVERNMENTAL	613	42,059,736	579	36,010,924	27	6,021,096	7	27,710
3. NONPROFIT INSTITUTION OR ORGANIZATION	176	2,697,931	173	2,022,181	2	675,000	1	750
4. SMALL BUSINESS - TOTAL	6482	14,466,277	6401	11,112,542	73	3,297,826	8	55,909
a. Advertised	594	1,735,627	554	581,835	40	1,153,792	-	-
b. Negotiated Competitive	2432	5,442,402	2417	3,986,711	15	1,630,696	-	-
c. Negotiated Non-Competitive	3369	7,158,330	3271	5,144,613	18	512,808	8	55,909
d. Government Schedule	159	129,918	159	129,918	-	-	-	-
5. LARGE BUSINESS - TOTAL	3432	129,197,061	3273	116,231,723	146	11,927,498	33	1,038,290
a. Advertised	169	5,591,609	77	399,565	92	5,192,044	-	-
b. Negotiated Competitive	887	64,284,021	875	61,988,687	12	2,295,334	-	-
c. Negotiated Non-Competitive	1889	57,942,090	1843	53,427,951	40	4,448,034	6	76,105
d. Government Schedule	507	1,379,341	559	415,070	2	2,086	27	962,185

PART B: NEGOTIATED PROCUREMENT ACTIONS

Negotiation Authority 10 U.S.C.	Number	$ Value	Negotiation Authority 10 U.S.C.	Number	$ Value
6. TOTAL	8681	137,524,774	2304(a) (9)		
2304(a) (1)	509	9,523,642	(10)	210	14,578,340
(2)			(11)	166	101,939,320
(3)	7738	3,735,543	(12)		
(4)	12	211,012	(13)		
(5)	14	2,436,764	(14)	29	4,725,153
(6)	3	375,000	(15)		
(7)			(16)		
(8)			(17)		

NASA FORM 508 (JUNE 1960)

YEARLY REPORT OF PROCUREMENT ACTIONS

NASA Installation __GODDARD SPACE FLIGHT CENTER__   FISCAL YEAR 1962

PART A: PROCUREMENT ACTIONS BY NASA APPROPRIATION

Category (a)	Total		Research & Development		Construction & Equipment		Salaries & Expenses	
	No. (b)	$ Value (c)	No. (d)	$ Value (e)	No. (f)	$ Value (g)	No. (h)	$ Value (i)
1. TOTAL	20717	209,292,154	20432	188,234,691	205	19,824,349	80	1,233,114
2. INTERGOVERNMENTAL	616	5,752,844	612	5,746,868	1	1,736	3	4,240
3. NONPROFIT INSTITUTION OR ORGANIZATION	188	13,209,413	183	12,456,011	2	744,980	3	8,422
4. SMALL BUSINESS - TOTAL	14436	23,299,070	14367	22,274,592	50	835,665	19	118,813
a. Advertised	252	3,194,931	232	2,909,887	17	244,332	3	40,712
b. Negotiated Competitive	3374	5,721,710	3362	5,645,711	11	75,201	1	798
c. Negotiated Non-Competitive	10370	13,676,111	10335	13,143,676	22	516,132	13	16,303
d. Government Schedule	440	636,318	438	575,318			2	61,000
5. LARGE BUSINESS - TOTAL	5477	167,100,827	5270	147,757,220	152	18,241,968	55	1,101,639
a. Advertised	517	7,039,954	428	4,626,221	88	2,410,733	1	3,000
b. Negotiated Competitive	1336	73,554,241	1308	66,829,131	17	6,401,550	11	323,560
c. Negotiated Non-Competitive	2874	82,281,111	2806	75,325,984	41	6,504,601	27	450,526
d. Government Schedule	750	4,225,521	728	975,884	6	2,925,084	16	324,553

PART B: NEGOTIATED PROCUREMENT ACTIONS

Negotiation Authority 10 U.S.C.	Number	$ Value	Negotiation Authority 10 U.S.C.	Number	$ Value
6. TOTAL	18,142	188,442,554	2304(a) (9)		
2304(a) (1)	736	15,934,895	(10)	853	42,056,080
(2)	12	625,380	(11)	235	103,911,638
(3)	16,192	7,683,152	(12)		
(4)	18	291,477	(13)		
(5)	59	8,897,255	(14)	16	4,144,396
(6)	20	4,895,388	(15)		
(7)			(16)		
(8)			(17)	17	2,893

NASA FORM 508 (JUNE 1960)

CORRECTED COPY

QUARTERLY REPORT OF PROCUREMENT ACTIONS (Use reverse for remarks)	FOR THE QUARTER ENDING July thru June FY '63	INCLUDES NASA FORM 507 REPORTS NOS. 63-1 / THRU. 63-1347
TO: Procurement and Supply Division Headquarters, NASA	FROM: (NASA Installation) Goddard Space Flight Center	

PART A - PROCUREMENT ACTIONS BY NASA APPROPRIATION

CATEGORY (a)	TOTAL NO. (b)	TOTAL $ VALUE (c)	RESEARCH DEVELOPMENT AND OPERATIONS NO. (d)	RESEARCH DEVELOPMENT AND OPERATIONS $ VALUE (e)	CONSTRUCTION OF FACILITIES NO. (f)	CONSTRUCTION OF FACILITIES $ VALUE (g)
1. TOTAL (Lines 2 thru 7)	30,477	303,506,335	30,333	286,272,935	144	17,233,400
2. INTRAGOVERNMENTAL	657	11,863,487	654	8,167,387	3	3,696,100
3. LARGE BUSINESS - TOTAL	8048	232,265,627	7968	220,984,570	80	11,281,057
a. Advertised	354	10,977,133	318	3,676,747	36	7,300,386
b. Negotiated Competitive	2050	116,527,557	2031	116,077,758	19	449,799
c. Negotiated Noncompetitive	5644	104,760,937	5619	101,230,065	25	3,530,872
4. SMALL BUSINESS - TOTAL	21,115	41,261,657	21,059	39,602,072	56	1,659,585
a. Advertised	493	7,399,117	470	6,647,832	23	751,285
b. Negotiated Competitive	4359	6,694,960	4351	6,401,434	8	293,526
c. Negotiated Noncompetitive	16,263	27,167,580	16,238	26,552,806	25	614,774
5. UNIVERSITIES	568	11,567,934	566	11,494,276	2	73,658
6. OTHER NONPROFIT INSTITUTIONS	52	162,170	52	162,170		
7. OUTSIDE U.S. & POSSESSIONS	37	6,385,460	34	5,862,460	3	523,000
8. SMALL BUSINESS SET ASIDES - TOTAL (included in line 4)	50	1,298,922	50	985,780	2	313,142
a. Individual Set Asides	50	1,298,922	50	985,780	2	313,142
b. Class Set Asides						

PART B - NEGOTIATED PROCUREMENT ACTIONS

NEGOTIATION AUTHORITY 10 U.S.C.	NO.	$ VALUE	NEGOTIATION AUTHORITY 10 U.S.C.	NO.	$ VALUE
9. TOTAL	28,973	273,266,598	2304(a) (9)		
2304(a) (1)	1257	12,856,686	(10)	2323	45,414,090
(2)	78	2,858,638	(11)	1396	166,536,433
(3)	21,494	9,737,867	(12)		
(4)	36	448,113	(13)		
(5)	567	11,193,496	(14)	21	4,669,876
(6)	43	6,735,026	(15)		
(7)			(16)		
(8)		—	(17)	1758	12,816,373

QUARTERLY REPORT OF PROCUREMENT ACTIONS *(Use reverse for remarks)*			FOR THE QUART. NDING 7/1/63 thru 6/30/64		INCLUDES NASA FORM 507	
					REPORTS NOS. 64-1	THRU. 64-1703

TO:　Procurement and Supply Division　　　　　　FROM: *(NASA Installation)*
　　　Headquarters, NASA　　　　　　　　　　　　Goddard Space Flight Center SS/SA/T&D/FS/IS

CATEGORY (a)	TOTAL		RESEARCH DEVELOPMENT AND OPERATIONS		CONSTRUCTION OF FACILITIES	
	NO. (b)	$ VALUE (c)	NO. (d)	$ VALUE (e)	NO. (f)	$ VALUE (g)
1. TOTAL *(Lines 2 thru 7)*	32,922	370,142,643	28,767	306,687,437	212	59,400,417
2. INTRAGOVERNMENTAL	705	55,404,400	613	13,937,359	11	41,192,329
3. LARGE BUSINESS - TOTAL	9,963	243,168,380	9,055	230,394,362	110	11,875,768
a. Advertised	876	13,099,707	691	8,149,178	73	4,648,384
b. Negotiated Competitive	2,760	113,125,846	2,521	107,548,214	17	5,245,392
c. Negotiated Noncompetitive	6,327	116,942,827	5,843	114,696,970	20	1,981,992
4. SMALL BUSINESS - TOTAL	21,872	49,336,800	18,759	42,132,023	83	4,335,440
a. Advertised	1,116	10,516,818	816	7,185,488	40	2,365,770
b. Negotiated Competitive	5,298	14,320,914	4,316	11,586,770	18	1,238,550
c. Negotiated Noncompetitive	15,458	24,499,068	13,627	23,359,765	25	731,120
5. UNIVERSITIES	143	12,884,535	143	12,884,535	-	--
6. OTHER NONPROFIT INSTITUTIONS	186	497,058	150	473,648	2	10,920
7. OUTSIDE U.S. & POSSESSIONS	53	8,851,470	47	6,865,510	6	1,985,960
8. SMALL BUSINESS SET ASIDES - TOTAL *(included in line 4)*	477	6,254,181	249	2,779,236	27	2,313,031
a. Individual Set Asides	412	4,496,060	236	2,517,291	6	1,173,930
b. Class Set Asides	65	1,758,121	13	261,945	21	1,139,101

PART A - PROCUREMENT ACTIONS BY NASA APPROPRIATION

NEGOTIATION AUTHORITY 10 U.S.C.	NO.	$ VALUE	NEGOTIATION AUTHORITY 10 U.S.C.	NO.	$ VALUE
9. TOTAL	30,225	291,121,718	2304(a) (9)		
2304(a) (1)	259	2,649,618	(10)	2,766	48,112,526
(2)	7	100,098	(11)	3,534	180,551,372
(3)	22,059	7,952,478	(12)		
(4)	57	1,100,861	(13)	3	1,364,441
(5)	139	12,887,129	(14)		
(6)	72	8,848,980	(15)		
(7)			(16)		
(8)			(17)	1,329	27,554,215

PART B - NEGOTIATED PROCUREMENT ACTIONS

Appendix F
Organization Charts

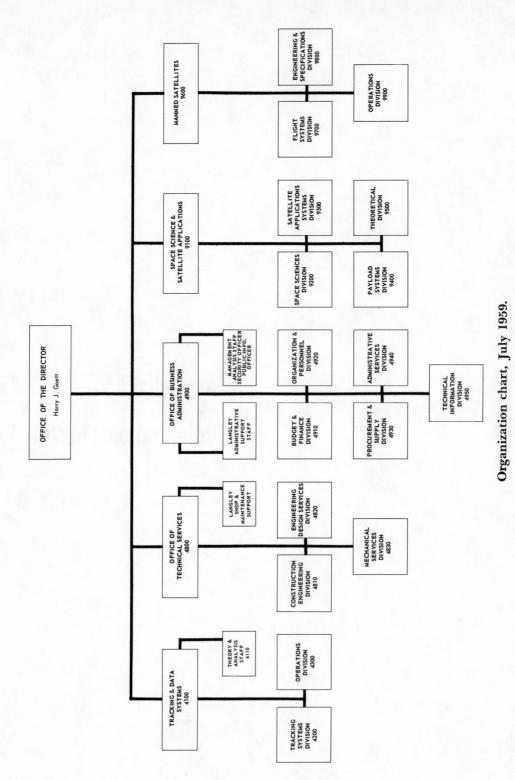

Organization chart, July 1959.

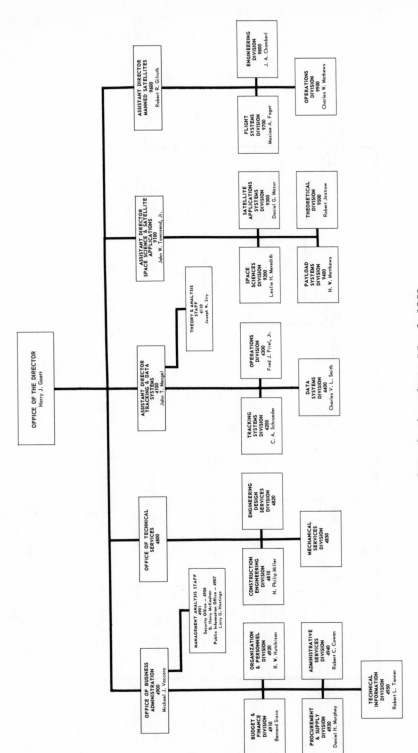

Organization chart, March 1960.

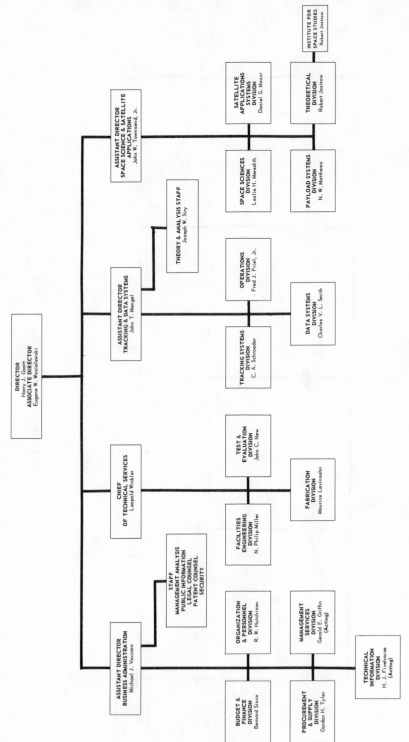

Organization chart, January 1961.

DIRECTOR
Harry J. Goett

ASSOCIATE DIRECTOR
Eugene W. Wasielewski

ASSISTANT DIRECTOR FOR ADMINISTRATION
M. J. Vaccaro
DEPUTY
B. Sisco

LEGAL COUNSEL
C. Kearney
PATENT COUNSEL
L. Rowicz
PUBLIC INFO OFFICER
E. Mason

PROJECT SUPPORT OFFICE
J. Cook

SECURITY OFFICE
W. Jenkins

ORGANIZATION & PERSONNEL DIVISION
R. Hutchison

FINANCIAL MANAGEMENT DIVISION
K. B. Foster

PROCUREMENT & SUPPLY DIVISION
G. Tyler

MANAGEMENT SERVICES DIVISION
H. Fivehouse

TECHNICAL INFORMATION DIVISION
D. Hutchison

CHIEF OF TECHNICAL SERVICES
L. Winkler

TEST & EVALUATION DIVISION
J. New

FACILITIES ENGINEERING DIVISION
N. Miller

FABRICATION DIVISION
M. Levinsohn

ASSISTANT DIRECTOR TRACKING & DATA SYSTEMS
J. T. Mengel
DEPUTY ASS'T DIRECTOR FOR OPERATIONS
O. Covington

SPACE PROJECTS INTEGRATION OFFICE
C. Looney

OPERATIONS & SUPPORT DIVISION
F. Friel, Jr.

TRACKING SYSTEMS DIVISION
C. Schroeder

PLANS OFFICE
F. Vonbun

SPACE DATA ACQUISITION DIVISION
R. Coates

DATA SYSTEMS DIVISION
J. Fleming

THEO. & ANAL. OFFICE
J. Siry

MANNED SPACE FLIGHT SUPPORT DIVISION
N. Heller

ASSISTANT DIRECTOR SPACE SCIENCE & SATELLITE APPLICATIONS
J. W. Townsend, Jr.

SYSTEMS REVIEW GROUP
H. Lagow

INSTITUTE FOR SPACE STUDIES
R. Jastrow

SPACECRAFT SYSTEMS & PROJECTS DIVISION
D. Mazur

SPACECRAFT INTEGRATION & SOUNDING ROCKET DIVISION
R. Baumann

THEORETICAL DIVISION
W. Hess

SPACE SCIENCES DIVISION
L. Meredith

SPACECRAFT TECHNOLOGY DIVISION
N. Matthews

AERONOMY & METEOROLOGY DIVISION
W. Stroud

Organization chart, November 1962.

Appendix G

Scientific Exploration of Space and Its Challenge to Education*

Harry J. Goett
First Director, Goddard Space Flight Center

IT IS A PRIVILEGE to be with you in these halls which sparked the mind of the father of the Space Age, Dr. Robert H. Goddard. Those of us engaged in the space program have a very special regard for Dr. Goddard. We see in him the embodiment of the curious and far-seeing scholar who best exemplified the theme of this convocation— the partnership of engineering and science in progress. Two generations ago, well ahead of his time, he gave us the theory and tools with which to reach into the universe in our never ending quest for knowledge. Those who read his reports cannot help but being impressed by the fact that it was due to the unique combination of the scientist and engineer in a single individual that enabled Dr. Goddard to be as far ahead of his time as he was.

We are now on the threshold of the Space Age which will require the same combination of the vision and practical application which characterized Dr. Goddard's work. Just as some 500 years ago man ventured beyond the Mediterranean, leading to the discovery of the New World, so today, man is breaking his earth-bound shackles to venture into space. Aside from the technological advances to which we are witness today, we must expect possibly even greater changes to our political, social, and educational concepts.

Those earlier explorations extended the horizons of the times in a literal sense, but even more important, they opened up new possibilities and concepts. They forced the people out of their established patterns of thought and produced an intellectual ferment and interest in new ideas necessary for the scientific revolution and for the political and social advances of the 18th century. These explorations were the most important events of that time; now some 500 years later, the space program can potentially play that same role.

The challenge posed by the Space Age is therefore addressed not only to the scientist and the engineer who are directly engaged in its projects; more importantly, it is a challenge to our society and, in particular, to its educational processes. The physicist, the astronomer, the geodesist, the meteorologist, the geologist, and the astrophysicist, all have new frontiers open to them. Their job as scientists is to bridge the gap between

---

* Presented at Centennial Convocation Luncheon, Worcester Polytechnic Institute, Worcester, Mass., October 8, 1964.

the known and the unknown. The question we must ask ourselves is whether they are being educated in such a manner as to prepare them to meet the challenges which the new laboratory of space has opened up to them.

The job of the engineer, in contrast to that of the scientist, is to use the resources of nature for social ends—to bridge the gap between the known and the desired. The laboratory of space has already opened up a new "known" to the engineer in the field of communications and meteorology. The experimental communication satellites—Syncom, Relay, Telstar, and Echo—have answered many of the questions that used to exist relative to the use of satellites for communication. The job of the engineer now is to translate this knowledge into a system that will be better than the under-ocean cables.

The experimental meteorological satellites—Tiros and Nimbus—have demonstrated the utility of cloud pictures taken from satellites as an additional operational tool for weather forecasting. The job of the engineer is to translate this knowledge into a practical and economical operational system.

The second question we must ask is whether the engineer is being educated in such a manner as to enable him to exploit these new developments in space.

We have seen the changes made during the past 30 years to adapt engineering education first to the new field of aeronautical and guided-missile engineering, later to the use of radar, still later to the adaptation of nuclear energy to practical uses. Space explora-

Goddard Center missions.

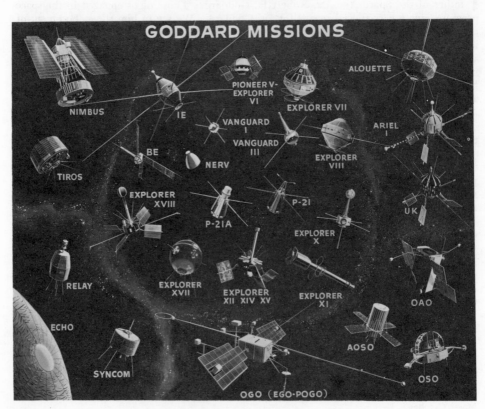

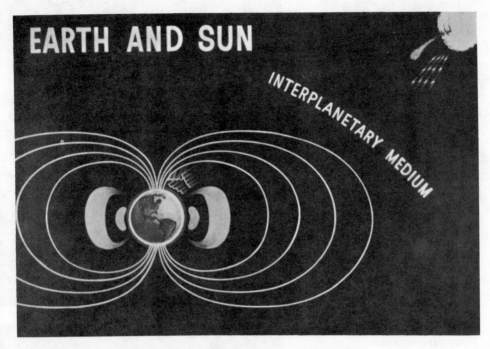

Divisions of space in the earth-sun region.

tion will continue this trend. I think that even closer collaboration than heretofore is going to be required between the scientist and the engineer. Also there is growing a need for closer interdisciplinary collaboration between scientific specialists in various fields. Have our universities who are now training these scientists and engineers reacted to this trend?

To seek a basis for an answer to the questions I have posed, I would like to digress and describe our space efforts from the viewpoint from which I see it. This viewpoint tends to emphasize, as you will see, the involvement of the various scientific disciplines and the close collaboration that is required with the engineer.

The first illustration gives a somewhat kaleidoscopic view of the variety of the projects involved. We have launched some 35 major U.S. satellites for various scientific communication and meteorological purposes. You can see the Syncom, Relay, and Echo communications satellites. Tiros and Nimbus satellites have served as experimental meteorological satellites. The group on the remainder of the illustration are the scientific satellites with which we are literally exploring space. Quite appropriately many of them are named Explorers.

This next picture shows our map of space which is being explored by these satellites. This map might be compared with the maps of the world that were probably available to the early maritime explorers. Space is not an empty void but can be divided into various regions of distinctly different characteristics that are emphasized on this picture. First, there is the near-earth region, the upper atmosphere and the ionosphere. Then, there is the region called the magnetosphere in which the magnetic field lines anchored in the earth extend out to space. They form a gigantic magnetic shield around the earth which makes this region quite different from that on out

Scope of Tiros photographs.

Tiros coverage,
May 20, 1960

further. This region, labeled the "interplanetary medium," is essentially uninfluenced by the earth's magnetic field. Finally, there is the sun which might on our map be given the same prominence as was India on the map of the early explorers, since, as you will see, the sun is the basic cause of many of the variations observed in the other regions of space.

Just as the early explorers initially ventured out only a short distance from their home ports, our first ventures into space were in the near-earth region. Satellites such as Tiros and Nimbus go up into orbits some 300 to 600 miles and look down on the earth as shown in the next illustration. From a satellite such as this, we have obtained data on the upper atmosphere. This next picture is a striking example of the result. On the lower portion, you can see a montage made up of some 64 successive pictures taken by Tiros. You can observe the huge cyclonic disturbance that has been mapped extending

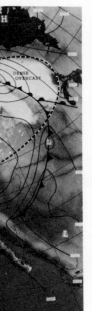

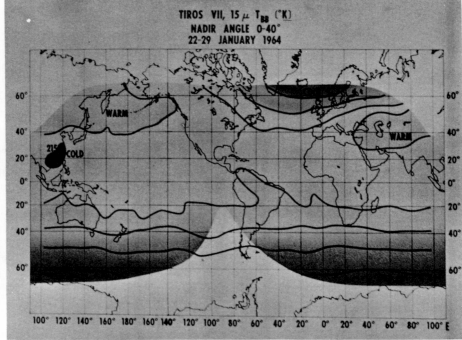

Temperature distribution derived from *Tiros VII*.

all the way from Wake Island in the Pacific to the Great Lakes. This was the first opportunity for meteorologists to observe weather patterns on such a massive global scale. Cloud pictures such as this are now being used daily by the operational meteorologists in their weather predictions. They are also serving a more basic research purpose in that they give an insight into the dynamics of the weather. We can look forward to much more accurate long-range weather forecasting as our understanding of this phenomenon improves.

Another type of experimental information made available by Tiros to the upper altitude physicists is shown in the next illustration. This is a plot of global temperature distribution obtained from infrared instrumentation. It is especially notable because it depicts the phenomenon of stratospheric warming shown in this region. This phenomenon has been suspected to be the trigger of weather disturbances and to be traceable

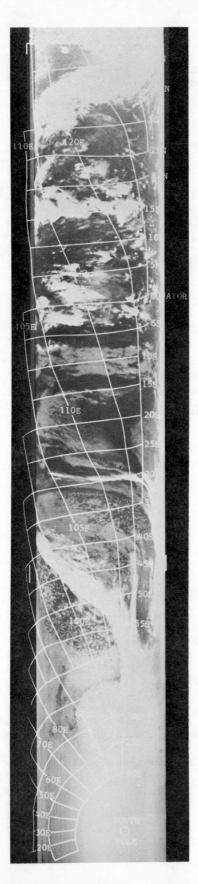

in some manner to solar activity. The data are now being studied by upper altitude physicists in an attempt to obtain a better understanding of this phenomenon, with the eventual hope of using observations such as this for long-range weather prediction.

The picture on the left shows a photograph made by Nimbus infrared techniques. Here you see a strip approximately 1,500 miles extending all the way up from the Antarctic to close to the North Pole. These pictures are less than a month old but already they are under detailed scrutiny by meteorologists who consider them to be a gold mine of data. They give a global picture of the cloud patterns and enable an understanding of cause and effect in the movement of the weather, not heretofore obtainable in observations from the ground. Features observable include:

  Antarctic ice shelf
  Low pressure system generated at polar fronts
  Location of jet streams
  Intertropical convergence zone
  Volcanoes
  Ocean currents

To analyze this global picture some of the following disciplines are involved: meteorologist, upper altitude physicist, geologist, and oceanographer.

The next area of exploration has been the ionosphere—the region of highly ionized particles that exists above what is conventionally considered the upper atmosphere. We have launched several satellites into elliptical orbits; they traverse the altitudes from 200 to 800 miles. These satellites are still pretty close to the earth in terms of our total area of exploration. From such satellites, we measured for the first time the temperature in this region and found that it fluctuated in a 27-day cycle corresponding to the time of rotation of the sun which shows clearly the close link between solar activity and events in our upper atmosphere. These satellites also discovered a helium layer which fluctuates and varies in thickness with solar conditions. Finally, there were measured flows of currents in the ionosphere and observations were made of the patterns of whistlers into outer space.

Our exploration was next pushed out into the

Infrared data obtained from *Nimbus I.* Shown is a "slice" of the globe from the Arctic to the South Pole.

magnetosphere. Satellites were sent up to investigate the energetic particle population of the Van Allen radiation belts. This information is not only important in our understanding of sun-earth relationships but also is essential if we are to acquire the engineering information required for the design of communication and meteorological satellites. Their lifetime will be strongly dependent on the radiation environment found in this region.

The next figure is a pictorial description of what this latter group of satellites found. As you can see, there is shown the orbit of the first Interplanetary Monitoring Platform (IMP) which carried it out to 122,000 miles. When it got there, it found that there was a "solar wind" blowing. This wind sometimes is a gentle breeze and on other occasions grows into what might be termed a hurricane. Of course it is not a wind in the conventional sense but is a stream of energetic particles (electrons and protons of varying energy) that are ejected by the sun. During quiet sun conditions, there is gentle breeze and during a solar flare, the number and intensity of these particles increase. It is through this solar wind that the sun has a profound effect on what goes on in our upper atmosphere. The earth is like a rock in a stream with a bow wave in front of it formed by the shock front that marks the boundary of the solar wind and the magnetosphere. Not shown is a wake behind the earth. One of our orbits is shown here—the satellite got in the moon's wake and we were able to observe the effect of the moon on this solar wind.

As you will observe, the sun has been the basic cause of all the phenomena that were observed by these various satellites. Therefore, the results obtained from the Orbiting Solar Observatory were of particular interest since they enabled us to observe what was going on in the sun and causing these variations. Man has been observing the sun for thousands of years. The existence of the early sun worshipers attests to the fact that the importance of the sun to terrestrial conditions has been appreciated for many centuries. However, during all this time, we have been looking at the sun as if through translucent blindfold. The earth's atmosphere and the magnetosphere filter out much of the solar radiation. Thus, earth-based instruments have only been able to observe the sun in a relatively narrow visual band and at radio wavelengths. The Orbiting Solar Observatory was able for the first time to observe the sun in the shorter wave ultraviolet, gamma ray and X-ray regions. New light has been shed

The upper atmosphere.

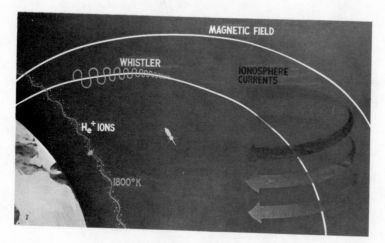

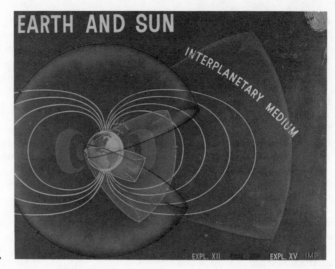

Earth-sun relationships.

The earth and "empty" space.

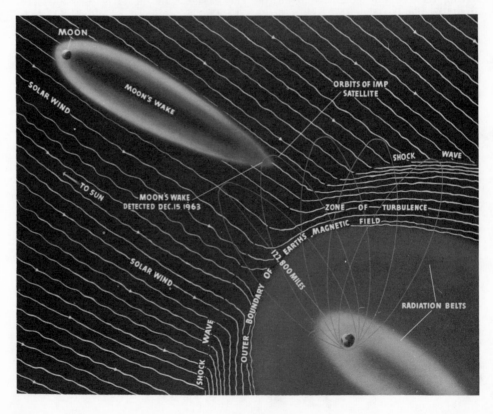

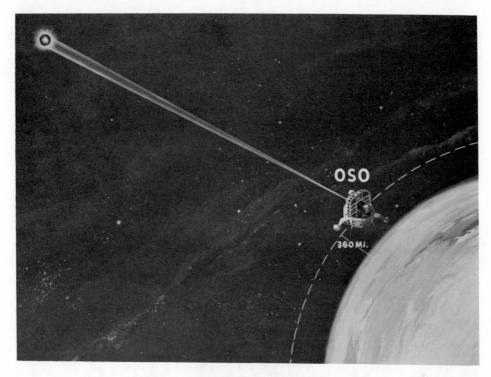

Orbit of *Orbiting Solar Observatory I.*

on the relation between solar flares and the associated variation in the solar wind fluctuations observed from IMP.

When there is a solar flare there apparently is a huge magnetic bottle that is exploded from the sun. Contained within this bottle are energetic particles, electrons, and protons traveling at varying speeds. Anything external to the bottle, such as galactic cosmic rays, cannot penetrate within the bottle and bounces off. This magnetic bottle gradually expands and if headed toward the earth impinges on the earth's magnetosphere and distorts it. Many of the energetic particles bounce off the magnetic shield formed by the magnetosphere, others get injected into the magnetosphere and in due course form the Van Allen belt, as they are commonly called. These particles ride the magnetic lines which exist in the magnetosphere and in due course impinge on the upper atmosphere in the auroral regions and cause changes in temperature that I have previously referred to and in some manner influence our cyclic variations in climate.

My object in giving this broadbrush sketch of the information that has been brought back from space has not been to convey any detailed understanding of the implications of these results. The point that I hope has been conveyed is that it has commanded the efforts of a broad spectrum of scientific disciplines. These include the solar physicist who is involved in the observation of the sun, the nuclear physicist who applies his techniques to the observation of the energetic population in the interplanetary space and the radiation belts; the magnetic field specialist who has been mapping the variation in the magnetic lines of the magnetosphere and studying the collision process with the solar wind; the ionospheric physicist who has been studying the electron distribution in the ionosphere and its variation with the solar cycle; the upper atmosphere physicist

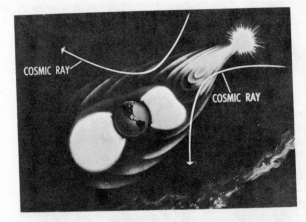

Deflection of cosmic and solar particles by the earth's magnetic field.

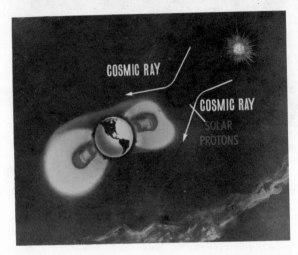

Effect of solar flare on the earth's magnetic field.

who has been trying to correlate observed atmospheric temperature and composition variations with the events in the other regions; and, finally, the meteorologist who has been trying to put together the interrelated effects of all these phenomena on the earth's weather. This interrelation between the various disciplines, I suggest, is a unique feature of space science which should be taken into account in the educational process. It is in distinct contrast to the trend toward specialization that has characterized the past 30 years. The aerodynamicist could concentrate on his wind tunnel with relatively little reference to other disciplines; the nuclear physicist could work with his reactor and the biologist with his microscope in the same relative isolation. Creativity could flourish because it was the era of the individual worker; there were fewer technical committees, budget reviews, administrators and the like; who could kill an idea while it was still in the formative stage.

The new era promised by the Space Age perhaps connotes a return to what was once called natural philosophy. The unifying element of these developments of the space program is a general spirit of inquiry into the nature of the external physical world. It represents a redirection of interest away from the increasingly narrow specialization which has characterized the physical sciences in the last decades.

276

The second distinguishing feature of research in space is the fact that scientists have only been able to make the observations that I have discussed by virtue of the hardware developed by the engineer. This is in distinct contrast to the biologist who could invest in a good microscope and do research comparable with the best.

The control equipment which enables the pointing of instruments with precise accuracy at the sun, the solar power supplies which supply the energy to run the experiments, the communication devices which bring back the information from outer space, all are developments which must come from engineers. In one sense, the normal situation has been reversed. Generally, the engineer exploits and puts to practical use the knowledge acquired by the scientist. But in space research, the scientist seems to be particularly dependent on the engineer to develop new devices and techniques. Engineering, in this context, has become a more creative and trail-blazing profession.

The third and possibly most imposing challenge of the Space Age is the potential feed-back of its developments into the civilian economy. In the long run, the justification of our space budget must stand on this "fallout."

Everyone knows the drive for miniaturization of electronic components to reduce weight and size of space applications. We can foresee the pressure for electronic components to operate at very high temperature. There is a need for new developments for electronic apparatus to operate in the hard vacuum of space. New materials must be developed for the space environment. There are applications for cryogenics and new power sources. There is a special need for insuring long periods of unattended operation of mechanical equipment in space. Development is needed of methods of lubrication in high vacuum and the creation of new sensing and control devices. Means of medical research of man in space must be developed.

These are some of the most immediate returns of space exploration. In due course, they will surely be exploited by our civilian economy. But I submit that the engineering profession is confronted with a new challenge in its job of converting the known into the desired. These developments will not find their way into the civilian economy unless the engineer has the creative initiative necessary for their application.

These three developments of the Space Age present a new challenge to our educational process. They are, in the first place, the interdisciplinary collaboration of various scientific specialists. Secondly, the leadership of the engineer in developing new techniques to enable the scientist to achieve his objectives in space. And thirdly, the creative thinking which is required to apply the new developments of space to our civilian economy.

If I were an educator, I would conclude this talk by suggesting some solutions. However, I claim no competence in the educational field; my job is to produce reliable satellites. There, I will terminate my discussion by suggesting a reexamination of the educational process and its curriculum by those competent in this field to see whether they think it has been properly adjusted to meet these new challenges of the Space Age.

Appendix H
Exhibits

XHIBITS COLLECTED in this appendix are available to the general public.
ver, it was felt that the value of this work as a historical tool would be much
d if it contained some of the pertinent historical documents collected in one
herefore, selected key documents considered important for the formation and
ars of Goddard Space Flight Center have been assembled in this appendix.

Exhibits

EXHIBIT 1
COPY

Release by Senator J. Glenn Beall, Maryland, at Washington, D.C. office
    August 1, 1958

U.S. Senator Beall today announced that the new "outer space agency" will establish its laboratory and plant in Maryland. "The location at Greenbelt, Md., is an ideal location for the new Government agency," Senator Beall said, "because of its accessibility to the nation's capital and its proximity to numerous important highways and others to be built."

Senator Beall has been in consultation on the matter of location with officials of the new agency to be known as the National Aeronautics and Space Administration and expressed himself as "greatly pleased with the decision" to locate in Maryland. The senator pointed out that the space laboratory and plant are to be established on land already owned by the federal government, "thus saving the taxpayers what would have been added expense of land purchase."

"The Greenbelt laboratory will employ 650 technicians, mostly electronic engineers and some chemists," Sen. Beall said, adding that, "all research work in connection with outer space programs will be conducted at the Greenbelt installation."

Sen. Beall said further: "Construction work on the new plant is expected to get underway immediately in view of the fact that legislation authorizing appropriations of $47,800,000 for the construction and installation of the space project center (S4208) was passed by the Senate on Friday and is expected to clear the House on Monday."

EXHIBIT 2
COPY

NATIONAL AERONAUTICS AND SPACE ADMINISTRATION
Washington, D.C.

September 25, 1958

NASA GENERAL DIRECTIVE NO. 1

Subject: Proclamation on organization of the National Aeronautics and
Space Administration

On this date I have issued the following proclamation, to be
published in the Federal Register:

A P R O C L A M A T I O N

"1. By virtue of the authority vested in me by the National
Aeronautics and Space Act of 1958 (Public Law 85-568, approved July 29,
1958, 72 Stat. 426, 433) I hereby proclaim that as of the close of
business September 30, 1958, the National Aeronautics and Space
Administration has been organized and is prepared to discharge the
duties and exercise the powers conferred upon it by said law.

"2. In accordance with the provisions of the Act, all functions,
powers, duties, and obligations, and all real and personal property,
personnel (other than members of the Committee), funds, and records of
the National Advisory Committee for Aeronautics are hereby transferred
to the National Aeronautics and Space Administration.

"3. The existing National Advisory Committee for Aeronautics
Committees on Aircraft, Missile and Spacecraft Aerodynamics; Aircraft,
Missile and Spacecraft Propulsion; Aircraft, Missile and Spacecraft
Construction; Aircraft Operating Problems; the Industry Consulting
Committee and the Special Committee on Space Technology and their
subcommittees are hereby reconstituted advisory committees to the
Administration through December 31, 1958, for the purpose of bringing
their current work to an orderly completion.

"4. Existing policies, regulations, authorities, and procedural
instructions governing the activities of the National Advisory Committee
for Aeronautics, not inconsistent with law, and which are applicable
to the activities of the National Aeronautics and Space Administration,
shall be continued in effect until superseded or revoked.

"5. The Langley Aeronautical Laboratory, the Ames Aeronautical
Laboratory, and the Lewis Flight Propulsion Laboratory are hereby
renamed the Langley Research Center, the Ames Research Center and the
Lewis Research Center, respectively.

"DONE at the City of Washington, District of Columbia this 25th day
of September in the year Nineteen Hundred and Fifty-Eight."

/s/ T. Keith Glennan

FOR RELEASE AT 2:00 P.M., EDT   October 1, 1958

James C. Hagerty, Press Secretary to the President

THE WHITE HOUSE

The President today signed an Executive Order transferring certain functions with respect to space activities from the Department of Defense to the new National Aeronautics and Space Administration which comes into existence today under the National Aeronautics and Space Act of 1958 enacted by Congress last July.

Under the Act, the National Aeronautics and Space Administration is to be responsible for aeronautical and space activities sponsored by the United States, except that activities peculiar to or primarily associated with the development of weapons systems, military operations, or the defense of the United States shall be the responsibility of the Department of Defense. The determination as to which agency has responsibility for any such activity is to be made by the President with the advice of the National Aeronautics and Space Council

The present Executive Order transfers from Defense to the National Aeronautics and Space Administration responsibility for non-military space projects such as lunar probes and scientific satellites which have been initiated by the Advanced Research Projects Agency of the Department of Defense pending the establishment of the new civilian agency. It also transfers from Defense certain space-related projects of the Air Force, principally in the field of "super-thrust" propulsion systems which are primarily applicable to future space vehicles. The order also gives to the National Aeronautics and Space Administration responsibility for Project Vanguard, the United States Scientific Satellite program which has heretofore been the responsibility of the Department of the Navy.

The order transfers from Defense to the NASA the amount of $117 million in connection with the Advanced Research Projects Agency and Air Force projects being transferred. This is the same as the amount anticipated to be transferred for these activities in the initial budget estimates for the National Aeronautics and Space Administration submitted to Congress in August. The particular projects to be transferred are to be identified in one or more supplementary Executive Orders. The transfers of funds necessary in connection with Project Vanguard are to be determined by the Director of the Bureau of the Budget.

Details regarding transfers of records, property, facilities, and civilian personnel, in connection with all of the transfers covered in the present Executive Order, are to be carried out as agreed upon between the National Aeronautics and Space Administration and the Department of Defense.

EXHIBIT 4
COPY

EXECUTIVE ORDER

- - - - - - - - - -

No. 10783
TRANSFERRING CERTAIN FUNCTIONS FROM THE
DEPARTMENT OF DEFENSE TO THE NATIONAL
AERONAUTICS AND SPACE ADMINISTRATION

By virtue of the authority vested in me by the National Aeronautics and Space Act of 1958 (Public Law 85-568; 72 Stat. 426), and as President of the United States, it is ordered as follows:

Section 1. All functions (including powers, duties, activities, and parts of functions) of the Department of Defense, or of any officer or organizational entity of the Department of Defense, with respect to the following are hereby transferred to the National Aeronautics and Space Administration:

(a) The United States Scientific Satellite project (Project Vanguard).

(b) Specific projects of the Advanced Research Projects Agency and of the Department of the Air Force which relate to space activities (including lunar probes, scientific satellites, and super-thrust boosters) within the scope of the functions devolving upon the National Aeronautics and Space Administration under the provisions of the National Aeronautics and Space Act of 1958, and which shall be more particularly described in one or more supplementary Executive orders hereafter issued.

Section 2. (a) The Secretary of the Treasury shall immediately transfer to the appropriation of the National Aeronautics and Space Administration for "Research and Development", from such appropriations of the Department of Defense as the Secretary of Defense shall designate, the following amounts:

(1) In connection with the transfer of functions provided for in section 1(a) hereof, such amounts as shall be determined by the Director of the Bureau of the Budget pursuant to section 202(b) of the Budget and Accounting Procedures Act of 1950 (31 U.S.C. 581c (b) and section 1(k) of Executive Order No. 10530 of May 11, 1954.

(2) In connection with the transfer of functions of the Advanced Research Projects Agency provided for in section 1(b) hereof, $59,200,000.

(3) In connection with the transfer of functions of the Department of the Air Force provided for in section 1(b) hereof, $57,800,000.

(b) In connection with the transfer of functions provided for in section 1, appropriate transfers of records, property, facilities, and civilian personnel shall be carried out as may be agreed upon from time to time by the National Aeronautics and Space Administration and the Department of Defense.

/s/ DWIGHT D. EISENHOWER

THE WHITE HOUSE
October 1, 1958

EXHIBIT 5
COPY

NATIONAL AERONAUTICS AND SPACE ADMINISTRATION

Washington 25, D.C.

For immediate release
Tuesday, October 1, 1958

FACT SHEET ON THE TRANSFER OF CERTAIN FUNCTIONS FROM DEPARTMENT
OF DEFENSE TO THE NATIONAL AERONAUTICS AND SPACE ADMINISTRATION

The National Aeronautics and Space Administration (NASA) was
established by Public Law 85-568 on July 29, 1958. In accordance with
the Act, T. Keith Glennan, Administrator of NASA and president-on-leave
from Case Institute of Technology, issued a proclamation on September
25, 1958, which stated in part. "I hereby proclaim that the National
Aeronautics and Space Administration has been organized and is prepared
to discharge the duties and exercise the powers conferred upon it . . ."
Prior to the enactment of this legislation, the President wrote
to the Secretary of Defense and the Chairman of the National Advisory
Committee for Aeronautics concerning his special message to the
Congress on April 2, 1958 which recommended establishment of NASA.
In his memorandum, the President said: "The Department of Defense
and the National Advisory Committee for Aeronautics should jointly
review the pertinent programs currently underway within or planned by
the Department, including those authorized by me on March 27, 1958, and
should recommend to me as soon as possible which of these programs
should be placed under the direction of the new (space) Agency. It
should be noted that Public Law 85-325 authorized the Department of
Defense for a period of one year; period will come to a close February
12, 1959. Since the new agency will absorb the going organization
of the National Advisory Committee for Aeronautics, it should be capable
of assuming the appropriate programs prior to the date."
The executive order of the President, which transfers certain
functions from the Department of Defense to the NASA, is a result of
the above stated review.
In accordance with the executive order, the following projects are
being transferred to the NASA by the Department of Defense.
1. The United States Scientific Satellite Project (Project
Vanguard). The transfer of this project will include approximately 150
civilian scientific personnel under the direction of Dr. John P. Hagen,
Director, Project Vanguard, Naval Research Laboratory.
2. Four Lunar Probes and their instrumentation, and three satellite
projects. These projects are being transferred from the Advanced
Research Projects Agency. Two of the Lunar Probes are assigned to
the Air Force Ballistic Missile Division and two to the Army Ballistic

Missile Agency. The three satellite projects are assigned to the Army Ballistic Missile Agency and call for putting into orbit two inflatable spheres—one 12 feet in diameter, and the other 100 feet in diameter—and a cosmic ray satellite.

The total cost of these ARPA programs is approximately $35.5 million, most of which was funded in Fiscal Year 58. The Fiscal Year 59 funds, necessary to complete these programs, is $9.6 million and will be made available to NASA. Additionally, $49.6 million originally designated for scientific projects will be transferred to NASA from ARPA.

3. A number of engine development research programs now being carried on in the Department of the Air Force will be transferred to NASA. These include basic research programs in such areas as nuclear rocket engines, fluorine engines, and the 1 million lb thrust single chamber engine study and development. As specified in the executive order, $57.8 million will be transferred from the Air Force to NASA for these programs.

The Advanced Research Projects Agency will continue work in activities peculiar to, or primarily associated with, the development of weapons systems for the defense of the United States, including the research and development necessary to make effective projects for the defense of the United States. At the present time, while ARPA has underway projects of considerable priority related to anti-missile defense and solid propellants, it is devoting major attention to continuing military projects, which include satellite programs from warning, navigation, communications, meteorology, and other military exploratory space programs. Space components and activities necessary to these projects, such as the development of super thrust boosters and high energy upper stages are also being carried on by ARPA. A program to put man into space is being pursued jointly by ARPA and NASA.

The ARPA military budget for 1959 is approximately $420 million.

```
┌─────────────────────────┐
│      EXHIBIT 6          │
│       COPY             │
│                         │
└─────────────────────────┘
```

NATIONAL AERONAUTICS AND SPACE ADMINISTRATION
BELTSVILLE SPACE CENTER
Washington 25, D.C.

4102-AN:1ds
15 January 1959

GENERAL NOTICE NO. 1

Subj: Designation as Beltsville Space Center

1. By action of the Administrator, four divisions have been designated
as comprising the Beltsville Space Center of the National Aeronautics
and Space Administration. The official address is as follows:

> National Aeronautics and Space Administration
> Beltsville Space Center
> 4555 Overlook Avenue, S.W.
> Washington 25, D.C.
>
> Telephone: JOhnson 2-6610
> Dial Code: 172
> TWX: WA 134
> Military Routing: RBEPRL
> Messenger Mail: Stop 10

All members of the Beltsville Space Center are requested to use the
new address immediately, and to disseminate it as widely as is
necessary. The local Post Office and telephone company are being
notified of this action.

2. New stationery has been ordered, and will be distributed as soon as
it is received. The stationery masthead will give the address as it
appears above, and also will list the three scientific divisions and
the telephone and TWX numbers. The Vanguard Division may continue to
use its Vanguard stationery until the stock on hand is exhausted or
until directed otherwise. Vanguard secretaries should type above the
printed masthead the words BELTSVILLE SPACE CENTER.

3. The Space Sciences Division and Vanguard Division will be located
at NRL. Vanguard will continue to occupy its present spaces, but there
may be some adjustments from time to time, with a view toward achieving
better use of what space is available. The Space Sciences Division
will move into space being prepared for it in Building 5-7 of the NGF
annex, adjacent to NRL Building 71. This move will probably take place
within the next three months. The Theoretical Division will remain

physically with NASA Headquarters until the Beltsville facilities are ready.

4. All divisions of the Beltsville Space Center will receive their administrative support, generally speaking, from the central administrative group being established at NRL under my direction. There will be exceptions to this made necessary by the physical separation of units and individuals. For example, for the immediate future, pay-rolling, travel, and some supply support for the Theoretical Division will be furnished by Headquarters.

5. The NRL Code Directory will show some listings for the Beltsville Space Center, but unfortunately there is not enough space to show all of the listings we requested. All branch listings could not be accommodated, so no branches will be listed. Service functions will be listed since they are believed to be subject to call frequently enough to be appropriate to the NRL Code Directory. However, we have duplicated, and are distributing with this memorandum, a supplement to the NRL Code Directory. We shall publish a complete directory for your use as soon as we can.

6. The telephone JOhnson 2-6610 is answered at the NRL switchboard by NRL operators. The separate number differs from NRL's only as a matter of identification, but you are requested NOT to use JOhnson 3-6600 unless you are unable to reach the board through JOhnson 2-6610. The change in trunk line number has absolutely no effect on your extension number. The government interdepartmental dial code remains the same as for NRL (172). There will be installed in the near future a two-way tie line between the Headquarters switchboard, and the NRL switchboard, which will permit transfer of incoming calls between the two boards. This means that a party calling JOhnson 2-6610 for a person who is located at Headquarters can have his call transferred to the Head-quarters board without having to place a new call, and vice versa.

7. Various notices and instructions will be published from time to time, to advise all personnel of policies and procedures governing the administration of the Beltsville Space Center. Until policies and precedents are established, many actions will be taken on an individual case basis. This is necessary in day-to-day operations; however, the fact that changes in or new procedures are established frequently should come as no surprise under the circumstances.

A formal beneficial suggestion program has not yet been established, but constructive suggestions and the pointing out of deficiencies are always welcome.

/s/ T. E. Jenkins
Administrative Officer

Distribution:
Construction Division
Space Science
Theoretical Division
Vanguard Division

COPY

NATIONAL AERONAUTICS AND SPACE ADMINISTRATION
BELTSVILLE SPACE CENTER

VANGUARD DIVISION

Code

Code			Bldg.	Room	Tele
4100	Chief, Vanguard Division	Dr. J.P. Hagen	12	369	447
4103	Asst Chief for Operations	CDR L.I. Baird	12	372	673
4104	Management Coordinator	Mr. H.E. Canney, Jr.	12	371A	533
4105	Science Liaison Coordinator	Mr. R.W. Stroup	12	366	445
4120	Vehicle Systems Branch	Mr. D.G. Mazur	2	254A	502
4130	Space Tracking Systems Branch	Mr. J.T. Mengel	42	319	2427
4140	Theory and Planning Staff	Dr. J.W. Siry	30	322	2347
4150	Vanguard Operations Group Manager	Mr. R.H. Gray	AMR	ULster	3-4515
4162	Administrative Assistant	Mr. R.W. Batchelder	AMR	ULster	3-2618
4170	Payload Systems Branch	Mr. N.W. Matthews	60	406	384
4180	Data Systems Branch	Dr. J.P. Hagen	12	369	477

SPACE SCIENCES DIVISION

Code			Bldg.	Room	Tele
4200	Chief, Space Sciences Division	Mr. J.W. Townsend, Jr.	Hq.	T602	128-7815
4203	Consultant	Mr. J.C. Seddon	42	415	345
4210	Fields and Particles Branch	Dr. L.H. Meredith	42	314	594
4220	Planetary Atmosphere Branch	Mr. H.E. LaGow	42	424	358
4230	Astronomy Branch	Dr. J.E. Kupperian, Jr.	30	222	893
4240	Solar Physics Branch	Dr. J.C. Lindsay	Hq.	T605	128-7723
4250	Meteorology Branch	Mr. J.W. Townsend, Jr.	*Hq.	T602	128-7815
4260	Instruments Branch	Mr. K.R. Medrow	42	410	518

THEORETICAL DIVISION

Code			Bldg.	Room	Tele
4300	Chief, Theoretical Division	Dr. R. Jastrow	Hq.	T611	128-7721

CONSTRUCTION DIVISION

Chief, Construction Division	Mr. N.P. Miller	Hq.	T204	128-7523

ADMINISTRATIVE OFFICE

4100A	NASA Administrative Officer	Mr. T.E. Jenkins	12	370	668
4100B	Asst Administrative Officer	Mr. A.P. Nagy	12	371A	2504
4100C	Administrative Services Officer	Mr. R.C. Cowan	12	374	2339
4100D	Personnel Clerk	Mrs. M.C. Dytrt	12	364	2593
4100E	Mail, Records & Documents Clerk	Mrs. P.M. Egan	12	367	798
4100F	Travel and Voucher Clerk	Mrs. H.G. Jackson	12	364	2564
4100G	Supply Clerk	Mr. R.J. Fisher	12	374	2445

EXHIBIT 7
COPY

NATIONAL AERONAUTICS AND SPACE ADMINISTRATION
Washington, D.C.

January 22, 1959

NASA GENERAL NOTICE

Subject: Establishment of Beltsville Space Center

1. The NASA has recently established a new field office to be known as the "Beltsville Space Center." This Center will be operated under the direction of the Director of Space Flight Development—NASA Headquarters (Dr. Abe Silverstein).

2. Pending completion of permanent facilities at Beltsville, Maryland, program activities of the Space Center will be carried out at Washington, D.C. and at the Langley and Lewis Research Centers.

3. During this interim period, official communications with staff members attached to the Center should be addressed as follows:

Office	Address
a. Theoretical Division	) National Aeronautics and Space) Administration
b. Space Sciences Division	) 1520 H Street, N. W.) Washington 25, D. C.) (Telephone: Executive 3-3260 -) TWX: WA-755)
c. Vanguard Division	) National Aeronautics and Space) Administration) Beltsville Space Center) 4555 Overlook Avenue, S. W.) Washington 25, D. C.) (Telephone: JOhnson 2-6610 -) TWX: WA-134)
d. Langley Space Task Group	) National Aeronautics and Space) Administration) Langley Research Center) Langley Field, Virginia) (Telephone: PArk 3-3325 -) TWX: HA-198)

```
                            )    National Aeronautics and Space
                            )    Administration
c. Lewis Space Task Group   )    Lewis Research Center
                            )    21000 Brookpark Road
                            )    Cleveland 35, Ohio
                            )    (Telephone: WInton 1-6620 -
                            )    TWX: CV-520)
```

/s/ Albert P. Siepert
Director of Business Administration

EXHIBIT 8
COPY

NATIONAL AERONAUTICS AND SPACE ADMINISTRATION
BELTSVILLE SPACE CENTER
4555 OVERLOOK AVENUE, S.W.
WASHINGTON 25, D.C.

SPACE SCIENCES DIVISION   TELEPHONE: JOHNSON 2-6610
THEORETICAL DIVISION   TWX: WA 134
VANGUARD DIVISION   4100A-19:TEJ: vmb
                                           February 16, 1959

MEMORANDUM FOR THE RECORD

Subject: Organization and functions of the Beltsville Space Center;
           report of observations and stating of implications drawn
           during conference concerning, held in Mr. Wyatt's office,
           February 12, 1959

1. Conference Participants:
   Robert Gilruth, Assistant Director and Director, Project Mercury
   John P. Hagen, Chief, Vanguard Division
   Robert Jastrow, Chief, Theoretical Division
   Thomas E. Jenkins, Administrative Officer
   John W. Townsend, Jr., Chief, Space Sciences Division
   Abe Silverstein, Director, Space Flight Development
   DeMarquis Wyatt, Assistant to Director of Space Flight Development
   Herbert S. Fuhrman, Administrative Assistant to Dr. Silverstein
   Al Hodgson, Director of Management

2. Purpose of Meeting: To survey the organization and functions of the
Beltsville Space Center as it currently exists; the functions to be
performed by the Center in the National Space Program; the organization
these functions will require for successful program execution; and
to take a very rough cut at the overall staffing problem.

3. Based on this discussion, I am attempting in this memorandum to
synthesize the guidelines which can be drawn from the discussion.
Attached are organization charts which evolve from the current Space
Center groups at scattered locations into an integrated organization at
one center physical location.

4. Major functions of the Space Center. It was generally agreed that
the Space Center will probably perform five major interrelated functions
on behalf of NASA as follows:
   (1) Project Management. It is generally agreed that Space Center

292

technical staff will perform management functions in connection with
NASA space projects, both of the contract and "in-house" variety (or
more likely, combination of the two). A project in this sense is
a complete application of science and space technology to a given
objective such as Man-in-Space, Meteorological Satellite, Lunar Probes,
et cetera. In many cases, the feasibility of projects will be studied
by the Headquarters technical staff with the input from the Space Center
until the gross outline of the job becomes evident. Detailing of the
plan of attack and execution of the project will rest primarily with
the Space Center provided, of course, the systems responsibility for
the project is in-house. The Space Center will also germinate ideas for
projects and forward proposals to Headquarters for evaluation and
authorization. Management of a project by the Space Center will be
augmented by the Headquarters technical staff which will assign a senior
project coordinator to expedite the work of the project and to help
resolve management problems requiring Headquarters attention and
support.

(2) <u>Research.</u> The Space Center will perform research (a), as
required to meet the gaps in current knowledge to form a base for
future ideas and applications and (b), research-in-space in all the
scientific disciplines as dictated by the expanding knowledge of space
phenomena.

(3) <u>Development and Fabrication.</u> The Space Center will design and
develop, including prototype fabrication, components and systems which
advance the state of the art of space technology and for specific
project application. This in-house development effort is required to
translate the ideas of scientists and engineers into hardware where
the contracting process would prove infeasible. For instance, the
development of payload systems of a highly experimental nature requiring
many stages of development, each dependent upon advanced techniques
which in themselves are developed as the hardware takes shape, can best
be done with in-house development and fabrication facilities available
on the spot and under the detailed direction of the staff scientists
and engineers. In both industry and government experience shows that
this type of effort is very difficult to "farm out" on contract.

(4) <u>Advance Planning.</u> The Space Center is and will continue to be
staffed by leaders in their respective fields who will germinate many
of the ideas necessary to the future program of space science and
exploration. As the practitioners of the art, they will, like many good
contractors, develop as a fruitful source of ideas. In fact, the current
National Space Program, as expressed in various NASA documents, is in
large part a synthesis of ideas emanating from the NASA staff. All of
the ideas expressed in the space program are not, of course, exclusive
with NASA personnel, but the program does express the broad competence
of the staff. It is expected, as is currently the case, that Space
Center staff will continue to participate in the formulation of the
program and in this respect act as a technical staff to Headquarters.

(5) <u>Operations.</u> The Space Center will be in charge of technical
operations in the field in all programs assigned to the Space Center.
These programs will include in-house space center projects plus projects
carried mostly on contract from Headquarters but technically monitored
by the Space Center. Space Center technical teams at the launching

sites will, of course, be under the direction and control of project and functional heads within the Space Center. Space communications and tracking will be a prime operational responsibility of the Center. This function includes data handling, both orbital and telemetered scientific.

5. It was concluded that to satisfy the questions in the mind of the Administrator we should immediately come up with (a) an interim plan of organization and operations to assure full effectiveness and integration into the program of the groups which now exist for the Space Center and (b) a tentative ultimate plan of organization and functions to show what the Space Center may look like three years from now.

6. Functional versus Project Organization within the Space Center. These two fundamental bases for organization were discussed at some length, in terms of what would be the best form of organization for the Space Center.

It was concluded that each of these bases of organization has merit and each has some drawbacks. Both in industry and government, outstanding examples of each can be cited.

(1) Functional Organization. By this is meant organizing the Space Center into sub-elements identified with across-the-board scientific or space technology disciplines. For instance, guidance and control, astronomy, data handling, scientific instrumentation, and propulsion. In an R&D institution, this form of organization is necessary to advancing the basic state of various disciplines and arts, and functional applied areas. Specialists in a given area are grouped and are interested in evolving new knowledge and techniques without reference to a preconceived specific application, but with the full knowledge that whatever gaps are covered will benefit the program across the board. This type of organization is generally stable and develops specialists who can be tapped as consultants by the applied projects. Effort organized along this line, when staffed by competent people who are really research people, creates the store of knowledge which is absolutely required if program stagnation is to be prevented.

The disadvantage of this type of organization is that unless it is modified or subverted for this purpose, it results in diffuse project management when a major project is planned in the organization.

(2) Project Organization. A project manager should have under his control or as his responsibility all of the necessary resources prepared to fulfill the project's mission. In a functional organization dependent, of course, on personalities and other factors, the project manager is handicapped from "managing" and "directing" and is apt to become something of a coordinator-expediter. If the institution is charged with carrying out several major projects, the competition among projects for specialists' services, in-house central technical service support, and even use of certain contractors must be delineated by management by formal assignment and delegation. The easiest way to accomplish this is to assign resources including personnel to the project under the direct control of the project director. The "project" should use central services where they exist and it is feasible.

294

It is concluded from the above that the Beltsville organization
should be based on functional lines with organizational flexibility
allowing the Center to organize for major or "macro" projects. Small
or "micro" projects can and should be carried in the functional
divisions.

7. Program Requirements. The program currently assigned and contemplated
for the Space Center has not yet been detailed in full. However, the
major efforts which are listed below indicate a very large and active
program which will require a great deal of contracting plus a heter-
ogeneous, competent, and sizable Space Center staff. Some of these
assignments, active or to become active in the next eighteen months, are:

  (1) Science Program
     155 sounding rockets of various types
     30 satellites
     15 probes

  (2) Application Satellites
    — Communications and Meteorological, 6 or 7 vehicles,
    — Geodetic—number of satellites unknown at this time,
    — Other Vanguard Division follow-on programs—vehicles and
      numbers as yet undetermined.

  (3) Project Mercury
    — Phase I
    — Phase II

  (4) Vehicles and Engines
    Vega, Centaur, Thor-Vanguard (Thor-Delta), Juno V (1.5 meg engine),
    Nova (1.6 meg engine known currently as 1.0 meg engine).

  (5) Global Range and Operations
    — Space Communications and Tracking
    — Operational Telemetering
    — Ranges—Wallops, AMR, PMR

8. Numbers of Personnel Required. Currently, all segments of the
organization, in terms of personnel numbers, are merely nuclei of the
ultimate staffs needed to do the jobs to be done. There is the feeling
that budget planning for the next fiscal year does not include adequate
numbers for the Space Center to carry out its mission. In general the
program managers, that is Division Heads, feel that if adequate numbers
of competent personnel can be brought on the staff, this is more important
than studying at this point how the Space Center is to be organized. This
feeling is not to be interpreted as a cry for anarchy or lack of
organization, but as an expression that thinking about the Space Center
sometimes seems to ignore the fact that the Space Center is already very
much a going concern. Geographical dispersion and logistic support
currently supplied in part by NRL, Langley, and Lewis tend to cloud
thinking on immediate future requirements. The fact that the physical
plant does not exist should not deny the existence of the going major
components of the organization. The general feeling was expressed that we
are headed for trouble in 1960 unless the complement figures, in particular,
are raised above levels being cited currently.

9. Space Center functions in terms of existing nucleus capabilities.
The Space Center is not starting from scratch in organizing a technical

competence. The five groups at the Division level now in operation have a nucleus capability to perform work organized functionally or by project in the following areas:

    (1) Space Sciences,
    (3) Vehicle Systems,
    (3) Theoretical Research and Support,
    (4) Instrumentation Support,
    (5) Payload Systems,
    (6) Data Handling and Techniques,
    (7) Communications and Tracking,
    (8) Operations.

10. My suggestions for organization of the Space Center:
    (1) To fully integrate it into the National Space Program,
    (2) To fully capture and utilize the nuclei of existing capabilities, and
    (3) To fulfill the potential which the senior personnel of the Center feel can be brought into being realistically,

are attached hereto with explanatory notes.

/s/ T. E. JENKINS
Administrative Officer

296

```
┌─────────────────┐
│                 │
│   EXHIBIT 9      │
│   COPY           │
│                 │
└─────────────────┘
```

NATIONAL AERONAUTICS AND SPACE ADMINISTRATION
BELTSVILLE SPACE CENTER

6 March 1959

MEMORANDUM FOR ALL CONCERNED

FROM: T. E. Jenkins, Administrative Officer

SUBJ: BSC Divisions' Authorized Personnel Complements, FY 1959;
 summary of recent revisions

1. To sum up the current situation with respect to Beltsville Space Center
division approved personnel complements (ceiling points):
 a. We requested a total of 342 ceiling points to cover the Vanguard
Division, including 42 for my Administrative staff;
 b. Dr. Silverstein approved an allocation against the Vanguard money
of 400 but to include 90 for Space Sciences Division. Dr. Silverstein
also promised Mr. Townsend he could get an additional 10 from the 400 if he
needs it by 30 June. Space Sciences Division then can go to a total of 100;
 c. Dr. Jastrow requested relief for the Theoretical Division of 10
points. Abe approved 6 points for Jastrow (plus 30 points carried
against S&E for a total of 36);
 d. In summary, the total of 400 ceiling points authorized against
Vanguard funds reserved on Headquarters' books is tentatively allocated
as follows:

> Total authorized 400
>   Space Sciences Division (Townsend) 100
>   Theoretical Division (Jastrow) 6
>   Vanguard Division (Hagen) 252
>   Beltsville Administrative Office (Jenkins) 42
>   Total 400

2. Vanguard Division, in all likelihood, will require more than 252 points
prior to 30 June 1959. In the financial summary we presented to Dr.
Silverstein there is money reserved to cover some additional points. In
fonecon with Dr. Silverstein I agreed it was too early to forecast how
successful Vanguard recruiting efforts will be, but all indications are
that they will be highly successful. Currently, physical work space
is the limiting factor. Vanguard will not exceed this ceiling without
specifically getting an approval by the Director, Space Flight Development.
3. <u>Controls.</u> I am taking steps through the Beltsville personnel office to
control accessions within the above figures. <u>By this memorandum Division
Heads (Hagen, Jastrow, Townsend) are advised that all PAR Form 52s
must be submitted to the Beltsville Personnel Office, Attention Code</u>

4100B (Al Nagy) <u>for approval within authorized complement and money</u>
<u>before commitments to hire can be considered firm with the candidate.</u>
If the total ceiling of 400 proves inadequate I will request additional
authorizations from Dr. Silverstein based on division justifications.

/s/ T. E. JENKINS
Administrative Officer

Distribution:

Headquarters:	Beltsville:
A. Silverstein	J. Hagen
A. Siepert	J. Townsend
D. Wyatt	R. Jastrow
A. Hodgson	A. Nagy
R. Ulmer (3)	B. Sisco
R. Lacklen (2)	L. Best
H. Fuhrman	B. Cowan

EXHIBIT 10
COPY

NATIONAL AERONAUTICS AND SPACE ADMINISTRATION
1520 H STREET NORTHWEST
WASHINGTON 25, D.C.

OFFICE OF THE ADMINISTRATOR   May 1, 1959

MEMORANDUM from the Administrator

Subject: Functions and Authority — Goddard Space Flight Center (GSFC)

1. Purpose of this Memorandum.
   a. To establish the Goddard Space Flight Center, Greenbelt, Maryland
   b. To provide a statement of functions and authority for the Goddard Space Flight Center.
2. Functions. The Goddard Space Flight Center is assigned the following functions:
   a. Conducting advanced planning and theoretical studies leading to the development of payloads for scientific and manned space flights.
   b. Conducting necessary supporting research in scientific payloads, applications systems, instrumentation, communications, guidance, and vehicles.
   c. Developing payloads for approved scientific programs, applications programs, and manned space flights.
   d. Developing, subject to specific approval in each case, vehicles to launch payloads.
   e. Supervising Goddard Space Flight Center flight operations, integrating the activities of all participants as necessary to accomplish missions successfully.
   f. Supervising tracking, data acquisition, communications and computing operations for the provision of orbital and reduced flight data from satellites and space vehicles for NASA space flight programs assigned to or monitored by the Center and for other space programs as requested by the Director of Space Flight Development.
   g. Interpreting results of flight programs for which the Goddard Space Flight Center is responsible.
   h. Furnishing technical management of projects, including monitoring of contractors, to insure timely and economical accomplishment of objectives.
   i. Exercising such procurement and contract administration authority as may be delegated by the Director, Office of Business Administration.
   j. Upon request by the Director of Space Flight Development, providing support for space program activities of other

organizations, e.g., military establishments of Department of Defense.

k. Reporting on the status of approved programs and recommending changes or modifications as necessary to meet program goals and schedules.

l. Providing necessary administrative and management support as required for carrying out assigned programs.

3. Responsibility of Director, GSFC. The Director, GSFC, reports directly to the Director of Space Flight Development and is responsible for the exercise of the functions assigned to the Goddard Space Flight Center.

4. Scope of Authority. The Director, GSFC, is authorized and directed to take such action as is necessary to carry out the responsibilities assigned to him within the limitations of this and other official NASA communications and issuances.

5. Relationships with Other Officials. In performing the functions assigned to him, the Director, GSFC, is responsible for recognizing the responsibility and authority of heads of divisions and offices, Headquarters and for assuring that actions he may take are properly coordinated with Headquarters groups having joint interests and are in accordance with NASA policies.

6. Approval of Organization. The basic organization of the GSFC is outlined on the attached organization chart. Modifications or changes in basic organization structure are subject to the approval of the Director, Space Flight Development and the Administrator, NASA.

/s/ T. Keith Glennan
Administrator

Encl
  Chart

EXHIBIT 11
COPY

NATIONAL AERONAUTICS AND SPACE ADMINISTRATION
GODDARD SPACE FLIGHT CENTER

4100A-89:TEJ:vmb
May 1, 1959

MEMORANDUM TO ASSISTANT DIRECTORS AND DIVISION CHIEFS

Subject: Organization and Functions of the Goddard Space Flight Center

1. Effective May 1, 1959 the Beltsville Space Center became the Goddard
Space Flight Center. The change in name accompanies the first formal
announcement of the Space Flight Center organization, mission, functions,
and appointments of many of the key personnel.

2. Attached is the official statement on organization and functions
accompanied by the official organization chart for the Space Flight Center.
As with most documents of this type, the wording in some cases may carry
different meaning to different people. Therefore, it should be stated
that the spelling out of the mission was not done to be restrictive so far as
activities conducted by the Space Center are concerned. The mission
is broad and the functions certainly spell out more responsibilities than
we can fully carry out or will be able to carry out until our capabilities
have been built up much beyond the point where they now exist.

3. There are many administrative details to be sorted out and published to
gear internal operations to the new organization structure. Such workaday
things as time cards, directories, job order numbers, delegations of
authority, et cetera are in the process of being published. We did as much
preplanning work as possible, but since all organization details were not
nailed down until a very late hour it will take us a couple of days to
publish the necessary instructions. In the meantime, you are advised that
all previous instructions remain in effect until superseded. For
instance, job order and account numbers to be used on time cards, stubs,
et cetera will remain the same until changed by specific notice. This
paragraph is not to be interpreted in any way as abrogating the
authority of any appointed official.

(signed)
T. E. JENKINS
Administrative Officer

```
┌─────────────────┐
│                 │
│     COPY        │
│                 │
└─────────────────┘
```

NATIONAL AERONAUTICS AND SPACE ADMINISTRATION
WASHINGTON 25, D.C.

ORGANIZATION OF ACTIVITIES
OF GODDARD SPACE FLIGHT CENTER

<u>Mission and Functions</u>

1. Operating as an integral part of the NASA space flight program, under the overall guidance and direction of the Director of Space Flight Development, NASA Headquarters, the Goddard Space Flight Center will be a major field arm of NASA. It will carry out assigned missions in the planning, research, developmental, and operational phases of the nation's space flight program. Specifically, personnel of the Center shall:

a) Conduct advanced planning and theoretical studies leading to the development of payloads for scientific and manned space flights.

b) Conduct necessary supporting research in scientific payloads, applications systems, instrumentation, communications, guidance, and vehicles.

c) Develop payloads for approved scientific programs, applications programs, and manned space flights.

d) Develop, subject to specific approval in each case, vehicles to launch payloads.

e) Supervise Goddard Space Flight Center flight operations, integrating the activities of all participants as necessary to accomplish missions successfully.

f) Supervise tracking, data acquisition, communications and computing operations for the provision of orbital and reduced flight data from satellites and space vehicles for NASA space flight programs assigned to or monitored by the Center and for other space programs as requested by the Director of Space Flight Development.

g) Interpret results of flight programs for which the Goddard Space Flight Center is responsible.

h) Furnish technical management of projects, including monitoring of contractors, to insure timely and economical accomplishment of objectives. In this connection, the Goddard Space Flight Center will execute contracts, in accordance with delegated authority, for performance of work necessary to accomplish program objectives.

i) Upon request by the Director of Space Flight Development, provide support for space program activities of other organizations, e.g., military establishments of Department of Defense.

2. These missions will be carried out through the execution of major functions as described below:

a) <u>Advance Planning.</u> The Goddard Space Flight Center staff will include leaders in the several space science fields who will be responsible for the formulation of ideas and concepts which are essential to the effectiveness of the space flight program. This advance planning will be of value to the Space Flight Center in carrying out its mission. Also, the Space Flight Center will assist and advise the Office of Space Flight Development, NASA Headquarters, in the formulation of the national space flight program.

b) Research. The Space Flight Center will perform two broad types of research: scientific and engineering research necessary to serve as a base for future ideas and applications; and research in the disciplines of the space sciences as a basis for acquiring ever-increasing knowledge of space phenomena.

c) Development and Fabrication. The Goddard Space Flight Center will design and develop, including prototype fabrication, components and systems which advance the state-of-the-art of space technology or which have direct project application. A part of this activity will be in-house, while the remainder will be on contract. The development and fabrication activities to be handled in-house will normally be those which cannot be handled as economically, expeditiously, or effectively by a contractor, either because they are so intimately related to other activities being carried out at the Center or because they involve matters so fundamental to major in-house project operations of the Center that they cannot readily be separated therefrom.

d) Operations. The Space Flight Center personnel will be in charge of technical operations in the field for all programs assigned to the Center. These programs will include in-house projects as well as those on contract for which the Center has the monitoring responsibility. Space Flight Center technical teams at launches will be under the technical direction and control of project and functional heads within the Center. Space communications and tracking, as well as data reduction and interpretation, will be operational responsibilities of the Space Flight Center. For other NASA space flight programs, the Center, upon request of the Director of Space Flight Development, will assume operational responsibility for tracking, data acquisition, communications and computing operations and for the provision of orbital and reduced flight data from satellites and space vehicles.

e) Project Management. The Space Flight Center will be responsible for the management of projects and parts of projects as necessary for the accomplishment of its assigned missions. A project in this sense is the application of scientific and engineering technology to a specified objective, such as man-in-space, meteorological satellites, lunar probes, and so forth. Ideas for projects may originate in Headquarters, in the NASA field organizations, or from other sources. Projects will be undertaken following authorization by Headquarters. Projects will be carried out on either an in-house or a contract basis. Monitoring responsibility may from time to time be assigned to the Space Flight Center on contracts let by NASA Headquarters. Project officers will be designated from the NASA Headquarters staff to advise and assist the Goddard Space Flight Center in projects execution and in resolving management problems which require Headquarters attention and support.

Relationships

1. **With Office of Space Flight Development, NASA Headquarters**
    a) The Goddard Space Flight Center will participate with the Office of Space Flight Development in the definition and establishment of national program objectives.
    b) Within the defined national program objectives, the Goddard Space Flight Center will carry the full responsibility for accomplishing the missions assigned to it, subject to such technical advice and assistance as the Office of Space Flight Development, NASA Headquarters, may provide.
    c) The Goddard Space Flight Center will keep the Office of Space Flight Development fully informed at all times concerning problems arising and progress made in connection with the Center's assigned responsibilities.
    d) The Goddard Space Flight Center will be responsible for its own internal administration, in accordance with the provisions of applicable statutes and policies, procedures, and regulations issued by NASA Headquarters.
2. **With JPL**
    The missions and functions of the Goddard Space Flight Center and the Jet Propulsion Laboratory complement each other. There will be no contractual relationships between the two, but there will be frequent interchange of data and technical information to the extent warranted by the common interests of both or as necessary for the operations of either. The relationships between these two organizations, both active in the space flight development field, will be essentially the same as those which exist between the NASA Research Centers.
3. **With NASA Research Centers**
    The Goddard Space Flight Center will have no formal relationships with the NASA Research Centers except through NASA Headquarters. The channel of communications in matters requiring formal action will normally be: Goddard Space Flight Center to Office of Space Flight Development, NASA Headquarters, to Office of Aeronautical and Space Research, NASA Headquarters, to the Research Centers. Such matters originating in the Research Centers will be referred to the Goddard Space Flight Center through the same offices, but in opposite sequence. Interchange of information and data, however, may be carried on freely between the Space Flight Center and the Research Centers without regard to these channels, except that information copies shall be furnished to the Office of Space Flight Development and the Office of Aeronautical and Space Research, NASA Headquarters.
4. **With Contractors**
    The Goddard Space Flight Center will be authorized to enter into contractual arrangements with private contractors in accordance with applicable NASA policies, regulations, and procedures. Subject to the limitations imposed by such policies, regulations, and procedures, the Goddard Space Flight Center will have the authority to develop contract specifications, including engineering design where appropriate, invite bids, evaluate proposals, make awards and monitor performance.
5. **With Governmental Agencies**
    There will be contractual relationships between the Goddard Space

Flight Center and other governmental agencies as authorized by
NASA Headquarters.

Organization of the Goddard Space Flight Center

1. Attached is an organization chart reflecting the components which
are proposed as major segments of the Goddard Space Flight Center.
This organization provides:

    a) Integration of the missions and functions of the Goddard Space
Flight Center with the national space program objectives.

    b) Coordination of the direction of the scientific and
technical functions of the Center with the supporting engineering
and business management activities.

    c) A staffing pattern that anticipates and provides for the
orderly integration of the personnel and functions now separately
located at Langley Research Center, Lewis Research Center, and
Naval Research Laboratory.

    d) A management structure capable of full execution of both
technical and support activities with the same degree of delegated
responsibility that characterizes the operation of other major
NASA field establishments.

2. The scientific and technical programs of the Center are grouped
under three Assistant Directors.

    a) The Assistant Director, Space Science and Satellite Applications,
will be responsible for:

      1) Space Sciences Division — responsible for conduct of a
broad program of basic research in the space sciences through
the use of experiments carried in rockets, earth satellites,
and space probes.

      2) Theoretical Division — responsible for conduct of a broad
program of study and research in phases of theoretical physics,
mathematics, and mechanics associated with the exploration of space.

      3) Payload Systems Division — responsible for integration
of scientific experiments and equipments into complete
earth satellites and space probes; conducts research and
development in the fields of space environment and special
electronic devices such as telemetering systems, command
receivers, control circuitry, and power supplies; designs,
fabricates, constructs, and tests satellite and probe space systems.

      4) Satellite Applications Systems Division — responsible for
research and development on applications systems, including:
applications satellites, such as the meteorological,
communications, and geodetic satellites; space techniques such
as advanced control and stabilization systems; and space and
booster vehicle systems.

    b) The Assistant Director, Tracking and Data Systems, will be
responsible for:

      1) Tracking Systems Division — responsible for research and
development on new systems for tracking, data acquisition, and
communications between satellites and/or space vehicles and ground
receiving stations; provides evaluation capability for all
system proposals plus calibration capability for systems
which are in operation; provides technical and engineering

support for all modifications and enlargements of technical equipment at the field stations, by furnishing prototype equipment, contract monitoring, and field installation and technical inspection services.

2) Data Systems Division — responsible for the application of data reduction techniques to: launching of vehicles, orbit calculation, and satellite and space probe scientific data; conducts research and development on new data handling techniques as required for Space Flight Center programs, and furnishes theoretical support for all phases of data techniques and analyses; responsible for data reduction and computation activities connected with NASA space flight programs assigned to, or monitored by, personnel of the Center; provides computation service for all areas of the Center as required, as requested by Director of Space Flight Development, assumes operational responsibility for data reduction and computation activities for other NASA or Department of Defense programs.

3) Operational Support Division — responsible for establishment and continuous operation of global tracking, data acquisition, and communications network, furnishing personnel and technical and logistic support therefore; operates control center of the Goddard Space Flight Center, furnishes continuing technical support of space flight operations, including range support and operations necessary to initiate communication, tracking and data sequences after vehicle launch; coordinates operations to assure utilization of the net and adequate service to user teams, both inside and outside NASA.

c) The Assistant Director, Manned Satellites, will be responsible for:

1) Flight Systems Division — responsible for conceptual design, integration and performance of complete manned space flight systems, including on-board equipment and subsystems; carries out preliminary design and performance analyses and specifies requirements for advanced systems; monitors or performs the required basic and applied research in support of space flight systems.

2) Operations Division — responsible for establishing operational procedures associated with the launch, in-orbit, reentry and recovery phases of manned space flight missions; accomplishes detailed trajectory analyses associated with each mission in the Mercury Program to ensure that test plans and test schedules are met; conducts necessary pre-flight checking and in-flight monitoring in order to maintain flight safety; selects and trains flight crews appropriate for each flight test.

3) Engineering and Specifications Division — responsible for engineering studies of proposed manned space flight vehicles and components to determine their feasibility; prepares specifications and cost estimates; supplies and monitors technical information required for the procurement and administration of contracts.

3. There is also included in the organization a Special Projects Group, currently identified as the Lewis Space Task Group, which has program

responsibility for engineering development and design of a special
high energy rocket stage.

4. The Office of Business Administration will provide the Center
with the full range of central administrative support functions, including:
personnel administration; budget and financial administration; plant
and personnel security programs; management analysis activities;
administrative services, including plant and fire protection; procurement
and supply, including contract administration; and technical information,
including library services.

5. The Office of Technical Services initially will include only
the construction group which is already in existence. As construction
progresses, however, and the Space Flight Center becomes a physical
reality, it will be necessary to staff this Office to perform the full
range of its functions. These will include: fabrication and shop operations;
construction and repair; buildings and grounds maintenance;
utilities operations, automotive operations, and industrial safety.

/s/ Abe Silverstein
Director of Space Flight Development

Attachment
  1 Chart
Date: 1 May 1959

EXHIBIT 12
COPY

NATIONAL AERONAUTICS AND SPACE ADMINISTRATION
Washington 25, D. C.

NASA RELEASE NO. 59-125   FOR RELEASE:
EX 3-3260   Friday P.M.
Ext. 7827   May 1, 1959

NASA'S NEW SPACE PROJECTS FACILITY NAMED
GODDARD SPACE FLIGHT CENTER

T. Keith Glennan, NASA Administrator, announced today the Government's space projects center at Greenbelt, Maryland, will be named the Goddard Space Flight Center in commemoration of Robert H. Goddard, American pioneer in rocket research.

The Goddard Space Flight Center, under the overall guidance of the Director of Space Flight Development at NASA Headquarters, will perform basic space research and will be responsible for the development of satellites, space probes and vehicles, tracking, communications, and data reduction systems. In addition, the facility will eventually be a command control center for NASA space flight operations.

The organization of NASA's new Space Center includes a director, not yet appointed; three major research and development groups, each headed by an assistant director; and business administration and technical services departments.

John W. Townsend, Jr., formerly Chief of NASA's Space Sciences Division, has been appointed Assistant Director for Space Science and Satellite Applications. Divisions reporting to him are: Space Sciences, Theoretical, Satellite Applications Systems, and Payload Systems. The Vanguard Operations Coordinating Group also reports to Townsend. Beginning today, the staff of the Vanguard Division will be integrated into other major NASA space flight projects.

John T. Mengel, former head of the Space Tracking Systems Branch in the Vanguard Division, has been named Assistant Director for Tracking and Data Systems. Reporting to him are the Tracking Systems, Data Systems, and Operational Support Divisions.

Robert R. Gilruth is the Center's Assistant Director for Manned Satellites. He currently heads the Mercury manned space flight project. Divisions under his direction are: Flight Systems, Engineering and Specifications, and Operations.

Michael J. Vaccaro, formerly assistant head of the Administrative Management Office and Personnel Director at the Lewis Research Center, Cleveland, Ohio, has been appointed Business Manager of the Space Center. The head of Technical Services has not been announced.

The Goddard Space Flight Center will be built on an approximately

550-acre tract acquired from the Government's Beltsville Agricultural
Center, north of Washington, D. C. Located east of the Baltimore-Washington
Parkway, the site is bounded on the south by Glendale Road.

The contract for the first two major buildings at the Center — Space
Projects Building and Research Projects Laboratory—was let
April 10, 1959, to Norair Engineering Corporation of Washington, D.C.,
at a total cost of $2,882,577. These two-story buildings, scheduled
for completion in mid-1960, will total about 100,000 square feet of
laboratory and office floor space. They will house a staff of about 450. The
remainder of the staff of the Goddard Space Flight Center will be
housed at the U.S. Naval Research Laboratory in Washington, and
at the Langley Research Center, Langley Field, Virginia, until the
completion of the facility.

EXHIBIT 13
COPY

NATIONAL AERONAUTICS AND SPACE ADMINISTRATION

NEWS RELEASE

GODDARD
SPACE FLIGHT CENTER
GREENBELT, MD.

OFFICE OF PUBLIC INFORMATION
PHONE: GRanite 4-9000, Ex. 555

RELEASE NO. 3-10-61-5

FOR RELEASE
SUNDAY A.M.'s
March 12, 1961

The National Aeronautics and Space Administration will dedicate
its $27-million Goddard Space Flight Center at Greenbelt, Md., on
March 16. The Dedication date marks the 35th anniversary of the world's
first flight of a liquid-propelled rocket engine by Dr. Robert H. Goddard,
father of American rocketry, for whom the Center has been named.

The Center, which will be completed by the end of next year, is the
first completely new complex to be constructed and staffed for the peaceful
exploration of space since NASA was established in October, 1958.

Center personnel conceive, develop and fabricate satellite and
sounding rocket instrumentation that probe space in the immediate vicinity
of the earth. The Center also has the world-wide responsibility for
tracking, communications and data analysis for both manned and unmanned
spacecraft.

Several hundred invited guests are expected to attend the
Dedication ceremony which will begin at 2 P.M. The ceremony will be
followed by a guided one and one-half hour tour of the Center's facilities.
The Dedication will not be open to the public. Open house for
employees and their families will be held Saturday, March 18 from 10:30 to
3:30 P.M. It is planned to hold a public open house later as the
Center nears completion.

The Center will be dedicated by Dr. Detlev Wulf Bronk, President of
the National Academy of Sciences. He will be introduced by James E. Webb,
NASA Administrator. An honored guest will be Mrs. Esther Goddard,
widow of the Clark University rocket pioneer. She will be presented a
Congressional Gold Medal, authorized by the 86th Congress. The
presentation will be made jointly by Senator Robert S. Kerr (D-Okla.),
Chairman of the Senate Committee on Aeronautical and Space Sciences, and

Overton Brooks (D-La.), Chairman of the House Committee on Science and Astronautics.

Mrs. Goddard and Dr. Bronk will unveil a sculpture of Dr. Goddard which later will be placed in the Center's Administration Building. It was created by Washington sculptor, Joseph Anthony Atchison, noted for his creative work in the Shrine of the Immaculate Conception in Washington, the World Flight Memorial for the Smithsonian Institution, and the Second Inaugural Medal of Franklin D. Roosevelt.

Invocation for the ceremonies will be delivered by The Rev. Kenneth B. Wyatt, pastor of the Greenbelt Community Church. The benediction will be said by Father Victor J. Dowgiallo, pastor of St. Hugh's Catholic Church, Greenbelt.

The tours, both for invited guests and the "open house" for employees and their families, will embrace the full spectrum of the Center's activities. Included will be a Control Room demonstration with simulation of a pre-rocket launch and countdown procedures, followed by a simulated satellite injection into orbit.

Lectures will be given on the Center's operation of global satellite tracking networks, including Minitrack and Project Mercury. The Center's cooperative role for the international exploration of space will be explained. Guests will see an animated miniature tracking station, and a scale model of the forthcoming S-51 spacecraft being instrumented by the United Kingdom which will be flown by Goddard.

There will be an extensive display of spacecraft instrumentation along with many of the Goddard Center's family of sounding rockets used for scientific experiments. Included will be an Iris Sounding Rocket and an Aerobee 150A with a new attitude (or pointing) control system. A similar rocket will be fired March 15 for the first test of controlling a rocket's three axes of pitch, yaw and roll. The experiment also will carry equipment aimed at measuring gamma ray intensities and the solar illumination.

Other models will include the Tiros weather satellite; the P-14 magnetometer (or radiation-counting) spacecraft; the S-3 energetic particles measurement satellite; the Explorer VIII and Vanguard I. Guests will also see a demonstration of a micrometeorite detector.

Tours will be conducted through the Center's extensive laboratory facilities where guests will see vacuum, vibration and spin-balancing equipment used to simulate space environmental conditions.

NATIONAL AERONAUTICS AND SPACE ADMINISTRATION
NEWS RELEASE

GODDARD
SPACE FLIGHT CENTER
GREENBELT, MD.

OFFICE OF PUBLIC INFORMATION
PHONE: GRanite 4-9000, Ex. 555

RELEASE NO. 3/14/61-1

GODDARD SPACE FLIGHT CENTER

FACT SHEET

The National Aeronautics and Space Administration Goddard Space Flight Center is the first completely new scientific center created since the NASA was established October 1, 1958. It is the nation's newest facility devoted exclusively to the peaceful exploration of space.

Formally organized on May 1, 1959, it was named for the late Dr. Robert H. Goddard, recognized as the Father of American Rocketry. He designed, developed and flew the world's first liquid-fuel rocket.

The Center was dedicated March 16, 1961, the Thirty-fifth Anniversary of that launching by Dr. Goddard.

The Goddard Space Flight Center is one of ten field laboratory facilities of the N.A.S.A., and is one of several integrated units under the direction of the Office of Space Flight Programs. The Center carries out assigned missions in the theoretical, planning, research, development and operational phases of space flight, utilizing laboratory studies and experiments, sounding rockets, earth satellites and space probes.

Organization

Dr. Harry J. Goett is Director of the Goddard Space Flight Center. Principal operating executive is Eugene W. Wasielewski, Associate Director. Other major officials and their duties are:

Mr. John W. Townsend, Jr., Assistant Director, Space Sciences and Satellite Applications, supervises four divisions:

    a. The Space Sciences Division, headed by Dr. Leslie H. Meredith, conducts basic research in the space sciences through the use of experiments carried in rocket sondes, earth satellites, and space probes. It supports the NASA National Sounding Rocket Program and provides management and contract monitoring.

b. The Theoretical Division, headed by Dr. Robert Jastrow, studies and conducts research in theoretical physics, mathematics, and mechanics associated with space exploration. Included are special analytical problems involving the use of large computers. The Division is now organizing an Institute for Space Studies in New York City, where it will draw on talent from universities and research groups.

c. The Payload Systems Division, headed by N. Whitney Matthews, is responsible for the integration of experiments and equipments into complete earth satellites and space probes; and for the basic satellite structure, thermal balance, and integrity of the entire system through all anticipated environmental conditions.

d. The Satellite Applications Division, headed by D. G. Mazur, is concerned with research, preliminary design and project management of meteorological, communications, and geodetic satellites.

Mr. John T. Mengel, Assistant Director, Tracking and Data Systems. This office supervises three divisions:

a. Tracking Systems Division, headed by Clarence A. Schroeder, which concerns itself with research and development of new tracking, data acquisition and communications systems between space vehicles and ground receiving stations.

b. The Data Systems Division, headed by Dr. Charles V. L. Smith, applies data reduction techniques to launchings of vehicles, orbit calculations, and satellite and space probe findings.

c. The Operational Support Division, headed by Fred S. Friel, establishes and operates NASA's global tracking, data acquisition, and communications network.

d. The Theory and Analysis Staff, headed by Dr. Joseph W. Siry, provides orbital and system analysis support for tracking and data systems.

Dr. Michael J. Vaccaro, Assistant Director, Business Administration. This office provides business management support functions, including personnel, budget and finance, security, procurement and supply, administrative, and public information.

Mr. Leopold Winkler, Chief, Office of Technical Services. This office is charged with fabrication and shop operation, construction and repair, buildings and grounds maintenance, utilities and automotive operation, and industrial safety.

The Goddard Mission

Specific areas of Goddard's responsibilities are:

• Advanced planning and theoretical studies leading to development of spacecraft for manned and unmanned scientific space investigations. This work includes formulation of concepts and ideas essential to the effectiveness of the NASA program.

• Supporting research in spacecraft, applications systems,

instrumentation, communications, guidance, and rocket vehicles as assigned.

• Development and fabrication of spacecraft for scientific and applications programs and manned space flight. The Center designs, develops, and fabricates prototypes of components and systems to advance space technology or to foster practical applications. Although the Center directs all such work, most of it is contracted out to industry and universities. For reasons of economy, urgency, efficiency or effectiveness, about fifteen percent of such activities are performed internally by the Center.

• Development and supervision of worldwide tracking, data acquisition, communications and computing operations for all NASA space programs except deep space probes.

• Interpretation of results of experiments under Goddard management.

• Management of projects, including technical direction and the execution and monitoring of contracts.

Staff and Facilities

Located on a 550-acre tract of land near Greenbelt, Maryland, about fifteen miles from Washington, D.C., the physical plant when completed in 1962 will consist of eight facilities costing approximately $27 million. Facilities now in operation are: Space Projects Building, Research Projects Laboratory and Central Flight Control and Operations.

First elements of the Goddard Staff were drawn from the Vanguard Project Team of the U.S. Naval Research Laboratory. The complement now numbers more than 1,300 and will total 1,800 by the end of 1961. It is expected to rise to about 2,000 when the Center construction is completed.

Facilities at the Center will enable scientists and engineers to subject payloads to the complete range of flight environments without having to risk an actual launch with untried hardware.

As one example, the Center's environmental test facilities include centrifuges, dynamic balancing machines, vibration machines, and thermal vacuum chambers. Of the last, there will be four when the present construction program is completed—including some of the largest chambers in the country. The largest will measure thirty feet by forty feet and will be capable of producing the complete range of near-space vacuum and temperature conditions.

Scientific Exploration in Space

Goddard Center programs embrace unmanned scientific research and exploration of space; study of the earth's upper atmosphere; study of the earth itself from the space viewpoint; unmanned technological utilization of space for practical purposes, such as weather forecasting and global telephone, radio and television communications; and near-space tracking and data handling.

During the present decade, in the execution of this program, the Center plans to launch at least ninety-six scientific satellites and twenty-eight applications satellites.

Launching of sounding rockets and space probes will total

hundreds. Purchases of sounding rockets in the current fiscal year include 22 Aerobees, 18 Nike-Asps, 20 Nike-Cajuns, 4 Argo D-4's (Javelins), 2 Argo D-8's (Journeyman), 5 Iris. Frequency of rocket launchings is expected to increase steadily over the next decade, particularly in support of the Tiros-Nimbus weather satellite programs.

The Center plays a major role in NASA's international cooperation for the peaceful exploration of space. Scientists of twenty-one nations are participating in the Tiros meteorological satellite experiments; Canada is designing the payload for a swept-frequency topside ionosphere sounder satellite to be launched and tracked by Goddard; United Kingdom will supply the experiments for an international ionosphere satellite to be built and launched by Goddard; and a number of scientists and technicians are in cooperative study and training at the Center.

Accomplishments

Since its organization, the Goddard staff has made significant contributions to knowledge of space and the earth.

The VANGUARD III satellite, designed and launched by the Goddard Staff, provided information on the distribution and intensity of the earth's magnetic fields; detailed location of the lower edge of the Van Allen Great Radiation Belt, and made an accurate count of micrometeorite impacts.

The EXPLORER VII satellite, in which Goddard played a key role in cooperation with the NASA Marshall Space Flight Center and the Jet Propulsion Laboratory, provided valuable information on radiation balance, Lyman-Alpha x-rays, heavy primary rays, micrometeorite impacts, solar exposure, temperature, magnetic storms and detected large-scale weather patterns.

The PIONEER V space probe experiment, jointly conducted by Goddard and the Space Technology Laboratories, transmitted valuable data on solar flares, particle energies and their distribution, and magnetic fields. The probe, second U.S. spacecraft to orbit the sun, transmitted data to earth from a record distance of 22,500,000 miles.

The TIROS I and II meteorological satellite experiments, launched by the Delta rocket developed under Goddard supervision, provided many thousands of photographs of the earth's cloud cover and mapped radiation and heat balance on a global scale.

ECHO I, the first passive communications satellite, was launched in cooperation with the NASA Langley Research Center. This 100-foot inflatable sphere proved the feasibility of communications over long distances by bouncing radio signals off its reflective surface. Messages were transmitted across the continent and across the Atlantic and photographs were sent by the same means.

The EXPLORER VIII satellite, another joint project of Goddard, the Jet Propulsion Laboratory and Marshall Space Flight Center, carried out the first intensive direct measurements of the earth's ionosphere, by measuring concentrations of charged particles and their temperatures.

In its sounding rocket programs, Goddard made the first measurements of auroral absorption events and solar proton beams; first flew an alkali vapor magnetometer to measure the earth's magnetic field at altitudes above 600 miles, and obtained the first ultraviolet stellar spectra.

The NERV, or Nuclear Emulsion Recovery Vehicle, launched by sounding rocket from the Pacific Missile Range to a height of 1,260 miles, was recovered from the ocean. The experiment produced exact measurements of the lower Van Allen Great Radiation Belt.

HISTORICAL BACKGROUND AND COMMUNICATIONS SATELLITE ACT OF 1962

On August 31, 1962, the President signed H.R. 11040, and the
Communications Satellite Act of 1962 became law. At the time of
signing, the President congratulated the Congress for "a step of
historical importance." He stated further: "It promises significant
benefits to our own people and to the whole world. Its purpose is to
establish a commercial communications system, utilizing space satellites
which will serve our needs and those of other countries and contribute
to world peace and understanding."

Major steps in the development of this legislation were as follows:

a. June 15, 1961, the President asked the Chairman of the National
   Aeronautics and Space Council to have recommendations prepared
   for communications satellite policy. Under direction of the
   Council staff, interagency meetings were held; policy recommendations were drafted; and those recommendations were acted upon
   unanimously by the Council.

b. July 14, 1961, the President approved and released the policy
   statement, which stressed the public interest objectives in
   obtaining a global system as soon as technically feasible. This
   policy stated that private ownership and operation of the U.S.
   portion of the system is favored, provided that the public
   interest is adequately protected through opportunities for
   foreign participation, non-discriminatory use of and equitable
   access to the system, and effective competition in the acquisition of equipment and in the structure of ownership and control.

c. In the fall of 1961, the President requested the staff of the
   Council to draft recommendations in order that the communications
   satellite policy could be effectively implemented. Under the
   direction of the Council staff, interagency drafting sessions
   were held, and the proposed bill was prepared and transmitted
   to the President.

d. February 7, 1962, the President sent the proposed legislation
   to the Congress and, in his accompanying message, urged that it
   be given prompt and favorable consideration.

e. Extensive hearings were held in the Congress. Six different
   committees called witnesses and participated in a thorough
   examination of the communications satellite policy and proposed
   legislation. After such committee actions, explanation and
   debate took place prior to votes in both the House and the
   Senate. The House passed a bill by a 354 to 9 vote on May 3;
   the Senate passed its corresponding version of a bill by a 66
   to 11 vote on August 11; and the House acted to accept the
   Senate bill by a 377 to 10 vote on August 27.

f. August 31, 1962, the bill was signed by the President and
   became law.

g. October 4, 1962, the President nominated 13 distinguished citizens to be Incorporators, with the statutory responsibility for taking the necessary actions to establish a Communications Satellite Corporation.

The Incorporators, under interim appointments, have held a number of meetings to consider and initiate the steps required to organize the corporation and to apply for a charter under the District of Columbia Business Incorporation Act, as provided under the terms of the Communications Satellite Act.

The Communications Satellite Act of 1962 incorporates the major objectives of the President's policy statement of July 24, 1961. It provides authority for the creation of a private corporation to serve as the United States portion of any global system. It will be privately financed and the essential business management will be in the hands of 12 directors elected by the stockholders and 3 directors appointed by the President and confirmed by the Senate. At the same time that the benefits of profit-making incentives and private management are obtained, the Act is most careful to identify national policy objectives in relation to the use of commercial communications satellites and to provide the machinery within Government for the regulation of and assistance to the corporation. In such a framework, it is expected that the services the corporation provides and the way it conducts business will be wholly responsive to the several objectives of the Act.

Public Law 87-624
87th Congress, H. R. 11040
August 31, 1962

An Act

76 STAT. 419.

To provide for the establishment, ownership, operation, and regulation of a commercial communications satellite system, and for other purposes.

Be it enacted by the Senate and House of Representatives of the United States of America in Congress assembled,

TITLE I—SHORT TITLE, DECLARATION OF POLICY AND DEFINITIONS

SHORT TITLE

SEC. 101. This Act may be cited as the "Communications Satellite Act of 1962".

DECLARATION OF POLICY AND PURPOSE

SEC. 102. (a) The Congress hereby declares that it is the policy of the United States to establish, in conjunction and in cooperation with other countries, as expeditiously as practicable a commercial communications satellite system, as part of an improved global communications network, which will be responsive to public needs and national objectives, which will serve the communication needs of the United States and other countries, and which will contribute to world peace and understanding.

(b) The new and expanded telecommunication services are to be made available as promptly as possible and are to be extended to provide global coverage at the earliest practicable date. In effectuating this program, care and attention will be directed toward providing such services to economically less developed countries and areas as well as those more highly developed, toward efficient and economical use of the electromagnetic frequency spectrum, and toward the reflection of the benefits of this new technology in both quality of services and charges for such services.

(c) In order to facilitate this development and to provide for the widest possible participation by private enterprise, United States participation in the global system shall be in the form of a private corporation, subject to appropriate governmental regulation. It is the intent of Congress that all authorized users shall have nondiscriminatory access to the system; that maximum competition be maintained in the provision of equipment and services utilized by the system; that the corporation created under this Act be so organized and operated as to maintain and strengthen competition in the provision of communications services to the public; and that the activities of the corporation created under this Act and of the persons or companies participating in the ownership of the corporation shall be consistent with the Federal antitrust laws.

(d) It is not the intent of Congress by this Act to preclude the use of the communications satellite system for domestic communication services where consistent with the provisions of this Act nor to preclude the creation of additional communications satellite systems, if required to meet unique governmental needs or if otherwise required in the national interest.

319

DEFINITIONS

SEC. 103. As used in this Act, and unless the context otherwise requires—

(1) the term "communications satellite system" refers to a system of communications satellites in space whose purpose is to relay telecommunication information between satellite terminal stations, together with such associated equipment and facilities for tracking, guidance, control, and command functions as are not part of the generalized launching, tracking, control, and command facilities for all space purposes;

(2) the term "satellite terminal station" refers to a complex of communication equipment located on the earth's surface, operationally connected with one or more terrestrial communication systems, and capable of transmitting telecommunications to or receiving telecommunications from a communications satellite system.

(3) the term "communications satellite" means an earth satellite which is intentionally used to relay telecommunication information;

(4) the term "associated equipment and facilities" refers to facilities other than satellite terminal stations and communications satellites, to be constructed and operated for the primary purpose of a communications satellite system, whether for administration and management, for research and development, or for direct support of space operations;

(5) the term "research and development" refers to the conception, design, and first creation of experimental or prototype operational devices for the operation of a communications satellite system, including the assembly of separate components into a working whole, as distinguished from the term "production," which relates to the construction of such devices to fixed specifications compatible with repetitive duplication for operational applications; and

(6) the term "telecommunication" means any transmission, emission or reception of signs, signals, writings, images, and sounds or intelligence of any nature by wire, radio, optical, or other electromagnetic systems.

(7) the term "communications common carrier" has the same meaning as the term "common carrier" has when used in the Communications Act of 1934, as amended, and in addition includes, but only for purposes of sections 303 and 304, any individual, partnership, association, joint-stock company, trust, corporation, or other entity which owns or controls, directly or indirectly, or is under direct or indirect common control with, any such carrier; and the term "authorized carrier", except as otherwise provided for purposes of section 304 by section 304(b)(1), means a communications common carrier which has been authorized by the Federal Communications Commission under the Communications Act of 1934, as amended, to provide services by means of communications satellites;

(8) the term "corporation" means the corporation authorized by title III of this Act.

(9) the term "Administration" means the National Aeronautics and Space Administration; and

(10) the term "Commission" means the Federal Communications Commission.

TITLE II—FEDERAL COORDINATION, PLANNING, AND REGULATION

IMPLEMENTATION OF POLICY

SEC. 201. In order to achieve the objectives and to carry out the purposes of this Act—

(a) the President shall—

(1) aid in the planning and development and foster the execution of a national program for the establishment and operation, as expeditiously as possible, of a commercial communications satellite system;

(2) provide for continuous review of all phases of the development and operation of such a system, including the activities of a communications satellite corporation authorized under title 'II of this Act;

(3) coordinate the activities of governmental agencies with responsibilities in the field of telecommunication, so as to insure that there is full and effective compliance at all times with the policies set forth in this Act;

(4) exercise such supervision over relationships of the corporation with foreign governments or entities or with international bodies as may be appropriate to assure that such relationships shall be consistent with the national interest and foreign policy of the United States;

(5) insure that timely arrangements are made under which there can be foreign participation in the establishment and use of a communications satellite system;

(6) take all necessary steps to insure the availability and appropriate utilization of the communications satellite system for general governmental purposes except where a separate communications satellite system is required to meet unique governmental needs, or is otherwise required in the national interest; and

(7) so exercise his authority as to help attain coordinated and efficient use of the electromagnetic spectrum and the technical compatibility of the system with existing communications facilities both in the United States and abroad.

(b) the National Aeronautics and Space Administration shall—

(1) advise the Commission on technical characteristics of the communications satellite system;

(2) cooperate with the corporation in research and development to the extent deemed appropriate by the Administration in the public interest;

(3) assist the corporation in the conduct of its research and development program by furnishing to the corporation, when requested, on a reimbursable basis, such satellite launching and associated services as the Administration deems necessary for the most expeditious and economical development of the communications satellite system;

(4) consult with the corporation with respect to the technical characteristics of the communications satellite system;

(5) furnish to the corporation, on request and on a reimbursable basis, satellite launching and associated services required for the establishment, operation, and maintenance of the communications satellite system approved by the Commission; and

(6) to the extent feasible, furnish other services, on a reimbursable basis, to the corporation in connection with the establishment and operation of the system.

(c) the Federal Communications Commission, in its administration of the provisions of the Communications Act of 1934, as amended, and as supplemented by this Act, shall—

(1) insure effective competition, including the use of competitive bidding where appropriate, in the procurement by the corporation and communications common carriers of apparatus, equipment, and services required for the establishment and operation of the communications satellite system and satellite terminal stations; and the Commission shall consult with the Small Business Administration and solicit its recommendations on measures and procedures which will insure that small business concerns are given an equitable opportunity to share in the procurement program of the corporation for property and services, including but not limited to research, development, construction, maintenance, and repair.

(2) insure that all present and future authorized carriers shall have nondiscriminatory use of, and equitable access to, the communications satellite system and satellite terminal stations under just and reasonable charges, classifications, practices, regulations, and other terms and conditions and regulate the manner in which available facilities of the system and stations are allocated among such users thereof;

(3) in any case where the Secretary of State, after obtaining the advice of the Administration as to technical feasibility, has advised that commercial communication to a particular foreign point by means of the communications satellite system and satellite terminal stations should be established in the national interest, institute forthwith appropriate proceedings under section 214(d) of the Communications Act of 1934, as amended, to require the establishment of such communication by the corporation and the appropriate common carrier or carriers;

(4) insure that facilities of the communications satellite system and satellite terminal stations are technically compatible and interconnected operationally with each other and with existing communications facilities;

(5) prescribe such accounting regulations and systems and engage in such ratemaking procedures as will insure that any economies made possible by a communications satellite system are appropriately reflected in rates for public communication services;

(6) approve technical characteristics of the operational communications satellite system to be employed by the corporation and of the satellite terminal stations; and

(7) grant appropriate authorizations for the construction and operation of each satellite terminal station, either to the corporation or to one or more authorized carriers or to the corporation and one or more such carriers jointly, as will best serve the public interest, convenience, and necessity. In determining the public interest, convenience, and necessity the Commission shall authorize the construction and operation of such stations by communications common carriers or the corporation, without preference to either;

(8) authorize the corporation to issue any shares of capital stock, except the initial issue of capital stock referred to in section 304(a), or to borrow any moneys, or to assume any

obligation in respect of the securities of any other person, upon a finding that such issuance, borrowing, or assumption is compatible with the public interest, convenience, and necessity and is necessary or appropriate for or consistent with carrying out the purposes and objectives of this Act by the corporation;

(9) insure that no substantial additions are made by the corporation or carriers with respect to facilities of the system or satellite terminal stations unless such additions are required by the public interest, convenience, and necessity;

(10) require, in accordance with the procedural requirements of section 214 of the Communications Act of 1934, as amended, that additions be made by the corporation or carriers with respect to facilities of the system or satellite terminal stations where such additions would serve the public interest, convenience, and necessity; and

(11) make rules and regulations to carry out the provisions of this Act.

TITLE III—CREATION OF A COMMUNICATIONS SATELLITE CORPORATION

CREATION OF CORPORATION

SEC. 301. There is hereby authorized to be created a communications satellite corporation for profit which will not be an agency or establishment of the United States Government. The corporation shall be subject to the provisions of this Act and, to the extent consistent with this Act, to the District of Columbia Business Corporation Act. The right to repeal, alter, or amend this Act at any time is expressly reserved.

PROCESS OF ORGANIZATION

SEC. 302. The President of the United States shall appoint incorporators, by and with the advice and consent of the Senate, who shall serve as the initial board of directors until the first annual meeting of stockholders or until their successors are elected and qualified. Such incorporators shall arrange for an initial stock offering and take whatever other actions are necessary to establish the corporation, including the filing of articles of incorporation, as approved by the President.

DIRECTORS AND OFFICERS

SEC. 303. (a) The corporation shall have a board of directors consisting of individuals who are citizens of the United States, of whom one shall be elected annually by the board to serve as chairman. Three members of the board shall be appointed by the President of the United States, by and with the advice and consent of the Senate, effective the date on which the other members are elected, and for terms of three years or until their successors have been appointed and qualified, except that the first three members of the board so appointed shall continue in office for terms of one, two, and three years, respectively, and any member so appointed to fill a vacancy shall be appointed only for the unexpired term of the director whom he succeeds. Six members of the board shall be elected annually by those stockholders who are communications common carriers and six shall be elected annually by the other stockholders of the corporation. No stockholder who is a communications common carrier and no trustee for such a stockholder shall vote, either directly or indirectly, through the votes of subsidiaries or affiliated companies, nominees, or any persons subject to his direction or control, for more than three candidates for membership on the board. Subject to such limitation, the articles of incorporation to be filed by the incorporators designated under section 302 shall provide for cumulative voting under section 27(d) of the District of Columbia Business Corporation Act (D.C. Code, sec. 29-911(d)).

(b) The corporation shall have a president, and such other officers as may be named and appointed by the board, at rates of compensation fixed by the board, and serving at the pleasure of the board. No individual other than a citizen of the United States may be an officer of the corporation. No officer of the corporation shall receive any salary from any source other than the corporation during the period of his employment by the corporation.

FINANCING OF THE CORPORATION

SEC. 304. (a) The corporation is authorized to issue and have outstanding, in such amounts as it shall determine, shares of capital stock, without par value, which shall carry voting rights and be eligible for dividends. The shares of such stock initially offered shall be sold at a price not in excess of $100 for each share and in a manner to encourage the widest distribution to the American public. Subject to the provisions of subsections (b) and (d) of this section, shares of stock offered under this subsection may be issued to and held by any person.

(b)(1) For the purposes of this section the term "authorized carrier" shall mean a communications common carrier which is specifically authorized or which is a member of a class of carriers authorized by the Commission to own shares of stock in the corporation upon a finding that such ownership will be consistent with the public interest, convenience, and necessity.

(2) Only those communications common carriers which are authorized carriers shall own shares of stock in the corporation at any time, and no other communications common carrier shall own shares either directly or indirectly through subsidiaries or affiliated companies, nominees, or any persons subject to its direction or control. Fifty per centum of the shares of stock authorized for issuance at any time by the corporation shall be reserved for purchase by authorized carriers and such carriers shall in the aggregate be entitled to make purchases of the reserved shares in a total number not exceeding the total number of the nonreserved shares of any issue purchased by other persons. At no time after the initial issue is completed shall the aggregate of the shares of voting stock of the corporation owned by authorized carriers directly or indirectly through subsidiaries or affiliated companies, nominees, or any persons subject to their direction or control exceed 50 per centum of such shares issued and outstanding.

(3) At no time shall any stockholder who is not an authorized carrier, or any syndicate or affiliated group of such stockholders, own more than 10 per centum of the shares of voting stock of the corporation issued and outstanding.

(c) The corporation is authorized to issue, in addition to the stock authorized by subsection (a) of this section, nonvoting securities, bonds, debentures, and other certificates of indebtedness as it may determine. Such nonvoting securities, bonds, debentures, or other certificates of indebtedness of the corporation as a communications common carrier may own shall be eligible for inclusion in the rate base of the carrier to the extent allowed by the Commission. The voting stock of the corporation shall not be eligible for inclusion in the rate base of the carrier.

(d) Not more than an aggregate of 20 per centum of the shares of stock of the corporation authorized by subsection (a) of this section which are held by holders other than authorized carriers may be held by persons of the classes described in paragraphs (1), (2), (3), (4), and (5) of section 310(a) of the Communications Act of 1934, as amended (47 U.S.C. 310).

(e) The requirement of section 45(b) of the District of Columbia Business Corporation Act (D.C. Code, sec. 29–920(b)) as to the percentage of stock which a stockholder must hold in order to have the rights of inspection and copying set forth in that subsection shall not be applicable in the case of holders of the stock of the corporation, and they may exercise such rights without regard to the percentage of stock they hold.

(f) Upon application to the Commission by any authorized carrier and after notice and hearing, the Commission may compel any other authorized carrier which owns shares of stock in the corporation to transfer to the applicant, for a fair and reasonable consideration, a number of such shares as the Commission determines will advance the public interest and the purposes of this Act. In its determination with respect to ownership of shares of stock in the corporation, the Commission, whenever consistent with the public interest, shall promote the widest possible distribution of stock among the authorized carriers.

PURPOSES AND POWERS OF THE CORPORATION

SEC. 305. (a) In order to achieve the objectives and to carry out the purposes of this Act, the corporation is authorized to—

    (1) plan, initiate, construct, own, manage, and operate itself or in conjunction with foreign governments or business entities a commercial communications satellite system;

    (2) furnish, for hire, channels of communication to United States communications common carriers and to other authorized entities, foreign and domestic; and

    (3) own and operate satellite terminal stations when licensed by the Commission under section 201(c)(7).

(b) Included in the activities authorized to the corporation for accomplishment of the purposes indicated in subsection (a) of this section, are, among others not specifically named—

    (1) to conduct or contract for research and development related to its mission;

    (2) to acquire the physical facilities, equipment and devices necessary to its operations, including communications satellites and associated equipment and facilities, whether by construction, purchase, or gift;

    (3) to purchase satellite launching and related services from the United States Government;

    (4) to contract with authorized users, including the United States Government, for the services of the communications satellite system; and

    (5) to develop plans for the technical specifications of all elements of the communications satellite system.

(c) To carry out the foregoing purposes, the corporation shall have the usual powers conferred upon a stock corporation by the District of Columbia Business Corporation Act.

TTLE IV—MISCELLANEOUS

APPLICABILITY OF COMMUNICATIONS ACT OF 1934

SEC. 401. The corporation shall be deemed to be a common carrier within the meaning of section 3(h) of the Communications Act of 1934, as amended, and as such shall be fully subject to the provisions of title II and title III of that Act. The provision of satellite terminal station facilities by one communication common carrier to one or more other communications common carriers shall be deemed to be a common carrier activity fully subject to the Communications Act. Whenever the application of the provisions of this Act shall be inconsistent with the application of the provisions of the Communications Act, the provisions of this Act shall govern.

NOTICE OF FOREIGN BUSINESS NEGOTIATIONS

SEC. 402. Whenever the corporation shall enter into business negotiations with respect to facilities, operations, or services authorized by this Act with any international or foreign entity, it shall notify the Department of State of the negotiations, and the Department of State shall advise the corporation of relevant foreign policy considerations. Throughout such negotiations the corporation shall keep the Department of State informed with respect to such considerations. The corporation may request the Department of State to assist in the negotiations, and that Department shall render such assistance as may be appropriate.

SANCTIONS

SEC. 403. (a) If the corporation created pursuant to this Act shall engage in or adhere to any action, practices, or policies inconsistent with the policy and purposes declared in section 102 of this Act, or if the corporation or any other person shall violate any provision of this Act, or shall obstruct or interfere with any activities authorized by this Act, or shall refuse, fail, or neglect to discharge his duties and responsibilities under this Act, or shall threaten any such violation, obstruction, interference, refusal, failure, or neglect, the district court of the United States for any district in which such corporation or other person resides or may be found shall have jurisdiction, except as otherwise prohibited by law, upon petition of the Attorney General of the United States, to grant such equitable relief as may be necessary or appropriate to prevent or terminate such conduct or threat.

(b) Nothing contained in this section shall be construed as relieving any person of any punishment, liability, or sanction which may be imposed otherwise than under this Act.

(c) It shall be the duty of the corporation and all communications common carriers to comply, insofar as applicable, with all provisions of this Act and all rules and regulations promulgated thereunder.

REPORTS TO THE CONGRESS

SEC. 404. (a) The President shall transmit to the Congress in January of each year a report which shall include a comprehensive description of the activities and accomplishments during the preceding calendar year under the national program referred to in section 201(a)(1), together with an evaluation of such activities and accomplishments in terms of the attainment of the objectives of this Act and any recommendations for additional legislative or other action which the President may consider necessary or desirable for the attainment of such objectives.

(b) The corporation shall transmit to the President and the Congress, annually and at such other times as it deems desirable, a comprehensive and detailed report of its operations, activities, and accomplishments under this Act.

(c) The Commission shall transmit to the Congress, annually and at such other times as it deems desirable, (i) a report of its activities and actions on anticompetitive practices as they apply to the communications satellite programs; (ii) an evaluation of such activities and actions taken by it within the scope of its authority with a view to recommending such additional legislation which the Commission may consider necessary in the public interest; and (iii) an evaluation of the capital structure of the corporation so as to assure the Congress that such structure is consistent with the most efficient and economical operation of the corporation.

Approved August 31, 1962, 9:51 a.m.

Appendix I

Robert H. Goddard Contributions and Memorabilia

Robert H. Goddard's Basic Contribution to Rocketry and Space Flight

First American to explore mathematically the practicality of using rocket propulsion to reach high altitudes and to traject to the moon (1912)

First to receive a U.S. patent on the idea of a multistage rocket (1914)

First to prove, by actual static test, that rocket propulsion operates in a vacuum, that it needs no air to push against (1915–1916)

First to develop suitable pumps for liquid-fuel rockets (1923)

First to develop and successfully fly a liquid-fuel rocket (March 16, 1926)

First to launch a scientific payload (a barometer, a thermometer, and a camera) in a rocket flight (1929)

First to use vanes in the rocket thrust for guidance (1932)

First to develop gyro control apparatus for rocket flight (1932)

First to fire a liquid-fuel rocket faster than the speed of sound (1935)

First to launch successfully a rocket with a motor pivoted in gimbals controlled by a gyro mechanism (1937)

Robert H. Goddard Memorabilia

National Air Museum, Smithsonian Institution, Washington, D.C.—Exhibit of the four complete extant Goddard rockets, made in 1926, 1935, 1938, and 1941; also some rocket parts, an oil portrait of Dr. Goddard, and a few personal memorabilia.

Institute of the Aerospace Sciences, New York City—Goddard collection of early rocket literature, one of the best in the U.S., which was transferred to the Library of Congress. The Institute had, from 1950 to 1959, an exhibit of numerous devices and parts developed and used by Dr. Goddard from 1918–1945, on long-term loan to the Roswell Museum, Roswell, New Mexico.

Roswell Museum, Roswell, New Mexico—Largest exhibit of parts of Goddard rockets, housed in the Goddard Wing of museum (dedicated April 25, 1959), including piping, drawings, murals of life-size photographs of four Smithsonian rockets, etc. On the grounds of the museum is the launching tower used by Dr. Goddard, with a copy of the 1940 rocket in it. His observation tower is also on display.

Clark University, Worcester, Mass.—Physics Department owned rocket parts, with additional items given by Mrs. Goddard. Also life-size photos, used as murals, of the four Smithsonian-held rockets, and bronze tablet at entrance to Physics Building, a gift of the class of 1959.

Worcester Polytechnic Institute, Worcester, Mass.—Collection of solid-propellant rockets, some of which were developed in WPI building and grounds. Also set of four murals of life-size Smithsonian rockets.

Robert H. Goddard Professorships, at Guggenheim Jet Propulsion Centers, at Princeton University, and at the California Institute of Technology, established by The Daniel and Florence Guggenheim Foundation.

Goddard Award, given by the American Institute of Aeronautics and Astronautics annually to one selected by its Directors as having made the greatest contribution to rocket development during the year; the oldest award in rocketry.

Goddard Power Plant, multimillion dollar plant at the Naval Proving Ground, Indian Head, Maryland, in memory of Dr. Goddard's work there in 1920–1922.

WPI 1908–Goddard Memorial Fund—Established by the class of 1908 of Worcester Polytechnic Institute in June 1958; income to be used for prize or scholarship.

Hill Transportation Award, of the Institute of the Aerospace Sciences—Carrying $5,000 and citation, accepted for Dr. Goddard by Mrs. Goddard at the annual dinner of IAS, January 1959.

Golden Replica of 1926 Goddard Rocket—Accepted for Dr. Goddard by Mrs. Goddard at the Missile Industry Conference at Washington, D.C., June 1958. Now on view at the Goddard Space Flight Center, Greenbelt, Md.

Goddard Memorial Dinner—Sponsored annually since 1958 on the anniversary of the first liquid-fuel flight, in Washington, D.C., by the National Space Club.

Goddard Trophy and Goddard Scholarship—Given annually at the Goddard Memorial Dinner at Washington, D.C., sponsored by the National Space Club.

Air Force Academy Goddard Award, Colorado—Established by the American Ordnance Association, to the cadet with the highest standing in mathematics in each graduating class.

Langley Medal—Dr. Goddard was the ninth recipient of this coveted medal from the Regents of the Smithsonian Institution, Washington, D.C. Presented to Mrs. Goddard, in Washington, June 28, 1960.

American Rocketry Society Goddard Memorial—Granite marker at site of the first flight of a liquid-propellant rocket, March 16, 1926, at Auburn, Mass., with a granite tablet beside road nearby, explaining significance of the marker. Dedicated July 13, 1960.

Congressional Medal—Presented posthumously to Dr. Goddard on March 16, 1961, at the dedication of the Goddard Space Flight Center, Greenbelt, Md.

Goddard Institute for Space Studies, extension in New York City of the Goddard Space Flight Center; established January 1961.

Goddard Alumni Award—Established by the alumni of Worcester Polytechnic Institute, June 1961, awarded annually to an outstanding alumnus.

Robert H. Goddard Squadron—Air Force Association, Vandenberg Air Force Base, California, established 1961.

Robert H. Goddard Industrial Center, Worcester, Mass.—Dedicated June 19, 1961.

Goddard Science Symposium of the American Astronautical Society—Annually on March 16, in Washington, D.C.

Robert H. Goddard Historical Essay Competition of the National Space Club—Prize of $200 and trophy awarded annually for the best essay on the historical development of rocketry and astronautics; established March 1962.

Robert H. Goddard Achievement Award—In Civil Air Patrol Cadet Aerospace Education and Training Program, National Headquarters, Ellington Air Force Base, Tex.

Robert H. Goddard Memorial Library, Clark University, Worcester, Mass., depository of Dr. Goddard's papers, established 1964.

Robert H. Goddard Memorial—Tower and rocket at Fort Devens, Mass., at the site of the Goddard testing tower, 1929–1930. Dedicated May 1963.

Appendix J
Selected Bibliography

Books

AARONS, J. (ed.), *Radio Astronomical and Satellite Studies of the Atmosphere* (New York, 1963).

AKENS, DAVID S., *Historical Origins of George C. Marshall Space Flight Center* (Huntsville, Ala., 1960).

American Institute of Aeronautics and Astronautics, *AIAA Unmanned Spacecraft Meeting*, AIAA Publication CP-12 (New York, 1965).

BERGAUST, ERIC, *Reaching for the Stars* (Garden City, N.Y., 1960).

BERKNER, LLOYD V. (ed.), *Manual on Rockets and Satellites* (New York, 1958).

—— AND ODISHAW, HUGH, *Science in Space* (New York, 1961).

BESTEV, ALFRED, *The Life and Death of a Satellite* (Boston, 1966).

BLANCO, V. M., AND McCUSKEY, S. W., *Basic Physics of the Solar System* (Reading, Mass., 1961).

BOEHM, J., FICHTNER, H. J., AND HOBERG, O. A., "Explorer Satellites Launched by Juno 1 and Juno 2 Space Carrier Vehicles," in *Astronautical Engineering and Science*, Ernst Stuhlinger et al., eds. (New York, 1963).

BOYD, R. L. F., *Space Research by Rocket and Satellite* (New York, 1960).

BRANDT, J. C., AND HODGE, P. W., *Solar System Astrophysics* (New York, 1964).

CARTER, L. J. (ed.), *The Artificial Satellite: Proceedings of the Second International Congress on Astronautics*, British Interplanetary Society (London, 1951).

CHAMBERLAIN, JOSEPH W., *Physics of the Aurora and Airglow* (New York, 1961).

CHAPMAN, JOHN L., *Atlas: The Story of a Missile* (New York, 1960).

CHAPMAN, SIDNEY, *Solar Plasma, Geomagnetism and Aurora* (New York, 1964).

DEUTSCH, ARMIN J., AND KLEMPERER, WOLFGANG B. (eds.), *Space Age Astronomy* (New York, 1962).

EMME, EUGENE M., *Aeronautics and Astronautics, 1915–60* (Washington, D.C., 1961).

—— (ed.), *The History of Rocket Technology* (Detroit, 1964).

Franklin Institute: *Earth Satellites as Research Vehicles*, Monograph 2 (Philadelphia, 1956).

FRUTKIN, ARNOLD, *International Cooperation in Space* (Englewood Cliffs, N.J., 1965).

GARTMAN, HEINZ, *The Men Behind the Space Rockets* (New York, 1956).

GATLAND, KENNETH W., *Project Satellite* (London, 1958).

GLASSTONE, S., *Sourcebook on the Space Sciences* (Princeton, 1965).

GODDARD, ROBERT H., *Rocket Development: Liquid Fuel Rocket Research, 1929–1941* (Englewood Cliffs, N.J., 1961).

GRIMWOOD, JAMES M., *Project Mercury: A Chronology*, NASA SP-4001 (Washington, D.C., 1963).

HALE, EDWARD E., *The Brick Moon and Other Stories* (Boston, 1899).

HAVILAND, ROBERT P., AND HOUSE, C. M., *Handbook of Satellites and Space Vehicles* (Princeton, 1965).

HESS, WILMOT N. (ed.), *Introduction to Space Science* (New York, 1965).

JASTROW, ROBERT (ed.), *The Exploration of Space* (New York, 1960).

—— AND CAMERON, A. G. W. (eds.), *Origin of the Solar System* (New York, 1963).

JETER, IRVING E. (ed.), *Scientific Satellites, Mission and Design* (North Hollywood, Calif., 1963).

JONES, BESSIE Z., *Lighthouse of the Skies: A History of the Smithsonian Astrophysical Observatory* (Washington, D.C., 1965).

JOHNSON, FRANCIS S. (ed.), *Satellite Environment Handbook* (Palo Alto, 1965). Second edition.

KALLMAN BIJL, HILDE (ed.), *Space Research* (New York, 1960).

KAULA, WILLIAM M., *Theory of Satellite Geodesy* (New York, 1965).

KING-HELE, D. G., *Satellites and Scientific Research* (New York, 1965).

——, MULLER, P., AND RIGHINI, G., *Space Research V* (New York, 1965).

KURNOSOVA, L. V. (ed.), *Artificial Satellites* (New York, vols. 1–6, 1960–1961).

LASSER, DAVID, *The Conquest of Space* (New York, 1931).

LEGALLEY, DONALD P. (ed.), *Space Science* (New York, 1963).

—— AND ROSEN, ALAN, *Space Physics* (New York, 1964).

—— AND MCKEE, JOHN W., *Space Exploration* (New York, 1964).

LEHMAN, MILTON, *This High Man: The Life of Robert H. Goddard* (New York, 1963).

LEY, WILLY, *Rockets, Missiles, and Space Travel* (3 rev. ed., New York, 1961).

MCMAHON, A. J., *Astrophysics and Space Science: An Integration of Sciences* (Englewood Cliffs, N.J., 1965).

MOORE, PATRICK, *Earth Satellites* (New York, 1956).

MORGENTHALER, GEORGE (ed.), *Unmanned Exploration of the Solar System* (New York, 1965).

MUELLER, I. I., AND ROCKIE, J. D., *Gravimetric and Celestial Geodesy* (New York, 1966).

MULLER, P. (ed.), *Space Research IV* (New York, 1964).

NAUGLE, JOHN E., *Unmanned Space Flight* (New York, 1965).

NEWELL, HOMER E. (ed.), *Sounding Rockets* (New York, 1959).

——, *Express to the Stars* (New York, 1960).

ODISHAW, HUGH (ed.), Research in Geophysics series; Vol. 1, *Sun, Upper Atmosphere and Space* (Cambridge, 1964).

—— AND RUTTENBERG, S. (eds.), *Geophysics and the IGY*, American Geophysical Union, Monograph 2 (Washington, 1958).

PENDRAY, G. EDWARD, *The Coming Age of Rocket Power* (New York, 1945).

PRIESTER, WOLFGANG (ed.), *Space Research III* (New York, 1963).

ROSEN, MILTON, *The Viking Rocket Story* (New York, 1955).

ROSHOLT, ROBERT L., *An Administrative History of NASA, 1958–1963*, NASA SP–4101 (Washington, D.C., 1966).

SCHWIEBERT, ERNEST G., *A History of the U.S. Air Force Ballistic Missiles* (New York, 1965).

SHTERNFELD, ARI, *Artificial Satellites* (Washington, 1958).

SMITH-ROSE, R. L. (ed.), *Space Research VI* (Washington, 1966).

STEHLING, KURT R., *Project Vanguard* (Garden City, N.Y., 1961).

SWENSON, LOYD S., GRIMWOOD, JAMES M., AND ALEXANDER, CHARLES C., *This New Ocean: A History of Project Mercury*, NASA SP–4201 (Washington, D.C., 1966).

SULLIVAN, WALTER, *Assault on the Unknown: The International Geophysical Year* (New York, 1961).

THOMAS, SHIRLEY, *Satellite Tracking Facilities: Their History and Operation* (New York, 1963).

VALLEY, SHEA L. (ed.), *Handbook of Geophysics and Space Environments*, U.S.A.F. Office of Aerospace Research (Hanscom Field, Mass., 1965).

VAN ALLEN, JAMES A. (ed.), *Scientific Uses of Earth Satellites* (Ann Arbor, 1958).

VAN DE HULST, H. C., DE JAGER, C., AND MOORE, A. F. (eds.), *Space Research II* (New York, 1961).

VEIS, G. (ed.), *The Use of Artificial Satellites for Geodesy* (New York, 1963).

WILLIAMS, BERYL, AND EPSTEIN, SAMUEL, *The Rocket Pioneers on the Road to Space* (New York, 1955).

Official Reports

ADAMS, JAMES L., *Space Technology*, Vol. II, "Spacecraft Mechanical Engineering," NASA SP–66 (Washington, 1965).

ALEXANDER, J. K., AND STONE, R. H., *A Satellite System for Radio-astronomical Measurements at Low Frequencies*, NASA TM X–55089 (Washington, 1964).

ASHBY, JOHN, "A Preliminary History of the Evolution of the Tiros Weather Satellite Program," NASA HBN–45.

AUCREMANNE, MARCEL, JR. (ed.), *The Ionosphere Beacon Satellite, S–45*, NASA TN D–695 (Washington, 1961).

Bell Laboratories: *Final Report on Bell Telephone Laboratories Experiments on Explorer XV*, NASA CR–67106 (New York, 1964).

BLUMLE, L. J., FITZENREITER, R. J., AND JACKSON, J. E., *The National Aeronautics and Space Administration Topside Sounder Program*, NASA TN D–1913 (Washington, 1963).

BOECKEL, JOHN H., *The Purpose of Environmental Testing for Scientific Satellites*, NASA TN D–1900 (Washington, D.C., 1963).

BOURDEAU, ROBERT E., ET AL., *The Ionosphere Direct Measurements Satellite Instrumentation (Explorer VIII)*, NASA TN D–414 (Washington, 1962).

CASPER, JONATHAN D., *History of Alouette: NASA Case-Study of An International Program*, NASA HHN–42, 1964, revised 1965.

COFFEE, CLAUDE W., BRESSETTE, WALTER E., AND KEATING, GERALD M., *Design of the NASA Lightweight Inflatable Satellite for the Determination of Atmospheric Density at Extreme Altitudes*, NASA TN D–1243 (Washington, 1962).

CORLISS, WILLIAM R., *The Evolution of the Manned Space Flight Network*, NASA GHN–4 (Greenbelt, Md., 1967).

——, *The Evolution of the Satellite Tracking and Data Acquisition Network (STADAN)*, NASA GHN–3, X–202–67–26 (Greenbelt, Md., 1967).

——, *Scientific Satellites*, NASA SP–133 (Washington, D.C., 1967).

CORTRIGHT, EDGAR M., *Unmanned Spacecraft of the United States* (Washington, 1964).

D'AIUTOLO, CHARLES T. (ed.), *The Micrometeoroid Satellite Explorer XIII (1961 Chi)*, NASA TN D–2468 (Washington, 1964).

FRANTA, ALLEN L., *Integrating Spacecraft Systems*, NASA TN D–3049 (Washington, 1966).

GIACCONI, R., *An X-Ray Telescope*, NASA CR–41 (Washington, 1965).

GODDARD, MRS. ROBERT H., "Account of Dr. Goddard's World 1917–18," in *Congressional Record*, September 9, 1959.

—— AND PENDRAY, G. EDWARD, "Biographical Data: Dr. Robert H. Goddard," reprinted in *Congressional Record*, May 6, 1960.

HABIB, E. J., KEIPERT, F. A., AND LEE, R. C., *Telemetry Processing for NASA Scientific Satellites*, NASA TN D–3411 (Washington, D.C., 1966).

HAYES, E. NELSON, *The Smithsonian's Satellite-Tracking Program: Its History and Organization*, in *Annual Report*, Smithsonian Institution (Washington, D.C., 1962).

HEPPNER, JAMES P., NESS, NORMAN F., SKILLMAN, THOMAS L., AND SCEARCE, CLELL S., *Goddard Space Flight Center Contributions to 1961 Kyoto Conference on Cosmic Rays and the Earth Storm* (Washington, D.C., 1961).

HESS, WILMOT N., MEAD, G. D., AND NAKADA, M. P., *Bibliography of Particles and Fields Research*, NASA X–640–65–37 (Greenbelt, Md., 1965).

LUDWIG, GEORGE H., *Particles and Fields Research in Space*, NASA SP–11 (Washington, D.C., 1962).

——, *The Orbiting Geophysical Observatories*, NASA TN D–2646 (Washington, D.C., 1963).

NASA, *Astronautics and Aeronautics, 1963: A Chronology on Science, Technology, and Policy*, SP–4004, prepared by the NASA Historical Staff (Washington, D.C., 1964).

——, *Goddard Projects Summary: Satellites and Sounding Rockets*, Goddard Space Flight Center (Greenbelt, Md.; published periodically).

——, *Ariel I, The First International Satellite, Experimental Results*, Goddard Space Flight Center (Washington, D.C., 1966).

——, *Ariel I, The First International Satellite,* NASA SP–43 (Washington, D.C., 1963).

——, *Goddard Space Flight Center Contributions to COSPAR Meeting, May 1962,* NASA TN D–1669 (Greenbelt, Md., 1962).

——, *Goddard Space Flight Center Contributions to COSPAR Meeting,* June 1963, G–545 (Washington, D.C., 1963).

——, *Orbiting Solar Observatory,* Goddard Space Flight Center, NASA SP–57 (Washington, D.C., 1965).

——, *Historical Sketch of NASA,* NASA EP–29, prepared by the NASA Historical Staff (Washington, D.C., 1965).

——, *Juno II Summary Project Report, Vol. I, Explorer VII Satellite. Vol. II, The S–46 Satellite,* NASA TN D–608 (Washington, 1961).

——, *Launch Vehicles of the National Launch Vehicle Program,* NASA SP–10 (Washington, D.C., 1962).

——, *Proceedings of the NASA-University Conference on the Science and Technology of Space Exploration,* NASA SP–11 (Washington, 1962).

——, *Semiannual Reports to Congress, October 1, 1958* and *October 1, 1959* (Washington, D.C., 1959 and 1960).

——, *Significant Achievements in Ionospheres and Radio Physics, 1958–1964,* NASA SP–95 (Washington, 1966).

——, *Significant Achievements in Particles and Fields, 1958–1964,* NASA SP–97 (Washington, 1966).

——, *Significant Achievements in Satellite Geodesy, 1958–1964,* NASA SP–94 (Washington, 1966).

——, *Significant Achievements in Satellite Meteorology, 1958–1964,* NASA SP–96 (Washington, 1966).

——, *Significant Achievements in Solar Physics, 1958–1964,* NASA SP–100 (Washington, 1966).

——, *Significant Achievements in Space Astronomy, 1958–1964,* NASA SP–91 (Washington, 1966).

——, *Space Measurements Survey, Instruments and Spacecraft, October 1957–March 1965,* ed. by Dr. Henry L. Richter, NASA SP–3028 (Washington, D.C., 1966).

——, *The Observatory Generation of Satellites,* NASA SP–30 (Washington, 1963).

——, *United States Space Science Program: Report to COSPAR, Sixth Meeting, Warsaw, Poland, June 1963* (Washington, D.C., 1963).

United States Space Science Program: Report to COSPAR, Seventh Meeting, Florence, Italy, May 1964 (Washington, D.C., 1964).

National Academy of Sciences-National Research Council, *United States Space Science Program: Report to COSPAR, Fifth Meeting, Washington, D.C., May 1962* (Washington, D.C., 1962).

National Research Council, *A Review of Space Research,* Publication 1079 (Washington, 1962).

——, *Proposed United States Program for the International Geophysical Year* (Washington, 1956).

——, *Space Research, Directions for the Future* (Washington, D.C., 1966).

NEW, JOHN C., *Achieving Satellite Reliability through Environmental Tests,* NASA TN D–1853 (Washington, 1963).

——, *Scientific Satellites and the Space Environment,* NASA TN D–1340 (Washington, D.C., 1962).

SOUTHWICK, A. B., "The Memorial Which Dr. Goddard Would Have Liked Best of All," Worcester *Evening Gazette,* May 9, 1958, reprinted in *Congressional Record,* September 9, 1959, p. A7904.

STAFFORD, WALTER H., AND CROFT, ROBERT M., *Artificial Earth Satellites and Successful Solar Probes, 1957–1960,* NASA TN D–601 (Washington, 1961).

STERHARDT, J. A., *NASA Sounding Rocket Program: Summary of Sounding Rocket Flights,* NASA X–721–66–515 (Greenbelt, Md., 1966).

TIMMINS, ALBERT R., AND ROSETTE, KENNETH L., *Experience in Thermal-Vacuum Testing Earth Satellites at Goddard Space Flight Center,* NASA TN D–1748 (Washington, D.C., 1963).

U.S. Congress, *NASA Authorization for Fiscal Year 1961—Part I,* 86th Congress, 2nd Session, Testimony by Homer E. Newell, Jr., Office of Space Flight Programs (Washington, D.C., 1961).

House, Committee on Science and Astronautics, *Aeronautical and Astronautical Events of 1961,* prepared by the NASA Historical Staff (Washington, D.C., 1962).

House, Committee on Science and Astronautics, *Astronautical and Aeronautical Events of 1962,* prepared by the NASA Historical Staff (Washington, D.C., 1963).

Senate, Committee on Aeronautical and Space Sciences, *Documents on International Aspects of the Exploration and Use of Outer Space, 1954–1963,* Staff Report (Washington, D.C., 1963).

Space Handbook: Astronautics and Its Applications (Washington, 1959).

Virginia Polytechnic Institute, *Conference on Artificial Satellites,* NASA CR–60131 (Blacksburg, Va., 1963).

Speeches

BOUSHEY, BRIG. GEN. HOMER A., "Vignettes of Dr. Robert H. Goddard," Address at Third Annual Goddard Memorial Dinner, February 17, 1960.

GLENNAN, DR. T. KEITH, "The Nation's Program in Space Exploration," Speech at the Economic Club, Worcester, Mass., February 15, 1960.

——, Speech, Science, Engineering and New Technology Committee, Oregon State Department of Planning and Development, Portland, Ore., October 12, 1960.

GOETT, DR. HARRY J., "Scientific Exploration of Space," Address to Franklin Institute, Philadelphia, Pa., May 9, 1962.

——, "Scientific Exploration of Space and Its Challenge to Education," Address at Centennial Convocation, Worcester Polytechnic Institute, Worcester, Mass., October 8, 1964.

JASTROW, ROBERT, "Results of Experiments in Space," 25th Wright Brothers Lecture (IAS), Washington, D.C., December 18, 1961.

WEBB, JAMES E., Address before the American Institute of Aeronautics and Astronautics, New York, October 21, 1963.

——, Address to Webb School Alumni Association Testimonial Dinner, Los Angeles, Calif., April 26, 1962.

Articles

ARNOLDY, R. L., HOFFMAN, R. A., AND WINCKLER, J. R., "Observations of the Van Allen Radiation Regions During August and September 1959," Part I, *Journal of Geophysical Research,* LXV (May 1960), 1361–1376.

AUGENSTEIN, B. W., "Scientific Satellite—Payload Considerations," RAND Corp., RM–1459, 1955.

BELLER, WILLIAM S., "New Delta May Prove Most Economical," *Missiles and Rockets,* XVII (Aug. 16, 1965), 24–29.

BOURDEAU, ROBERT E., "Ionospheric Research from Space Vehicles," *Space Science Reviews,* I (1962), 683–718.

——, "Research Within the Ionosphere," *Science,* CXLVIII (April 30, 1965), 585–594.

BOYD, R. L. F., "In Space: Instruments or Man?" *International Science and Technology,* No. 41 (May 1965), 65–70.

——, "Techniques for the Measurement of Extraterrestrial Soft X-Radiation," *Space Science Reviews,* IV (Feb. 1965), 35–90.

BURGESS, ERIC, "The Establishment and Use of Artificial Satellites," *Aeronautics,* XXI (Sept. 1949), 70–82.

CAHILL, LAURENCE J., "Magnetic Fields in Interplanetary Space," *Science,* CXLVII (Feb. 26, 1965), 991–1000.

——, "The Magnetosphere," *Scientific American,* CCXII (March 1965), 58–68.

CANNEY, H. E., AND ORDWAY, F. I., "The Uses of Artificial Satellite Vehicles," *Astronautica Acta,* II (1956), 147–179; (1957), 1–15.

CHAZY, J., "Sur les Satellites Artificiels de la Terre," *Comptes Rendus,* CCXXV (Sept. 22, 1947), 469.

CLARKE, ARTHUR C., "Extraterrestrial Relays," *Wireless World* (Oct. 1945).

COLEMAN, P. J., JR., SONETT, C. P., JUDGE, D. L., AND SMITH, E. J., "Some Preliminary Results of the Pioneer V Magnetometer Experiment," *Journal of Geophysical Research,* LXV (June 1960), 1856–1857.

CROSS, C. A., "The Fundamental Basis of Power Generation in a Satellite Vehicle,"

Journal of the British Interplanetary Society, XI (1952), 117–125.

DICKE, R. H., AND PEEBLES, P. J., "Gravitation and Space Science," *Space Science Reviews*, IV (June 1965), 419–460.

EDSON, J. B., AND SNODGRASS, R. J., "Prelude to Missilry," *Ordnance*, XLIII (July–Aug. 1958), 67–70.

EHRICKE, KRAFFT A., "The Satelloid," *Astronautica Acta*, II (1956), 63–100.

EHRLICH, EUGENE, "NASA Particles and Fields Spacecraft," AIAA Paper 64–337 (1964).

EMME, EUGENE M., "Yesterday's Dream . . . Today's Reality; A Biographical Sketch of the American Rocket Pioneer, Dr. Robert H. Goddard," *The Airpower Historian*, V (Oct. 1960), 216–221.

FAN, C. Y., MEYER, PETER, AND SIMPSON, J. A., "Experiments in the Eleven-Year Change of Cosmic-Ray Intensity Using a Space Probe," *Physical Review Letters*, V (Sept. 1960), 272–274.

FINDLAY, JOHN W., "Radio Astronomy from Space Vehicles," *Astronautics and Aeronautics*, IV (Oct. 1966), 10–14.

FRIEDMAN, HERBERT, "The Next 20 Years of Space Science," *Astronautics and Aeronautics*, III (Nov. 1965), 40–47.

——, "X-Ray Astronomy," *Scientific American*, CCX (June 1964), 36–45.

GATLAND, K. W., KUNESCH, A. M., AND DIXON, A. E., "Minimum Satellite Vehicles," *Journal of the British Interplanetary Society*, X (1951), 287.

GODDARD, ROBERT H., "An Autobiography," *Astronautics*, IV (April 1959), 24 ff.

——, "A Method of Reaching Extreme Altitudes," Smithsonian Miscellaneous Publication No. 2540 (1919), reprinted by the American Rocket Society, 1946.

——, "Liquid-Propellant Rocket Development," *Smithsonian Miscellaneous Publication* No. 3381 (March 1936), reprinted by the American Rocket Society, 1946, and in *The Air Power Historian*, V (July 1958), 152–160.

GOLDMAN, D. T., AND SINGER, S. F., "Studies of a Minimum Orbital Unmanned Satellite of the Earth (MOUSE), Part III," *Astronautica Acta*, III (1957), 110–129.

HABER, HEINZ, "Space Satellites, Tools of Earth Research," *National Geographic Magazine*, CIX (April 1956), 487–509.

HAGEN, JOHN P., "The Viking and the Vanguard," in Emme, Eugene M. (ed.), *The History of Rocket Technology* (1964), 122–141.

HAGERMANN, E. R., "Goddard and His Early Rockets," *Journal of the Astronautical Sciences*, VIII (Summer 1961), 51–59.

HALL, R. CARGILL, "Early U.S. Satellite Proposals," in Emme, Eugene M. (ed.), *The History of Rocket Technology* (1964), 67–93.

——, "Origins and Development of the Vanguard and Explorer Satellite Programs," *The Air Power Historian*, XI (Oct. 1964), 101–112.

HEPPNER, J. P., "The World Magnetic Survey," *Space Science Reviews*, II (1963), 315–354.

HINES, COLIN O., "Sounding Rocket Resurgence," *Astronautics and Aeronautics*, IV (1966), 8–13.

——, "The Magnetopause: A New Frontier in Space," *Science*, CXLI (July 12, 1963), 130–136.

HINTEREGGER, H. E., "Absolute Intensity Measurements in the Extreme Ultraviolet Spectrum of Solar Radiation," *Space Science Reviews*, IV (June 1965), 461–497.

HOOVER, GEORGE W., "Instrumentation for Space Vehicles," American Rocket Society Paper 157–54 (1954).

JASTROW, ROBERT, AND CAMERON, A. G. W., "Space: Highlights of Recent Research," *Science*, CXLV (Sept. 11, 1964), 1129–1139.

KALLMANN, H. K., AND KELLOGG, W. W., "Scientific Uses of an Earth Satellite," RAND Corp., RM–1500 (1955).

KRULL, A. R., "A History of the Artificial Satellite," *Jet Propulsion*, XXVI (May 1956), 369–383.

KUPPERIAN, JAMES E., AND ZEIMER, ROBERT R., "Satellite Astronomy," *International Science and Technology* (March 1962), 48–56.

LAGOW, H. E., "Instrumenting Unmanned Satellites," American Rocket Society Paper 281–55 (1955).

LEHMAN, M., "The Strange Story of Doctor Goddard," *Reader's Digest*, LXVII (Nov. 1955), 147–152.

LEY, WILLY, "The Satellite Rocket," *The Technology Review*, LII (Dec. 1949), 93.

LUDWIG, GEORGE H., "Cosmic-Ray Instrumentation in the First U.S. Earth Satellite," *Reviews of Scientific Instruments*, XXX (April 1959), 223.

MALINA, FRANK J., "Origins and First Decade of the Jet Propulsion Laboratory," in Emme, Eugene M. (ed.), *The History of Rocket Technology* (1964), 63–65.

MAXWELL, W. R., "Some Aspects of the Origins and Early Development of Astronautics," *Journal of the British Interplanetary Society*, XVIII (1962), 415–425.

MAYO-WELLS, WILFRID J., "The Origins of Space Telemetry," *Technology and Culture*, IV (Fall 1963), 499–514.

McGUIRE, JAMES B., SPANGLER, EUGENE R., AND WONG, LEM, "The Size of the Solar System," *Scientific American*, CCIV (April 1961), 64–72.

NESS, NORMAN F., "Earth's Magnetic Field: A New Look," *Science*, CLI (March 4, 1966), 1041–1052.

——, "The Earth's Magnetic Tail," *Journal of Geophysical Research*, LXX (July 1, 1965), 2989–3005.

NEWELL, HOMER E., "The Satellite Project," *Scientific American*, CXCIII (Dec. 1955), 29–33.

NEWTON, ROBERT R., "Geodesy by Satellite," *Science*, CXLIV (May 15, 1964), 803–808.

OBERTH, HERMANN, "From My Life," *Astronautics*, IV (June 1959), 38–39, 100 f.

O'BRIEN, BRIAN J., "Review of Studies of Trapped Radiation with Satellite-Borne Apparatus," *Space Science Reviews*, I (1962), 415–484.

ORDWAY, FREDERICK I., "Project Vanguard—Earth Satellite Vehicle Program," *Astronautica Acta*, III (1957), 67–86.

PENDRAY, G. EDWARD, "Pioneer Rocket Development in the United States," *Technology and Culture*, IV (Fall 1963), 384–392.

PIERCE, JOHN R., "Satellite Science and Technology," *Science*, CXLI (July 19, 1963), 237–244.

RAND Corp., "Preliminary Design of An Experimental World-Circling Spaceship," (May 1946).

ROGERSON, JOHN B., "The Orbiting Astronomical Observatories," *Space Science Reviews*, II (1963), 621–652.

SCHUESSLER, RAYMOND, "How America Muffed Space Supremacy," *American Mercury*, XC (May 1960), 25–30.

SINGER, S. F., "A Minimum Orbital Instrumented Satellite—Now," *Journal of the British Interplanetary Society*, XIII (1954), 74–79.

——, "Research in the Upper Atmosphere with Sounding Rockets and Earth Satellite Vehicles," *Journal of the British Interplanetary Society*, XI (1952), 61–73.

——, "Studies of a Minimum Orbital Unmanned Satellite of the Earth (MOUSE)," *Astronautica Acta*, I (1955), 171–184; and II (1956), 125–144.

SPITZER, LYMAN, JR., "The Beginnings and Future of Space Astronomy," *American Scientist*, L (Sept. 1962), 473–484.

STAMBLER, IRWIN, "The Explorers," *Space/Aeronautics*, XLI (Feb. 1964), 38–46.

——, "The Orbiting Observatories," *Space/Aeronautics*, XLII (Sept. 1964), 34–42.

——, "The OGO," *Space/Aeronautics*, XXXIX (Feb. 1963), 70–76.

STONE, ROBERT G., "RAE—1500-ft. Antenna Satellite," *Astronautics and Aeronautics*, III (March 1965), 46–49.

STUHLINGER, ERNST, "Army Activities in Space —A History," *Transactions of the IRE*, MIL-4 (April–July 1960), 64–69.

THOMAS, J. O., "Canadian Satellites: The Topside Sounder Alouette," *Science*, CXXXIX (Jan. 18, 1963), 229–232.

THOMAS, SHIRLEY, "Robert H. Goddard," *Men of Space*, Vol. I (1960).

——, "Harry J. Goett," *Men of Space*, Vol. VII (1965).

TOUSSEY, RICHARD, "The Extreme Ultraviolet Spectrum of the Sun," *Space Science Reviews*, II (1963), 3–69.

TRENT, N., "Early Days in Rocketry," *Christian Science Monitor* (July 24, 1963).

VON BRAUN, WERNHER, "The Explorers," *Astronautica Acta*, V (1959), 126–143.

——, "The Redstone, Jupiter, and Juno," in Emme, Eugene M. (ed.), *The History of Rocket Technology* (Detroit, 1954), 144–145.

WHIPPLE, FRED L., "Scientific Value of Artificial Satellites," *Journal of the Franklin Institute* (Aug. 1956).

INDEX

The Author

ALFRED Rosenthal has been the Historian of the Goddard Space Flight Center of the National Aeronautics and Space Administration since 1962. He is responsible for documentation and preparation of historical monographs covering over 50 major satellite programs as well as the other important activities at the Goddard Center with regard to space science, tracking, and advanced technology. Mr. Rosenthal is also Deputy Public Affairs Officer and published a series on space-science-oriented mathematics developed in cooperation with the U.S. Office of Education.

Before joining NASA, Mr. Rosenthal was with the U.S. Army Corps of Engineers, preparing studies on civil works programs and military projects, including a series on the development of U.S. water resources. He attended Charles University in Prague, Czechoslovakia. During World War II he served with the 88th Division in Italy.

NASA Historical Publications

HISTORIES

- Robert L. Rosholt, *An Administrative History of NASA, 1958–1963*, NASA SP–4101, 1966; for sale by Supt. of Documents ($4). (Management History Series)
- Loyd S. Swenson, James M. Grimwood, and Charles C. Alexander, *This New Ocean: A History of Project Mercury*, NASA SP–4201, 1966; for sale by Supt. of Documents ($5.50). (Program History Series)

HISTORICAL STUDIES

- *History of Rocket Technology*, edited by Eugene M. Emme, special issue of *Technology and Culture* (Fall 1963); augmented and published by Society for the History of Technology (Detroit: Wayne State Univ., 1964).
- *Space Medicine in Project Mercury*, by Mae Mills Link, NASA, SP–4003, 1965; for sale by Supt. of Documents ($1).

CHRONOLOGIES AND SPECIAL STUDIES

- *Aeronautics and Astronautics: An American Chronology of Science and Technology in the Exploration of Space, 1915–1960*, compiled by Eugene M. Emme, Washington: NASA, 1961 (out of print).
- Aeronautical and Astronautical Events of 1961, published by the House Committee on Science and Astronautics, 1962 (out of print).
- *Astronautical and Aeronautical Events of 1962*, published by the House Committee on Science and Astronautics, 1963; for sale by Supt. of Documents ($1).
- *Astronautics and Aeronautics, 1963*, NASA SP–4004, 1964; for sale by Supt. of Documents ($1.75).
- *Astronautics and Aeronautics, 1964*, NASA SP–4005, 1965; for sale by Supt. of Documents ($1.75).
- *Astronautics and Aeronautics, 1965*, NASA SP–4006, 1966; for sale by Supt. of Documents ($2.25).
- *Astronautics and Aeronautics, 1966*, NASA SP–4007, 1967; for sale by Supt. of Documents ($1.50).
- *Astronautics and Aeronautics, 1967*, NASA SP–4008 (1968).
- *Project Mercury: A Chronology*, by James M. Grimwood, NASA SP–4001, 1963; for sale by Supt. of Documents ($1.50).
- *Historical Sketch of NASA*, NASA EP–29, 1965; for sale by Supt. of Documents ($0.25).
- *Project Gemini Technology and Operations: A Chronology*, by James M. Grimwood and Barton C. Hacker, with Peter J. Vorzimmer, NASA SP–4002 (1968).
- *The Apollo Spacecraft: A Chronology*, Vol. I, through November 7, 1962, by Ivan D. Ertel and Mary L. Morse, NASA SP–4009 (1968).

☆ U.S. GOVERNMENT PRINTING OFFICE : 1968 O—285-083

W9-CLR-655

NOTHING BUT LIFE

BRENT VAN STAALDUINEN

DUNDURN
TORONTO

Publisher: Scott Fraser | Acquiring editor: Rachel Spence | Editor: Susan Fitzgerald
Cover desiger: Sophie Paas-Lang
Cover image: utility knife: istock.com/DeadDuck; textures: unsplash.com/BernardHermant and istock.com/sbayram
Printer: Marquis Book Printing Inc.
Lines from "26" © Rachel Eliza Griffiths, 2013. Used with permission.

Library and Archives Canada Cataloguing in Publication

Title: Nothing but life / Brent van Staalduinen.
Names: Van Staalduinen, Brent, 1973- author.
Identifiers: Canadiana (print) 20200155555 | Canadiana (ebook) 20200155563 | ISBN 9781459746183 (softcover) | ISBN 9781459746190 (PDF) | ISBN 9781459746206 (EPUB)
Classification: LCC PS8643.A598 N68 2020 | DDC jC813/.6—dc23

We acknowledge the support of the Canada Council for the Arts and the Ontario Arts Council for our publishing program. We also acknowledge the financial support of the Government of Ontario, through the Ontario Book Publishing Tax Credit and Ontario Creates, and the Government of Canada.

VISIT US AT

 dundurn.com | @dundurnpress |  dundurnpress | dundurnpress

Dundurn
1382 Queen Street East
Toronto, Ontario, Canada
M4L 1C9

For Nora and Alida,
who love stories.

How quiet the bells of heaven must be, cold
with stars who cannot rhyme their brilliance
to our weapons. What rouses our lives each moment?
Nothing but life dares dying.

— *Rachel Eliza Griffiths, "26"*

PART 1
HERE

GRADUATION

I plead guilty, of course. It's the only option. No one else used a box cutter on Patrick Scheltz ten days ago. In math class. During the last regular period before our end-of-year exams. Now, I'm not that great at math, but these numbers are easy. Eight stitches. Twenty-seven witnesses. Seven days before summer freedom. One thousand times I've told myself how dumb it was to lose my cool.

The youth-court judge, a stern-looking woman no one in their right mind would mess with, asks me if I understand the consequences of pleading guilty. I nod, but she makes me say it out loud.

"I understand, Your Honour."

Then she clears the courtroom of everyone but me, Mom, the lawyers, the court reporter, my youth worker, and the bailiff, who sits in the chair at the end of my table. Even Gramma Jan and Aunt Viv have to go. The prosecution lawyer starts to object — he thinks Patrick and his parents should be allowed to stay — but the judge silences him with a look over her reading glasses.

"I'll bring them back for sentencing, but there's something I need to talk to Wendell and his mother about first."

First time she's called me Wendell. Until now, I've been "the defendant." I think about what that could mean as I watch everyone file out of the courtroom. Patrick — who everyone calls Pat, which he hates — glares at me as he leaves. A single person remains in the gallery, a woman who's been scribbling madly in her notebook the entire time.

"You too, Ms. Walters," the judge says.

"Judge, I —"

"Especially you."

The woman frowns but gets up without another word and leaves. The judge sighs and nods at the bailiff. "Watch the door, please. I don't want anyone 'accidentally' bursting back in."

I can tell the judge is talking about Walters, a reporter from the local paper — which my mom calls "that right-wing rag" — who lives in my neighbourhood. The bailiff gives a small smile and heads to the door. He shares the judge's opinion.

The judge removes her reading glasses, looks down, and takes a long, deep breath. Her eyes are softer when she looks up and over at the table where I'm sitting. I've seen that kind of look before. It's how people who weren't there look when they talk about it. All helplessness and sadness. She's going to talk about Windsor. My lawyer brought it up in my defence, but I was hoping it would stay locked up in the court records. But no. Now the judge will say my full name again and want me to talk about it.

But I won't. I won't tell anyone. Not in a way they want, anyway. I have memories that live inside my head that are just for me. I was in the Windsor High library when the shooter walked in and opened fire. I didn't see much while it was happening. I was behind a table with my eyes closed. I heard the angry sounds of the bullets destroying everything around me. And the other noises I can't talk about. We all did.

The shooter was my stepdad, Jesse. I found that out later, at home, at the same time my mom did. When the police came to interview her. And me. I also found out that Jesse went to my classroom first. I don't know why. He didn't leave a note or anything. After the shooting, in the strange quiet of our house, I tried to figure it out. Mom hid the TV remote, but there were dozens of reconstructions on the internet. Hashtags and protests and rage and so many people wanting to fight. So much information but so few answers. Computer-generated animations and diagrams and arrows and dotted lines and red *X*'s wherever someone had died. Kids and teachers. The horrible math of it. But I can't say that number. I hope that's all right.

The judge coughs gently.

"A few things have come to light since you were charged," she says, "including the fact that you were at Windsor High School on the day of the shooting. When I call everyone back in, I'm going to pass sentence, but I wanted to tell you in private how sorry I am for what you've gone through. And how much I respect your mother for bringing you home to Hamilton for a fresh start. I've spoken to your math teacher and principal — who both speak very highly of you — and we talked about your situation. They, of course, had no idea."

I sneak a look back at Mom. She's leaning forward on the gallery bench, her arms folded, looking at the judge with narrowed eyes. My lawyer using Windsor is one thing, but Mom won't like that the principal and my teacher know, too. She made me promise not to say anything to anyone, not that I would. Not that I can. I turn back to the front of the courtroom. The judge is still talking.

"You'll be relieved to hear that your expulsion has been reversed and you'll be allowed to graduate from grade ten after all. Quietly, of course. They feel that this one mistake shouldn't keep you from moving forward. I agree. Your school records will be filed away with full confidentiality, which is important to you and your mother. By law these court records will also be sealed. Wendell, I sincerely hope you and your mom can find some peace here. You're a strong young man, and I'm lucky to have met you, despite the circumstances." She leans back and puts her glasses back on. "That said, you broke the law, so what happens next is very, very important."

And with that the judge nods at the bailiff and he opens the door and everyone comes back in. I force my eyes to stay open to keep them dry. I never cry, but I get close a lot. My eyes fill all the time. I can't look back at Mom right now because she'll be a mess. Like me. I can't hear the word *Windsor* without my insides twisting themselves into ropes. But she feels it worse. She feels everything.

BIG BROTHER'S BEST

My probation officer's name is Sean, and he meets me at our house the next morning. He's dressed in khakis and a black golf shirt. He has a thick leather belt with a phone pouch and a gold badge on one side and a handcuff holster on the other. There's a thin cylindrical pouch next to the cuffs. Flashlight, maybe. Pepper spray. Or a collapsible baton. For the ones who don't co-operate.

He opens a map of our neighbourhood on the kitchen table. The boundaries of Churchill Park and Cootes Paradise have been outlined in pink highlighter. We live in an old neighbourhood with the city pressing in on one side and the park and marsh on the other, interrupting Hamilton's urban sprawl. The city, an old steel town tucked alongside the bay at the end of Lake Ontario, keeps growing. Our neighbourhood has seen better days. The houses are small and worn. "War homes," Gramma Jan calls them. Lots of senior citizens.

Lots of families looking to invest as soon as the older folks die off.

Sean repeats the judge's instructions. At-home supervision. Weekly meetings with Sean. Two hundred and forty hours of community service. Picking up garbage from the park and marsh trails from 9:00 a.m. to 3:00 p.m., Monday to Friday, every week until the first day of grade eleven. Then every day after school until the hours run out.

"Alone?" my mother asks.

"For the most part, yes," Sean says. "I'll drop by when I can, but Wendell —"

"Dills," I say. "Call me Dills."

I used to prefer Dilly, but at some point Mom started calling me Dills, and I've come around to liking it. A growing-up thing, I suppose. I'm fine with it. I guess someday I'll even think of myself as a Wendell.

He shakes his head. "Sorry, mate, but no. Let's keep this professional, yeah?"

Sean's about my mom's age but British, so everything he says sounds like it's been stretched out. My name, for instance. Wen-doe, he says. And he drops *yeah?* in behind so many of his sentences.

"Anyhow, I've made an arrangement with Gary, the park manager, for daily check-in. Here." Sean points to a building on the park's eastern side. "He says he'll be there at nine every morning."

"That's the old field house," Mom says. "I always thought it was abandoned."

Sean shrugs, slides the map over to me, and talks about boundaries and limits. Grassy parkland is my priority, but I'll clean the trails, too. The marked, official ones. The little scale marker at the top of the map tells me the area is huge. Bigger than I imagined. I looked it up online, but seeing it spread out on paper is different. I start to feel the weight of the summer ahead of me. Sean puts a plastic shopping bag on the table. Out of it comes a blaze-orange safety vest. Blue construction helmet. Work gloves. A box of industrial garbage bags. Bug spray. A huge blue bottle of sunscreen. SPF 45. My mom's eyebrows rise at that one.

"Uh, I threw that in there," he says. "I've done outdoor work before, and the sun'll burn you quicker than you think."

"That's thoughtful of you," Mom says.

Sean waves away her words, embarrassed. "But stay on this side of the marsh, yeah? South side only."

"Okay," I say.

"Which brings me to the last thing." He digs down to the bottom of the bag and takes out a length of nylon strapping with a black box attached. Unmarked.

"You've got to be kidding," Mom says.

"What is it?" I ask.

"It's a fu—" Mom closes her mouth and stops the word before it comes out. Not a word I hear from her very often. "It's a LoJack."

Sean gives her a look. "Let's call it an ankle monitor, yeah?"

"Big Brother's best."

"No need to be dramatic." He looks at me. "It's a GPS tracker, Wendell, to make sure you stay where the court says you need to stay."

"I can't believe this," Mom says.

"It's standard for house arrest." Sean hands it to me.

It's not heavy. It's not light, either. "I have to wear it all summer?"

He nods. "It also makes my job easier if I need to find you while you're working."

"What about showering? Exercising?" Mom asks.

"Water- and sweatproof. Just keep the strap clean. They can get pretty ripe." He takes the monitor back from me, kneels, and looks up at me. "I have to put it on you now. Which ankle?"

I hear myself telling him to put it on the right side. He talks about tampering and alarms and how violating the court's conditions puts me in a whole different category of youth offender. I've seen ankle monitors in movies, of course, so I get it. But it takes a special, wicked-looking tool to lock it tight and activate it, and the electronic tone as it connects to the satellite sounds sinister. Those scare the crap out of me. The sights and sounds of a screwed-up summer. Stretching out ahead of me a long, long way.

LISTEN

The park manager is a little guy, not much taller
than me. He has a mess of twisted scars all up his left
arm and bursting up the left side of his neck onto his
face. His ear is a ruin. You can see it when he isn't trying to hear anything. When he is, he turns his head to
catch the sound with his good ear and the messed-up
one disappears. He smells a lot like skunk. The office
does, too.

"This is Gary," Sean says.

"Gal," the guy says. "Not Gary."

Sean grunts, takes some folded papers out of his
shirt pocket, and squints through all the small lines of
text. Frowns. "Thought it was Gary."

No apology, though, even through the long silence
that follows. My mom would be pissed about that. *Make
it right, right now*, she'd say if she was here. I wonder
if Sean's having difficulty with the weed smell. A pot
smoker in charge. And if Gal is sensing Sean's issue

with his habits. Both of them tense, me dangling in the middle of all that awkwardness. Nothing to do until Gal speaks.

"So you have instructions for me?"

Sean grunts again and goes through his spiel, most of which I've heard before. This time he adds *geofencing* to the vocabulary, which I want to ask about but can't because the two guys are busy moving through the rest of the formalities. They both have accents. Sean's British and flat, Gal's something else: stiff and kind of nasal, with strange vowels, rolled *r*'s, and crumbly consonants, like old cement.

Finally, Sean turns to me. "So that's it, then. Stay busy, yeah?"

"Sure."

Sean walks out of the field house, leaving Gal and me to stand there for a few awkward moments. Gal gives me a quick once-over, head to toe, and waves me out.

"You are on your own, young man."

"Will I see you while I'm —"

"I will not be checking up on you."

Gal turns back to the tiny desk tucked against the wall and picks up his pen. The ratty office chair creaks a protest. Silence again. I feel forgotten already. Just me and my silly safety vest and a million acres of decaying trash.

"Is it gone?"

He turns his head, right ear exposed. "I am sorry?"

"The hearing. In the ear with the scars."

"Yes."

"How does a deaf dude get a job managing a park?"

It's a rude question. That little voice inside is telling me so as I say it, but I'm annoyed enough at the situation to ignore it. Gal scowls, saying something about a million-dollar question. Then he tells me to fuck off and go pick up my garbage. No, really, he says that to me, like I'm somebody his own age and not a teenager he should watch his mouth around. "Feck off and go peck up yoorr rrruhbesh."

BABY

I used to swear. A lot. Sharpening my tongue as soon as I left the house, savouring the taste of the perfect F-bomb, blending in with the other guys. Mom didn't like it. She said it was going to get me in trouble. But after Windsor, those foul words started sounding empty. Puffed up without anything inside. So I stopped. The guys at my new school are just like the guys I left behind. Now that summer's here, they must be blinding themselves with the swearing they can do. I don't miss it. Jesse thinks swearing is a weakness. "It means you've run out of words — a poor substitute for substance," he says. Or, he would say. I wonder if he still thinks about things.

"I feel like swearing now," I say to the trees at the edge of the soccer field.

Specifically, I want to swear at the heat and the bugs and the disgusting stuff that can still come out of long-forgotten garbage when I impale it on my spike.

But I won't. I'll tough it out and head home at lunch. Whenever that is. I've caught myself reaching for my iPod a few times to check the time, but I'm not allowed to have it with me. Part of my sentence.

And I don't own a phone. Mom says I can decide later this year, when I turn sixteen, whether I want one or not but I'll have to get a job to pay for the data. A year ago I'd have said, *Of course I'll want one. I'm a teenager, after all*, but now I'm not sure. Of course, I can do pretty much anything on my iPod I could do on a phone, but between nudie apps and sexting and cyberbullying and the trolls who look to make life miserable for anyone who's experienced tragedy, there's so much wrongness online. You think a lot about safe places after a thing like Windsor.

I've followed a well-worn path into the bush to try to cool down a bit. I didn't know a guy could sweat like this. Ever. I've played sports and felt the little beads running down my face, but this is different. I'm soaked through. Even my undies. I'm getting a rubbed-raw patch between my legs. I should drink more, but the little plastic water bottle has been empty for a couple of hours now. I'll have to get Mom to buy me a bigger one. I've only peed once, running into the bush to go behind a tree — it was dark yellow, and thick, like syrup.

"Hydrate, hydrate, hydrate. Water is the most important thing, troop."

Jesse's words again. Yes, out loud. I do that a lot more these days, ever since the shooting. That's how I got on Patrick's radar. At lunch one day he came around a corner to find me alone, having one of my conversations with Jesse. He told everyone else I was talking to myself, like a baby. But I don't talk to myself — I talk to Jesse. I say his words, too, sometimes. He used to be home all the time, so I could talk to him whenever I needed to, morning, lunchtime, after school.

I feel faint. This is not good. Plus there's a suspicious burning on the back of my neck. Sunburn. Or more chafing from the cheap, rough collar on my safety vest. Both, maybe. *I should head home now*, I think as I spear another faded, collapsed can and put it into my bag. Would Sean know that I left, the stupid box on my ankle broadcasting where I am, my deviation from my work locations? Would he care?

Whatever. I'm going. I stash the stick and the garbage bag and walk out of the woods. Home is right across the field. Sean and the courts would go easy if they knew I was dying out here, right?

Ah, man. Something claws its way up from behind my ribcage and I have to stop midstep and take a few deep breaths to push it down. I can't think about the word *dying* anymore. Even when I'm obviously exaggerating.

"Aww, is Baby crying now?"

Patrick. Sitting on one of the park benches pushed up against the edge of the field. I blink away the blurriness. He's wearing shorts and a sleeveless green and yellow jersey, the scar I gave him on his bicep pink and angry. He flinched when I lashed out at him. Just in time to keep me from cutting his face. We were doing one of those combined lessons that are supposed to teach us how science and math and life are all connected. The teacher gave everyone a box cutter, one of those clicky yellow utility knives. There was a lot of leaf cutting and counting and dividing. Pat and I were assigned as partners. Him whispering taunts. Me lashing out in a moment of pure weakness.

"I heard you got stuck here," he says.

"How'd you hear that?"

"Nice vest."

"What do you want?"

"I want to beat the shit out of you, but who needs the hassle?" He points at my ankle monitor.

"Pat, I said I was sorry —"

He's up and in my face before I finish the thought. "And I told you never to call me that."

Must've been the back of my brain throwing his nickname out there. It's almost funny, but even though he's afraid to hurt me because of my supervision, I know better than to laugh. He can't stand that Pat can be a girl's name. So much that his stupid lizard brain might make the decision for him. Mom says that there are "glands and mysterious forces" that make guys do things. Especially the ones whose parents started them in school late so they could be "more ready." Pat relishes being bigger than everyone. He actually gets five o'clock shadow when he forgets to shave.

I hear myself apologize again.

"Punch me," he says.

"What?"

"Anywhere you want. I won't even hit back."

I'd be lying if I said that the thought of punching him has never crossed my mind. Or that I'm not tempted to bury my fist in his gut to see him fall. But there's a wicked little glint in his eye and a suspicious burn in my throat telling me not to. That's how *I'd* fall. I'd get busted for breaking the conditions of my sentencing. You're not allowed to get in fights, much less with the person you're doing time for hurting.

Jesse would tell me to walk away. I can hear him. *He just wants to bring you down. Don't drop to his level. Clear as mud?*

"Clear as mud," I say.

Patrick is confused. "Huh? What are you talking about, Baby?"

Clear as mud is one of Jesse's favourite sayings. He picked it up in the army, one of a thousand things that sound like gibberish to non-army people. Mud's not clear. It's muddy. You say it when you know what you have to do even when it's not entirely sensible or logical. Jesse always explains the sayings to me. *Get a jag on. On the bus, off the bus. We're all mushrooms, fed shit and kept in the dark.*

Or maybe it's explain*ed*. Past tense. In reality, he can't explain anything to me any more than one of the trees can. He's still in that Windsor Regional Hospital bed. When the police finally swept the school, they found him in a bathroom. Almost dead but not quite. He'd tried to kill himself. At first the cops kept Jesse in restraints and stationed an officer outside the intensive care room. They hoped he'd wake up so they could charge him and lock him away forever. But the doctors say he'll never wake up, that it's not a coma but a "persistent vegetative state." Now everyone is waiting for him to die, which is a little sad. There's been so much death already.

"You shouldn't be here," I say.

"Be a man and hit me."

I shake my head and walk away. I think, *Don't you get it, Pat? I'm not a man. I'm not supposed to be. Not yet.*

Why does everyone expect me to be older than I am? I hear him say dumb things to my back about how sorry I'll be and how he'll be around every day but I'll never know when. Even my own lizard brain knows that you only say those kinds of things when you're out of other options.

S&C

Our cool, air-conditioned house is five minutes from the park, my massive, sweltering prison cell. Sean didn't say I can't go home during the day while I'm doing my time, but it still feels like I'm doing something wrong. Even though it makes sense for me to use our own bathroom and eat lunch there. I've been torturing myself.

There's a bright blue Elantra parked at the curb out front, and Mom is talking to someone on the step. It's the reporter from court. Walters. Mom isn't happy to be talking to her. Her arms are folded and she's standing in the middle of the doorway like she's blocking it. You don't stand that way when you're friendly with the other person. You lean against the door frame or turn aside so they can come in.

Walters turns and sees me coming up the walk. She smiles. "Wendell, hello. I'm Cathy, a reporter from —"

"Stop talking to him."

"Vicky, I just have a few questions for your son."

"No, you don't. And you don't get to call me Vicky."

"Hey —"

"I said no. He's still a minor, so it's my call. Dills, come inside and don't say a thing."

She turns slightly to allow me access, but the reporter hasn't moved. I stop. Awkward.

"Get out of the way," Mom says.

"Why did the judge ask everyone to leave the courtroom?"

"Inside, kiddo. Now."

Mom says the last word with extra weight. I know that tone. I call it "Do Not Argue with Me Right Now, Young Man." Walters steps aside and lets me past.

"Don't come here again," Mom says.

She closes the door in her face, cutting off the next question. With a low groan, the door eases open a bit. Mom has to thunk it closed twice more before it catches. Old doors and twisted frames, I suppose. But it steals some of Mom's thunder — Walters is probably out there laughing at the dramatic but missed attempt.

I make for the sink and drain four full glasses of tap water, Mom's eyes on my back the entire time. I put the glass down, my belly as tight and round as a medicine ball.

"Are you all right?"

"I need a bigger water bottle."

"Let me see your neck." Mom moves behind me and grabs my shoulders. Tut-tuts under her breath. "You got some sun, too."

"I'll be fine."

"You're already burned. Didn't Sean give you sun-screen?"

"It was cloudy when I started this morning."

She reaches up and takes down the first-aid kit stashed above the cupboards and hands me a bottle of green aloe vera. It's cool on the back of my neck. Funny how the good feeling makes me more aware of how much I'll feel the burn tomorrow.

"Thanks."

"You're welcome."

I expect her to ask me more questions about how my day is going so far, but she doesn't. She leans against the counter with her arms folded, watching an indistinct point on the fridge across from her. Thinking. Mom's good at keeping things in, like she can lock them up in strongboxes in her heart and mind, but Walters's visit has pulled Windsor back to the surface again.

"She doesn't know anything," I say.

"For now. She's tenacious. Always was. Even in high school."

"You went to school together?"

"She was in the grade below me. Always running around for the school paper and yearbook. Always bug-ging everyone for stories."

"I'll stay away from her."

"And she's still here. Seems like everyone else left."

"You came back. *We* came back."

"Not by choice."

Her eyes fill, and she's back in Windsor, missing everything about what was good before Jesse walked into my school. Fighting against all the bad that followed.

That we tried to leave behind. Mom is a good fighter. But the tears break free, like they often do. She lets them flow for a bit, then sleeves them away. Stretches tall, breathes in deep.

"I love you, Dills."

"Love you, too, Mom."

Then it's silence in the house. Mom and me and all of this old house's hollow echoes, which I'm coming to know as well as my own breathing. The house has been in the family for a few generations, built by my great-grandpa Gene after the Second World War. He agonized over every joist, every nail, then retreated into the basement workshop and stayed there until he died. Gramma Jan, my grandmother, who was Gene's only child, said the war pushed him down there so he wouldn't have to talk to anyone. "He saw things no one should ever see," she said to me once. I get that.

The workshop is Mom's studio now. My room is down there, too, in the basement guest room, the quietest place in the house. Gene finished the guest room right after the workshop and slept down there every night. The whole basement is soundproofed. Against his nightmares, I guess. And now mine, although for me it's pools of sweat and a racing heart. Dream images fading like the flashes you get when you look at the sun. Not knowing where I am until I can identify the house sounds around me.

My stomach growls. "Okay if I stay for lunch?"

"Of course you can. Why wouldn't you?"

"I almost didn't come home. I don't know if I'm allowed to leave."

She laughs, wiping away a latecomer tear that shines on her cheek. "The judge assigned you to Churchill Park for a reason."

I frown. I don't like being laughed at. "Mom."

"You're supposed to stay close to home."

"Sure, but —"

"I'm sorry, Dills. I sent you out today without talking logistics. Bad mommy moment for me, okay?"

I wish she wouldn't say things like that. Even when I'm pissed at her, I know she's a great mom. I hear myself saying that it's fine, that I'm glad I have the option of a home lunch. I'm glad, too, that I can say that to her. When I'm at my maddest, I don't always give her a break, though she deserves it. Anger is funny that way. Your brain and your heart saying different things, and you know the right thing but your angry heart wins anyhow.

"Actually, I have something you can —"

Mom disappears for an instant without finishing her sentence. Then she's back, holding a faded olive-drab sling pouch. There's a flap over the top, but I know what's in there. Jesse's old army-surplus canteen. He never would have used it when he was in the service — they use hydration bladders now — but he loved to collect old military things. It's a dull olive-green blob with a screw top. Thick, thick plastic. Feels indestructible. I can't believe Mom's holding it. It's not like it was sitting on the hallway shelf, waiting for her to grab it on our way out of the house. It was in Jesse's old footlocker, down in the basement, with his collectibles and other dusty army things. She would've had to go out of her way to get it. Way out.

Mom's speaking as I take the canteen, something about not being able to live with herself if I got heat-stroke and passed out in the woods without anyone knowing. Something like that. I notice she's stopped talking and is waiting for me to respond.

"Huh?"

"So you'll use it?"

"I guess. Are you sure? It's Jesse's."

"It's supposed to carry water."

"Well, yeah, but —"

"He'd be fine with you having it. He'd want you to, actually."

"He didn't really share his army stuff with me."

She tilts her head. "Oh, I don't know about that. You should hear all the army-isms that come out of your mouth."

"That's different."

"It is, and it isn't. Just rinse it out before you use it, okay?"

I twist open the cap. A mustiness wafts up, faint but just strong enough for both of us to smell it. Mom makes a face, I make a face, and we speak the same words at the same time. "Sin and corruption," we say. And we laugh because we've both heard it a thousand times and now it's coming out of us almost with one voice. Jesse's voice. "Jesus! Look at the sin and cor-ruption in there!" Something his superiors would yell during inspections when they found anything not completely clean. Dust in corners. Mud in the tread of a combat boot. Smudges on a window. Soot in a rifle's chamber. Sin. Corruption. Both impossible to see or do anything about, yet the saying is so nonsensically, impossibly perfect.

Mom goes serious again and her eyes get all glittery. Mine, too. The canteen didn't do it, but that ridiculous saying did. She wipes her eyes and proceeds to assemble two ham-and-cheese sandwiches, cut them diagonally, and spread them out on two plates. Kettle chips and an apple go in the wedge-shaped gaps. Two meals, made without speaking or thinking.

I don't feel like saying much, either. I never say it out loud, but I miss Jesse so much it's an actual hole in the middle of me. I hate what he did, obviously, but still. Mom misses him, too, though for her the betrayal is so much worse. I can't even imagine. I hope it's all right, but I enjoy our quiet lunch. Sometimes you don't need to say anything.

HEARING JESSE

I'm better prepared when I go out after lunch. White zinc oxide on my nose and ears and the back of my neck. Mom says you can't sweat the zinc oxide away. Sean's sunscreen everywhere else. It smells like coconut, so I smell like the beach.

Before I left, Mom filled the canteen for me and also made me chug another two glasses. Rolled her eyes when I said it would just make me pee more. "You guys love to piss in the woods," she said. Which is true, of course. Although I must've been pretty dehydrated, because even with all the water I drank at lunch, I still don't feel like I have to go. My body needing everything I can give it.

Pat is nowhere to be seen. I half expected him to be waiting for me. Is it likely he'll be out all day, every day, to get me back? No. But knowing doesn't mean I won't worry.

About midafternoon, the temperature drops and the clouds return, this time dark and heavy. I hope it doesn't rain. Sean was clear that I have to work in all conditions. Rain. Wind. Shine. "But not in a thunderstorm, yeah?" he said. "The moment you hear thunder or see lightning, you head for the nearest shelter. Safety first." Mom said she'd go out to buy a bigger water bottle this afternoon, but we didn't talk about rain gear. If I get dumped on this afternoon, all I can do is get wet and keep going. I work my way onto one of the forest paths again, this one linking the park and the marsh, wondering if the forest counts as shelter.

Then, the strangest thing: as the wind picks up, making the leaves rush against each other and the tree trunks creak and groan, I hear Jesse's voice.

I'm here, Dills. Come see me.

I practically jump out of my running shoes. (I have to wear them — "Sturdy trainers, Wen-doe," Sean said. "No sandals, yeah?") What I heard was not the gentle, kind of blurred voice I hear when I talk out loud and imagine Jesse responding. This was as clear as if he was standing on the path next to me. Talking deep and slow, like he always does, like he has all the time in the world. Clear enough to imagine him on his feet and living normally, like before. I feel like I've been punched right above the waistband of my shorts.

I don't want to miss him as much as I do. I want to forget about him and what he did. All those lives. I want to forget that he might've been in the school to get me first. But here's the thing: I can't. He's family. In spite of all his demons, he loved our life together. *Demons.* That's Mom's word for what he carried back from his tours in Afghanistan and Iraq. But we chased them away. On mornings when he'd come into the kitchen with eyes so dark you knew he hadn't slept a wink, or after days away in the woods, he always smiled. For us. "What's up, favourite people?" he'd say.

I wait for him to say something else in his real, right-now voice, but all I hear is the wind and the trees. I wait a long time. I must look like an idiot. Kid in an orange safety vest, standing ridiculously still in the middle of a dirt hiking trail, garbage-sticker in one hand and black plastic bag in the other, staring at the tree canopy. Excitement, anticipation, and disappointment moving across his face like the clouds he can barely see.

Jesse always says I need to work on my poker face. "Two things," he'll say. *Two things* is another Jesse favourite. Keeps a point or an argument simple and easy to break down. "One, people respond better to a little mystery. Two, never give anything away — if they can't know how you feel or what you're thinking, you get the advantage." I always lose the battle for the poker face. Jesse has it down, I can tell you, especially away from home. No road rage or snapping or anger from him, no matter what. Even when he has every reason to rage.

Mom loves that about him. I've seen her watching him as he talks to me, his face calm even when I've screwed up bad. I'll be a mess of knotted ropes inside or as furious as boiling water and he'll remain as still as anything. Mom used to get this little smile when she watched him or talked about him to me. She still does, sometimes. Way less than she used to.

"Jesse?" My voice is low. Even though I'm not talking to myself, saying it out loud is a risk. No one else would understand. Pat, especially. But I still do it — I want to hear more. "Is it really you?"

Nothing.

I wait another minute or so, then put my head down and get back to the garbage. A faded candy wrapper here, a cigarette butt there. There's enough to get into a kind of dirty, distracting rhythm. I wonder if Sean would let me listen to music while I work. I could use Jesse's old MP3 player that Mom uses for yoga, which can't connect to the internet. It only has a few hundred songs on it, all of Jesse's music. She has an iPhone, too, and she listens to streaming music and podcasts on that while she's working in her studio. But the little yellow music player always comes out for her workouts.

The afternoon passes quickly. Just me and the trash and a hundred questions about that voice I heard. Or thought I heard. The rain never materializes.

DEPENDENT

I have this dream where we stay in the classroom and Jesse finds me. There's no talking or shooting. He stands in the doorway and looks at me with his rifle at port arms, an army term he taught me. Held in front, muzzle up. Used in ceremony but nowhere else. Formal. Impractical. He's dressed in his standard jeans and T-shirt, but his face is a mess of camouflage grease-paint. Darker shades on the high points, lighter on the low, which confuses perception and detail. He taught me that, too. The kids in my class are screaming and running to the back. I stay in my desk because I want to hear what he has to say. That's when I wake up. I don't scream like you see in the movies, so no one comes running. I'm always alone when I open my eyes.

I used to get the dream every night. At first, I tried to keep it to myself. Mom would try to make a joke of it and call me "zombie" in the morning, but I could tell she was worried. Eventually, I told her. For her and me.

You can only hold so much for so long. She said I should wake her up, but I never do. No need to have two of us tired in the morning. Two zombies. Since moving to Hamilton, I only get it once in a while, but Mom always knows when I do. Like today.

"Did you see Jesse again last night?"

I nod and reach for the cereal.

"Same dream?"

"Yeah."

"Want to talk about it?"

"No thanks."

She gives me a long look but doesn't press. She sips her tea, the little tag swinging with the movement, and goes back to her iPad. She only drinks green tea flavoured by burnt rice. "Nokcha," she calls it. Orders it online from Korea. Says she got hooked on the stuff in Gwangju when she babysat kindergarten ESL students for a year after university. It just smells like burning to me, though.

I'm annoyed she doesn't want to know more. Usually I'd be fine with it, but today I want her to stop looking at the iPad and tell me it's not healthy to bottle things up. "We're a sharing family," she likes to say. Or used to. We're both a lot quieter these days. Her with her business, the online store where she sells stainless-steel art and jewellery she makes in the basement studio. Me with my nightmares and school troubles.

She asks, "Ready for today?"

"Sure."

"I'm glad you're doing this."

"This?"

"Cleaning the park. Staying close to home. It'll be appreciated."

The word digs at me. Appreciated? How? By who? Churchill Park is huge — I'll never clean it all. A place can look spotless until you're responsible for it. Until you have to pay attention to how little people really care about beauty. Each day takes forever, and I pick up a thousand pounds of garbage, but no one will notice.

"It's not like I have a choice," I say.

"No, but the judge did. There are homes and facilities."

"I wish she'd put me there."

"No, you don't."

"I hate the park."

"It could be wor—"

I stand and slam my hands on the counter. My cereal bowl jumps, the spoon clattering onto the counter, the milk and cereal splashing, forming a soggy constellation. Mom jumps, too. "How, Mom? How could it be worse?"

"Dills …"

"I'm alone all day. There's the heat, the bugs, the garbage — there's so much of it. And I'm on full display. At least at one of those other places, I could be out of sight."

"Doing nothing. Getting —"

"Keeping my dignity."

Mom lets out a slow breath. Her eyes widen a little. I see real hurt there. She folds her arms. "There's no dignity in those places."

"I just —"

"Stop, Dills! Be quiet and listen to me."

The sudden sharpness in her voice makes me sit down again. Mom almost never interrupts like this. "Sometimes all we have is our ability to listen," she likes to say. She takes another deep breath.

"I've never told you this, but I spent some time in one of those facilities."

"Wait, what? You?"

"Yeah, me. I was a little older than you are now. Some friends and I stole a car and drove into a minivan full of kids."

"But —"

"I was driving. No one was killed, but people got hurt."

I kind of hear her tell me the rest, but it doesn't sink in fully. I manage to absorb a few details, like how she and her friends found a car with keys in it, how it was supposed to be a joyride and not a theft. How she bore the weight of the crime because she was driving, so she was sent away for a few months to a juvenile facility. "Juvie," she calls it. Prison for young people. She was incarcerated in a girls' wing with drug pushers, thieves, and murderers. There were fights and injuries and threats and a hundred sleepless nights. But she's sitting in front of me. No criminal, just Mom.

"What happened afterwards?"

"I came home."

"So Gramma Jan and Aunt Viv ..."

"We don't talk about it."

"Why?"

"Because I got to come home, kiddo. Because I had help to get back into my studies, because I lived with people who cheered for and loved me, I was able to get past it."

"Couldn't I do the same?"

"I have no doubt you could. But nothing good happened in there. And boys' juvie is much worse. You can't help but change."

"You changed?"

"Yes."

"How?"

"I used to love loud places, concerts, crowds, protests. I was always the one at the microphone."

I can't imagine her like that. She's all about quiet reflection, listening, thinking twice before speaking. She loves to protest — or she used to, before Windsor — but for her that has always meant writing op-eds and essays for the newspapers, magazines, the little hand-stapled zines she collects. Climate change. Gender parity. Marriage equality. Gun reform. Since moving to Hamilton, though, she's been so subdued. Limiting her anger to the insensitive things the local paper sees fit to print. Small rants over the dinner table.

"Is that why you do what you do? Sitting in your workshop making things?"

"Partially, but —"

"So you're a criminal."

Mom smiles. "No more than you'll be, after the summer. Juvie records are sealed, remember?"

"Right."

"I love making my art. And it sells, too, which allows me to support our family, which is especially important now that —"

"Now that Jesse's out of the picture."

Wow. I can see the physical pain on Mom's face as I say it. Another barb out before I can stop it. I think, *Out of the picture? Come on, Dills, that wasn't fair at all.* "Sorry, Mom, that was —"

She holds up a hand. "It's okay. You're not wrong. The army pension scheme is a nightmare at the best of times, but let's just say they're not sure what to do with him."

"But you can access our accounts from here, right?"

"I can, but I haven't."

"Why not? Aren't we still his dependents?"

"Yes."

"So …"

"I'm still processing things, too. I'm not sure I want his money anymore."

"He was sick, Mom. *Is* sick."

She exhales and nods. Falls silent. She stares into her teacup, where the green leaves and brown grains of rice will be sitting at the bottom, soggy and swollen. I'm quiet, too. I think about families and how we give everything to each other, even when we don't mean to. About the box cutter and Mom's misadventures, how she paid for her crimes. About what she might still be paying for. About how I'm paying for mine. About Jesse and family and influences and the possibility that hurting others might be part of us. In our DNA and bones.

MIA

Every day feels as long as all of human history, yet before I know it, I'm a few weeks into my sentence. Slow days passing fast. A strange, blurry mess of time.

I hear Jesse a lot. Not the imaginary Jesse I used to talk to, but the new voice, all his, that seems right next to me. It happens more frequently now, sometimes four or five times a day. I don't know what to do with it.

I'm here. Come see me.

I've stopped talking out loud to him, though. Two things. First, it feels weird to have the same conversations with him — me talking, him responding in my mind — when his real voice might drop into my day at any time. Second, it keeps Pat away. Without ammunition, he faded quick. I see him from a distance sometimes. He looks bored.

I've tried to tell Mom about Jesse talking to me, but I always bail out. She's so quiet these days. Like every day we're away from Windsor moves us farther away, even though we're still in Hamilton. She's so pissed at him but misses him, too, I can tell. And she worries. Every day, she calls her lawyer in Windsor, who has power of attorney and can receive updates so Mom doesn't have to call the hospital. She'll walk out onto the sidewalk with her phone and pace the width of our property. Voice low. Talking about the man who's legally her spouse, though there's no paperwork to prove it. Apart from army pension cheques he picked up from a post office box somewhere, he never got mail. Everything else was in her name.

I was four months old when Jesse made his vows to Mom. She loves to talk about how Jesse retired from the army and drove from Fort Bragg to Hamilton in a single push as soon as his discharge paperwork was finalized. How he managed to find a tiny tuxedo for me to wear to the church. How cold the church was because it was January and the middle of the week when the building didn't need to be heated. How you couldn't see my tux because of all the blankets. How perfect the service was, though there were only six of us: Mom, me, Jesse, Gramma Jan, Aunt Viv, and the pastor. How they didn't actually get married, because Mom didn't believe in the institution, but the pastor was a family friend who let them trade vows and "forgot" to file the marriage licence. How Gramma Jan and Aunt Viv showed up even though they both thought the relationship was impulsive — a new mom with some nameless other guy's baby in her tummy hooking up with a wounded warrior. Not fitting the mould of what families hope for. I don't know who my bio-dad is. That's Mom's and Jesse's term for the guy who got her pregnant and bailed.

All sorts of gaps, it feels like. The hole of not knowing. The canyon of pain and questions we're going through now. The space between our name and Jesse's, which I'm thankful for. Enough to keep mostly everyone from making the connection. Once the police ID'd him in the hospital, there were warrants for all his records and they found us quickly. Our names appear in detective reports and court documents and more than a few of the little notebooks investigators write in. After it became clear we had nothing to do with what Jesse had done, for the most part they left us alone. They kept our secret. Mom's been so careful about it.

Today, Jesse's voice doesn't arrive until the afternoon. I'm out by the splash pad, which is surrounded by playing fields. On hot days, it seems like every exhausted parent in the neighbourhood brings their kids here. Crowds of squealing, crying, laughing, running, falling kids. But the temperature has dropped before tonight's predicted storm, so there's no one around. A good day to pick up garbage. No one to recognize me. No one to ask what I'm doing.

I'm here. Come see me.

I will, I think. Well, I've decided to try, anyhow — it's a long way to Windsor. Longer still on my own. I haven't worked out the details. There are so many.

I get a good pace going by the splash pad. Out in the open you can walk and stab and keep moving while you work. In the bushes around the park, it feels like you could fill ten bags and not travel more than a few feet.

Trash under every bramble. The poison ivy you want to ignore, but you still have to clear under it.

It's a calm day, too, like the cooler temps convinced the wind to stay away. So I hear Gal singing before I see him. He walks in a strange way, his head turned to the left to take advantage of his good right ear. It always looks like he's about to run into something. He never does, though. And he sings with every step. Low, sad songs in his language. I've never seen him walking without some song keeping him company. Always brutally out of tune, I assume because of the ear thing.

I never know when I'll see him. He goes all over the park, usually carrying a backpack holding whatever tools he'll need for the small repair jobs he does. Rebolting a trail sign to its post. Repainting a playground fixture. That kind of thing. But today he doesn't have the backpack. He's just walking. Sometimes he does that, too. Walks and sings all day, and I'll see him popping in and out of the trailheads at the edge of the grassy areas. He seems to like his job.

I see him stop by the hedges at the far end of the field. The hedges are the remnants of an old living maze. Cedar, I think. Hundred-year-old bushes, with thick, gnarled trunks. Lots of dark hiding spots. There's a faded tourist sign nearby that suggests the park used to be popular with visitors to Hamilton. Grainy black-and-white pictures of people strolling in the park. Women with parasols. Men in top hats.

The woods have mostly reclaimed the area. If you walk through the trees, you can still see the rusted iron framework from the tropical gardens and crumbled stone foundations from mystery buildings. The only remaining feature still in operation is the aviary, a loud, smelly place filled with parakeets, peacocks, all sorts of rainbow birds.

Gal ducks into the hedge and disappears. I haven't worked up the nerve to go in myself, the twisted bushes a bit too mysterious for me. You don't find good things in hidden places like that. There will be lots of garbage. Broken bottles. Beer cans. Used condoms. All sorts of discarded objects from the stoners and love-drunk teenagers who probably hang out there.

So it's weird that Gal would go in. Now I'm curious. I pull out my watch, an ancient silver thing with a cloudy face. I actually have to wind it up every morning. It was Gene's. Gramma Jan said I could use it for the summer since I can't have my iPod with me. It has no band so I keep it in my pocket, a short length of braided paracord acting as a lanyard. Jesse gave me a roll of the skinny green rope and taught me how to braid. Box braid. Running. Trilobite. Herringbone. Cobra. "Once you have paracord around, you'll always find a need for it," he said. "You can use it for anything. Lanyards, laundry lines, belts, you name it." He was right. I'd made a cobra-pattern bracelet for myself the night before the shooting and had it on my wrist when Jesse came into the library. I unravelled it and used it as a tourniquet on my classmate Dakota. On her leg, which one of the bullets almost destroyed. It worked, but her other injuries were too serious and she died anyway.

The watch's blurred hands tell me that it's almost noon, so I walk to a nearby rubbish bin and drop my bag in, stick my picker-upper in the ground, and walk over to the hedges. I can hear Gal's voice as I get close. Then a girl's voice. Both speaking another language. Arabic, I think. Gal says something and the girl laughs. I can smell weed smoke, too. I stop. Shit. There are reasons guys and girls meet in the dark to smoke up. But I hear Gal calling out my name from inside, and I'm busted. Awkward.

"I'm heading home for lunch. I —"

"No, no, please come in," Gal says.

"Uh, that's okay."

"Please. I insist."

"I don't think … I don't need to …"

"Do not be shy. Come."

The girl says something too low for me to hear. Gal laughs. She giggles.

Well. If it wasn't awkward before, it sure as heck is now. I start to walk away.

"Wendell, stop," I hear the girl say to my back, laughter still in her voice. "We're not making out or anything."

The curiosity comes back in a rush. She knows my name. Huh. I feel my feet carrying me back to the opening in the hedge, into the darkness. Branches arch up and over the path. My eyes take a moment to adjust, but there's enough light to see them meet overhead, like the bones of a big church. A cathedral, even.

Gal and the girl are sitting together on the ground, their backs against the worn trunks of a pair of trees. Gal's head is turned, ready to hear me though I'm not saying anything. He's not smiling but he looks content. He has a tiny joint in his hand, the smoke swirling lazily around the space. The girl has a blanket over her legs, a book face down on her lap to mark the page. I recognize her right away. From my class. In the dim light, her short hair and her eyes are the same dark colour, almost black. She's wearing a tank top, and I can see her arms. Muscular. Lean. Strong. I don't know much about her. She's a competitive wrestler away from school, so she doesn't hang around. Always sits at the desk closest to the door. Last to arrive, first to leave. No one in my class talks to her. The girls can't relate. The guys are just plain scared.

"You're Mia," I say, a little stupidly.

"Yep. And you're Wendell. Or should I call you Cutter, like everyone else?"

"I'm not —"

Mia laughs. "I know. Kidding. Personally, I think Pat had it coming. The knife was maybe a bit far."

"It was definitely a bit far."

"Most entertaining thing to happen all year."

"Knife?" Gal asks. "Who is Pat?"

Mia laughs again and gives him the ten-second version of my story. Laid out plain and brutal. Hearing it feels like thorns behind my eyes. Am I a terrible person or what?

At the end, Gal simply nods. "So that is why you are here."

"You didn't know?" I ask.

"Not specifically. Your caseworker did not tell me. Confidentiality rules, I imagine." He shrugs. "It is no matter. You are doing a fine job, so I have no need to know."

Between his scowling face and the scars, it doesn't seem like a compliment.

"Want to sit for a bit?" Mia asks. "I have some protein shake, if you'd like."

"I shouldn't. I'm on lunch and then back to work."

But there go my feet again, carrying me in farther. Maybe it was the offer of protein shake, which I have no idea about. It sounds gross. And yet.

I feel some branches snagging on my socks and the ankle monitor. I'm wearing shorts all the time now. It's too hot to wear pants. At first I thought the little black box on my ankle would be like a billboard advertising my delinquency, but no one pays attention to me. I reach down to clear the —

"Wait-a-minute branches." Jesse's voice drifts forward from the past, from the one time he took me hunting. That's what he called the loose branches that snag your clothes. "Two things," he said. "One, never hurry through the brush. Too many bad things can happen when you're not careful and you're carrying a rifle. Two, never break the branches out of the way. No one needs to know you've been there. Clear as mud?" Mom was so pissed at him when we got home. That he'd take me out of school without telling her. That he'd sneak me into the woods to shoot at things. To kill for sport.

Jesse tried to explain that he didn't hunt for fun, but it didn't matter — Mom's mind was made up. Jesse never took me out again. He taught me things at home. I was so mad at her. The memory is as scorching and heavy as the sun, and the dim corridor through the hedges becomes a blurred, conflicted tangle of black and green and blinding white all at once.

"Wendell?" Mia's voice. Concerned.

"I have to go," I say. "I'm sorry."

I can't get home fast enough.

COLD CARROTS

I blunder in through the side door, kick my shoes off, and nearly bowl Aunt Viv over as I rush into the kitchen. I mumble an apology, open the fridge, and stick my head in, savouring the cool air on my hot, red face.

"Hey, kid," she says behind me. "Everything okay?"

"I'm fine."

"You look like someone pantsed you in church."

I shake my head. Then her hand is on my back. Patting, like a new father when he gets his first chance to burp the baby. "Uh, breathe, Dills. Breathe."

It works, though. I calm down enough to close the door and face her. "Thanks."

"So, are you going to greet your auntie properly or what? It's not like I've been gone for a week or anything."

"Oh, shit. Sorry."

I go to give her a hug but she's clearly expecting a high five. There's an awkward clash of hands and arms and shoulders. Some laughter, which is good. I sit down on one of the barstools at the counter. She goes to the fridge and pulls out an old lidded container full of leftovers, sniffs it, shrugs, and leaves it on the counter near me. Not in front of me. She's not like that. I pull it toward myself. Baby carrots and potatoes. I pinch out a carrot and eat it cold.

She leans against the sink and looks long at me. I have to look away. There's an intensity to her gaze I can never meet. She has the darkest, most penetrating eyes ever. Black hair framing her thin face. She's Korean by heritage. Born there. Gramma Jan adopted her when Koreans could get away with sending girl babies away. They wanted boys. Mom's adopted, too. Gramma Jan could never have kids of her own so she took motherhood seriously. All sorts of rituals. She and Grampa Vernon, who died before I was born, had some matching vision for parenthood and resolved to give all their kids *V*-names. Victoria. Vivian. But they're so different. Mom's rounded corners versus Aunt Viv's hard angles. There was a younger brother, Vincent, who died young. He's in only one of the photographs on the living room wall, his dark brown skin in dramatic contrast to the rest of the family, although it's everyone's smiles you see first. Great big grins. No one talks about him, though.

"So," Aunt Viv says. With purpose.

"So?"

"Saying 'shit' now are we?"

"No, I —"

"Next thing it'll be drugs and F-bombs and tattoos. And pregnant girls. The horror of adolescent malehood. The crisis of —"

"Okay, okay. I got it."

"Good. Definitely don't let Gramma Jan hear you talk like that. She'll have you scrubbing the bathroom floor with your tongue."

"Or Mom."

"Or your mom, exactly."

"You sound like you have some experience."

"I should tell you about the time Gramma Jan washed my mouth out with an actual bar of soap. I was picking bits out of my teeth for days."

"I think you just did."

"Smartass."

"How was your trip?"

With that she lights up, and you could forget that she's as tough as a calloused heel. She explains some obscure internet protocol she's initiated, but I don't understand a word. She's some kind of online-security expert. Travels all over the place to help corporations beef up their online protection. A hacker for hire, although I'd never say that to her face. Mom says that Aunt Viv could bring the world to its knees if she wanted. She's that good.

I sit back and eat the cold leftovers, letting her monologue wash over me. Her enthusiasm is a nice distraction from my embarrassment at having lost it in front of Gal and Mia. Sometimes the memories arrive so quick and huge, I don't know what to do with them. Mom and Gramma Jan and Aunt Viv are used to the moments when I need to stop and get away. But Mia and Gal aren't. Gal? Whatever. But Mia is so strong and never lets anything get to her. The other kids talk, but she walks through the halls at school like she's bullet-proof. Made of Kevlar. I like that strength.

CALL ME DILLS

I'm here. Come see me.

Windsor is about three hundred klicks from Hamilton. Klicks are kilometres in army-speak. Jesse grew up in some hilly place in Pennsylvania before he joined up, hoping for a career. Mom says the war knocked the nobility out of military service for him. He doesn't talk specifics about Afghanistan or Iraq but still has lots of those army-isms, like *klicks*. The army uses them instead of miles. Jesse calls himself "reformed to metric" and now hates that everything is in miles in the U.S. Says it's a stupid way to measure distance. I've never seen him get angry at other drivers, but he sure can rant about the imperial system of measurement.

Mom agreed with him but still ribbed him whenever we were driving and he got into it. "So the Brits aren't civilized?" she'd ask. Then they'd argue in a laughing way about bad teeth and colonialism and the legacy of fish and chips, and they'd look at each other a lot, and she'd run her nails through the stubble on the back of his head and give him goosebumps. When we got home they'd send me to my room. When I was really young they said I needed quiet time. When I was older they said they needed a nap, though they didn't nap and were obviously having sex. Anyhow.

Klicks or kilometres or miles, Windsor is a long way away. No matter how many times Jesse calls to me, getting to him is going to be hard. Not old enough to drive. No job, so Uber or bus or anything requiring money is a bust. Can't ask for the cash. Won't steal it. Can't ask anyone for help or everything will come out, so no. Deal breaker.

The height of the sun and the saturation of my boxers are telling me it's almost lunchtime. I take my helmet off and let the air evaporate some of my sweat. I'm in the woods cleaning the Princess Point Trail so the shade helps, but it's a scorcher today. Thirty-five degrees, feels like. Ninety-five in Fahrenheit, which Jesse never talks about, but I bet he thinks it's another dumb system. Why not measure up and down from zero, rather than from a freezing point of thirty-two? Weird.

I put my helmet back on, tie the garbage bag off, and walk it out. There are large oil-drum trash bins beside every set of benches throughout Churchill Park. The bags go in there when they're full. Well, as full as I can comfortably carry, which is usually about half. Things that decompose on damp ground get heavy.

I heave the bag into the garbage can, stepping back from a cloud of yellow jackets that drones into the air. I haven't been stung yet, but it's only a matter of time. You can't understand how many kinds of bees and wasps and hornets there are until you work outside. They do their thing and don't seem to care much, but you never know when you'll disturb them in the wrong way. Next thing you know, you're being swarmed and stung and they're leaving their stingers in you and dying. I always forget whether it's the bees or the wasps that leave their stingers.

Out here the sun blazes straight down and I have to squint against it. Through the humid haze I can see Mia walking across the grass and waving. I want to wave back, but for an agonizing instant my hand won't work. I just stare. Then my hand creeps up to a low wave and I feel almost human again.

"Hi," I manage when she comes close enough for conversation.

"Hi yourself."

She's wearing another tank top today, a light-blue one this time, and khaki shorts. A few wisps of hair escape from her baseball hat. As she walks up, I can't help but notice how her muscles flex on her legs. Not an ounce of fat on her. She's about my height but wider than other girls our age. But not awkward wide. Powerful wide. Like she's already been given her set of adult dimensions. It feels odd to think of her as a girl. Maybe I should say young woman. A young woman who could bench-press me.

"Leg-press, definitely," she says. "My bench isn't quite there yet."

"Sorry?"

"You were wondering if I could bench-press you."

Oh my god, I think. "I said that?"

A bemused smirk. "You talked to yourself at school, too."

And now I'm blushing and stammering and embarrassed. *Why, Dills?* I ask myself. *This is not news.* And then she looks embarrassed that she embarrassed me. A chorus of awkward noises and apologies. Finally, we both let ourselves off the hook with a good nervous laugh. We meet, kind of.

And for the first time in a long, long time I have a new friend. Just like that. No worries, no doubts, just the pleasant company of another person who can stand you. You lose that feeling early in your life, don't you? Moving to Hamilton in the middle of a school year and not being able to talk about my former life because I might let it slip that it was my stepdad who killed all those kids at another high school like this one is a difficult formula for finding friends. Much less one who makes me itch in a pleasant way. Maybe more than friends. At some point.

"I'm sorry for running away yesterday," I say. "That was awkward."

"Totally."

"And it's Dills."

"Huh?"

"Call me Dills, not Wendell."

"Oh, okay."

"It's weird, but I like it better."

"No, that makes sense. Wendell seems like a birth-certificate name, not a real name."

"Exactly. I like that. I may use it."

"Make sure you footnote me."

I smile and agree to make sure that every time I say it, she'll get the credit. I like that explanation. I *really* like it, in fact, and not because she's a girl and I'm not and there's a kind of magic when a girl notices things like that. I think it explains things. That tension I've always felt about my own name. How Mom avoids my questions about why she named me Wendell, which is a name for old men who wear dark socks and sandals on sweaty days like today. I kind of tune out for a moment thinking about it, and return only to find that Mia is saying something that sounds important.

"Huh? Sorry?"

"I was saying I should apologize for yesterday, too," Mia says. "For how it must've looked over by the aviary."

"Oh, that. Uh …"

"Gal's a friend. A strange friend, but still a friend. That's all."

"I shouldn't have barged in."

"I don't own the hedge."

"No, that's not what I meant. You were having a private talk."

"Yes and no. We were in private, but it was just a conversation. He speaks Arabic, too. I don't get many chances to practise."

"Don't you speak it at home?"

She frowns. "Not anymore. We used to, all the time, but my parents are trying to improve their English. And not get noticed so much."

"Is it okay if I ask where you're from?"

"Hamilton."

Another blush. "No, I mean, uh, where is your family from?"

Nothing.

"Your ethnic background? Your, uh, heritage, culturally speaking? The part of the world, maybe, where you and your parents and their parents and —"

Mia laughs and holds up a hand. "Okay, stop. Watching you squirm was fun at first, but now it's painful."

"Sorry. I've never asked anyone that before. Windsor, where we came from, is pretty white, and —"

I cut my voice off as cleanly as if I've used a box cutter on it, too. Shit. "Windsor" was out before I could stop it. Definitely one of the pieces of information we're trying not to advertise. My mind turns over itself, tumbling damage control around like wet clothes in a dryer. Heavy and ungiving. But Mia looks concerned, like she's gone an inch (2.54 centimetres) too far.

"That's okay," she says. "Hamilton's pretty white, too."

"That's true."

"We're Palestinian, although we hold Jordanian passports."

"Why?"

"Our family was cut off when Israel built another one of its walls. Jordan gives stateless Palestinians passports, and we were able to come here."

"Oh wow."

"Yeah. You couldn't know. Sorry for giving you such a hard time about it."

"I'm sorry, too, for … uh, can you forget I told you where we came from? I'm not supposed to talk about it."

"Windsor's where —"

"Yeah."

A beat. A nod. "I'll keep your secret, Sir Dills. As long as you promise never to tell anyone about my conversations with Gal."

"Of course. I —"

"He's Israeli. That's why it could be a big deal. Plus, smoking up isn't my thing at all, and I don't want that to get attached to my stellar reputation."

"I don't care about that."

"I do. Not about the assholes at school, but what my coaches would think. Weed's terrible for athletes."

"Okay."

"Gal needs the dope. You've seen the scars. He has severe pain almost all the time."

"Oh wow."

"You said that already."

"Right."

As I speak I feel that heat, like it could turn into yet another round of blushing. But it doesn't. A plain old smile rises instead. Mia doesn't seem to notice. She talks some more about her odd friendship with Gal, how he noticed that she likes to spend a lot of time reading in the park. About how her parents would go postal if they ever found out she was speaking with an Israeli, much less developing a fondness for the older, formal, scarred guy in the park who basically represents everything they escaped. She actually said "go postal" like it was no big deal, and I get that itch behind my eyes again. Mass shootings normal enough to create everyday slang. Most people don't think about their language.

"I know all about the hardships Mom and Dad faced," Mia says. "But I can't seem to hate Gal because of where he's from. He agrees that things are messed up over there."

"Why is he here? In Hamilton, I mean."

"He immigrated after he got injured in the army. It was like twenty years ago."

"What's with the scars?"

"His vehicle got hit by a rocket when they attacked Ramallah."

"They?"

"The Israelis."

I shake my head. "Unreal."

"Yeah."

"And now he looks after a park."

Mia smiles. "Can't get much more peaceful than that."

It occurs to me that I'd be fine with staying right here. Now is about the time when you'd ask if the other person would like to sit down on the bench. Maybe carry on the conversation until the sun sets. Or forever. But the ever-present abrasion of my safety vest reminds me that I'm not in the park for fun. How do you tell someone that you can't stay? Such a simple thing. And yet. Mia's gone quiet. A slight breeze feathers the loose hairs, and she tucks them under her hat with an absent, habitual gesture. She looks long across the park. Relaxed. Like she's looking at a good kind of future. Not making it any easier for me to walk away.

"Now that's a woman on a mission," she says.

I follow her look. Mom is striding across the grass toward us. She's in her workshop clothes: stained jeans and tattered UBC sweatshirt and bandana headscarf. The only thing missing is her tool belt, which is full of pliers and solder and other metalworking things. She was born with fair skin, but right now her face looks as white as printer paper, ninety-two bright. I've never seen her walk so fast.

"We need to go," she says when she arrives, slightly out of breath.

"What's wrong?"

"Gramma Jan's at the hospital."

"When? How? For what?"

"Chest pain." Mom exhales quick, exasperated, almost like a growl. "She actually drove herself, then called me. Took Viv's car. Stubborn, stubborn woman!"

"Gramma can drive?"

"She can, but shouldn't. I'll tell you more on the way."

"Okay. But my backpack is by the field house."

"You can get it later."

"I was going to get my water bottle to refill it over lunch, but Mia came, and …"

I don't finish the sentence, distracted by the surprise I see on Mom's face when she looks at Mia. Like she hasn't seen her, though Mia has been standing right here the whole time.

"Mom, this is, uh …"

I can't pluck her name from my brain. I know it. I swear I know it. Really. But she steps forward without a blink of hesitation, her hand extended, and she smiles at Mom. And suddenly I'm aware that no matter what, I'll always be a little in awe of her. Clear as mud for sure.

"I'm Mia, Mrs. Sims. Mia Al-Ansour."

"Oh! I'm Victoria. Vicky, actually. Just Vicky. Not *Mrs.* Sims. I was never a missus. I kept my name."

Mom stops, apparently aware that she might be rambling. Gives me a look. Pleased as sunrise for me, in the middle of everything. Mortifying, all of it. Obviously because it's my mom looking at Mia like she can actually see grandchildren in the shape of her. But also the timing. Poor Gramma Jan. But mostly because, well, Mia. And me. Or not me. The risks and chances I haven't glimpsed yet.

"Mom? Gramma Jan?"

"Right. You're set? Let's go. Nice to meet you, Mia."

"You too."

I give Mia a little wave as we leave, unable to say much more. As we walk across the park, I catch Mom giving me another look, this time with a hint of frustration making lines around her mouth. Well, I know that look. I call it "Boy, Are We Going to Talk About This Later."

METALLIC

Mom usually drives her old Corolla easy, like it'll fall apart at any moment, but today she's treating it like it's a stubborn pack animal that needs to be tamed. Whipping the steering wheel around corners. Mashing the gas pedal to the floor. Crunching the gearshift into place. She's had the car a long time — it's the only car I've ever seen her drive. Its poor little engine screams a few too many times for my liking. I imagine car bits flying off with every bump. Wheel covers. Mirrors. The veteran licence plates Mom insisted on that annoyed Jesse because it made him visible to others. I don't dare ask about Gramma Jan and driving; I won't be the reason Mom wraps us around a telephone pole. We arrive at the hospital and she zooms into the luxury parking lot at the front of the building. Ordinarily she'd circle wider and wider until she found free parking on the street, even if it meant we'd have to walk a few blocks.

"My mother is here somewhere," she says to the nurse at the desk. "Can you tell me —"

"Last name?" the woman says without looking up, her voice a monotone mix of exhaustion and practised boredom.

"Sims."

The nurse manipulates her keyboard and mouse. The computer screen glows blue on her face, dull blue stars glinting in her glasses. There's a waiting room full of sick people behind us. Lots of drawn faces and subdued voices. The nurse doesn't seem to care about any of it. She actually sighs, like she's the one holding the worries of the patients in her tired arms. Mom stares daggers at her, both of her hands on the counter like she might hurdle over it and reduce the nurse to her component elements.

Finally, the nurse looks up. There must be something in Mom's face she recognizes, because her eyes widen for an instant and her expression softens a bit. As she gives us the floor and room number, I'm thinking that she'll never know how much she owes that glimpse of compassion. People have been torn apart for lesser offences than indifference. I can barely keep up with Mom as she bolts down the hallway toward the elevators.

We find the room.

If my mom is a force, Gramma Jan is ten times that. Torn jeans and college T-shirts and baseball hats. No job too demanding. Handy with a hammer and wrench. A garden that's afraid of her. But all of that seems like a memory. Gramma Jan looks like she's weighed down on her bed by wires and pads and sensors. Her face as pale as the hospital gown she's been forced to wear. Her skin is an atlas of veins and spots and wrinkles I've never noticed before. She lies there at the mercy of medicine and all those unanswered questions. I guess I've never thought of her as old. Right now I can't help but think of her as anything else, and it feels wrong.

Her eyes, though. They burn as brightly as ever. She looks like she could spit. "Bastards won't even give me a goddamn glass of water," she says.

That's more like her.

"Mom, language," my mom says, but there's nothing behind it. Her voice drops and she moves to her mother's bedside. The equipment could be barbed wire, it's so scary, and all she can do is place a hand on Gramma Jan's arm. And take deep breaths. Try to, anyhow. It's hard to breathe deep when worry thins the air like it does.

"Shit, Vicky, don't be like that."

"'Shit, Vicky?' That's what I get?"

"I'm fine."

"You're not."

"You shouldn't be here," Gramma Jan says.

Mom snorts. "I called Viv. She'll be here soon. She's grabbing an Uber."

"I told you I didn't want you to come."

"Stop acting like we could possibly stay away. Besides, you stole her car, Mom."

"I borrowed it."

"Good luck explaining that to her."

"She'll be fine."

"And you?" Mom asks. "How —"

"This is all a damn embarrassing mess, is what it is."

Mom goes quiet. Not satisfied with Gramma Jan's response but not wanting to push too hard. Gramma

Jan doesn't say anything more, either. There's not much more they can say, and the silence isn't too awkward. A comfortable tension, if there's such a thing. Like they're reflecting each other in a cracked mirror.

Most of the time you never have reason to see it. Sickness brings it forward. Injury. Death. The last time I saw it was in the ER where they brought us after the shooting. Lots of families momentarily aligned. Divorced parents walking in hand in hand. Working moms and dads, feeling guilty for being so far away, wandering around with their phones in hand, calling names. Everyone shocked at the blood everywhere. Mom, too. The paramedics had bundled me into an ambulance. All that blood and you can't blame them for thinking I'd been hurt. Blood has a smell, did you know that? Kind of metallic. I could smell it on myself, soaked into my clothes from when I slipped and fell beside Ethan, who died with a library book in his hand. And from Dakota, whose leg bled more than I thought possible.

"Hey, Dills, since you're here against orders anyhow, how about a hug and a kiss?" Gramma Jan says.

I try to smile as I move next to the bed. There's a hug of sorts. As awkward and cardboard as it was yesterday with Aunt Viv, but more so because I don't want to hurt Gramma. Who's scared, though she's trying to be brave. Fear has a smell, too. I smelled it while I was waiting for Mom in the Windsor ER hallway where they'd put all the kids who'd been cleared and were waiting to be released by the police back to their parents. Under the blood smell. Fear is sour.

And just like that, I'm back in that hallway, sitting on the floor with everyone else who has been deemed well enough to wait. My friend Maddie and I have given up our chairs because even though none of us have been injured too badly, it seems like everyone else needs them more than we do. There's a sling here, a bandage there, and a lot of bloodstains on all our clothes. Turning dark and kind of brown. We're tagged with our names. There's a cop with a clipboard who checks ID when parents come in for their kids. I think we're all crying. It's cold. The smells of blood and fear fill my nose. Metallic. Sour.

Wait. I can hear voices. Mom's. And Gramma Jan's.

"Dills? Are you okay?" Mom asks.

"I think so?"

Now I'm in a hospital room with my mother and grandmother, who's had some kind of heart thing. It's bad. Must be. Otherwise there wouldn't be so much stuff on her. Wires and pads and clips. The little green and orange and red lights of all the equipment, the fluttering readout screens, the whiteness of the bed and gowns and the open window. I'm all right. But I can still smell that fear. And not only from Gramma Jan. It's everywhere, in the air of the hospital. And it's coming from me again. Why does the room seem all shimmery, like I'm looking at it through water?

I'm here. Come see me.

Jesse's voice. Right next to me, as real in this room as it has been in the park. Is he here? Can he be? Then there's a sudden blackness and I feel myself falling. I don't feel where the fall ends, though.

SCARS

Voices. Familiar ones, I think. But they're all muddy and lost in a swimming darkness made worse by the fact that my eyes won't open. I want them to. Why won't they? Wait. Maybe it's not completely dark. There's a distant redness, like when you shine a flashlight through your hand.

I feel rested. Like I've slept a full night through and am waking up when my mind and body are perfectly ready. What a strange thought to have, given that I don't seem to be in control of either mind or body. And I don't remember dreaming, which is new. No dreams, good or bad. When I was a kid I used to have the wildest, most fantastic dreams. Space adventures and ten-headed creatures and heroics. But they were often gone in the morning, even though I wanted to hold on to them. Now I just have the kind of dreams you're glad to forget in the morning, if you can. I remember too many. Dreams of Jesse's rifle and his camouflaged face. Also ones that feature gunfire or blood or the screams of the other kids.

"Memory dreams," I call them. I think the universe makes you remember those.

"Dills."

That voice is less muddy. Am I waking up? Was I sleeping, or something else?

"Dills, open your eyes."

It's Mom. I can tell because there's the tiniest gravel in the back of her voice. Like she smoked for a while and quit, but not before the hurt took hold. Or maybe the fumes from all the welding and soldering she does in her workshop have seared her vocal cords. I'm glad she's here. It makes it okay to try again to open my eyes.

More light. Flashes. A room that's kind of bright, kind of not. Oh, right. Hospital. Window blinds. Equipment and screens, tiny lights and numbers. Lots of the off-white plastic that everything in hospitals seems to be made of. Mom's face. And Aunt Viv.

"Hi," I say.

"Hi yourself," Mom says.

"What happened?"

"You fainted. How are you feeling?"

I want to say that I feel great, rested, ready to jump out of bed, but I'm not sure how Mom will take that. There's concern in her eyes. And parents have expectations. "Not bad," I say. "Uh, maybe a bit confused."

"Really? You did hit your head on the way down." She looks more concerned now. Parents and expectations and a constant fear of concussions.

Time to downplay. Reassure. Parents can be needy, too. "No, not that kind of confused. I'm wondering what happened."

"Are you sure?"

"My name is Wendell Bartholomew Sims. I'm fifteen years old. I live in Hamilton. I come from a long line of Sims, son of Victoria, grandson of Jan, nephew of Vivian. I'm a criminal mastermind wearing a LoJack —"

"Okay, okay, we get it," Aunt Viv says, rolling her eyes. "Smartass."

"I'm fine."

"Dills, I won't —"

"Mom, chill, okay? I'm good."

"Can you blame me?" Mom asks. "You blacked out, dropped like a stone. Gramma Jan's bed broke your fall, and ..."

She stops and points at my forehead. Ah. That explains the strange tightness I feel on my brow, above my left eye. I lift a hand — which feels remarkably heavy, given that it's mine and I've been moving it my whole life — and feel the bandage there. A distant, slight pain behind the dressing. A tightness.

"Stitches?" I ask.

"A few, yeah," Mom says, frowning.

"You'll have a little scar," Aunt Viv chimes in. "And chicks dig scars."

"Cool," I say.

For an instant I believe myself. Maybe every guy dreams about getting just the right scar for just the right story for just the right person. But all my recent history flashes forward. Windsor. Hospital. Pat. Box cutter. I wince. My relationship to scars has changed forever.

"Dills?" Mom asks. "What's wrong?"

"Anyway …" I stretch out the word. I'm so aware of their eyes on me. *Distract, distract, distract.* "How's Gramma Jan?"

Mom and Aunt Viv glance at each other, then practically climb over each other to tell me. The docs think Gramma Jan has an arrhythmia, an irregular heartbeat. She needs to stay in hospital for a few days for further tests. She insisted that Mom and Aunt Viv go with me to make sure I was all right. I can almost hear her peppering her orders with choice language. There's more detail, but I tune out their voices and look around. The bed is in a fishbowl room right across from a nurse's station. Glass on three walls. Curtains on either side of me. In front I can see the top of a woman's head above the station desk. Ducked down, busy, but positioned to look into the room in a nanosecond if need be. A trauma room. For a kid with a cut forehead. It all seems like monstrous overkill.

There are bloodstains on my dingy work shirt and shorts. I'm thinking about the physics of how they ended up there, given that I fell and the blood should've ended up on the floor, when I see the back of someone stopping at the desk and speaking to the nurse. She looks up and nods at the room behind him and he turns, pocketing his wallet. He must keep his probation officer ID there.

Sean.

And he looks annoyed. Not concerned.

He strides into the room and opens his mouth to speak but stops when he sees Mom and Aunt Viv sitting on the stiff chairs. His eyes lock on to Aunt Viv and his mouth closes, this blank expression taking over his face, like he had a speech all ready to go but the sight of her has forced his brain to reboot itself.

"Yes?" she asks, her eyes narrowing.

Her expression is not uncertain in the least. It could cut him into ribbons. Aunt Viv has always had this built-in mistrust of anything institutional. Schools. Courthouses. Churches. She came to my sentencing but steadfastly refused to place a single foot into any of the other buildings associated with my correctional life. "I'm here for *you*, Dills," she said, "not *Them*." The words coming out like they'd been dipped in sewage.

"Well?"

By the way Aunt Viv is disassembling Sean with her eyes — *field-stripping*, Jesse would say — it's clear she views him as the System. Not representing a single portion of it, but embodying the entire thing. There's no response from Sean. Maybe his lower jaw moves a little? I begin to feel bad for him.

Mom steps in. "What are you doing here, Sean?"

Her voice reaches him, and he blinks a few times. You have to do that when you've stared at the sun for too long. "Oh, right. I'm here because, uh, Wendell is in breach."

"In breach?" Mom asks.

"Of his sentencing conditions."

Aunt Viv folds her arms. "What the hell?"

"Um, well, he's geofenced, yeah?"

Aunt Viv's left eyebrow rises a bit. "How?"

"The ankle monitor is GPS-linked, so —"

"Dynamic or static nodes?"

"Dynamic, but only from my workstation."

"Contextually retargeted, undoubtedly."

"In real time, if need be."

"Trigger intervals?"

"Every fifteen minutes."

"Pushed."

"Of course."

Sean holds up his phone and taps open an app. Aunt Viv steps around the bed and stands right beside him, shoulder to shoulder. Their conversation continues as though we aren't there. Which we aren't. Not really. They talk so fast, using terms I don't recognize. It could be their own language. Digitalese, or something. Mom and I give each other a sidelong glance. This conversation has taken a turn toward the surreal. Viv laughs, and Sean lights up like he's glimpsed something golden. Now it's my mother's turn to get grumpy. And my turn to get it. Sean and Aunt Viv are into each other. Flirting. Or some data-stimulated version of it, anyhow.

Mom snaps her fingers in Aunt Viv's direction. "Hey! How about coming back down to reality for a moment?"

"But he —"

"Sean," he supplies, helpfully.

"Right. Sean is e-conduited to the court database. It's —"

"Viv," Mom says.

"— pretty cool, if you think about it."

"Vivian So-Eun Sims."

Hearing her Korean given name, which Gramma Jan insisted she keep on her adoption papers, snaps Aunt Viv back to the present. She shakes her head like she's clearing it of radar jamming and moves back to my bedside. She folds her arms and her face regains its composure, which in her case means the hard stare returns and is directed right back at Sean. He doesn't seem to know what to do with the jarring shift. He fiddles with his phone, suddenly preoccupied by some dirt trapped at the edge of its protective case, before putting it back in his pocket.

"Sean?" my mother asks. "What's going on?"

"Wendell's ankle monitor is linked to a specific geographical location. It alerted me when he left the park area."

"Oh."

"It's sensitive, especially during work hours."

Aunt Viv frowns. "He can't leave our neighbourhood?"

"Of course he can. He's not wearing a shock collar, yeah?" Sean looks at the three of us in turn, his expression brightening a little, but his attempt at humour falls flat. "Right. Well. In off hours, there's some leeway programmed in. If the monitor moves to, say, a grocery store or school or church, we don't worry. But if Wendell suddenly dashes across town in the middle of the day, it'll trigger."

"This is a hospital, Sean," Mom says. "Wouldn't you assume he'd been hurt?"

"I didn't think about it much, to be honest."

"Your concern is heartwarming."

He shrugs. "People go to hospitals for all kinds of reasons."

"You should've told us," Mom says.

"It's common sense. Plus, we went over this at the field house on day one, didn't we, Wendell? You should know better than to desert your post on a workday."

"Desert his what?"

My post, Mom, I want to say. The park. That place where I'm supposed to stay. I can imagine Jesse narrowing his eyes if he was here to hear this. *One, you have a job to do. Two, people are depending on you to stick it out. You don't leave in the middle. Clear as mud?*

Mom leans forward. "So what are you saying, Sean? Spit it out."

"I have to report this to the court. They'll probably look at the circumstances and excuse the breach, but that's up to the judge."

Sean's face has grown harder, too. I hate that. I hate that what I do makes people angry.

"His grandmother is upstairs in the heart ward and you're worried about … about …"

"Breaching, apparently," Aunt Viv offers.

Sean ignores Aunt Viv. "I don't think you appreciate how serious this is, Mrs. Sims. He has to meet the conditions of his sentencing."

"First, don't call me 'missus.' Call me Victoria or nothing at all. Second, I understand that you're processing data and ticking boxes on a thousand bureaucratic forms, but this was a family emergency."

"I have a job to do, Mrs. … Victoria."

"And third, if you think I don't *get* what my kid's been through —"

"He still has to meet the conditions of his sentencing, even if he was at Windsor."

Mom slaps the edge of my bed. "He wasn't just *at* Windsor! Reporters were *at* the school. Parents were *at* the school. Hell, most of the other kids were *at* the fucking school. Dills was —"

Mom stops herself from saying *in the library*. Just a few of our many words to choose from, but they always generate a frenzy of strong opinions and horror and expressions of sympathy. I can't say them. Thinking them is enough. Knowing what they mean is enough.

Mom and Sean and Aunt Viv have all gone quiet. Silence is a strange sort of space, isn't it? You want to fill it. Sean has been knocked into a not-knowing-what-to-say variety of silence. Aunt Viv has retreated into a kind that the loved ones of survivors go into, where there are no words. Mom is looking at me, her silence a mix of the helplessness parents feel and the hope that I'll fill the void. Parents want their kids to say the words, sometimes.

I don't, though. Words can be too easy.

In the days after, during what Mom called "the media storm," news outlets tended to alphabetize the names. Scrolled them like stock tickers. I always knew when Ethan's name and picture would come up. He was my best friend, and his last name began with a *G*, so his was always the fourth. The fourth photo and name listed or slideshowed across all those screens. The same school picture from last year because he was sick on picture day this year. Grade nine and his new braces. Silver hardware and army green for the backings. Mom always looked away when it happened, like when we went shopping or got my hair cut or bought a drink from places where the TVs were always on.

I didn't. In the picture, though he's smiling and clean and polite, which wasn't like the everyday Ethan I knew, he was still so much more him than the Ethan I had to leave on the floor in the library. People can die without faces.

I watch Sean and Mom and Aunt Viv fill the space, but I'm not listening. Mom will tell me the important stuff later.

BELIEVED

The next day, I wake up to a quiet house, which is unusual — I live with three early risers who are always up long before me. But it's a strange morning, all right. Gramma Jan is at the hospital for her tests. Mom's nowhere to be seen. Probably sleeping. Aunt Viv is the only one around, sitting at the kitchen table behind a laptop. Her oatmeal — her breakfast always consists of coffee and a single pack of plain instant oatmeal — congealing and cold beside her as she manipulates the keys.

"Hey, kid," she says when I walk in and begin to assemble my breakfast of Mini-Wheats and OJ. Doesn't look up, though.

"What're you doing?"

She types a long string of code or something, gives a satisfied grunt, and looks up. "Checking out the tech your friend Sean uses to keep tabs on you."

"He's not my friend."

"Just an expression."

"In fact, I'd say he might be more your friend than mine. You two were pretty tight yesterday."

A dismissive wave. "Professional interest."

"Uh huh."

"The tech got me, is all."

"Find anything out?"

"Always."

"What does that mean?"

She points at the computer. "You can find pretty much anything if you have the right keystrokes."

"Please tell me you didn't hack him."

She smiles, a glint in her eye from the laptop screen, sky blue. "Well, *I* wouldn't call it a hack."

"What would you call it? Wait, don't answer that. I don't want to know, do I?"

"No."

"Make sure you don't —"

"Don't worry, Dills. I know how serious this is for you. I'd never jeopardize that."

And I believe her. She has this way of moving through life like it's hers for the taking. Mom told me once that Aunt Viv was top of her class, that she'd been courted by all the tech giants. A bunch of high-six-figure salaries dangled in front of her like golden apples. But she went out on her own. Makes her own hours, chooses her own clients. Mom says she's rich as hell, but you'd never know it by looking at her. Clothes from the same stores everyone shops at. A nicely detailed but small Toyota hybrid in silver, the beige of car paint. Still lives with Gramma Jan in this quiet little neighbourhood. Sleeps in the bedroom she grew up in. Like she doesn't need anything beyond the basics. I like that. You have to respect the lines between need and want.

"Okay, Doc," I say.

She grunts again, reaches over, right into my cereal bowl, and throws a soggy Mini-Wheat at me. She has at least two PhDs, but never talks about them. Hates the prestige factor. It's fun to bug her.

"How's the head?" she asks.

"Fine. No pain."

"Good. Your bandage fell off."

I raise a hand to the tight place. I can feel the roughness of the knots and clipped thread. No pain, though. "How does it look?"

"Like you cut your forehead on the side of a bed."

"Really? I should —"

"It looks fine, Dills. Relax."

I reach for the first-aid box, take it to the bathroom, and check myself out in the mirror. She's right. There's some bruising. But no blood — the wound is clean. I stick a plastic bandage over it and go back to the kitchen.

"You blacked out pretty good yesterday," Aunt Viv says as she spoons coffee beans into the grinder. Her back is to me as she works.

"I guess I did."

The tinny sound of the grinder's blades smashing through the coffee beans fills the kitchen for a few seconds. She pours the freshly ground beans into a basket filter and drops it into the top of the coffee maker. Reaches over to the sink, fills the carafe about halfway, and dumps the water into the coffee maker before hitting the power switch. The machine chugs and hisses.

She watches every drip, not wanting to take the coffee before it's ready. A Jesse thing, something about the proper grind and saturation and timing that he learned in the army. Whenever we'd visit Hamilton, he'd get up first and make coffee for everyone. He'd block the machine if anyone tried to take a mug before it was done. "It'll be worth the wait, troops. Promise," he'd say. Somehow the habit crept its way into our family. Aunt Viv, Mom, and Gramma Jan observing the ritual. They don't realize. I do.

"Do you know what you said before you fell?"

"I said something?"

"You did. 'No, Jesse!' Clear as anything."

The inflection she puts into the words is startling. It sounds like pleading. Like I was pleading. Begging.

"We all heard you, Dills. No one talked about it — I suppose we all figured it was being in the hospital that did it — but I wanted to ask."

"I don't remember saying anything."

"The way you said it —"

And I suddenly know why she's asking. She's imagining what the tone in my voice was saying. Like I was afraid of Jesse. That he could hurt me somehow. In all the ways people fear grown-ups can hurt us.

"Aunt Viv, no, he never —"

"Because you can tell us if anything happened. You know that, right?"

What an odd moment. The hacker aunt I've never lived with asking me if my stepfather abused me. The questions my own mother never asked about my stepfather. The stepfather who, despite a footlocker full of flaws, would never do anything to hurt me. Yet the same stepfather who could march into a school and start shooting. We still don't understand his flaws. And we're afraid of them. Afraid enough to assume. Like Aunt Viv is doing right now, her controlled face a wash of emotions all fighting to take over. *He could never do that*, I want to say. With all of myself I want to defend Jesse, but I've never seen Aunt Viv wrestling so hard with herself, either. What do you do when the could-have-beens are eclipsed by what actually happened?

I guess you begin with what's in front of you. By offering other things. "He talks to me."

"What do you mean? Who talks to you?"

"Jesse."

Aunt Viv tilts her head. "Jesse talks to you."

What seems so clear to me is clearly not so for her. I must sound crazy. "Yes. No. In my head, I think. I mean, I can hear him. When I'm working."

"You've always talked to yourself, Dills."

"No, it's not that."

"Okay."

"He's calling me. I don't know how else to say it."

She exhales, unfolds her arms, and pushes herself away from the counter. Opens the cupboard with a jerky, rushed movement. Grabs a mug. I can tell she's still not able to hold on to what I've told her. And who can blame her? Even I'm starting to hear myself, to hear the crazy in the words.

"Don't worry about it," I say. "I must've hit my head a bit too hard."

"No, keep going."

"Can you not say anything to Mom? She won't like that I —"

"Dills. Keep. Going."

Her eyes have cleared and she's leaning toward me. The body language suggests a change in my favour. But I wait an instant. Not daring to hope too much.

"I believe you," she says, finally.

"Really?"

"Yes."

Okay, then. Her words have settled me. I hear myself telling her everything, the whats, whens, wheres, hows. Telling her that Jesse's voice is a real thing I can almost feel, how it's different from memory or imagination. At the end, I sit back in my chair and watch her as she sips her coffee. She drinks it black. "Full strength," she likes to say. Jesse drinks his the same way. "One, it's easier when you're pressed for time," he once said. "No muss, no fuss. Two, what's the point otherwise? Coffee has to be strong. For the blood. For the brain." Aunt Viv puts down her mug. She's having trouble with the whys.

"So, he wants you to go back."

"Yeah."

"I can't stop thinking about what he did. And now he's talking to you, which is hard to fathom."

"You don't believe me after all."

"I think I do. But I'm worried about what it means for you, in terms of your healing."

"Healing?"

"I'm not going to talk about moving on or anything — God knows you've heard enough of that — but accepting what happened."

"I don't hate him, Aunt Viv."

"You don't have to."

"Everyone expects me to. They don't say it, but they do."

"People think hate is the answer for what they don't understand. It's not. But no one can ask him, which makes it worse."

"I can't even hate him when I think that he might've been coming for me."

"Ach, Dills, aside from thinking about all those dead kids, and that you might've —" Her voice breaks and she winces. There is real, physical pain there, pain I've never seen uncovered like this. She swallows, coughs, blinks away a sudden misting of her dark eyes. Tries again. "Thinking about Jesse hurting you is the toughest part for any of us. The wondering. Especially for your mom. You can understand that, right?"

"Do you hate him?"

"I hate what he did. The rest of it, who knows?"

"Does Mom?"

"Would you blame her if she did?"

"He's still Jesse."

"He is and he isn't, if that makes sense."

"I miss him, Aunt Viv. I want to go."

"I know. But can I offer a suggestion?"

"I suppose."

"Keep this to yourself. I'm glad you told me, but your mom might not …" She pauses. "Let's say that she might not get it. Not that I want you to keep secrets from her, but we don't talk about Jesse much these days."

"I get why, I do. But it still feels like a hole in our family."

Aunt Viv puts her mug down and nods. Thanks me for the talk, like we've worked out some everyday thing. There's another awkward hug that she hangs on to for a few extra beats. Then she picks up her laptop and walks out of the kitchen, telling me as she goes to "get out there and pick up some trash." Like she's my coach. Like all that rot and garbage is the goal, rather than the struggle.

DETAILS

Mia finds me before lunch. I've been in the same spot for more than an hour. Near the soccer pitches, there's an access road for the city maintenance fleet to use when they come for their weekly grass mowing and trimming. A dozen iron posts linked by rusted heavy chain line the road from the gate to the soccer field. Hard to know how old the posts and chain are, although they go far enough back to when iron and chain seemed appropriate for kids' play areas.

Only one of the hollow posts still has its original decorative ball screwed to the top. The rest are open to the sky, filled with what seems like a century of garbage. Everything from crushed pop cans to chip bags to cigarette butts to tattered, unidentifiable pieces of clothing. Like a park history in layers of decaying trash. More rotten the farther down you go. The first post cleared out easy, so I thought I'd get the rest. Bad idea. Between the dirt and the rust and the fetid things, each grosser than the last, I'm filthy. And pissed for doing this to myself.

"Serves you right for being so stubborn," I tell myself as I dig into a post with my spike — which I've decided is a far cooler word than *picker-upper* — and lift another dripping, smelly piece of cloth into the sky. This one was black at some point, but is now a faded mess of grey and rust.

A sudden voice behind me. "Stubborn? I'd say you're being thorough, but —"

"Shit!" My heart in my mouth. I fumble the cloth, which falls to the ground and flops open, revealing a cracked silkscreened skull and a single word. *Misfits*. An old band T-shirt. I turn.

It's Mia. Laughing. Hard. "But surely this wasn't part of the deal."

I groan inwardly. I'm blushing to burst. *Please let me not have squeaked out loud. Okay, universe? That's not too much to ask, right?*

"Uh …"

"Hi," she says. Just like that.

"Hi."

"What happened to your head?"

"My head?"

"You have some shiny new stitches."

"Oh, that." I raise my spike-holding hand — it's a tiny bit cleaner than the other one — to my forehead and feel the rough suture knots. I've sweated the bandage away again. I tell her I fainted and banged it against the hospital bed when I went to visit Gramma Jan. I explain it away as an aversion to hospitals and a reaction to how sick Gramma Jan looked. I finish with a dramatic statement about how worried I was and that I wasn't prepared for what came next. Truth mixed with a strategic omission of truth. I'm getting pretty good at leaving things out of my stories.

She nods at the poles and the mess at my feet. Makes a face. "So you're stressed. I suppose it helps explain the reason you gave yourself this particular challenge. Which is totally gross, by the way."

"I didn't think it would take so long. I did the first one, which was easy, and then kind of —"

"Got obsessed."

"Totally."

She smiles. I try to smile. I don't really know whether I'm still embarrassed or not. Caught talking to myself again. Ethan used to make fun of me for it, but in a best-friend way, where you hassle each other for the least important things. He knew about Jesse, how he wasn't my dad but I treated him like he was. How I wanted him to be. When I was a kid, sometimes I'd call Jesse "Dad" to see if it would stick. He didn't like it, though. "Just Jesse, little man," he once said. "One, you know that your dad left your mom when he found out you were on the way. But two, even though you don't like to think of him that way, he's still your dad. I'm not. Clear as mud?" I'd try to argue and say that he was my real dad, but he'd smile and say something like he was lucky to be in my life and he'd take whatever he could get. Though I'm clearly the lucky one. Was, maybe.

"Who's Ethan?" Mia asks.

First, mortal embarrassment. As in *Oh my god, oh my god, oh my god*. Second, I discover another shard of what happened. Right in my middle. And it slices in. Again.

I take a deep breath. "He was my friend. From before."

"From Windsor?"

"Yes."

"Sorry. I was supposed to forget about that, but I can't. I kind of want to know your story, Wendell Sims, a.k.a. Dills Sims."

The nicest feeling in the universe happens when you realize that someone else really wants to know you. I almost miss this one. If her words had arrived at any other time than right now, I'd tell her. Maybe not everything, but enough. Enough to return the interest, at least. My guts, though, are currently focused on stitching themselves up, so I have to let the moment pass.

"Dills Sims …" She lets her statement trail away, like a question that needs an answer.

"Yes?"

"Sounds awkward, am I right?"

"I suppose so."

"Your mom seems nice, too."

"Huh?"

"She said to call her Vicky, but I think I'd like to call her Victoria. Do you think she'd mind?"

I smile. If there's anything I do know, even amid my confusion, is that my mother hates it when people use her proper name. "That woman named me after a silly Englishwoman," she'll say, sometimes right in front of Gramma Jan. I also know that Gramma Jan reacts as strongly to being called "that woman" as my mom

does to being called Victoria. They argue about it sometimes. Which is funny to watch because it's such a small
thing to get worked up about, I think. Mia, by asking
an innocent question, has landed right in the middle
of it, creating a nanosecond of escape for me. My smile
becomes a grin, which cracks open my face and releases
a laugh so sudden it steals a little of my breath.

"I do think she'd mind, yes," I manage to gasp at the
end of it.

Not what Mia is expecting. Her eyebrows pinch, perplexed. She's unprepared for my bluntness to her earnest
question. Which is even funnier, and I can't stop myself
from laughing more. I have to put down my spike and
my bag. I take my helmet off because it seems too small,
unable to contain the swell of unexpected funniness.

Mia watches me for a few moments. But there
comes a point when even the most well-meant laughter
begins to cut those who aren't sharing it. She frowns and
pulls out her phone and swipes through something or
other. Those familiar movements are like a heavy curtain falling. You worry whether you'll be able to lift it
back up again. My laughter fades, leaving the everyday
sounds of a park in motion and leaving me with that
tight, crinkled feeling you get in your face when you've
laughed too long.

I notice the tiniest shimmer in Mia's dark eyes.
Harsher stabbing and swiping across her touchscreen.
The slight turn of her body away from me. I feel as small
as the point of my trash spike. And as sharp.

"I'm sorry."

"Whatever."

She blinks and continues to manipulate her phone. I wait for her eyes to reclaim their normal mystery. But they stay hard.

"It's just that my mom is so stubborn about some things," I say. "Like her name. It's a perfectly fine name, but she hates it."

"She could change it, if it bugged her enough."

That's a thought I'd never had before. Huh. I hear myself saying "sorry" again, telling Mia that my reaction surprised me, too, that I didn't mean to be so harsh. That the laughter came out so quickly I couldn't hold it back. What I didn't say is that it was the first out-loud laughter I could remember having in a long time. Maybe since before Windsor. Through half a school year at a new school. The cutting incident. Court and sentencing and a daily grind of prying and digging and plucking discarded things from where they'd lain too long. And truthfully, although I was sorry for cutting into her, it felt good, too. Which of course feels horribly wrong. And yet.

Finally, Mia smiles and tells me that it's okay. But I worry that it's not. That I've carved too deep, and maybe the scars won't heal right.

Mia seems to sense my worry. She holds out a hand. "Give me your phone. I'll put my number in there for you."

"I don't have one."

"Oh. Right. The judge doesn't want you to —"

"No, I actually don't own one."

"Really?"

"Sorry."

"Why would you say sorry?"

I don't know. Before Windsor, me having a phone was an "End of Discussion, Young Man" topic. Mom has this thing about cellphones and kids and how rotten their brains are becoming. She can be empowering and progressive about a whole whack-load of other things: religion is misdirection for ignorant people, social justice is everyone's battle, talk to me about anything, there are no stupid questions, you're twelve but here's a box of condoms just in case, et cetera. But on the issue of me having a phone, it's the early 1990s and the web hasn't taken hold yet. She and Jesse are in lockstep about it, too. "No way, kiddo. One, this is your mom's call, but my job is to have her back, so don't triangle me against her. Two, I happen to agree with her. No one knows how to look each other in the eye anymore. Read a book. Get outside. Build something. Get a job." I tried a thousand angles and pitches, but Mom's resolve on this one issue was plate armour. Sixteen for my first phone, and the words "Don't ask again" delivered with a real edge to her voice. I haven't tested it in a while, of course.

"My mom hates cellphones," I say. "She jokes about them being a sign of the end times. I'm not allowed to have one."

"That's —"

"Shitty. I get it."

But I really mean *embarrassing*. Mortifying. Frustrating. Life-alteringly backwards. And yet I don't mean those things, either. I haven't had the urge to use social media since before the shooting, haven't wanted a phone. But here I am, trying to make some offering to the girl in front of me, that obviously it's Mom's issue, right? I know it isn't, yet I can't stop myself.

"No, I was going to say that it's cool," she says. "Sometimes I wish I didn't have to carry one around."

I breathe again. Mia has managed to surprise me and put me out of my misery all at once. "But don't you use all the apps and stuff?"

"Some. Mostly to stay in touch with my wrestling peeps. The rest of it is" — she glances down at her phone — "complicated."

"How?"

"Me being Muslim. Immigrant family. Wrestling body shape. All that. Let's say that social media isn't a safe space."

"I get that."

"Yeah, but boys don't have nearly the —"

"I like how you look."

Her eyes narrow. Ugh. My mouth took over. One silly heart short-circuiting the rest of the system, contacting my lungs, throat muscles, vocal cords, and tongue without first consulting my brain. I'm struck by a sense that it was the wrong thing to say. *Nice one, boss. That was unexpected. Foot in mouth much? Women are more than a sum of their looks, you know.* But right as I'm about to assemble another crack team of apologies — there are some things a guy can never unsay to a girl — Mia smiles. Big and bold and all for me. And beautiful. I hope I can say that.

"Thanks," she says.

And that is how a single word can pull a person back. Give him back his breath. "You're welcome."

"That is literally the first time anyone has ever said that to me."

"No way. That's —"

She holds up a hand. "It's okay, Dills. I've seen the movies and magazines. I know what everyone seems to want."

"I like how you look."

Another smile. "Yeah, you said that already."

"I wanted you to hear it from me for the second time, too."

She rolls her eyes. "Yeah, yeah, that's enough. Now, if you don't have a phone, how —"

"Landline. And email on my iPod. Mom has an iPhone, but I'm not allowed to use it."

"You don't use social media, either?"

I shake my head but don't say anything. The school therapist assigned to me after the shooting advised me to stay away from all things online. "There's too much ugliness there right now," she said. "Too much hate and misinformation. Focus on your real-life relationships and try to lean on them, okay?" It sounded like something she'd gotten used to telling other survivors. I did look at the news reports at first, but I wasn't that big on the online web of social intrigue before, so it wasn't hard to break up with it. I haven't had the desire to go back.

But Mia doesn't question my reasons. She nods and asks for my contact info, tapping it into her phone. Maybe she saw a shadow cross my eyes as I remembered my therapy, another one of a million small but jagged things that feel like they'll be hooked into my insides from now on.

"All right, you, now back to work," she says.

I throw up a salute. "Yes, ma'am. Right away, ma'am."

Parade-worthy, Jesse would call it. Tip of the right middle finger brushing the right eyebrow, hand straight, upper arm parallel to the ground.

Mia giggles and salutes me back. Sloppy and wrong, but that's fine.

"Later, Dills."

"Bye, Mia."

She walks away, and I put on my helmet and adjust my vest on my shoulders. My scratchy, sweaty armour against the rest of the summer. I jab my spike down on a piece of garbage on the ground. No more digging wrong things out of ancient fence posts for me today. I resume my usual rhythm. Look, stick, lift, slide whatever crud I've picked up into the garbage bag. And repeat. This time, though, I let myself include a few extra looks. To anyone observing me, it'll look like I'm scanning for more trash, but I'll actually be watching Mia cross the park as she heads back toward her place. Which I do. Maybe more than a few times.

I'm here. Come see me.

"I know, Jesse. I hear you," I say low, under my breath. "I'm working on it."

But that's not quite the truth, is it? I want to go, but there's a lot of my present life happening around me. Keeping me busy. And keeping me strangely interested in the right now.

SURPLUS

Midmorning snack break is my new thing. When hunger strikes, pretty much wherever I am, I'll drop my bag and stick my spike in the ground and eat. Today I'm close enough to the park chapel to take a couple of steps over and eat in its shadow. Before leaving home, I stuff my pockets. Some days it's cookies or raisins or apples or nuts — whatever I can get, however much — but today it's granola bars. I dig out one of the four I grabbed from the cupboard. Mushy from my body heat, the dark chocolate almost liquid. Gone in two bites. Hunger hits so quick these days, it's almost painful. All the walking and sun and fresh air, I suppose.

The chapel is in the main part of the park, where you'll find the sports fields, the play structures, and the splash pad. The small white cross at the top of the chapel's steeple is visible from almost anywhere in the park. You look there first and next your eyes are drawn down to the white walls and doors. Right now the sun is late-morning high and hitting the place with full force. Blinding against the greens of trees and grass. The chapel sits between four ball diamonds, one at each corner. If you stood at home plate on any of them, the miniature church beyond the home-run fence would be a tempting target. An iceberg to smack a ball at.

I'm not here very often. There's nothing to clean. Everywhere else, the garbage seems to defy physics, wedged tight into impossible places by the smallest breeze. I'll clean another corner of the park until it sparkles, only to find it the next day looking like a rogue garbage truck dumped its load overnight. To spite me. The chapel, though, never seems to get dirty, and trash never collects along its angles.

I wonder how on earth the place stays so white. How anything does. I can't own anything lighter than beige. You can't tell if beige things get dingy because they start that way. Shoes, especially. I gave up on asking for white ones a long time ago. They look great in the store, but on my feet they're scuffed in seconds. By the end of the first day, they look like I've run ten kilometres in them. On a mix of gravel and new asphalt. While kicking old tires. Tagged by rival gangs as I ran.

As I stand and chew, I catch the faintest whiff of burning weed. I wipe the chocolate from my hands and circle the building but see no one. Has to be from inside. I imagine some neighbourhood kid sneaking into the chapel, lighting up, filling the interior with greasy smoke, and dropping the roach on the floor. Grinding the residue into a cross pattern. Giggling at God to do something about it.

And it pisses me off. I have no idea why. We're not a religious family. Maybe I don't like the idea of some kid mocking the chapel's wide-open, welcoming doors by messing the place up. Maybe it's a tiny bit of loyalty because the chapel is cared for by the same local church where Jesse and Mom did their thing and I wore that tiny tuxedo. Maybe it's because it's a clean, cool spot where anyone can escape the sun, sit on polished wood pews, and stare at stained glass.

I step inside and squint against the startling contrast between the light outside and the colourful dimness inside. As my eyes adjust, I see a dim figure sitting in one of the pews. Gal. Leaning forward with his scarred forearms on the pew in front of him. A smouldering joint lightly pinched between forefinger and thumb.

"Mr. Sims," he says.

He brings the joint to his lips and tokes long and hard on it. Exhales. A strange offering. But he looks comfortable here, at peace, like this is routine. I can only see the right side of his face. Almost normal, if you tune out the twisted flesh on his arm.

"You look angry," he says.

"No, I'm not … it's just that …" I fall silent.

"Nice canteen."

He's still looking straight ahead, and I've only just arrived, but he's already taken everything in with his peripheral vision, right down to my accessories. Unsettling.

"Uh, thanks," I say. "Mom's idea."

"Hydration is important."

We're speaking in our normal voices. It's so quiet in here Gal doesn't have to turn his good ear to hear me.

"You sound like her," I say.

"This is a compliment, I am sure."

He tokes again and pinches out the joint with his fingers. No hesitation. No smoke at all. Wow.

"How'd you do that?" I ask.

"Long practice."

"But it was so quick."

He holds up the extinguished end. "If it is small, it is possible. You must do it quickly. Take all the oxygen. No chance to burn."

"That sounds like something Jesse would've —"

That was out before I could stop it. Gal's action like an army thing. *Tactical*, Jesse would call it. Where you act in ways that make you difficult to be seen or heard or found.

"Jesse?"

"Nothing," I say. "He's no one."

Gal looks at me and grunts. Doesn't look convinced. Hard to convince a person if I'm not convinced myself.

"Where did you learn it?" I ask, testing my theory.

"The army."

His voice clipped and final. He doesn't say more. He drops the half-burnt joint into his chest pocket, rises from the pew, stretches, and slides over to the aisle, where he goes down on one knee and crosses himself.

"You're a Chr— uh, a churchgoing type?"

Oh, that was smooth. Nice terminology. Say Christian, *for crying out loud.* Mom fought against the paperwork and rigidity of marriage and she doesn't believe in organized religion anymore, but she still thought it was important to exchange the vows in church. Jesse never had religion and only went along with it because he loved her. Mom grew up attending services twice every Sunday because Grampa Vern was a dyed-in-the-wool church person. Bible studies. Prayer before and after every meal. Church school and catechism every week until he died when she was fifteen. Strict. "Too strict. And no place for women," she told me. "That's why I don't do church." Gramma Jan stopped going after Grampa Vern died. Mom thinks watching him decline wore Gramma Jan's faith away.

Gal tilts his head. "Why would I not be?"

"Mia says you're from Israel, so —"

"You assume I am Jewish."

"Don't you have to be?"

"I was, then. But not now."

"Why not now?"

A long pause. "You might say what happened to me, and what I saw, has complicated my relationship with my heritage."

It almost feels like an opening to ask him about the scars. I want to. But something keeps me from the question. Maybe it's the violence of the past. It complicates everything for me now, too.

Gal doesn't seem to mind my hesitation. He points at the canteen slung across my chest like a satchel. "May I?"

I remove it from its carrier and hand it to him. He smiles a bit when he flips open a miniature cap embedded in the middle of the main lid and points at a small doughnut of faded black rubber resting inside. Tells me it's a hydration port. A straw can be passed through the seal in the canteen and another through an identical seal in a military gas mask. Soldiers can drink in a chemical weapons environment.

"But I could never get the mask to work," Gal says. "Not many could. It is an American design. Useless."

Jesse said the same thing. He said that older NCOs — non-commissioned officers — would talk about them. Practising in gas huts with CS gas, which is like tear gas. Failing because the rubber was too grabby for the straw and they'd give up and breathe and end up on the ground outside, their eyes fused shut, gagging and vomiting from the exposure. Training for NBC warfare, Jesse said. Nuclear. Biological. Chemical. Training for the unthinkable. Bunny suits and booties and gloves and seam tape and decontamination powder. All against poisons and pathogens that you can't see or smell and will probably kill you anyway.

Gal flips the little flap closed. Click. The sound makes him chuckle, his eyes crinkling, lines bursting outward. Like a glimpse of sun between storm clouds. But he grows serious almost right away. His scars don't wrinkle the way the rest of his skin does. They have to feel different. An ever-present reminder keeping him from laughing too long.

He hands the canteen back to me and moves back into the pew. He kneels on the kneeler, crosses himself again, and sits back in his former position. This time he closes his eyes. Folds his hands on the back of the pew in front of him. Serious. Mouthing words of some kind.

EXILED

I can't eat lunch at home today. I walk across the park toward Mia's hedge — that's what I'm calling it now — with a plastic shopping bag dangling by my legs. I don't know if she'll be there, but sitting and eating by myself is better than dealing with the storm brewing at my house.

Mom and Aunt Viv are in a sour mood, arguing about every little thing. Gramma Jan is coming home either today or tomorrow, which you'd think would be good news. But the sisters are jumpy about it. Bickering about who should drive her home. What to prepare for her first meal back. That kind of thing. They tried to bring me into it, but I told them I didn't want to play referee. And could they get over it so Gramma Jan didn't have to deal with their shit when she got home and could concentrate on getting better?

Me dropping the S-word got a half-hearted rebuke from Mom and silenced them for a bit. But by the time I'd assembled a couple of PBJ sandwiches and grabbed an apple and cookies and a few more granola bars, they were at it again. They didn't say goodbye when I left.

Every family argues, right? A good argument is like a pressure valve for all that unconditional love. Mom doesn't talk about it much, but Aunt Viv is happy to share the details of their most extreme shouting matches. A passionate family. Except for Grampa Vern. Mom says he was the calm one in the family. The rain to dampen Gramma Jan's perpetual grass fires. When he died, there was no one to balance Gramma Jan out, so she raised Mom and Viv by her own methods. It was a house where no opinion went unchallenged, no infraction unpunished. Mom says it's why she tries so hard to be gentle with me. Counterpoint to her upbringing. "Building new legacies" was how Jesse put it. "Your mom is changing the game."

But she can still argue. I grew up listening to their flare-ups, which always seemed inevitable. Mom, Jesse, and I would visit Hamilton every now and again. Not very often — Gramma Jan never warmed to Jesse, so the visits were always tense. No one in this family likes to be the first to give in. Gramma Jan and Aunt Viv are different generations of the same person. Mom is calmer but still strong-willed. The three of them feeding off each other is something to watch. Jesse had to take me out of the house a lot when the family would get together.

So the arguments aren't new. There are fewer blowups these days, but when they do happen, what comes out is multiplied. Hotter. Like the fury's been stored up. And though no one says his name anymore, Jesse is the cause of all of it. Gramma Jan and Aunt Viv wrestling not only with the horror of the shooting but also with the fact that the shooter is family. Mom fighting against what he did, trying to help me cope, and grieving the loss of their relationship all at once.

This one happened one night a few weeks after we moved to Hamilton, when they thought I was asleep:

"I don't want to talk about it," Gramma Jan said.

"Mom, we need to set some ground rules."

"Victoria Sims, this is my house and I'll decide the rules. You take care of your own."

"I do. He's downstairs and sleeping. That's why I'm bringing this up. He's who we should be worried about."

"Feel free to thank you-know-who for that."

"You're blaming me?"

"*I* didn't bring him into the family!" Gramma Jan said. Like she was spitting. "And I won't say his name one more time. No one will. Not in this space. Ever."

Mom fell silent, hurt and raging all at once. Bearing all of it. Blame. Guilt. Grief. Heartbreak.

You probably can't know what it takes to banish a name from a home. How painful it is, even though it should be easy, given what happened. We were already tiptoeing around it, but anger pushes things. I'd just had one of my first run-ins with Pat at school. He'd pushed my face into the drinking fountain and I'd shoved him back against the opposite row of lockers. Witnessed by a teacher and every student in the hall. A quick phone call and an uncomfortable meeting in the principal's office. Mom took me home. She was calm and reassuring. Gramma Jan was not. Aunt Viv tried to be the referee. They carried the argument into the night. I couldn't sleep and sat on the steps to hear what was being said about me.

"Jesus, Mom. You can't police what we say," Aunt Viv said.

"Watch me. That goes for Dills, too."

"He answers to me," Mom said, although her voice was small against my grandmother's anger.

"He's not answering to anyone right now, is he?"

"Mom —"

"What's Vicky supposed to do with that?" Aunt Viv asked. "The kid's traumatized, for crying out loud."

"He needs structure. Discipline."

"No, he needs time," Mom said. "And love and lots of space. He saw his best friend killed, for —"

Her voice broke, and all three women went quiet. Something reaching all of them at the same time. And of course I was thrown back to that library. Ethan's body. In full HD. I clenched my stomach tight against what could burst out of me.

"That's exactly what I'm talking about," Gramma Jan said, her voice softer but still full of acid. "*He* did that to Wendell. That fucking monster."

"No!" That was me. On my feet and storming into the kitchen. Seeing the emerging horror on three faces, the realization that I'd been listening the whole time. My anger blazing its own supernova. "Stop talking about him that way!"

Gramma Jan stood. "We're just —"

"You think you know why! Everyone thinks they know why! But no one knows anything. Not you, not me. Maybe not even Jesse."

"That doesn't matter. What matters is he took every-thing away, and he —"

"*Jesse*, Gramma. Say his name."

"No, Wendell. I won't."

And the supernova surged so white I couldn't see anything. I had to burn through. Scream. "You're the fucking monster!"

I turned and rushed out of the kitchen and back down to my room, stomping a thousand pounds on every stair. Thinking about the fact that Mom hadn't spoken at all after I burst into the kitchen. Hadn't defended me. I wanted her to, though there wasn't much she could have said. I screamed into my pillow and made my throat sore. I stared at the little strip of light that cut under my bedroom door. I lay awake for a long time, my anger simmering. Mom never came down, like she always does when we fight. I fell asleep, and of course the dreams came back. I would've preferred to stay awake with the anger.

Today, as I walk toward Mia's hedge, my irritation with Mom and Aunt Viv fades. Like it did after that early argument about Jesse's name. There's something about anger. I find that it can't stay around long, and at some point you're back to normal. It's like the heat of a dis-agreement seizes up the family engine for a little while but can't hold the tension as the machinery cools. Next thing, you're laughing. Back to the everyday movement of a family. Defending a gramma who sometimes says indefensible things.

A thin layer of cloud has covered the afternoon sky and the air has gone perfectly still. Capturing the humidity, it feels like. The mosquitoes, usually trapped in shadow and waiting for sunset, love this weather. Without the sun to dry them out, they travel far and wide to bite me. Halfway across the park I'm tempted to turn back to grab my insect repellent, a greasy organic concoction cooked up in some herbal kitchen somewhere. Smells like cough syrup and mint and oregano. I don't go back, though. I'm too excited to see if Mia is at the hedge.

She isn't. Pat is. He looks up from the crumpled magazine he's reading.

"Found your spot, Baby," he says with a sneer.

"It's not mine."

"I really like it."

"You shouldn't be here," I say.

"Why not? It's a public park."

He's not wrong. But I don't respond.

He sniffs. "That's what I thought. Too weak to give a shit. Now fuck off and don't come back."

His eyes go back to the magazine. Porn. What a shocker. There's a woman on the front. Jean shorts and a bikini top. Huge breasts. What Pat would call *tits*, I'm sure. *Tats. Jugs. Funbags.* Words my mom would crucify me for if she ever heard me using them. Still, whatever you might call them, it's hard to pry my eyes away.

Pat sees me looking. "Oh, you like this?"

Turns the magazine around and flops it open to the centre. An extra page flips open. Like my jaw. The dimensions of her. Such a volume of pink, pink flesh. I feel an uncomfortable warmth down below and my shorts are suddenly smaller. A distant part of me feels guilty for responding. Porn's wrong. No one wins. Objectification of women's bodies. All that.

But Pat laughs and closes the magazine, rolling it into a tight tube. Points it at my face. "Nope. Not for you. You're gay as fuck. You and your butch friend."

Now, I don't care if Pat calls me gay. For him, it's an insult of the worst kind, but for me, whatever. I'm not gay, but Jesse and Mom always made it clear that I'm allowed to feel whatever I need to feel. I shouldn't care if he calls Mia butch, because it's the same empty nothingness he threw at me. But I do. It's the casualness of how he does it. As though his messed-up opinions are unbreakable by their certainty. I clench my fists and take a step toward him, like someone else has taken control of my body. He sees it. Drops the magazine and gets up. Those dumb, narrow eyes. I take another step.

I'm here. Come see me.

This time the words aren't spoken, but whispered. Almost hissed. Like a warning. Close enough that my ear seems to itch from Jesse's breath. The discomfort of it, the urgency, knocks me into myself again. I feel this suggestion of imminent shame, like I could disappoint everyone who loves me by stepping wrong. I shake my head and drop my hands and turn away.

Pat doesn't know what to do with the change. As I leave Mia's hedge, I hear him calling me back, huffing and puffing, a comic-book dragon at a loss. Before my next step takes me out of the shadows and onto the park grass once again, my right foot clips against my left and I fall. A classic tripping move. Impossible to recover at speed. I land in the long, uncut grass at the park's fringe, right on my chest, my hands not having time to break my momentum. Lunch bag and watch and granola bars and canteen go everywhere. My breath knocked somewhere into the grey, grey sky.

I get onto my hands and knees, trying to breathe. It's all I can think about as Pat stands next to me, his stupid knees in my peripheral vision. Worst feeling in the world, maybe, to get the wind knocked out of you. Pat is yelling something. I don't hear. I've been sucked into a soundproof tube.

But I feel it when he kicks me in the side, his shoe digging deep into the space between my hip bone and ribcage. There's no breath to drive out, so there's only the pain. The helplessness as I flop over on my back. Half a second in motion but a forever moment on the ground. I close my eyes to concentrate on getting that one elusive breath back. *Focus, Dills*, I think. *Breathe*.

The first sound that reaches me is the scratch of Pat's button and fly. Then he's pissing on me. Still shouting. His urine is warm and yellow and it soaks through my clothes so quickly. Another brief eternity to endure. My lungs finally fill as he finishes. The thick stink of his dehydration is sharp in my nostrils. I open my eyes to see him zip up, almost expecting him to spit on me. The perfect finishing touch to the perfect insult.

Pat sees the canteen. Picks it up, unscrews it, and sniffs the contents. Shakes his head. Holds the canteen over me. A thin stream of water, still cool from the faucet at home, arcs out and lands on me, soaking into my shirt. I hear him mocking me, "Baby playing army" and whatnot, but I'm distracted by his need to sniff the canteen. What did he expect to find? Tea? Vodka?

"Stop," I gasp.

He's surprised enough at the sound of my voice that he does. "Why?"

"You should have it."

"Have what?"

"The rest of the water."

He snorts. "Like I'd drink —"

"You're obviously dehydrated. Your piss stinks."

"Fuck you, Baby."

Pat raises the canteen and pours the rest out all over me. Mixing with his urine. I don't know where his piss begins and the water ends, or vice versa. I'm simply wet. He looks at the canteen for an instant and slings it over his shoulder, thanking me for it, telling me how awesome it is, telling me I should take better care of my things.

"Hey!"

Pat turns toward the voice. It's Gal, striding across the field in his unique sidelong way, hand up and pointing. Pat doesn't know what to do with it. His confusion would be satisfying if I couldn't still smell his piss, now cooling. Reminding me of the humiliation that has put me down here.

"Get away from him!"

Pat's sneer returns. He is emboldened, no doubt by the unusual appearance of the reclusive park manager. He sees a non-threat there. A disabled opponent. But then Pat's face changes. Gal's face is dark, his scars pale against his anger, his body tense. I've been distracted by the scars and the weed and his surly manner and have ignored the compact power he still holds. It's fearsome. Pat glances at me on the ground, then back at Gal, and runs away after giving me one final, calculating look. *This isn't finished*, the look says. The canteen bounces against his back as he runs. That's suddenly all I can see.

Gal stands next to me. "Get up now. Go home."

He reaches out a hand to help me up, then draws it back as I reach out my own. Like one of those cruel playground jokes. *Psych!*

"What?"

He frowns. "It is better for me not to touch you."

I exhale through my nostrils, mad at the world for bringing fear into adult-and-kid relationships. Imagining Gal feeling a last-second tug of hesitation about touching the pissed-on kid on the ground. Appropriate boundaries. Bodily fluids. And so on. But then I see him looking all around me. My eyes follow.

"Aw, come on," I groan.

I've landed in a patch of poison ivy. "PI," Jesse called it. "Leaves of three, let 'em be." The memory of Jesse whispering and pointing at foliage as we stalked the bush on our hunting trip. How it all looked the same to me. So much of the forest undergrowth having three-leaf bunches. I didn't take the lesson seriously. Now I do. These low, greasy little plants are defiantly obvious.

"You must wash. With soap. Now."

I stand, my eyes scanning every centimetre of exposed skin. Already feeling the itch, though the reaction is a ways away. Gal's nose wrinkles as the air I disturbed reaches him. Shame drapes me in a blanket soaked in urine. I actually feel like crying. But there's more shame at the idea that I might. I don't cry. Won't. Not anymore. I left my last tears in the triage hallway of a Windsor hospital.

"Don't tell anyone," I say.

Gal doesn't respond. Maybe he doesn't know the proper next steps. His role in all of this, whether he bears any responsibility. Finally, he looks me in the eye. "You have problems with this boy."

"Yeah."

"Is this the one Mia called Pat?"

I nod. "His full name is Patrick, but we call him Pat to bug him. He hates it."

Gal makes a face and a sucking noise behind his teeth. "I would also."

Gal making the connection is worrisome. This can't get back to Sean, who'd obviously have to report it. Or not. Maybe Pat assaulting me isn't his problem. But I wonder about the follow-up. What if it's bigger than him and me? Pat pissed on me, after all. What if the police have to be brought in? I can't imagine the courts ignoring this.

And I think of the box cutter. The one I used to cut Pat. I still have it. I lied to everyone when I said it must have gotten lost afterwards. The principal and the police officer pressed a bit, but not much. Laws and rules about interrogating kids, I guess. But it wouldn't be hard to find. It's in my room, yellow and clicky and stainless and wicked sharp, in a white shopping bag in the bottom drawer of my desk. No blood on it or anything, but still. It could get found and make things worse for me. Any remaining compassion would evaporate faster than the first raindrops on a hot day.

"This is not something he should get away with," Gal says.

"Please don't tell anyone," I say again.

A long pause, thoughtful. A nod. "Go home. And clean yourself."

I pick up my things and walk away, leaving the bag and my lunch on the ground. I'll come back later and use the spike to pick it up and dispose of it all properly. But it bothers me to leave it there. On top of everything, I've made more work for myself. And I'll have to see it again when I come back.

I walk back across the park, taking the shortest possible route home. My worry about poison ivy and the school's knife growing exponentially by the second. I can smell Pat's piss the whole way.

CLEAR

I'm here. Come see me.

The next morning I open my eyes way too early. My single window, which looks south at the world at ground level, is bright. I forgot to close my curtains last night. I wait, feeling as though Jesse might say more. But he doesn't. I close my eyes again to try to grab a little more sleep, but it's clear that my body has had all it needs. Such a good sleep. There were no dreams. Only pure, clear rest. I want more of it. My stomach growls, too, louder than any alarm.

And my right wrist is itching like mad. The rash has arrived. A red, bubbled line up the inside of my forearm, straight as a ruler. Ten centimetres long.

I get up and pad up the stairs to the washroom, a set of clean clothes under my arm. The house is silent. No one else is awake. I strip out of my sleep shorts and T-shirt and stare at myself in the full-length mirror on the back of the door. Bracing for the worst. The wrist undoubtedly a foreshadowing of what's to come. I'm getting a wicked farmer's tan on my face and arms. Body and thighs pale as winter. Pale enough that a rash would be neon lights. But my body is clear. Just sad white skin (and it is a little sad, how pale we can be) and the single rash line on my arm. Itching hot and bright, like it's making up for being the only one. I'll have to cover it. Not to keep it from spreading but to keep my fingernails from wearing a path down to the bone.

As soon as I got home yesterday, I scoured my helmet, shoes, vest, and gloves with a horsehair brush and some ancient soap I found in Gramma Jan's garden shed. I carried the pissy, soapy pile inside to the laundry room, stripped down to what Mom calls "the truth," and dumped everything but the helmet into the washing machine. Poured in a single capful of detergent, then added a bit more for good measure. Set the wash to normal, but on hot, and with an extra rinse. The house was all mine, so I risked a naked dash to the shower and scrubbed myself for what felt like an hour. Did everything right. Urban myth says the blisters spread the rash, but PI only spreads if the oil is still on the skin. The blisters aren't contagious. So I'm good. I know. I googled it.

I called Sean to tell him. About the PI, not Pat. He said I did the right thing by cleaning up and calling him and it was fine to take the rest of the day off. "But assuming you're not lousy with rash, right back at it tomorrow, yeah?" Then he actually thanked me. His thanks were kind of passive, thrown out there before he hung up, but still. I don't think many of his clients do much to keep him in the loop.

The bandage on my forehead has fallen off again in my sleep. The scar is narrow and pink. One of the sutures has come undone, the blue thread sticking out. I pull at one of the loose ends and cringe at a glint of pain as the thread slides through. I use a single square of toilet paper to dab away the tiny bead of blood that has risen from the suture hole. I decide not to replace the bandage — it never stays on for more than an hour or two anyway.

I pull on my clothes and go to the kitchen. My first stop is the first-aid kit, where I cut a length of gauze and then tape it loosely over the rash, an action which is super awkward with only one hand. Then I dig into the cupboard for cornflakes. I'm on my third bowl when I hear Aunt Viv get up. The old house tells me where she is, groaning and popping as she crosses the floor above me. She and Mom each have an upstairs bedroom, the old painted doors facing each other across the small hallway. Aunt Viv comes down, each step creaking, and yawns her way into the kitchen. Ignores me until the coffee maker is hissing and sputtering.

Finally, the last of the water drips through the coffee grounds and filter. The machine groans a final time and falls silent. Aunt Viv clunks the carafe out, sloshes coffee into her mug, and clunks the carafe home again. Morning sounds. She turns and leans back against the counter, taking her first tentative sips with her eyes closed. The mug moves up and down, up and down, flashing a combination of fruits and flowers faded by time and wear and dishwasher heat, the outlines long gone but the shapes themselves still oddly bright. Morning colours. She opens her eyes, sees me, and nods a kind of good morning.

"What's with the bandage?"

"Dressing, actually," I say.

She rolls her sleep-puffy eyes. "Sorry. *Dressing*."

"It's poison ivy."

"From the park."

"Yep."

"God, it's everywhere there. I wish the city would do something about it."

"Ever had it?"

"Once. On my arm, actually, like you. Maybe the other one, though. Itched like a b—" She stops herself and grins into another sip.

"Like a ...?"

She shakes her head. "Can't say that stuff anymore."

"Sure you can. Everyone does."

"Getting older means you figure out what needs to get said, what doesn't."

She smiles again, like she's figured out what's good and proper when it comes to bad language. She and I share a few minutes of silent morning. Talking about the PI has made the rash itch a little more. It's probably in my head, but that doesn't make it feel less real.

Aunt Viv doesn't make a move for any food. *The coffee doing the job quite nicely indeed*, Mom would say. I bring my bowl and spoon to the sink.

"So, have you figured it out?" Aunt Viv asks.

"Figured what out?"

"Jesse. How you're going to go see him."

I shake my head. "How could I do that? It's a long way."

"Not too far."

"It is for a guy with no money and no driver's licence."

She shrugs. "You sounded so sure."

I am sure. But it still feels odd that someone knows about it. Like I should keep a little back, maybe to protect my plans, maybe to protect Aunt Viv if I go through with it. Maybe a bit of both. There'd be so much trouble. She doesn't press me about it, though. She retrieves an old, battered travel mug from the cupboard and fills it with the dregs of her first cup. She tops it up from the carafe, steam swirling and disappearing into the air, disturbed by her movement, until she twists the cover on. Sees me looking.

"I've got the morning shift at the hospital."

"Huh?"

"With Mom.

"Mom? Why?"

"My mom. Gramma Jan to you. Your mom stayed last night, so I get today. Like I did yesterday."

"Mom stayed there all night? Why would she?"

"The chair in the room lays flat. They call it a cot, but it's more like a torture device."

"No, I meant why the need to stay? Is Gramma Jan all right?"

A brief shadow moves across Aunt Viv's features, like that single cloud that passes directly overhead on a sunny day. The sudden dimness surprises you. She snorts and makes a joke about how pissed Gramma Jan is that her girls are making all this fuss. When I try for a few more details, Aunt Viv dodges and weaves, chastising me for the shirt and shorts I dropped on the bathroom floor. Uses the old this-isn't-a-hotel standby for whenever adults gripe about the stuff we leave behind. There's grumpy work talk — "I don't get to take a day off," "Can't believe the hospital charges for Wi-Fi," etcetera — as she gathers her car keys, wallet, and laptop and tosses them into her shoulder bag. As though any of it has answered my questions.

DEADLINES

I'm working the near side of the park this morning. I can almost see my house from here. The field is an oval cricket pitch, with a strip of hardpacked crushed stone splitting the middle for the wicket. I work the edge, stabbing garbage along the treeline.

My arm itches like crazy. I was neck deep in PI, so it's a miracle I didn't pick up more. Still, it feels like every itch I've ever had has decided to join forces with every other itch and they're eating themselves into my forearm. All at once. Right now. I find myself having the craziest thoughts as I work. Using knives and forks for the scratching. Pouring boiling water on the rash to distract myself from the burn. Finding the roughest tree in the woods and sandpapering my arm against the bark. That kind of thing.

I let my mind go where it wants because as crazy as they are, those thoughts are also keeping me from thinking too much about the job. Another day in paradise.

Picking up its trash. They work for a while, anyhow. At some point the image of me using that box cutter to cut off my forearm to cure the itch pops into my head, and that's when I decide to stop being so dumb about it. Making light of crudely amputated limbs? I should know better. I've seen what the crazy physics of bullets can do. How fragile we are. But that's all I'm going to say about it. I hope that's all right.

Weird as they might seem, those grim thoughts were also keeping me from thinking about Gramma Jan. And Mom. Now the concern comes back, full force. Of course, there are all sorts of reasons daughters might need to stay at the hospital with their sick moms. But my heart isn't buying the arguments. All it can do is worry.

I'm more worried about Mom. I love Gramma Jan, but she's not the one I grew up with. She's the grand-parent you need to love from a distance. Who you only see a few times a year but who your mother would still drop everything for. You would, too. But to make sure your mom is taken care of. The concern for Gramma Jan more an abstract thing.

I'm here. Come see me.

Jesse's voice arrives at the precise moment I think about heading home to check on Mom. As though he can read my mind and is worried that I might not have enough concern to go around. Like he'd get forgotten if I dared to think about Mom for too long. A flash of pure annoyance washes out the morning.

"Now, Jesse? Really?"

He doesn't respond. Of course. As soon as I close my mouth, the words lost to the grass and trees, I feel stupid about losing my cool. A bit guilty. I haven't been thinking about Mom a whole lot. I should do better. I will.

I walk over to the tree where I've stashed my water bottle and snack bag. The pissing thing with Pat has made me feel weird about stuffing my pockets with food. I don't know why. I take a long drink and walk out to the road. I'll probably find the house either empty or quiet with sleep, and there's no way I'll wake Mom up if she's making up for a sleepless night at the hospital. Still, I have to go and check.

A little blue Elantra pulls up to the curb. Walters. The last thing I want to do right now is talk to a reporter. The last thing I want to do ever. I think about turning around, but I'm still wearing my safety vest and there's no way she hasn't seen me. She doesn't get out. The car is perpendicular to me and I can see the dark outline of her head and shoulders through the tinted side glass. She's turned slightly toward me. Looking at me. Why isn't she getting out? I start to walk again, faster this time, so when I pass the car I can minimize my exposure.

Her car door opening is loud against the morning stillness. The park is quiet, like it always is in the middle of the week. There are a few people walking dogs and out for early hikes, but they're swallowed up by the size of the place. It'll get busier closer to lunch, when parents emerge from their homes, kids tumbling alongside, to head to the play structure and splash pad.

Walters steps around her door and removes a pair of white earbuds from her ears. "Hi," she says.

"You can't be here. My mom —"

She holds up a hand. "I'm not working right now."

Could be the truth. Her hair is tucked under a base-ball cap and tied into a ponytail in the back. She's in running tights decorated in a crazy broken-glass pattern and a neon-peach sports bra. And it's clear she runs a lot — she's tanned and fit, and her shoes are scuffed and dirty from the trails. I've seen a lot of trail runners in the park this summer. But the timing of it. And a car? She lives around the corner. Like me.

She watches me checking out the car. "You don't believe me. You think this is an ambush."

I shrug.

"I like to run before work. Usually I'm out here at six in the morning, but I was up late last night on deadline. I'm going in late today."

"Okay."

"And I don't interview in my running gear. Not the most professional."

She looks down at herself and laughs. It's the laugh that finally disarms me. It's genuine. Caught out. She was not anticipating seeing anyone. And the smile around the laugh peels away some of the years between us. Sometimes I have that sense that a lot of the adults in my life aren't that much older than me. Ms. Nieman, one of my teachers at Windsor, was like that. She was our teacher, so obviously she was older, but there were rare moments when she smiled and didn't seem like it. Moments we could sit back and not worry about school or homework or anything. She died behind the library counter, where she'd been helping the librarian check out our books. Research for some project I don't remember. The librarian was definitely an older woman. She held Ms. Nieman's hand as she died. She wouldn't let go when the police cleared the room and escorted us out, or later when they let the paramedics in to help the fallen. I heard she screamed at them to get away a bunch of times. Anyhow.

"There's that look again," she says, her eyebrows rising.

"Huh?"

"When we came back in for sentencing. You and your mom."

Why is it that the worst memories come back right when you're least able to handle them? Why can't you lock them away, bring them out when you need to? The therapist said, "You can't always control how you feel, but you can learn to manage the feelings that do come out." Managing them usually means fighting with them. Fighting back another black, boiling flood.

"And your sentence was so light. What happened?"

"You're not supposed to be talking to me," I say, and walk away.

"You're right. I'm sorry," she says to my back. "But, Wendell?"

I slow and turn back toward her. There's something about adults using kids' first names that's like a tractor beam. "What?"

"Telling your story can help you feel better."

"I don't think that's true."

A pause and a nod. "Okay."

"Okay."

"I'm going for my run."

"You do that."

She smiles at me, puts her earbuds back in, and turns to her phone, swiping into a song or podcast. She runs away, her ponytail swinging. Straight across the cricket pitch and onto the trail into the woods at the far side. A streak of neon disappearing into the gloom. As bright as me in my silly vest.

The morning is silent again. It's cool, too. As I walk home I can feel the dew that has soaked cold through my shoes and socks. Funny I didn't feel it before.

INBOX

The house is quiet. I lock the door behind me, kick off my shoes, and go right to the bathroom to change the dressing on my rash. It's hanging by a single strip of medical tape. How is it that medical people can transplant almost any body part but haven't figured out how to make tape that can stick to sweaty skin? I rinse my arm with cold water, which feels good. The rash is red and angry, as though it resents what I've put it through. I change into dry socks, laying my wet ones over the lip of the laundry hamper to dry. I think better of it, drop them on top of the dirty laundry, and carry the hamper downstairs to the laundry room.

The load from yesterday is a cold, wrinkled heap in the dryer, bunched slightly to the side. That last tumble a half-hearted effort. I lift the pile out and set it on top of the machine. There's no piss smell. Thank God. Nice to know you can normal-cycle away the smell of embarrassment.

I upend the dirty stuff and sort through it. Whites here. Darks there. Synthetics in their own pile. I like doing laundry. The mindless rhythm of it. Lug, dump, sort, wash, fold. Mom taught me the basics when I was six or seven, and now we both watch for the hampers to fill and throw in loads whenever they do. No such thing as laundry day in our house. Any day could be the day.

I see Mom's phone charging on the kitchen counter when I go upstairs. Confirmation that she's sleeping. No devices are allowed in our bedrooms, no phones or laptops or alarm clocks. The fear of blue light and constant connectivity killing proper sleep. My iPod is charging alongside. Both screens are dark. I tap Mom's home button to see if there are any urgent notifications she'd want me to wake her up for. Like phone calls or texts with lots of exclamation points. Her old phone had a code, so I could tap it in and see, but her new phone uses a fingerprint. She likes the security. I still check the screen out of habit. But there's nothing there, only an Etsy photo of one of her metal creations and the phone's clock.

I don't like the new picture. It feels sterile. Her old phone had a photo of Jesse and me doing something in our garage when I was younger. She left it in Windsor and bought a new one when we got here. She says it was a blessing in disguise that she forgot the old phone, because she needed a better camera and more speed. I don't buy it. Nobody forgets their phone when they leave the house to get groceries, much less moving to an entirely new city. It would be like losing a hand or something.

My stomach growls. Lunch hunger hitting me half-way through the morning. I raid the fridge and eat standing beside the sink. Leftover grocery-store chicken in its plastic spaceship. Cold, stiff potato wedges. I munch on some cucumber and celery sticks to "green up the meal," as Mom likes to say. A conscience thing. She is sleeping upstairs.

My iPod's screen blinks on across the kitchen and a low electronic chime announces the arrival of an email. I wipe the grease from my hands on a dishtowel and swipe in. A new message from Mia. Time-stamped now. In my excitement, I almost drop my iPod.

> *wendell. (feels weird to write Dills, i dunno why, sorry.)*
>
> *how r u? u left ur email address with me, so now u cant get away, ha ha. i guess that means were pen pals. or is it touchscreenlaptopkeyboard pals now? anyway.*
>
> *im at home and bored. not much wrestling in the summer but lots of weights and running (yawn). but im not writing because im bored. Really. im writing cuz 2day is my 16th bday (insert whistling and fancy bday sounds) and summer bdays are the worst — there are no friends around to spoil u.*
>
> *UNTIL NOW.*
>
> *thats right, lucky (only) neighbourhood friend, ur it. u get the job. (insert congratulatory clapping and polite cheering.) now,*

*this is totally last minute, but u have to come
to my bday picnic tonight. (i know, i know,
birthday picnic?! lame. but still, its my bday,
so u have to come.)*

*u probably finish ur trash-picking-upping
around 5, which gives u about an hr to shower
and dress in ur sunday best and come over to
the old lawn bowling green for 6. (yes, shower.
ull need one after sweating in the park all day.
believe me. i know. im bffs with vinyl mats
that stink of feet and sweat and unwashed boy,
so i know smelly. and yes, sunday best. mia is
birthdaying and will be playing dress-up herself (gag). DO NOT MAKE HER DRESS UP
ALONE.)*

so, ya, thats it. ur invited.

this was long. sorry. (i hope u read it all.)

mia

I read it again. And I nearly drop my iPod again. Me. Invited to her birthday. And she's funny. I laugh in the same places the second time through. Which has to mean something.

I look at the clock. It's not even lunchtime, yet I have this weird need to get ready now. Which is impossible because of garbage and courtrooms and charges and LoJacks and all the time I need to make things right again. I wonder who else'll be there. If I'm the designated summer friend, who does that leave? That thought carries me back to the park to finish my day.

SO GROWN-UP

Here's my afternoon: repeatedly grabbing the paracord lanyard and pulling my watch out to stare at it to see if time is moving any faster, but of course it isn't. I don't know how many times I do that. Takes forever.

When I finally get home, I hear clanging and cursing in the basement. Mom's awake and working. I yell a "Hey, Mom, I'm home!" down the stairs and make straight for the bathroom for a shower. Realize when I'm finished that the towel racks are bare. Mom must've done a load. I dry myself by squeegeeing my body with my hands, but it only goes so far. My clothes are a dirty, damp, not-an-option-dumbass pile on the floor. There's a closet in the hall with clean towels, but it's out there. For a millisecond, I debate a mad run in the buff down to my room, but only a millisecond. Today, the house is not my own.

I crack open the door. Steam wisps around me into the hall. "Mom!"

"What?"

Her response is muffled. Her workshop door is closed. I cringe. A closed door means "I'm Creating. Do Not Bug Me Unless There's Blood or the Apocalypse."

"Can you get me a towel?"

"In the closet! There's a whole pile of them right there! Folded and ready!"

"I'm naked!"

Awkward silence. A door opening, feet stomping up stairs, the closet opening, the soft movement of laundered towels. Annoyed mother muttering about finally getting some work done despite the distractions and teenage boys she'd like to strangle. Footsteps outside the bathroom. I hide behind the door and reach my hand into the hall. But all I grab is air.

There's a pause. A long, long pause full of a mom's unasked questions.

"I'm freezing here!"

"Uh huh. So, why the shower?"

"I always shower."

"Sure, but only after you grab a snack, drink a glass of milk, stare into the fridge for an hour while you scratch your guy parts."

"Mom."

"It's gross. Don't think I don't notice."

"I'm still naked, you know, right here behind this door. A foot away from you."

That's my trump card. My best play. Embarrass the mother who joked about guy parts into action by reminding her of teenage boys and puberty and the changes she never wanted to happen to her baby.

But no. She laughs instead. A dismissive little laugh. "Yeah, I got that. So what's up? Have an accident at work?"

"Mom!"

"I can wait all evening, my friend."

She's enjoying herself enough to make it happen, too. It's nice to hear the lightness that has been eclipsed for the past while. Haven't I been telling myself I need to do more for her? Part of me wants to let her savour it. A small part. The rest of me is butt naked and anxious about a certain girl waiting for me and about wanting to time things so I'm arriving precisely at six so she'll be impressed with my promptness and discipline.

"I'm meeting Mia."

"I figured. The mad shower dash was a classic move."

And the towel is placed into my hand and I can bring it in and close the door. I wait for her footsteps to head back downstairs so she can reimmerse herself in her work and leave me alone. Instead, I hear her head into the kitchen and rattle some things around to make tea. Stall tactic. She doesn't do tea when she's creating.

I dry off, wrap myself in the towel, go down to my own room, and get dressed in a light-blue golf shirt and a new pair of cargo shorts, the nicest clothes I own.

Well, the nicest non-funeral clothes. At the far-left side of my closet there's a suit and a dress shirt and a navy-blue tie with diagonal stripes. All hung on the same hanger in the same clear dry-cleaning bag that lets you see the stripes are red. And the stripes remind you of how you stared down at them all through a bunch of funerals for your school friends and teachers, who probably wouldn't have cared that the stripes look like blood, but you did and felt guilty through every eulogy and tribute. Of how you insisted on going to every service and insisted on wearing that tie even though your mom sensed that it was making things worse and said you didn't have to go. But you kind of did have to. Anyhow.

When I finally go upstairs, Mom is waiting for me. Leaning against the counter and drinking a steaming cup of something, holding the mug with both hands, like it could drop. No burnt-rice smell this time. Instead it's berries and cinnamon and something herbal, like hemp. Jesse called Mom's eclectic collection of rare teas "hippie brews." "Earth mom's getting all unified, man. Far out. Dig it?" he'd joke. It's been a long time since I've seen Mom make a cup of the hippie stuff for herself.

She levers a single finger from the mug and points at my wrist. "What's with the bandage?"

"Dressing," I say without thinking.

"Right. Dressing. PI rash from the park, right?"

"Yep."

"I'm not surprised. You should get your Aunt Viv to tell you some of her rash stories."

"Maybe I will."

She smiles. "You're getting some nice colour, too. From the sun. The white of the dressing really makes it stand out."

"Uh, thanks?"

"You look good. Older. Like your dad."

I don't know what to say to that. My bio-bad (never my *real father* — that title belongs to Jesse) gone but still always casting a shadow on the wall behind us. But Mom is smiling slightly, like she's all right with the reminder of him in me. That's a first.

"He'd like you, I think."

Like. A strange word for dads and sons. Even dads like him and sons like me.

Mom seems to read my face. "I'll have to tell you more about him sometime."

I shake my head. "This is so weird."

"How so?"

"You've always talked about him as the guy who left. Like you didn't want me to know more."

"He did leave me. And you. But he wasn't a bad person."

"Did he know about me?"

"Yes."

"And he still left."

"He was nice enough, but not dad material. He knew it."

We fall silent. A lot to process. Mom suddenly letting on that her relationship with my bio-dad was more than a passing thing. I wonder how long they were together. What they were like. If I might've liked him. That last thought burns. Emotional heartburn for the betrayal against Jesse. I suppose it's natural to wonder about the what-could-have-beens, but I feel like even admitting that I'm curious will stain what Jesse was to me. Is.

"Good thing Jesse stepped up," I say. I can hear an edge to my voice. Almost anger.

Mom looks at me and breathes deep. Nods. "Jesse stepping up was the best gift a mom could ask for, Dills. The two of you were such a good team."

"*Are*, Mom."

"Right. Are."

"How much of him do you see in me?"

"So much I can hardly stand it sometimes. So much goodness, I mean." Her eyes well up as she says it. The twist of heartbreak. Mismatching the man she loved — the man who made so much of me actually me — against the thing he did.

I say, "No, not Jesse. *Him*."

"Oh. I …" She tilts her head, considering. "I'm not sure, really. I'd have to think about it. I haven't thought about him in a long time."

"What was his name?"

"Alan."

"Alan what?"

She wipes her eyes and looks me in the eye. Shakes her head. A quick motion, sharp. "Just the first name, kiddo. Jesse made you who you are. That's where we leave this."

"We should —"

Mom's phone rings, the electronic chimes more like gongs in the quiet of the kitchen. Cutting through the intensity of this new discussion. Drowning it out. We both look over at it, our conversation falling away like a rope cut from a cliff. The screen is lit up and I can see Aunt Viv's face and name in the centre, her expression annoyed, like Mom caught her in the middle of something important when she took the photo for her contact list. The call buttons red and green and huge.

"Weird," Mom says. "She always texts."

Another cycle of chimes begins, as loud and brash as the first. Mom grabs the phone. "Viv, what's —"

Mom falls silent, listening. Some seconds pass. "No, tell me now."

Another few seconds. Five. A thousand, maybe.

"Okay, I'll see you in a few. Bye."

Mom pulls the phone away and stares at it, like she's trying to figure out how to end the call, though it's one of those things we've all done a million times. The red button fades as she watches it. Aunt Viv hit hers first. The screen goes dark to save power.

"Mom?"

"That was Aunt Viv."

"I know. What's up?"

She looks around the kitchen and at the living room beyond the counter, mumbling about corners and dust and doing a load of sheets. Staring at nothing, though. Not really seeing. Her eyes are so wide.

"Mom?"

She grabs a scrap of paper and starts a list of groceries, as though the fridge and cupboards are empty. They aren't. They're as full as we need them to be.

I put my hand on her shoulder. I've seen people do that when they need a person to respond. A person who isn't in the present. I've seen lots of hands on lots of shoulders. Lots of minds struggling to keep pace, struggling to process any of what's happened.

"Mom. Talk. To. Me."

Lots of voices that are firmer than they would be otherwise. So the person will hear them.

Mom turns toward me and her eyes clear. She tries to smile. "Gramma Jan's coming home. They'll discharge her in the morning."

"That's good, right?"

"She was supposed to be in for another few days. I guess the heart thing wasn't as serious as they thought. Your aunt said there was something else, something serious, but she wouldn't tell me on the phone."

"It's after working hours. I can come with you to the hospital."

Mom looks down at me. At my clothes. "Your thing with Mia. You should go."

I look down, too. Creases and laundered cloth. Skin so clean it's almost new. I want to go see Mia but I also want to go with Mom — she looks like she needs the support. I feel the conflict rising, that ancient tension between girl excitement and family obligation. I say that I can see Mia anytime, that this thing with Gramma Jan is more important, but Mom shakes her head.

"I should do this on my own. I don't know what Viv is going to say."

As though to protect me. I get that. "But —"

"Dills. Go get your girl. She's waiting for you."

And Mom turns away from me, ending the conversation. Sending me out. But not making me feel better in the least.

DEFIANT

It feels strange to walk through the park without my safety vest and helmet and trash spike. As though I've forgotten how to be a normal person. I have to resist the urge to stop at every tree and bush to make sure new trash hasn't wedged itself into the places I've already cleaned. Like getting all sweaty and dirty again would be an appropriate penance for abandoning my mother.

I'm here. Come see me.

Jesse's voice seems to walk with me. I can't tell whether it's more or less insistent. My resolve to go see him is finding all sorts of reasons to put itself on hold.

"I should turn around, right?" I ask, hoping he'll walk me through this. Knowing he won't. "Do you think she'll be okay?"

Mom, I mean. Gramma Jan, too. But mostly Mom.

Have you ever found yourself asking questions you already know the answers to? Not knowing why you're asking, yet not able to stop yourself? Jesse would say, *One, your mom is a tough cookie and can handle this. Two, she's not a person you go against. Ever. She told you not to come, so that's it. We honour the requests of people we love, Dills, and we follow orders from those who can order us around. And this was definitely an order. Clear as mud?* Jesse has this way of making everything plainer. Even when it's not.

It's still hot out, the low sun doing nothing against the humidity and heat. My clothes lost their laundry stiffness as soon as I stepped out the door. My rash is itching extra hard. I walk by the splash pad, where families on blankets sit and eat while miniature formations of kids attack the ice-cold spray and mist. Squealing and laughing. I frown at them, but no one notices. Their play like armour.

The bowling greens lie at the southern end of the park. When the community lawn-bowling club went out of business, no one stepped in to maintain the perfectly trimmed greens. Now they're covered in the same grass as the rest of Churchill Park, while the benches and sunshades rust away.

Mia and her family have set up under one of the old sunshades. Smoke from a trio of low silver barbecues rises straight up in the windless air. The smell of grilled meat and veggies makes my mouth water. Sudden, powerful hunger.

Mia sees me. Smiles. That smile like the sun. Melting my cold scowl away. I wave back, noting in a detached way that there are few things more awkward than waving while walking. But not caring.

A few adults stand in a loose circle around the food, men in collared shirts and dress pants offering advice to the guy working the grills, women in dresses and head coverings. There are a couple of toddlers hanging on to skirts. Grade-school kids dashing around like the only reasonable thing to do in such situations is to chase each other. A few older kids, various tweens and teens, sit at the appropriate distance from embarrassing families. When Mia waves, the conversation stops and suddenly every eye is on me, adult and otherwise.

My feet slow down. I don't tell them to, they just do. All that attention. Like I'm walking into the thousand-pound spray of a firehose. Mia turns to all the grown-ups and says something to them. No one moves, their need to stare as heavy as gravity. You can't move gravity. She hisses something at them — a bunch of words I can't hear, then "*Yella, yella!*" That makes them all chuckle and smile and return to their whatevers.

"Hi," she says.

"Hi."

"Thanks for coming. You look nice."

"You, too. You're ..." I stop. My goal was to come up with some astute, creative compliment, but my words refuse to try. The sight of her makes them impossible. She's wearing a sundress with a beige and green floral print that would look like camouflage on anyone else. She's tanned and strong, and the dress fits like it's supposed to make my down-belows get all worked up. What she wears isn't about me, I know. But in the moment? All that blood moving south? Sure feels like it is.

"You, too," I say again.

"Thanks."

"Your family?" I ask, nodding at the group, who're trying to respect her wishes not to stare but can't help themselves.

Mia nods and does a run-through of names, all of which I forget as soon as she says them. Except for her parents. The guy on the grill is her dad. The tall woman with the deep purple headscarf and her arms folded is her mom. Neither are smiling. This doesn't surprise me. Boys everywhere never expect anything resembling acceptance from parents. You're trying to steal their biggest accomplishment, after all. And obviously corrupt her beyond redemption.

"What happened to your arm?" She points at the dressing covering my rash.

And just like that, my mind returns to Pat pissing on me, and the buzz I had from seeing her in her dress is gone. Replacing it is a kind of abrasion, sand somehow getting behind my eyes. I didn't get the same feeling when Mom asked. But here, now, I do.

"Nothing much. A little PI."

"PI?"

"Poison ivy."

"I've never had it. Does it itch?"

"I don't want to talk about it."

I can hear my words and tone as they spill out like acid. I should stop them. I want to. Yet I can't. "Foul," Jesse would call it when Mom or I would get grumpy: "Wow. You're acting so, so foul." Saying that would, of course, make it worse. Nothing more annoying than someone else not playing along with your anger.

"Okay," she says, her smile dimming.

"Am I the only one here?"

"The only what?"

"Non-family member."

"Yes."

"Where are your wrestling friends?"

"I don't really have any."

"Why?"

"Well, I'm a girl, and I'm advanced for my age, so I win a lot. No one likes a girl who wins too much."

"That's dumb."

Her eyes narrow. "What's wrong with you? A second ago, you were —"

"I'm fine."

She folds her arms and turns a quarter turn away from me. Closing herself off. Regret in her body language. Inviting this idiot was a bad, bad idea.

What the hell, Dills? I want to ask myself. I've snapped at and interrupted her, which are the rudest things. But my gut is running the show now. My mind is merely a horrified spectator. And guess what gets added next? Replaying my departure, reliving the guilt and worry about leaving Mom to go to the hospital on her own. And I get even angrier at Mia, if you can believe it. Like she's to blame for all of it. My gut opens my mouth, ready to deliver the next perfect, biting remark, and —

"Mia, who is this boy?"

My mouth snaps shut. Her mother has come over to where we're standing. Her accent is strong, but her voice is flat. The tone says, *He looks like trouble and if he speaks to you like that again, I will kill him where he stands.* Up close, she is incredibly tall. Like professional volleyball player tall. Mia's father arrives after a moment, wiping his hands on his apron, which is black and decorated with the words DON'T LIKE MY COOKING? LOWER YOUR EXPECTATIONS. He isn't tall. But he looks strong enough to protect a daughter's honour by tearing questionable guys apart with his bare hands. A single hot bead of sweat trickles down my back, between my shoulder blades.

"Mom, Dad, this is Wendell Sims. My friend from school."

"We did not know he was coming," her mother says.

"I invited him." Mia glances at me as she says it. Is there regret in the look?

"Wendell, it is kind of you to come, but this is a family dinner."

Mia's father hasn't said a thing. But his eyes have moved to my shoes. No, wait, not my shoes. The ankle monitor. Shit. I don't think about it at all anymore, apart from when I need to wash around it in the shower. LoJack is the perfect name. Low Jack. Gritty and dishonest, like the kind of person who'd wear it. With shorts. To a birthday party.

"Mom, you're embarrassing me."

"Please ask him to leave. Wendell, it was nice to meet you."

That tone definitely tells me it wouldn't matter if I returned the courtesy. So I don't. I just nod.

"Dills, stay."

There's as much defiance against her parents in her invitation as there is desire for me to be a part of her celebration. I did that. My crappy temper making all this discomfort possible. Without another word, her mother and father turn away and move back to the party. I feel small. And mad. And wrecked. But mostly small.

These days I find myself measuring everything against a piece of metal I keep in the drawer next to the box cutter. I told you about that hospital hallway. The waiting and the blood and the crying and all the things damaged kids can't do for each other. But right after they sat me down, I saw a dark object lying against that smart little curve they put at the base of hospital walls to make sure there are no corners to gather germs. It looked out of place and dirty, so I got myself off the floor and walked over to it. It was small, about the size of a frozen kernel of corn, but heavy for its size, jagged and dense. I put it in my pocket and found it later that day when Mom took me home and let me go up to my room. Rubbing against the cloth in my pocket had shined it up a little. Dark, with flecks of copper. Bullet fragment. I should've given it to the police, but I didn't. I take it out sometimes. Wonder about its travels. Who it might have gone through or fallen out of. It's my new small and huge and every other size.

"You didn't tell your parents about me," I say.

"What would I tell them?"

"Something. Anything."

"Like what? Do *you* know what we are?"

No. Yes. Maybe, is what I think. What I say is "I should go."

"Please stay."

She puts her hand on my shoulder. Her body language opening up to me again, like a door of some kind, even though I'm being such an idiot. The hardness gone from her face, her hand warm through my fancy shirt. The best kind of low heat. She looks over at her family, her eyes moving between the kids, the teens, and the circled adults waiting to eat. Her eyes don't rest on anyone. I realize that she doesn't belong in any of the groups. That we can be strangers in our own families. That she's asking me to be her comfortable. If I'm the threatening outsider, she's the threatening insider, the daughter and niece and cousin no one can talk to. Maybe she's too strong.

"I want to," I say. "But I think you need to work on your parents a bit."

"It'll be fine."

"Maybe I can meet them again sometime when my friend is gone." I lift my foot a bit.

Her eyes go down to the ankle monitor. "Oh my god, I totally forgot!"

"Me, too. But your parents won't."

"We don't need their permission."

"*I* do, Mia."

"Why?"

Because I don't need another question mark in my life, Mia. Another day at odds with another set of parents, or step-parents, or whatever. Though I don't say that. I glance over at her folks, who've been reabsorbed into the adult group. Studiously not looking over at us. Parents are people you want to be loyal to. And you want to have the favour returned.

"Look," I say, "maybe it's too much right now."

"Wait. What's too much? We're hanging out."

"I'm just so … I just have …"

"You sound like you're about to make a lame excuse, Dills."

"No, it is a lot. This stupid LoJack. The sentence. New grade in the fall. Pat. Gramma Jan."

"What's going on with your grandma? Will she get to come home soon?"

I almost tell her. I want to. But, as if on the most awkward sort of cue, my rash lights up again, hotter and itchier than ever. Blots the evening out with the overwhelming urge to scratch and the need not to. And a fresh bloom of anger at the frame my life has been set into lights up, too. The urge to scream at the crappiness of it all. Like really scream at it, raise my sweating face to the sky and yell and shout and scream until my voice obliterates itself.

"No," I say. Mostly to myself. Knowing how little such an outburst would accomplish.

"No what?"

Mia's voice is now as flat and suspicious as her mother's. I read that as the final signal. Affirmation of every speck of not-worthy-and-not-ready in me. "Nothing. I'm going to go."

And I do. I turn away and walk back across the park and into the empty house. To a text on my iPod from Mom, telling me that she'll be staying overnight again. That I should stay put and that Aunt Viv will be home a little later. As though I'd dash across the city right then. She says that Gramma Jan needs to rest so I shouldn't call, that she'll tell me everything in the morning. That I shouldn't worry.

That last one does it.

"Oh, come on!" I yell, pounding my fists against the kitchen counter, hard, listening to the impact moving through the woodwork of the house.

Don't worry.

Right.

Telling someone not to worry is like spraying fuel vapour over a campfire while telling the flames they don't have to grow.

DIGGING

I suppose you could get used to an empty house in the morning. But not by choice. You look for the people you love. When they've always been part of your routines, like Mom, or have become part of them, like Gramma Jan and Aunt Viv, and they're not there, you notice. It feels weird to see every door ajar, every curtain and blind open, every bed unslept in. Everything exactly where you left it the night before. No caring person to reset the house after you go to bed.

I refresh my email on my iPod. Nothing from Mia. The world could've ended as I slept. *The Rapture*, Ethan would've called it. Sheep and goats and all the sinners having to stay on earth. His family was one of those that prays while doing everyday things and uses the word *blessings* a lot, that ends every discussion with "Praise Jesus." Ethan was obsessed with this retro series of books called *Left Behind*, where the Rapture comes and the survivors have to figure out how to survive. I bet he made those the most-read books in the school library. Anyhow.

I eat and get ready for the day in silence. I think about turning on some music loud to keep me company, but that seems crazy. Crazier than trusting myself alone with my worry and guilt about how I left things with Mia.

Before I leave, I wind and set Gene's watch and open the weather app on my iPod. Going to be a scorcher today. Heat alert in effect. Good. Not good for working, obviously, but good for my lunch break and after work. Coming home to a cool house is a rare kind of heaven. Gramma Jan has this thing against air conditioning unless the weather people declare that it is actually hot. The rest of the time, we open windows and use fans to push the hot air around. I turn on the AC. The appearance of the snowflake icons on the thermostat momentarily displaces my worry.

It's so warm there's no morning dew on the grass. The park is dry and still. Bracing itself against the heat. Nothing moves or makes noise, not even the sparrows, who are always moving, always flashing around in fidgety little flocks. A good day to be under cover. There's a path into the woods out past the soccer fields that I haven't gotten to yet. I smear sunscreen everywhere as I walk toward the trailhead.

I'm here. Please come see me.

Please come see me. The *please* is new. Not for Jesse — he's the politest person — but it's the first time he's said it out here. He says that *please* might be the most important word. "So many people don't say it these

days," he once said to me. "Like politeness is a weakness
or something. But people appreciate when you make the
effort. You get more flies with honey than with vinegar."
He even uses it when he asks for the time: "May I have
the time, please?" It sounds so formal. He'll ask someone at the store or gas station even though he wears his
old army watch everywhere and he carries a phone.
Creating chances to say *please* to strangers or something. It's weird. But kind of cool.

The trail is wide. Packed hard and well used. Not a
lot of garbage, maybe the occasional beer can or snack
wrapper. I cover a lot of ground, following the path up
and down, toward and away from the marsh, in and
out of small ravines and valleys. It's hot and I'm already
sweaty, but it's kind of nice to walk for a change.

"Wendell? Can you hear me, mate?"

Sean's voice somewhere behind me, dulled by the
heat and the trees but still killing the calm. I slow down
but stay quiet. He'll find me on his own — there's only
one path, and his GPS will get him here. I don't feel the
need to contribute to the noise. I round a bend and find
myself at one of the park's scenic lookouts, a wooden
platform hanging out over the marsh. Usually these
spots are cleaner than the paths, but today I see a jumble
of small plastic things, bright against the weathered grey
of the platform's pressure-treated lumber. Green. Red.
Blue. Yellow. Spent shotgun shells. Scattered all over the
lookout, like someone stood right here and shot them
all off in one session. For fun. Who does that?

I kneel and pick them up by hand, dropping them
into my garbage bag one by one. They landed on the

platform, so they're clean. There's the sharp smell of burnt gunpowder. The shooting smell is strong. Like a ton of gunpowder gets packed inside before the shooter blasts them out of his gun and destroys whatever he's pointing at. Not like .22-calibre rounds. They're small. They smell sharp, too, but lighter. Less volume. Jesse has a larger-calibre hunting rifle but also owns a .22 that he uses to shoot beer cans. "Plinking," he calls it. "To keep the hand-eye coordination fresh." One of his army buddies, who moved to Canada and bought a huge plot of land south of Windsor, lets Jesse shoot whenever he wants. I went down with him a few times, long before he took me hunting and got in so much trouble. He'll line up a bunch of cans on a rail and lie down a ways away. Prone is the most stable shooting position. He's so good at shooting, too. He'll tuck the rifle into his shoulder and slow down his breathing and *snap! snap! snap!* he'll knock the cans over one by one with almost no hesitation between them. He can shoot all day. And he does, sometimes.

"There you are."

Sean rounds the final bend, breathing hard. He's holding his phone. As I stand to face him, I can see a pulsing blue dot in the middle of the screen. That's me, I bet.

To my surprise, Aunt Viv appears right behind him. "Hey, kid," she says.

"You're really in deep this time," Sean says.

"But you said I could clean the trails."

"Not *in deep* like that," Aunt Viv says, laughing. "He meant deep in. Far back in the woods."

"What she said," Sean says, smiling at her. "You're fine, Wendell. This is a regular check-in."

"Okay," I say. "But what are you doing here, Aunt Viv?"

"I asked Sean to find you, and he said he was coming out today anyhow. Gramma Jan's being discharged today."

"Yeah, Mom told me."

Her eyebrows rise. "I didn't know that. I was on my way out when she got to the hospital, so —"

"On your way out? But you didn't come home."

"Oh. That. Well ..."

And insert awkward pause. So much weirdness happening all at once. Someone using Cootes Paradise as a shooting gallery. Sean in the woods looking like an urban alien. Aunt Viv following him out here. Aunt Viv choosing to follow anyone. Aunt Viv asking for help. If she can hack into his system, surely she can find me out here on her own. Her laughter at Sean's mixed-up words. His smile.

"*I* certainly had a nice time," Sean says.

"Sean," Aunt Viv says, drawing out the word long enough to glare at him. "We talked about this."

"Well, I did enjoy myself, Vivian. And it's pretty clear Wendell's figured it out, yeah?"

Aunt Viv makes a low growling sound and rolls her eyes. Probably because he called her by her proper first name. "Fine," she says.

Sean turns to me again. "But she did ask if you'd be allowed to break early today, so you can be there when your gran comes home. That's what she was going to tell you."

"Both of you had to be here for that?"

"Well, no, but her Prius wouldn't start this morning, so I had to give her a ride home."

"Sean!"

Aunt Viv looks like she could punch him. TMI, clearly. And I get it. It feels sloppy, how goofy he's being around her. What happened to "Let's keep this professional, yeah?"

"Does Gramma Jan know about all of this?" I ask. "She hates it when we make a big deal out of anything."

Aunt Viv nods. "She asked if you could be there."

"Why? What's wrong?"

"She'll tell you herself. She insisted."

"That's more like her, but come on, you can —"

"Be home for eleven."

"Aunt Viv —"

"Stop, Dills. Just be there."

And with that she turns and walks back up the path, disappearing around the bend.

"Sean, what's going on?"

"I don't know, mate. She didn't tell me, either."

He looks at his phone and swipes something away from the screen. Puts the phone in its pouch and looks at me long and hard. "Actually, this wasn't a regular check-in. I have to tell you something. Two things, actually."

"Okay."

"I spoke to the judge about your breach the other day. At the hospital. She's waived any further escalation, so you're off the hook."

"Well, that's good. Mom'll be happy."

"You should be, too."

"Oh. I am."

"You sure? You don't look it."

"I haven't had time ... I, uh, haven't thought about it much."

Sean gives me a look, like he can't believe I haven't been obsessing about it.

I ask, "And the other thing?"

"Right. It's about that reporter. From the trial."

"Walters."

"She's been poking around the office and the courts. Bugging me about you."

"I've seen her a couple of times. She knows that something's different about my case."

"So she says."

"Would you ever —"

"Not a chance, Wendell. We don't talk about our cases with reporters. The court, too — they're locked as tight as we are. Still," A pause, thoughtful. "I don't think she's going away. I wanted to warn you to be careful and not say anything."

"I won't."

"When reporters start chewing on something ..."

"Yeah."

Sean glances down and sees the shell that's still in my hand. This one is yellow. I drop it in the bag. He looks around the platform at the shells I haven't gotten to yet. Back at me. Sighs. It looks like he wants to say something about them, but he doesn't. Maybe there's a rule somewhere he's trying to interpret on the fly. They're spent, so there's no danger. Or maybe it's about guns and guys like me who live through the unimaginable. I kneel again to grab the next shell, this one signal red. And the next. Blue. Green. Another yellow.

Sean says, "You're all right?"

"All of this is weird, but I'm getting used to it."

"Protect yourself, yeah?"

"I will. Will you tell Aunt Viv?"

He shakes his head. "I have to tell your mum, of course, and I'll have to write it up in my own reports, but no one else. Confidentiality."

"Good."

"Right, then."

And he jogs away back up the path, awkward, looking like he's trying to put a spring in his step. Trying to catch Aunt Viv. He seems so certain about the security of my information, but Aunt Viv can slice through it and barely break a sweat. I trust him, but what about everyone else in the system? My story is different. My life is a scoop. My family is news.

I look at my watch. One hour to go.

COMPLICATED

I'm here. Come see me, Dills. Please.

As I work my way up and down the marsh paths for the remainder of the morning, Jesse calls to me often. As though the woods have provided some extra privacy. Safety to talk to me. Just for today, maybe.

"How, Jesse? How do I get to you?"

His words and voice have become more urgent, and I want to go more than ever. But I'm fifteen. I'm not one of those kids who has worked out how to leave, a plan in his back pocket. I never wanted to run away. Mom and Jesse and I have never been a perfect family, but there's love there. Safety. So many people have assumed that Jesse was always violent, but that's not the case at all. Irritable? Lonely? Impulsive? Sure, sometimes. But he always had time for me, too. Always made sure that his knowledge was my knowledge. Is. I never felt in danger. *We* never felt in danger.

Of course, Jesse doesn't answer. So I walk and spear the occasional trash, my black plastic garbage bag filling slowly, and let my mind wander.

There's the issue of how to get to Windsor. Google tells me there's a bus, but that takes money. Probably ID, too. My student card won't be good enough. Mom keeps my birth certificate and health card. And my passport, a few years old, with a photo of me so young I barely recognize myself. All ears and big new teeth. Hitchhiking is free, but no way. Mom has a car, but I'd bet all the money I don't have that she won't take me. Maybe Aunt Viv can drive.

And that's as far as my plotting gets me. Uncertainty. That three-hour drive might as well be across a demilitarized border, like in Korea. Landmined and razor-wired.

I think about Mia, too. Her parents a different kind of border, just as hard to cross. Me over here, carrying how I feel about her, and her over there with her own feelings. She made it sound so simple. Her parents don't need to know. Parents always find out, though. And I think about Aunt Viv and Sean and Mom and Gramma Jan, and I wonder why life has to be so complicated. *Here, Dills*, the universe is saying, *deal with all of this, will ya? You can handle it, right? It's not like you have any other issues to process.*

I trip over an exposed root. The dressing covering my rash catches on a low branch and tears off. The sudden air against it is a lit match against sawdust. Up it goes. The itch blooming like flame again. The perfect timing of it makes me stop midstep and close my eyes. I feel like swearing.

"Coming through!"

It's a big guy in sweaty running gear. The brightest shades of it. Soaked salmon shirt over his expansive gut, blue shorts covering his spindle thighs. Running hat in construction orange. He has a small dog, maybe a chihuahua, a tiny rat thing that yips and growls at me. I'm so stunned by the sight of them that I can't move, and they're forced to stop a couple of feet from me. Even the dog is decked out for a blinding jaunt though the woods, wearing a ridiculously tiny yellow bandana that matches my safety vest. It's surreal how intense they are against the gloom.

"Out of the way, kid!"

But I don't move. My eyes are locked on the dog as it bristles, teeth bared at me. All the dog shit I've had to clean over the past few weeks. Bagging it for the trash. Flicking it into the underbrush when I can so I don't have to carry it around. Fresh. Petrified. Somewhere in between. The hot, smelly mess of it.

"You should leash your dog," I say, removing my helmet and wiping the sweat from my forehead. "The bylaw's clear. I'm sick of picking up after them."

The guy, shiny with run sweat, folds his arms. "What are you, the cops?"

Instead of replying, I push past him and carry on up the path. The dog growls as I pass, the low burr of a tiny voice box. I can feel all four of their eyes on my back. There was nothing more to say that wouldn't have devolved into swearing and yelling and tearing into him. Not recommended for my situation.

The rest of the morning passes slowly but without further incident. Sweaty and slow. Thinking and waiting and worrying are the worst companions when you want the time to fly.

TERMINAL

I'm late getting home even though I paused my workday in time. At five to eleven I stashed my gear behind a tree and walked to the edge of the park. Something stopped me there, one foot on the end of the sidewalk, the other on the park grass. Awkward. But I remained in that position for five, maybe ten, minutes, staring at the neighbourhood and thinking about everything. Overwhelmed. Forcing myself to breathe. I hope no one saw me.

Mom's Corolla is parked on the street next to the side door. Odd. She's so fastidious about parking in the driveway, which is in the back of the house because we're on a corner lot. More traffic to worry about when you park streetside, more risk of dings and scratches. As I come near, I smell burning. Hot rubber and steel. The car's hood is open. The muffler and the long exhaust pipe rest on the asphalt under the car.

"Mom?" I yell as I close the door behind me.

"You're home," Mom says, appearing in the hallway. "Good."

"What happened to the car?"

"I don't know. It started making all sorts of horrible sounds on the way home from the hospital and died right as I pulled up."

Cars don't die, Mom. They just stop, is what I think. But I can't say that to her. Or to myself, maybe. I kick off my shoes. "It got you home."

"True, but now it won't start."

"That sucks."

"Yeah. Anyhow, come on in. We're in the living room."

We walk in together. Gramma Jan is seated in the easy chair at the far corner of the living room. Aunt Viv is sitting across from her on the good sofa. Mom sits down slowly, carefully, at the other end. A special occasion? Gramma Jan loves to sit and read in that chair, but the rest of the furniture rarely gets used. Aunt Viv and Mom look as stiff as only sitting on an off-white sofa can make a person. You're afraid to breathe. Your breath might stain the fabric. And there are biscuits on a fancy plate in the centre of the coffee table. They're called biscuits, not cookies, because they're in recognizable flower shapes, covered in chocolate, dusted with coconut. Gramma Jan, Mom, and Aunt Viv are each sipping coffee from proper cups and saucers, delicate things with gold edges and hand-painted flowers.

This all clashes. We're more a kitchen-table-and-family-room kind of family. We sometimes sit on the floor. We're mugs and cookies, never fine china, never biscuits. Four-finger mugs. Messy, homemade cookies with smeared chocolate chips. I am instantly on alert.

Gramma Jan smiles at me. She is still so pale, and she looks like she's lost half her body weight since I saw her a couple of days ago. It makes her smile too big. Her head like a grinning skull.

"Wendell!" she says. "Get your ass over here and give your gramma a hug."

I go over to her, but slowly. The language is her, but the instruction is not. I am not a Wendell in this house. You know by now that we are not hugs, either.

"Here, Mom," Aunt Viv says, rising from the sofa, "let me take your cup."

But Gramma Jan has shifted forward and risen from her seat, surprisingly strong.

"Don't worry about it, Viv."

"But the rug —"

"Is just a rug."

Aunt Viv stops, unsure. Glances at Mom, who shrugs. Gramma Jan steps forward and grabs me with a single bony arm. Her other hand somewhere behind me, the cup and saucer clinking an alarming tattoo. She smells of rubbing alcohol and hospital wards and the faintest whiff of urine.

"I missed you, kid," she says. Her voice low and husky. Breaking, kind of.

"Hey, Gramma."

That's all I can get out. Gramma Jan doesn't seem to mind or notice. She holds on for a long time. Tight. The details I've taken in since I walked through the door may have created a general sense of something being off. The hug, though, the length of her need to hold on, tells me with precision that something is wrong. When she finally lets me go and steps back, her eyes are red and shimmering, and the sense of wrongness grows. Gramma Jan is steel and edge, not crying and tears. She eases herself down into the chair again with an audible exhalation.

"Why are you home early?" I ask, finding my voice again.

"They needed the bed," Gramma Jan says.

"Mom," Aunt Viv says, leaving the sentence unfinished. *We talked about this*, the tone says.

Gramma Jan chuckles. "The girls tell me I shouldn't lie to you."

"Lie about what?"

"I said not to burden you, but they're stubborn. Like me."

"Is it your heart?"

"My goddamn heart's fine," Gramma Jan says. "Well, in context, anyhow."

"I don't understand."

"I'm dying, kid."

Mom exhales audibly and brings a hand to her mouth. Aunt Viv makes a face like she could punch the words Gramma Jan just said.

"But you're …"

I stop myself from saying the rest. *You're fine*, I was about to say. But obviously not. That would be stupid. Gramma Jan looks at me. Long. Without speaking. Like she's suddenly aware of how important it is to wait for others to respond to bad news. Mom and Aunt Viv both look like they want to take over. To tell me everything. But they don't. Gramma Jan's news to share.

"Tell me," I say.

So she does. So many details. The heart issue and the tests they ran uncovered certain things. Various elevated levels. Further testing and scans revealed more. Cancer. The Big C. Buried deep, spreading fast. Terminal. Gramma Jan already knew something was seriously wrong but didn't tell anyone. There's an argument about that, about responsibility and sensitivity and pridefulness. But I know that the argument is a symptom of Mom's and Aunt Viv's pain, rather than a need to work through anything. What's done is done.

For my part, I don't say anything. Instead, my mind tries to sort through the infuriating mystery of why bodies fail before their time. I'm still processing why and how the universe can extinguish so many lives by the horrible actions of others. How bodies can be torn apart from the outside. Now I have to process why and how our bodies can turn on us, too. How they can tear themselves apart from the inside. How defenceless we are against any of it.

LIKE NORMAL

"So, do you still hear him?" Aunt Viv asks late the next morning, sitting on the chair beside me.

I take my eyes from my iPod. "Huh?"

We're both in the family room at the back of the house, where the TV and beat-up furniture live. Aunt Viv has her laptop open and is working the keys, her hands a blur. Mom's puttering around in her workshop — she hates the word *puttering*, a Jesse word, and says it diminishes what a person does — more quietly than usual. Earlier, she had the Corolla towed and the tow-truck guy shook his head like it was all over, and now it seems like Mom's grieving the car's absence on top of everything else. Gramma Jan is upstairs, still sleeping. Sean called and said I could take the day off. Aunt Viv must've told him about the diagnosis.

"Jesse," she says.

"Oh. Yeah. Not right now, but every day."

"And Windsor? Still trying to get back?"

"Yes. No. It's complicated."

"Why?"

"Like I said. Mobility challenges."

"So jump on a bus. Get an Uber. Hitchhike, for crying out loud."

"Uh huh. Money? My safety? You haven't offered to drive, either."

"Car's in the shop."

"What about later, after —"

"No."

"Why?"

She scratches a spot behind her ear. "Uh, I don't do highways."

"So we take side roads."

"I can't do those, either."

"I don't understand."

"I have a thing. It has a name, but let's call it fear of road travel."

"A thing."

"A phobia."

"You're messing with me."

"Wish I was, kid. It's real. I've learned to function in the city, but I can't drive farther."

A thought arrives. Lands on me heavy. "That's why you never visited me and Mom."

"Yeah."

"And Gramma Jan doesn't drive."

"She had to give up her licence years ago because of some eye thing she won't talk about. I wonder if it's tied to her recent heart troubles …" She shakes her head and sighs. "Anyhow, before you and your mom came home with an extra set of wheels, I was her taxi."

"Even after Windsor, you couldn't —"

"It sounds weak, but between your gramma and me, it was easy to talk ourselves out of going."

"Mom knows."

"Yep."

"Which is why she never complained about you two staying back here in Hamilton. Huh. I never thought about it. I thought it was about Jesse."

"That, too. I'm sorry."

"I don't know what to say right now."

"But you should still go. I can give you the money."

"It's not just about getting there," I say, holding up my leg. "I'm LoJacked, remember? And why are you encouraging me? You were worried about my healing, didn't want me to tell Mom."

"You seem so preoccupied. And I think you need the chance to …" A pause. "Jesse and you were so … *are* so —" She smacks the table. "Shit, Dills. It's not your fault. Any of it."

"I know that."

"Do you?"

"Of course I do!"

"I don't want to intrude. And yet I do. Feel free to tell me to fuck off."

"No way, Aunt Viv. Never."

"I just want to help."

"I know that, too."

"Okay."

"Okay."

I glance at the screen again. Refresh my email. Again. Willing it to display a little *1* in red. For Mia to reach out, even though it was me who stormed off the other day. The irrational hope I won't have to do anything. That she'll love me for my brand of stubborn crazy. Like one of those scenes in a movie, where the other person appears at just the right time with just the right words in just the right place, even though real life isn't like that and there are so few right times and places. Like this:

> Him: *I am so glad you decided to read my mind and appear in the middle of my randomness.*
> Her: *You are so good to accept my apologies.*
> Him: *Why, of course it would be okay to call me again.*
> Her: *I want to kiss you now.*
> Him: *Yes, we should kiss.*
> Her: *And look at that sunset!*
> Him: *It is orange and attractive.*

Meh.

"You've been glued to that thing, Dills. It's the girl, right?" Aunt Viv looks excited. Like changing the topic was a kind of rescue.

"How did you —"

"Educated guess. People who stare at screens so much are usually waiting on someone."

"Not you."

"True. I don't wait for them to deliver POL. Proof of love," she explains before I can ask, looking pleased with herself.

"It's not like that."

"Not what your mom says. She says the girl seems nice."

"She told you?"

"She called you 'smitten.'" She makes a face. "I hate that word. It's like roses and chocolates and stupid crushes."

"Me, too."

"But you like her."

I nod. There's no point denying it. She isn't asking.

"Hard to fight, when it hits you like that," she says.

She gets a far-off look in her eyes as she speaks. Well. Who's smitten now?

"Like you and Sean?"

She frowns, coming back to herself. "Maybe. I don't know what to call us. We're having fun. But this isn't about us. What's her name?"

"Mia."

"Italian?"

"Palestinian. Her last name is Al-Ansour."

"Interesting."

"I think so."

"So why isn't she messaging?"

"She prefers email, actually."

Viv rolls her eyes. "How fifteen years ago. Quaint. Maybe you're more roses and chocolate than I realized."

"Aunt Viv …"

"Now I *am* messing with you, Dills."

She looks at her watch and stands. Looks back at her computer. Then moves off into the kitchen where I can hear the fridge door opening and closing. I'd call it aimless, but she's trying to connect. I'm sure her mind is on her computer, assaulting some stubborn code somewhere, racking up her billable hours. Mom's gone quiet in her workshop. It feels weird to have Aunt Viv and Mom not busy. Mom had to take time off from her work after the shooting, of course, but that was not by choice. Aside from Sean giving me the okay to stay home, nothing has been said, but I can tell they've cleared their schedules for the day. Making themselves available for Gramma Jan. And me.

But can we step out of our lives for more than a day? It took me a long time to fall asleep last night. Thinking about what Gramma Jan's diagnosis could mean. For her. Us. It's called "terminal" for a reason. It's not going anywhere. Suspended over us. Today feels like suspension, but tomorrow will push us back into our everyday stuff. Stuff that has to change but still try to stay the same. I have a feeling we'll be looking for a new normal.

Something has changed. Please come.

I know, Jesse. Here, too, I think. I lift my iPod and tap Reload. No change there.

HELD UP

We had a massive thunderstorm overnight. Arrived about three in the morning and rattled the foundations for about thirty minutes. Puddles everywhere and a new coolness in the air this morning when I went out for work. Like the heat and humidity's backs had been broken. I haven't been sweating today even though it's now after lunch, when the heat usually soars.

I'm back at it, working the main park today, dodging parents and kids and the city's grass-mowing crew. Everyone is smiling more. I catch one of the city workers humming as she walks back to her truck, gas trimmer slung over her shoulder. No, not walks. Strolls. She smiles and winks at me as she passes, saying something about being able to breathe again. Her teeth perfect white against her tanned face.

By three in the afternoon, when I usually sit in the shade somewhere and scarf down a couple of granola bars, the section of the park I'm focusing on today is spotless. Not a bit of garbage anywhere. But I'm not moving on. Mia's house backs onto the far side. Her family lives in a row of townhomes, the only ones in the neighbourhood. There are at least five separate occasions where I resolve to walk right into her small backyard and knock on her patio door. Immediately followed by five panicked ones where it doesn't happen.

So now I'm moving up and down the same stretch of treeline, visible from her place, actually pretending to stab things in the brush and put them in my garbage bag. Which remains almost empty, pathetically wrapping itself around my leg with every puff of wind. As limp and formless as my own resolve. I'm embarrassed for myself. Yet can I stop? No.

It's almost a relief to hear Gal's horrible singing. He'll see me and want to check on my progress. Anything to interrupt this ridiculous little play I'm directing and starring in. He emerges at a trailhead a short way down, stops, and heads in my direction. He looks at the ground and at my spike and at my bag, but no change comes across his features. You can't say his face is expressionless — his scars are a riot of expression.

He nods at the bandage on my arm. "The rash is not so severe. I am surprised. You fell into so much poison ivy."

I'd become comfortable with the itch, almost a constant crackling static in the background. But now it flares. I rub it through the bandage. "I was lucky, I guess."

"This is not luck."

This being everything that happened around the PI incident, of course. But there's no need to say anything further about it. I just nod.

"That boy, Pat, the one who pissed on you —"

"What about him?"

"He has been around more. I have had to tell him to leave a few times."

I don't know how I feel about Gal doing that. Fighting this battle for me. "Own your own shit, kid," Jesse says. "One, no one can shoulder it for you. Two, it feels good to be responsible." I remember asking him when to look for help. Jesse told me to try to do things myself but that if I needed to, I could ask him or someone trustworthy. I asked how a person knows if someone can be trusted. "I have no idea," he said. "Some you can, some you can't. Like I said, own your own shit. Remember that. Although if your mom ever asks, I said *stuff*, right?"

"I can take care of him," I say to Gal.

Gal's eyebrow rises. Questioning. Doubting. "I do not think that this boy has much respect for anyone. Be careful."

"I will."

He nods and takes a step away, as though he's heading back into the woods to carry on his walk, but then he stops. Scans the ground, the underbrush at the edge of the woods. Looks at me and across at the fence behind Mia's place and back at me again. The tiniest of smiles breaks on his face, his scars easing.

"This section of the park is very tidy," he says.

"Thanks."

"I would offer to go and tell her you are here, but I think you might like to do this yourself."

As though on cue, Mia appears, stepping out through her sliding glass door and walking across the small yard.

Sees Gal and me. Waves. Unlatches the gate and walks across the grass. Flip-flops, ragged cut-off shorts, and a dark tank top. Everything loose. Functional. Yet showing off her muscles, too. I like that she doesn't hide who she is.

"*Salaam 'alaikum*," she says to Gal when she arrives.

"*Wa'alaikum a'salaam.*"

They have a quick exchange in Arabic, rapid fire, back and forth. I'm the awkward spectator with nothing to say. Maybe not even present. I stand and listen, mute, as awkward as a third leg and foot facing the other direction. Mia says something that makes Gal chuckle, and I want to jump in and yell that I'm here, pay attention to me, I'm not pathetic. Gal waves and heads off, singing, his voice fading as he enters the woods at the next trailhead down from the one he emerged from. Leaving me and Mia to stand in silence.

I'm here. Please come.

The word Jesse doesn't say is *now*. He doesn't have to. Now is everything. I have this sense that there are no moments other than now, if you think about it. The past is done and mostly sucks. You can't guarantee a future. You can make plans and save and hoard, but you might never get to use any of it. So what's left? Only the right-nows you try to use as best you can.

"I'm sorry," I say. "About how I acted at your party. I can —"

"No, I'm sorry. I totally put you on the spot."

I'm speechless. Blinded. I was going to tell Mia that I can see her however she wants me to see her. In secret. Out loud. Whatever. Because I think Jesse would be pissed at me if he knew how easily I'd shrugged off this opportunity. His voice telling me without telling me to buck the hell up and to hold what I can. But Mia headed me off with her own apology, and now my words — any words at all — have resettled into the strange places they inhabit in my brain.

"I met your aunt," she says.

"Wait, what?"

"Vivian. She's cool. We had coffee this morning. Well, she had coffee. I had milk. Coffee's gross."

"I don't understand. Why w—"

"She said she wanted to meet me."

"How did she find you?"

"She knocked on our front door. Didn't you tell her where I live?"

I shake my head. "I mentioned your name. She must've googled you."

Now it's Mia's turn to shake her head. "We're not listed, Dills. My parents keep themselves private. Especially after 9/11 and all the crap happening in the States. And that information isn't anywhere on my social media."

And I can't respond to that. I might be used to Aunt Viv's mysterious online ways but only from a distance. Apart. You can trust the space. Not now, though. As I said the word *google*, I knew it was a weak version of what Aunt Viv is capable of. She doesn't need Google. But it's odd that she's taking such an interest in me and in Mia. Aunt Viv and I have never been that close.

Mia watches me thinking. "We made small talk. She said she was an online-security consultant."

"She's much more than that."

"Hacker?"

"She hates the word, but yeah."

"Seriously?"

"Seriously."

Mia looks at the ground, falling into her own thoughts. I think about how exposed she and her family are. She must be realizing the same thing.

Well, I did that. My stupid open mouth. I have to make this right. I have to help. "I'm sorry."

But a change happens. She looks up again, and in the piercing darkness of her brown eyes I can see a new clarity. New strength. No, wait. Not new. More. More of the abundant wonder stuff she is already made of. In a blink, she has weighed all the pluses and minuses and has made her decisions and has made my urge to help, to fix, irrelevant. Not needed.

"It doesn't matter," she says.

"It does, Mia. She shouldn't have hacked you."

"She won't hurt us. I like her. I think I can trust her."

"Still, it —"

Mia lays her hand on my forearm and my voice cuts itself off. There's a strong weight there. Warm. Nice. I'm glad it's a cool day, that my skin is sweat-free and clean so her hand won't slip off. I want to live right here for as long as I can. Soak her in. Her warmth and —

"She told me about Windsor High."

Aw, man, those words. From her, they're bullets. I've been shot through. Two military rounds piercing my body at 3,251 feet per second, 5.56 millimeter caliber, tungsten core, tumbling. All the now and truth and warmth that have filled me up for the past few minutes gush out of me. A trickle at the entrance wound in front, a torrent from the fist-sized exit wound in my back. I've seen those wounds. The blood and bone and bits of flesh that spray out of them, the horrific mess left behind.

Mia's mouth is moving. She's concerned. Asking if I'm all right. But I can't hear. There's a roaring in my ear, a hundred assault rifles on full auto. Drowning out the screams that are immediately behind.

I should have run sooner. Hidden. Behind the librarian's desk. That bookcase. The tables and chairs and catalogue computers. The witness stand. The judge's dais. A tree. Anything.

My legs feel weak. I guess that makes sense. I thought I'd kept it all in, protected, bandaged tight as I heal. But for some reason, Mia's knowing has torn the dressings off and I'm bleeding out. It feels like all that's left is to sink down and wait for it all to end.

Mia raises her hands to my face and kisses me. Not the awkward but tender, swirling, blush-of-romance kind of first kiss, but the who-you-trust-to-save-your-life kind. Firm, dry, strong, and brief. Long enough for my feet and legs and body to understand that they can support me after all. And her arms around me in a long embrace. She could hold me up if she needed to. She is that strong.

"Vivian told me about your stepdad, too. About what he did."

I take a deep breath, exhale into her shoulder. Where to begin? Maybe with the obvious. My obvious, anyhow. "I can't hate him, Mia. Everyone else does, but I can't."

"You don't have to. No one can know him like you do."

"That's so it. Exactly."

"She says he talks to you."

I pull back and look at her. To gauge her expression. Her belief. But her expression is as full of that wonder stuff as before. Wow.

"And you're going to go see him."

"Vivian told you that, too?"

A nod. "I can go with you. We could leave any time."

"I want to, but I can't just go." I explain about buses and unaccompanied minors, the expense of other options, the dangers of hitchhiking. The practical barriers. My ankle monitor. I don't explain about all the other things, the intangibles centred in my head and heart, that might be keeping me here even more.

"We'll figure it out," Mia says.

"I could get in a lot of trouble. You, too."

"I don't care."

"I do."

"You could ask your mom."

"No way. She's dealing with enough as it is. Plus, I think her car died."

"Vivian?"

I shake my head and tell her about Aunt Viv's fear of roads, how she can't leave the city.

"Oh."

We briefly fall silent before Mia's face opens up, bright as that first bit of eastern sun rising over the trees in the morning. "I know who can drive us."

"Who?"

A smile. Teeth as white as trust. "I got this, Mr. Wendell."

"You have it all worked out."

"I am owed a big favour, as they say."

Her tone is formal and serious, though her eyes are bright. I open my mouth to ask the obvious next question, but close it again almost immediately. *As they say.* You never know who *they* are, and yet saying it so often makes it a kind of truth. Especially when it's said by someone like Mia.

"All right, then, Ms. Al-Ansour," I say. "You have my encouragement to pursue this line of inquiry."

"Excellent. I will begin post-haste."

"That is acceptable."

"To me, also."

We laugh, the seriousness and formality feeling somehow right. If I could lift myself like a drone ten thousand feet into the sky, all of Churchill Park laid out below me, I'd see that we're standing precisely, impossibly in the centre of it. Surrounded by grass and trees and swamp. Lots of places to hide. Lots of places to bleed out all alone. But right now, my feet fixed to the earth, it's the place we just happen to be standing, and I have no idea about midpoints and geography and signs. Just that, for the first time in a long time, wholeness doesn't seem so alien. Maybe the dressing hasn't been torn off. Maybe it needed to be loosened. To gauge the healing. To let the air in for a little while.

PART II
THERE

GO

By the time we pull back onto the highway, the sun is below the horizon. We left Hamilton four hours ago but one hour out the rear left tire blew. It took five minutes for Gal to figure out that his spare was flat and almost three hours for the roadside service guy to find us. He was a greasy dude, perving Mia out as he filled and mounted the spare, like she might be ripe enough to squeeze. Gal got in his face, the service truck's flashing yellow lights turning his scars into a strobe-lit horror show. The guy left in a hurry, barely glancing at the cash Gal put in his hand. The original tire was a lost cause, like a shredded rubber corpse. We almost left it on the gravel shoulder, but Gal and I shared a look and put it in the trunk. One less piece of garbage for someone else to pick up.

"That took way too long," I say from the back seat.

"It is what it is," Gal says, and falls silent.

Gal unintentionally using Jesse's words. *It is what it is, kid. Lots of things can't be explained. And don't need to be. They just are.* You wonder how such sayings get passed between different groups of people.

Full dark comes quickly. Our headlights throw a small pool of brightness on the highway ahead. Out here there are no streetlights, so the highway is mostly dark, apart from tail lights on our side of the road and meteor headlights passing the other way.

Please, kid.

I'm coming, Jesse. Finally, I'm coming.

I feel like a coward for waiting this long. Taking a three-hour trip seems like such a simple thing. When you have your own resources, it's simple. When you have the time, it's simple. When you're not chained to the legal system by a sentence and an ankle monitor, it's simple. Yet, when you can have a million excuses but not a single reason that stands up against the reality that you haven't made the effort, it doesn't feel so simple. That you haven't cared enough, maybe. Or that deep down, you have reservations. Complicated reservations.

Gal hums to himself, as off-tune as always, content to drive his Kia hatchback twenty below the highway maximum. On cruise control. The tire guy warned against driving the doughnut spare faster than this, but Gal is in no hurry anyhow. Unlike me. I want to yell at him to speed up. Obviously, I don't. He's driving, after all. Willingly. And he waved away my weak offer to pay for the tire change, clearly sensing that finding the cash would be a challenge.

Mia did this. This trip. This chance to answer some of my questions. The edge of her face lights up and dims with every car passing by in the other direction. I didn't fight too hard back in Hamilton when she called shot-gun. The view of her may be the only thing keeping me from screaming that everything is taking too damn long.

"The highway is quiet," Gal says after a while.

"It's Friday night," Mia replies. "And we're in the middle of nowhere."

"Not nowhere," I say. "We're near London. Jesse and I stopped here once."

He called London "a sleepy college town," like the words explained everything. We stopped at a twenty-four-hour supermarket in the northern suburbs to buy some food for our hike into the woodlands nearby, and there were two sleepy students buying snacks in the checkout ahead of us. Not paying attention to the cashier. Jesse snapped at them to wake the hell up. There was an uncharacteristic edge to Jesse's voice. Maybe because he never went to college and wonders if he should have. He's so smart, so he could have, but he likes to talk about the home he made in the military, too. His army family. Mom talks about me going to college like it's a given thing, but Jesse doesn't participate in those discussions. "Education's important," he says, "but it's not school that makes a man who he is. Just keep your choices intact."

"Who is Jesse?" Gal asks.

"Wendell's stepdad."

"Is he the reason we are sneaking from Hamilton on a Friday night?"

I tap Mia on the shoulder. "You didn't tell him?"

"He knows where we're going. The rest of the story is yours."

"He must owe you a heck of a favour."

"Well, that's his story to tell, too. If he wants."

"This little drive will not begin to repay it." Gal says this like he's making a proclamation of some kind.

"Gal, I told you, this'll be enough," Mia says.

Gal makes that sucking sound behind his teeth again and she goes quiet. But in the car's low light, I can see she's smiling. All this history. Inside jokes and stories. I want to tell them to spit it out, that keeping secrets in front of others is rude, but that's not very diplomatic, is it? Or realistic. We keep all sorts of secrets from each other.

We drive in silence for a few more minutes before Gal sighs and glances at me in the rear-view. "You have seen my scars?"

"Of course he has. They're impossible to miss!"

Gal doesn't answer Mia's outburst, but glances at me again and then brings his eyes back to the front. Waits for me to answer. Making space. A kind of permission.

"I didn't want to be rude," I say.

Mia has told me some, of course, but I'm not sure whether Gal knows. Better to keep that to myself. Gal sighs again and expands on the version Mia told me. His national service in Israel. Stationed in a settlement near Hebron but shifted to Ramallah after a couple of Israeli soldiers were murdered there. The complications of control and violent suppression. A rocket attack and an unexploded warhead going off as he placed warning tape around it. Fragments all over his upper body, some of which are still there. Shrapnel. Jesse kept a jar on the dresser in the master bedroom in Windsor with a few shards of metal they took out of him after he got hit on one of his tours. Gal didn't keep his. The surgeries and rehabilitation and a desperate need to leave his country were reminders enough of what happened. Aside from the fragments in his body — the ones he'll carry forever. Or at least to the grave, where they won't decompose with his body. Like Ethan's braces.

"I am healed," he says. "Enough to function. But the pain persists. Especially in my head."

"He smokes pot for the pain," Mia says, excited, still wanting to participate.

"Cannabis has eased my symptoms, yes."

"Okay, but what does this have to do with why you're willing to drive me?"

"Before cannabis was legalized, I was registered to use it medically. But there were times when the amount I was allowed was not enough. Mia helped me a couple of years ago."

"You helped him get weed?"

She glances back at me, rolling her eyes. "Sure, Dills. I'm the neighbourhood dealer. I can hook you up. Did I forget to mention that?"

I give her a look, something along the lines of "Sarcasm Doesn't Help Anyone." But I realize that she can't see me. Right. I feel like an idiot. "So how —"

"She hid my supply when the police raided the field house."

"You did what?"

"It wasn't a big deal," she says.

"Yes, it was," Gal says.

"How much are we talking about?"

Turns out it wasn't a truckload or anything, but definitely enough to have gotten Gal and Mia in serious trouble. Now he can walk into a dispensary and pick out what he wants, but before legalization, his own dealer would sell him enough to keep him supplied for a while. One day Mia walked in on him when he was about to light up, just as the police rolled up, cherries flashing. He told her to leave. Instead, she hid the bag in the waistband of her shorts.

"The cops hardly even looked at me," she laughs. "They had a warrant to search everywhere else but didn't think twice about the bulge on my belly. Just another fat girl."

"Wait," I say. "That's … you're not …"

"Exactly," she says. "But kind of funny, too."

"They didn't wonder why a teenage girl was hanging out with the park manager in his gloomy office?"

"They joked about Gal robbing the cradle, but —"

"They had to leave when they could not find anything," Gal says.

I watch her and Gal laugh about it. But I'm not settled. Too close for comfort, in so many ways that I can't begin to pin them down. I'm glad for their strange friendship — you can't always decide which ones will survive, can you? — but feel lost, not playing much of a part in it. But that's not entirely true, is it? Here I am. Here they are, helping create this piece of my story. And Aunt Viv back home, her car still in the shop, taking Sean out for a long dinner and a movie to keep him from thinking about work.

She hacked the parole system for me. My little blue dot, which turns red when I'm in breach, now moving in short paths around the park and my house. The online equivalent of putting a bank's video feed on a loop while you rob it. The guard snoozing in front of the blinking monitor. No one the wiser. Leaving after work on a Friday was her idea. If anything goes wrong, maybe a reduced weekend staff or Viv supplying Sean with her own distractions will delay anyone noticing too closely. I asked her what would happen if Sean found out, but she laughed and said her digital trail is clean. All he could do is suspect her. They'd have to break up, of course. I said that would seriously suck. "Whatever," she said. "He's not in my league." I'm not sure I believed her.

Mia and Gal's conversation and laughter drop away, leaving the hush of the wind and the tires on the pavement. Mia pulls out her phone. The screen glows against her face, blue in the darkness. Softens her profile more. I want to reach out and rest the back of my hand against her cheek.

"Everything is still a go, team," she says.

"I do not like that your parents do not know," Gal says.

"We've been through this."

"They will be worried."

"Not until the morning."

Mia told them she was heading into the gym for a monster workout to prepare for her upcoming season. It's not unusual for her to be out late when she's at peak training, and they won't wait up. She said her father grumbled in his usual way about the appropriateness of her independence. Her mother simply made an extra-large protein smoothie, like she always does before an intense session. Knowing the importance of sustained energy. Tissue repair.

I agree with Gal and I agree with Mia. I hate the idea of our parents being in the dark. Most of the time we make mistakes in the moment and without a thought to the cost. But this trip to Windsor is on its own level. A more premeditated kind of disappointment for the people who've given everything so we can be safe and loved. Still, a necessity. Mia knows her parents, so the decision rests with her. Just before we left, she said, "It sucks, but there's literally no scenario that sees them being okay with this."

Mom would've locked me in the house rather than let me go. Or worse still, offer to drive, even though the car's dead and she isn't ready to face Jesse. Still, for me she'd stare down every demon and walk me right into the hospital so I wouldn't have to be alone. She'd feel everything yet again.

Up ahead, a police cruiser appears over a rise, moving fast in the other direction, lights on, red and blue. We all tense up, as though the plan has already crumbled and the authorities have been brought in to find us. The lights zip past, and Gal and Mia exhale. I have to close my eyes against the lights still burning behind my eyelids. They flashed all day and night after the shooting, the red of the ambulances and fire trucks, the red and blue of the police. Impossible strobe patterns glinting against the sunlight as we were escorted and carried from the school. Slashing through the night when I finally left the hospital.

"Dills? Are you all right?"

I open my eyes. Mia has turned to the back seat, concerned. I guess she can see me after all. All the light is behind her. I can't see her eyes, though. I nod and attempt a smile and turn my head to look out the side window. But you can't look through glass into darkness, can you? All I see is the darkened outline of my own self and the dimmed reflections from the car's interior.

Somewhere to the north, off to our right, are the woods where Jesse taught me how to walk without making a sound. He was so quiet when he stalked, which is what you call it when you hunt something. He became his surroundings. Watching him move like a spirit through the brush and trees made his former life clearer to me. The things he had to do to succeed and survive. Deadly things that needed absolute silence. "Never hurry," he said. "Speed makes you careless, and careless makes sounds. But you can't go too slow, either, because the deer won't wait for you. Clear as mud?" Hard ground? Heel first, roll to the toe. Leaves and debris? Toe first, testing the surface for the things that can crackle and snap and betray your presence. No talking, just hand signals and eye contact. Every step its own performance. Then the next, with the same considerations. Again and again. It was this exhausting mix of pause and motion, halting but intentional. Getting anywhere took forever.

But now? Twenty below the speed limit feels slow, but it'll get us there. And when we arrive, this will feel like nothing at all, like we arrived as fast as blue and red light. Faster than I thought possible.

INVOLVED

Mia uses her phone's GPS to direct Gal to a tall apartment building on Windsor's east side. We park in one of three visitor spaces below the building. It's late, about midnight, but most of the building's windows are lit up. A lot of nighthawks, doing late-night things. Catching the late shows. Writing the next great novel. Binge-watching Netflix. Feeding babies. Staring at phones.

Mia taps a contact on her phone, watches it dial. "Moment of truth."

"She doesn't know we're coming?" I ask.

Mia shakes her head and listens to the phone ringing on the other end of the line. On the way down from Hamilton, she told us about Noor, her wrestling friend who lives here. I assumed it had been all arranged. Another complication. More people involved. This whole trip becoming way, way more complicated than I anticipated. I closed my eyes when I saw the first city-limits sign from the highway, thinking I could avoid seeing the name *Windsor*. But it's everywhere. Gas stations. Corner stores. Faceless industrial buildings. Schools.

No one's answering. Mia frowns and ends the call. "I didn't want to take the chance that she'd tell someone we're coming. We're friends, but not good friends."

"Risky."

"Life is risk, Mr. Sims," she says, smiling.

"You both are behaving very strangely," Gal says.

His tone is deadpan. Hard to know whether he's trying to participate in the humour or genuinely perplexed. And no way to confirm either way, as he's not saying anything more to help.

Mia tries the call again. Another wait. No luck. "Now what?"

"Hotel?" I ask.

"Perhaps it would be best if a solitary middle-aged man did not attempt to check in to a hotel with two minors."

"Right," Mia laughs. "Good thinking."

"The hospital?" I ask. "I'm sure we could find a waiting area."

"Mmm ... hospital chairs," Mia says, drawing out the words like they're the world's best chocolate.

"Hey, come on," I say, feeling chastised. "I'm just trying to —"

Mia's phone lights up and buzzes, cutting me off, bright and loud in the confines of the car. A photo of a dark-haired, dark-skinned woman comes up on the screen. *NOOR* in big block letters. Mia smiles and taps the green emerald to accept the call. There is a quick exchange in Arabic and some laughter.

I glance at Gal. "Mia's friend must have asked if she should put on some clothing," he says, looking embarrassed. "Mia has told her that you and I are here, so yes, she should."

Now I'm embarrassed too. "Oh. Okay."

Mia ends the call and slaps Gal lightly on the shoulder. "She's putting on a housecoat over her pyjamas. She wasn't naked or anything. Let's go."

Gal winces and mutters something I don't understand under his breath as he gets out. She steps out, too. Their doors close with a metallic clunk, leaving me alone. They walk to the front of the car, talking. The parking-lot lights are bright enough to outline them in an amber glow. Like halos. I think about my earlier thought, about how the complications are becoming harder and harder to control, and I want to take it back. I'm glad they're here, these two odd people who have determined I'm worthy of their time and efforts. Unexpected angels, for sure. Even in their impatience, as they bend to look at me in the car and make hurry-up gestures, wondering why I haven't come out.

COOLING GLASS

"Done," Mia says, sliding the balcony door closed and joining me at the railing. "But wow, does it feel weird leaving my phone out there, hidden or not."

She went down to stash her phone in a park across the street from the apartment complex. Aunt Viv's idea. Just in case Mia's parents contacted the police, who'd track her phone before doing anything else. I offered to accompany Mia down, but she said no. Insisted, in fact. Telling me I needed plausible deniability, like we were sneaking state secrets out of the White House itself.

"Did you see anyone?" I ask.

"No. Still felt like there were a thousand eyes on me, though. Gal's out?"

"On the couch. Snoring about five seconds after he turned off the light."

Mia laughs. "Must be the weed cookies. Too tired to smoke, maybe."

"He did drive the whole way."

"He's good people."

"Quite the little crew we make. Noor, too."

"Our very own miniature UN."

"I'm not sure she got the memo that you two aren't close friends."

Mia smiles. "Sometimes my skin is thicker than it needs to be. There aren't too many Muslim girls in our sport."

Noor and Mia could be sisters, they're so similar. They look like they were cut from the same tree, raised from the same seed. The hardest wood. Grown for putting strong people down.

"Who's better, you or her?"

"She is, big time. Same weight class, but older. Smarter. Kicks my ass all over the mat every single time."

"Nice of her to let us stay."

"I actually laughed at her when she offered: 'If you're ever in Windsor …' I feel bad about that now."

"Does she have family?"

"In Toronto. She left them to come out here. College wrestling, full scholarship. She's that good."

You're that good, I almost say. But don't. Saving myself from a further layer of something embarrassing.

We lean on the railing and fall into a comfortable silence. Suburban Windsor lies before us, a spread of low buildings, yellowish street lamps, stoplights, and business signs. We're only eight floors up, but from here we can look out across the uniform roofs of a dozen master-planned communities and feel like we're in a skyscraper. Jesse and I climbed higher hills together, but this is the first time I've been in a building with more than a few floors. It's dizzying, being so high.

My house is out there. Our house. The home Mom and Jesse and I made. I can't see it in the street-lit darkness, but it's just south-southwest from where I stand, about five minutes away. And the school is another five minutes beyond that. I could find my way to both places with my eyes closed, but I won't go back. Ever. From the porch of our Windsor home, you can see the front doors of the houses where three dead kids used to laugh and yell at their parents. None of the wounded were from our street. Just the dead. I'm glad we arrived at night.

"Did you power off?" I ask.

"Huh?"

"Your phone. Down there."

Aunt Viv told us that powering off would make it even harder for the police to triangulate. "And make sure you stash it somewhere other than where you're staying," she said.

"Oh. Right. That's an affirmative, Agent Sims."

"Mia …"

"Right. No real names. You can be Agent Smith. Like in —"

"*The Matrix.*"

"You know it? It's kind of old school."

"Yep."

"I like that you know it."

I blush. And blush more when I realize it. And even more when I realize there's just enough light reflected onto our faces from the city below that Mia can see me. She giggles and kisses me on the cheek. Which of course, makes my face bloom even more.

She goes into a two-sided recitation of some of the lines from the movie, asking herself if she can dodge bullets and then telling herself when the time comes she won't have to. She laughs. I don't. I feel my blush cooling, fading to pale. Bullets in movies don't do the things real bullets do. And there's no supernatural dance around them. What they find, they destroy. It's that simple.

So instead of talking, I pull out the small phone Aunt Viv bought for me and power it on. I watch the screen brighten and the wireless bars dance as they search out the nearest tower. "It's a burner," she said. "We're safe for texting or calling, and you can use the GPS. No email or social media, though. Those are beyond my immediate, uh, powers." She has an identical device. Untraceable. "Can't very well have you using my real number, can I?"

The phone chimes as it connects. Text from Aunt Viv.

— Let me know when you arrive

I tap out a quick response.

— windsor

She responds in precisely fifteen milliseconds.

— Good. All clear here too
— sean?
— Clueless. The perfect crime

A smile at her choice of words sneaks onto my face.

— i bet

— ;) You ok?

— i think so

— ...

— well maybe a bit nervous

— Ok. (I would be, too.) G'nite

There's no reason to text more. Aunt Viv does not do extended goodbyes. Hates them, in fact. She railed about it just the other day after running an errand. Acted it out.

"They stand there right in the store, gushing over each other's farewells like they mean something. Like they're not going to see each other two minutes later in the car. 'No, you say goodbye.' 'No, *you*.' (Insert awkward, pregnant pause by both parties.) 'I was waiting for you!' 'And I was waiting for *you*!' (Insert giggles.) 'Okay, now really, you say goodbye.' 'No, *you*!' And so on. People are pathetic."

I slip the phone into my pocket.

Mia is watching. "You got so quiet before Viv's text arrived. Did I say something wrong?"

"No."

"Are you sure? I feel like I messed up somehow."

"It was just your words. Normal words. I'm just unprepared for them sometimes."

Her eyes get wide. "It was *The Matrix* scene, wasn't it?"

"Yeah."

"I'm so sorry."

I shrug. "You couldn't know."

"Does it happen often? Where you get sad, I mean?"

"It's not sadness!"

I say it too quickly. Too sharply. And I can see it on her face. When you speak like that, it stretches out before it's ready and becomes brittle. Like molten glass cooling into shape too quickly. It'll break if you don't ease some warmth back into it.

"No, wait," I say. "I am sad, of course, for everything we lost, but what hits me is more of a darkness. A shutting down, if that makes sense. And yeah, it happens often enough. You saw it the other day."

"Have you talked to anyone about it?"

"Not since leaving here. The school board had counsellors everywhere. For a little while, anyway."

"How was that?"

I pause, considering. You get this sense that there are all these people who want to help, but in the end, they weren't there. They haven't lived what you've lived. They haven't seen death like you've seen it. Counsellors all over the place for a few days. Daily sessions in offices far removed from the school. Then dwindling to once a week. Too big to imagine, much less fix. No one gets that. Every survivor will stay broken forever.

I wonder if Mia only wants to hear the good stuff. The TV news stuff. That I'm grateful for the help. One day at a time. Community heals. #windsorstrong #istandwithwindsor #neverforgotten. The stuff that makes politicians feel better about taking money from gunmakers. That kind of thing. Or maybe she doesn't — maybe she wants the truth.

"Useless," I say.

"For real?"

I nod. "It's not their fault. People think you can fix anything if you talk about it enough."

"You can tell me anything."

"I know."

Next comes the urge to call Mom. Surprising and not surprising all at once, out of nowhere but right inside me the whole time. I can feel the burner phone's warmth against my leg. It would be so easy to tell her I'm all right. I left a note saying I was meeting Mia in the park, but she'll have noticed I'm not home by now. She'll be carrying the worry as fully as she does everything else.

"What about your mom? Do you talk to her?" Mia asks, like she can reach into my mind with one of her strong, calloused hands and grab what I'm thinking. Turn it over. Inspect it for a while.

"I can, but we don't. Not much, anyhow. It's hard for her. She gets torn between loving Jesse and what everyone thinks about him."

"Like you do, too."

"For her it's multiplied by, like, a thousand. Because they're married. And Jesse is just —"

I pause, cutting off my own voice, feeling horrible about what was about to come out.

"Just what?"

"I was going to say *just* my stepdad, but —"

"Jesse was more than that."

"*Is* more than that. He's always been there, right from day one."

"I thought he and your mom got married after you were born."

"They did. They met while she was pregnant with me, though."

"By someone else."

I nod. "Jesse was on leave and met Mom, love at first sight, all of that. She told him about the baby. He said he was 'so rocked by her' he didn't care. He didn't drink for the rest of his leave so she wouldn't feel uncomfortable."

"To respect the pregnancy. Wow."

"Right? That's the Jesse I know. I know what happened at Windsor. I know he did it. But it wasn't him. Mom has tried to tell that story. I've tried, too, but —"

"No one wants to hear it."

"No one wants anything to do with it."

"Thank you for telling me."

"Thank you? You're thanking me? For —"

Well. That shatters me into a million and four pieces, and my voice hitches. I am that thin strand of cooling glass after all. Being thanked for sharing a bit of myself is enough to break me. It shouldn't be. My glass core should be vaulted in tempered steel rather than this delicate, fragile thing we call a body. Not defeated by a simple *thank you*, much less being thanked for being honest about a guy who made everything so dark and wrong but who built me up with such strength and light. Like I could be anything else. Because of him.

I open up for the first time since I was a kid. The flood we all hold back, every day, set loose on that balcony. Big and messy and raw. With the girl I'm crushing on resting at the railing beside me and watching the same city and not saying another word. Or doing anything you'd expect if you've watched anything on TV or online or in a theatre or anywhere at all. No hugs or kisses or attempting to say the right thing. You'd think it was an effed-up scene in the most effed-up, unsatisfying movie. Unless you were me, ugly-weeping for the mass murderer no one understands like you do. You'd be thankful for the space. And maybe a calloused hand on a shoulder. Warm and strong. Again.

JUST FINE

The next morning I sit at the kitchen table, staring at the massive breakfast Noor has loaded onto our plates. Eggs, beans, toast, fruit. Bowls of muesli and containers of yogurt, too. Noor and Mia eat like they're bulking up, chatting between mouthfuls. In English now, maybe for my benefit. Memories of holds, pin-downs, wins, almost-wins. Gal eats slowly but steadily, in silence. Everyone is up early. Visiting hours still a couple of hours away. My stomach has shrunk itself to the size of a marble. Two sips of orange juice and I feel like I've feasted.

Mia and I talked until well past midnight, then fell into a comfortable kind of quiet, watching the city and listening to a line of distant thunderstorms that never reached us. Then a quiet goodnight. Mia in the guest room and me on an air mattress on the living room floor, kept company by Gal's snoring. No attempt to sneak into the guest room to try anything more than what happened on the balcony. Content to rest, knowing about the big day ahead and that we'd be facing it together. Neither of us with the desire to talk all night or make out or get into trouble. Smashing teenage clichés by the dozen.

I can't look at this food any longer. I stand and excuse myself to the bathroom, leaving my heaping plate untouched. I lock the door and lean against it, drawing a long, deep breath. To still myself against the nerves and energy that are building.

Please come. I need you.

"I know!"

Jesse's voice is a surprise. My response too loud, too sudden. I hear Mia calling to me down the hall and asking if I'm all right. Me yelling back that I'm fine.

Come, Dills.

"As soon as I can, Jesse," I whisper. "Promise."

Noor has stacked clean towels on the vanity and triangled a couple of washcloths on top. A bowl next to the sink holds a motley assembly of wrapped hotel soaps and tiny shampoo bottles. There are a few new toothbrushes and travel tubes of toothpaste, all still in their packaging. Flourishes of unexpected hospitality. I run the shower full blast, steam quickly filling the small space, and step into the spray. It's too hot for comfort, but it feels right, too, the scalding water scouring my pores. I changed after work yesterday but putting clean clothes on a dirty body is like painting an old wall without stripping it first. All grit and flaking paint.

My clean skin feels like a kind of armour against the day ahead, too. I'm going back. Back to the hospital, where I was bathed in the sights and smells and sounds of an unimaginable aftermath. Where I really noticed the stains for the first time, the blood and the other things I can't mention even to myself. The stains I know are still there, just under my skin. This time, I'll arrive clean. Clean enough, maybe, to keep at least some of the worst of it from sticking to me again.

When I emerge from the bathroom a short time later, my skin singing and red, Noor and Mia are in the kitchenette, scraping and rinsing and stacking the breakfast plates. Still talking as though they're the only ones in the apartment. Gal is a shadow through the balcony-door curtain. There is the faintest smell of weed smoke. All is calm. I feel a sudden peace. And sudden hunger. I grab an apple and a small container of yogurt and sit at the table, watching Mia and Noor enjoy each other's company.

"So, what is the plan?" Gal asks when he comes in a few minutes later, closing the balcony door.

"Aside from being at the hospital for visiting hours," I say, "I don't have a plan, not really."

Gal grabs an apple and bites into it, waiting for me to say more.

"I was going to wait and see. I don't know what to expect."

"Will they allow you to see him?"

"I'm family, so —"

"But not blood family."

The wind leaves me. That's true. How, in all the time I've spent thinking about and agonizing over this, has that not occurred to me? Different last names. Nothing to prove that Jesse has been a part of my life from breath number one. No photos, appropriately linked ID, records of any kind, nothing the hospital would take as proof. Shit.

"Well, we're here now," Mia says, stepping out of the kitchenette and wiping her hands on a dishtowel. "Let's just go. There's no crime in trying."

"This is true," Gal says.

Noor says something about having to work later and doing a dark load downstairs in the laundry room and us staying as long as we want, then disappears. She emerges carrying a cracked beige laundry basket filled past the brim with tumbled clothing. Grabs her keys and walks out. Mia stretches high and rolls her shoulders and walks down the hall to the bathroom. The dull hiss of the shower bleeds through the door.

I dig the burner phone from my pocket to check the time. A splash of green. A text from Aunt Viv, time-stamped early.

— Good luck today. I hope you find some answers or closure or whatever
— thx. still good on ur end?

I wait a long moment for a response, but there's nothing. I put the phone down to find Gal looking at me. His scars and his expression are impossible to ignore. Or to remain silent around. The ultimate truth serum.

"I feel like I need to say something to Jesse, but I don't know what."

"You will."

"There's no playbook for this. I'm —"

"You speak well. You are intelligent and kind. You love him, yes?"

The flood of affirmation stuns me so much that all I can do is nod. These are not compliments. Gal is not a complimentary person. His words are always measured out as precisely as marijuana from a government pot shop. But I guess he's seen something in me. Jesse would probably like him. *Will* like him. I can picture them sharing a joint in the park and trading bits of army wisdom. *Hurry up and wait. Embrace the suck. Watch your six. Gotta live the dream, troop.* They wouldn't trade war stories, though. They're not like that.

"I have heard you speaking with him. In the forest."

"You're kidding."

"I wondered who would receive such careful words. But now I know your story."

"How much did you hear?"

"Enough. I may be deaf in one ear, but my other hears a lot."

Have you ever been around a person but kind of tuned them out to background noise? Gal is like that. He's a constant presence, but for some reason I never thought of him as an active one. Even after Pat's attack. Gal was just there to help. More than convenient, to be sure, but I still haven't allowed myself to think of him as having a part in this weird play I'm staging.

"Thank you again for helping me the other day. When Pat ambushed me."

"He is a small boy with small ideas. It was necessary."

"Maybe, but all I did was tell you not to tell anyone. I should've thanked you. And trusted you."

A dismissive wave. "It was nothing."

"Tell me what?"

Mia's voice, sudden enough to make both Gal and me jump a little. She has padded to the kitchen, soundless in bare feet. Her hair is a wet, spiky mess. A small canvas bag, which I hadn't noticed either on the drive or on our way into Noor's apartment, rests under her arm. A change of clothing. Of course. She's in fresh shorts and a new tank top, making me feel grubby by comparison. Me focused on the destination. Mia planning the journey.

I hesitate, but Mia's looking at me patiently, like I could admit I torture kittens and she'd still hear me out before passing judgment. So I tell her about Pat and his attack, feeling the tiniest bit embarrassed that I have that kind of story to tell at all. Another one to add to a pile that's already too tall for someone my age. She glances down at the bandages on my wrist, now a couple of adhesive strips covering the lesions that haven't fully healed. I must scratch them in my sleep. Her eyes narrow when I tell the part where Pat unzips his fly and pisses on me, where Gal arrives almost in time. Mia looks ready to run back to Hamilton to find Pat and put him down for me. Pin him. Grind him into his very own patch of the greasiest poison ivy.

"Why didn't you tell me?"

It should be obvious. Shame and pride and the last piece of embarrassing teenage guyhood I'd want anyone to know about. Bad enough that Gal had to rescue me. But I don't say those things. I shrug.

Then Mia does another unexpected thing. She steps close and puts one arm around me, the other holding her bag. It is the perfect pressure, soft but strong and warm. No one else gets these kind of hugs, I'm sure. My embarrassment melts into her and is gone by the time she releases me and nods at Gal.

"Thanks for being there," she says to him.

Like claiming me in her own way. The good kind of possession.

Gal's face twitches into a scarred lightning smile before returning to neutral. He moves to the front hall and pockets his wallet and keys. Just as he bends to put on his shoes, Noor returns, nearly knocking the door into him. They perform an awkward dance in the tiny hallway, trying to manoeuvre around each other and uttering low words of apology in Arabic, back and forth. They both laugh, honest and unselfconscious. There is a moment of eye contact. Slight smiles are exchanged. A spark of something.

I stare. I've never thought about his age. He's Gal. Too wise and world weary to be bothered by the sudden pinch of attraction. Old. Scarred. Half-deaf and broken. I've only seen him based on his appearance and the history of violence he carries. I open my mouth to say something, maybe a too-late apology, but Mia nudges me before I can. Through her pleased, I'll-take-credit-for-this-introduction look, her eyes tell me to keep quiet, to let the moment play out. Not about me. Right.

The moment ends, transitioning back to our previously scheduled momentum. Mia and I move toward the door, to our shoes, and toward the big out-there questions that still need to be answered. Noor steps aside as we ready ourselves to go.

"Good luck today," she says.

"Thanks."

That's all I get out. I was hoping to thank her for letting us stay. Not a prepared speech, but for sure more than a single mumbled word. You do that when people offer something of themselves to make your life easier. I've been raised to make sure people know when they're appreciated, and I can hear Mom's and Jesse's voices in my mind, telling me to say my thanks out loud. They're both so big on generosity and gratitude. But once again I stumble on *thanks*. My new breaking word.

I can see a weight in Noor's eyes, a shadowed knowledge, and I wonder how much Mia has told her. Noor nods at me, smiles, and reaches out, pulling me into a wrestler embrace. Hard enough to squeeze some air from me. No pain, though. Just that core strength she and Mia share. She breaks off and holds me at arm's length. Looks me up and down. Finds my eyes. The shadow is gone now.

"Yeah, you'll do," she says. "You'll do just fine."

NO ACCESS

The long-term-care duty nurse sits back in her chair and folds her arms. She is all business. Short blond hair in a pixie cut. Pens secure in their sleeve pockets. A clip-on watch dangling from her shirt pocket, next to an ID card. LTC 102234 / S CRUMMEY, it says underneath a grainy photo of the nurse when her hair was longer and darker. I wonder what the *S* stands for. She's dressed in purple scrubs that wash out her already pale skin, making the dark smudges under her eyes look like bruises. Teal running shoes fringed in neon yellow. No jewellery.

She says, "There's nothing I can do."

"But —"

"Your student ID tells me you're Wendell Sims, but you don't have anything showing a relationship to the patient. Besides, he's on restricted access because of who he is and what he did."

"I'm worried about him."

"Maybe so, but we have to think about his rights, too. You could be anyone. We've had a lot of gawkers. Not so many recently, but still."

Gal steps forward. "What if I told you I was his brother, and this young man is my nephew?"

In the harsh lighting of the hospital ward, Gal's accent and appearance seem more pronounced. The nurse tilts her head and sighs. Skeptical doesn't begin to describe it.

"And you have proof?"

"Only my word."

"Do I need to call security?"

I look down the hall, wondering which room Jesse could be in. But the doors all look the same to me. I see one with a small desk beside it, a bald security guy dressed in black seated behind. That has to be Jesse's room. I want to run over and burst into the room, but the guard looks strong and fit. Not a chubby rent-a-cop, but someone who knows his job. I'd be on the ground and in cuffs in a heartbeat. But I'm so close. Too close to give up now.

I turn back to the nurse. "Jesse is my stepdad. I came all the way from Hamilton to see him."

"Look, kid."

"His middle name is Dominic."

"I'm sorry."

Her apology sounds so final. More than her previous threat to call security. Those were testing words. Not ending words, like these. So I list off every piece of information I can about Jesse. Date of birth. Our street address. His eye colour. And so on. As I speak, the nurse checks her computer records against some of what I'm saying. Confirmed. But when I describe Jesse's scars, the horrific ones he brought home from combat, I see her weakening. Too much inside knowledge to ignore.

"I know those scars," she says.

"You do?"

A nod. "Very well. Too well. He's been here a while. But we have protocols."

She doesn't reach for the phone, though. She is softening. Looking for the final reason not to send me away. I take a deep breath. "I was in the school library."

"But that's where he ..." She can't finish her own sentence. She gives me a long, searching look. Another person rendered speechless. The breath stolen from so many conversations.

"Yes."

"Oh my god." Her eyes fill. She brings her fingers up to push the brimming tears away. "I'm so sorry."

I just nod. Me, too.

"It hasn't been that long," she says, "but I guess we've all tried to move on, you know?"

"I do."

I've reached her. I don't say anything, but part of me wants to ask about her connection to the shooting. I also don't want to. You worry how you could cut into a person by asking a question.

Another nurse appears from somewhere down the ward and steps into the duty station. The two nurses could be twins, but the new one's hair is a dark pixie, and her scrubs are aquamarine. She notices our nurse wiping her eyes. "Sarah? You good?"

So. *S* is for Sarah. She looks up and tries to smile. "Fine, Teresa, thanks."

The other nurse hesitates, as though she's not quite sure if she believes her, then nods. She walks past, too fast for me to catch any of the information on her ID badge, and sits behind a nearby computer. Lost in her data entry within seconds.

Sarah tries again. "It's not about moving on, I don't think. You'd know better than anyone that's not really possible. It's more like ..."

She pauses and wrestles with something. In that pause I can hear everything around me, from the hush of the ductwork to the faint rustling of Gal's and Mia's clothes as they breathe. And this moment of clarity arrives, and the sounds from that day come back. Not the screams and the moaning, or the weeping of shattered parents and loved ones, but the regular sounds. Beeps from machines. The *skkriik!* of the mesh dividers between the trauma bays. The clicks and clunks of medical supplies on tables. The tearing of sterile packages. Urgent but calm voices. The voices of people whose job is to stitch the broken back together when the unthinkable happens.

"You were here," I say. "Afterwards."

Sarah nods. "All day and all night. We all stayed."

They stayed. And were stained, too. And came back to this terrible, hopeful place, day after day.

"I didn't know that."

"God, there were so many kids. No one could leave. But it was too much. I asked for a transfer from the ER afterwards. And ended up here."

"On this ward, of all places," Mia says.

"With Jesse," I say.

"We're supposed to think of him as just another patient."

"But he's not."

"Not even a little."

Sarah fingers her ID badge, half obscuring her photo and other information. She looks at me and smiles, her eyes squinching up, trapping the overhead lights. She tilts her head down the hallway, lifting her chin toward the security guy, who's finished his coffee. He's popped the dark brown lid from the maroon paper cup and is looking into the bottom like he can refill it if only he thinks about it hard enough.

"It's too bad, really," Sarah says.

"I'm sorry?" I ask.

"That I can't help you. That I certainly can't tell you he always leaves about five minutes after finishing his coffee," Sarah says. "Magazine in hand. Post-colic thing, I imagine."

"Post what?" Mia asks.

"Colic," Sarah repeats patiently. "Of the colon."

"He has to take a crap," I say. Mia chuckles. Jesse would call it something else. *Gotta go to the shitter, Dills. The Thunder Jug. Drop the kids off at the pool. If I'm not back in ten minutes, wait longer. Ha ha.*

Sure enough, a short while later, the guard is fidgeting in his seat. He gets up from the chair and hitches his utility belt higher, his flashlight and handcuffs and pepper spray clicking. He picks up his magazine and folds it in half, tucking it under his arm. Yawns. Starts walking.

He passes by and nods at us, just another family seeing just another patient. One of a thousand faceless people hoping to get better.

Sarah looks at the watch on her scrubs and declares she has to go check something. She rises and stands next to her colleague, pointing out something on the computer screen. Her back to us.

Permission, kind of.

"Dills, go," Mia whispers, gently pushing me toward Jesse's room. "We'll wait."

GOODBYE

There are two beds in the room. Only one of them is occupied. Jesse's army pension paying for semi-private, but the hospital unwilling to fill the other bed. Even with another paying customer. Forcing that person to recover next to a mass murderer. Someone with loved ones who'd visit. Where would they stand? Where will *I* stand?

I close the door behind me and move deeper into the room, forcing myself to walk rather than run. The horizontal blinds on the window are partially closed. The divider between the beds is drawn partway, obscuring Jesse's bed from the hall, the curtain's gaudy peach and dusty blue further dimming the light into a depressing blush. The smell is depressing, too. A stale mix of floor wax, disinfecting agents, hand sanitizer, urine, and something dank underneath it all. There is a rhythmic sound of air moving in and out. Ventilator. My anticipation fades, the smells and sights and sounds unexpectedly bringing me lower.

I step past the divider.

You're here. Finally.

"I'm here, Jesse."

My voice is barely a whisper. Not to be stealthy, or because of that strange reverence you adopt when you encounter sleeping people in hospitals. My throat has constricted itself. There is truth to what people say when you're about to witness the horrific:

> Prepare for the change.
> Nothing can prepare you.
> You might not know the person in front of
> you.

This is not Jesse. Jesse is a stocky guy, of a height you'd forget but strapped in muscles you'd remember. He takes a hard life seriously. He kept his form after leaving the military. He stayed ready. I'm supposed to be looking at hands that can skin a bush rabbit without a knife. Baseball forearms. A body as thick and cut as a fighting dog's. Not an ounce of fat anywhere. Mom will joke with him about it, pinching her own waist and trying to get a grip on his. "You can have some of mine," she'll say. He'll grab her close and kiss her neck, making her squirm but also giving her more chances to try to grab his skin. "You know I love every inch and pound of you," he'll say before she slaps him and tells him never to be so specific about a girl's weight. Mom never refers to herself or other women as girls, only women. But she lets herself think of herself as one around him.

This is someone else. Under the thin sheet I can see that there's nothing left. A skeleton wrapped in paper-thin skin, faintly yellowing. A couple of taped-down IV tubes look like they have barely enough vein and flesh to be secured to.

And this face isn't Jesse's. It isn't anyone's. It's a mess of cavities and pits and scars where his smiles and frowns and laughter used to live. Holdout wounds that have refused to heal. No mouth. No nose. Eyes sutured closed. A breathing tube sewn into his throat, space-age whites and blues against the jaundice of his face. A couple of small bandages are stuck at the top and bottom of what's left. All this damage by his own hand as the police closed in. He kept one round for himself. Maybe the monster everyone thinks he is.

Stay. Please.

His voice is pleading, strained, like he's worried that my heart will propel me out of here.

I stay. I stand for a long time, listening to the air get pushed into him and drawn out again. Watching the machines and their polite LED lights. Tracking where all the cords and tubes go. Trying to decipher the mystery numbers and bars and lines on all those screens. Do they predict how long he'll hold on? Ten minutes? Thirty? A week?

All this time I've been holding on to nothing. Like a disappearing breath in the cold. I've been cultivating his voice in my head and his memories in my brain and the idea of what he still might be. But this is not someone who intends to wake up. There's nothing left to support a life. Nothing to recover. No justice. Not even a trial, a formal pageant in advance of a preordained verdict. No chance at redemption, even for the only person who refuses to hate him. Restoration. Reconciliation.

"You never meant to come home, did you?"

My voice sounds like I've swallowed a handful of sand. Why did I say that? As though Jesse could walk out. From the moment I saw his ruined face and wasted body, I knew my plan had to change. There can be only one destination for all of this. It was supposed to be simple. But all my simplest hopes are gone.

No regrets, kiddo. That's what he should be saying to me right now. He hates dwelling on things. He taught me about survival but he never told war stories. He didn't have to. I read online about where his unit was deployed, one of the most notorious cities in Iraq and the toughest valley in Afghanistan. They humped their gear and their hate all over hell. They spilled blood, had theirs spilled. He had to survive somehow.

I now see so clearly that when Jesse took me into the woods, it was more about movement than about being in the outdoors. "Keep moving. You can't kill what you can't hit," he told me. Hunting another way to keep form. To stay alive. On that one hunting trip, he taught me how to use a knife to dress a small deer. There was so much blood, but his expression remained calm. "Don't focus on the mess," he said. "Focus on the job. There will always be blood."

"So what happened, then?" I say. "If you had it all figured out, how could you —"

I stop. Of course I do. *Kill all those innocent people* are the words that usually come next. Unlike those who weren't there, I can't say them so easily. The faces arrive too quickly when I try. A best friend named Ethan who sat next to me in every class we shared. Teachers. Kids whose names I only know from the news. I feel bad about that, even though they were in other classes, other grades.

"Why did you come to my classroom first?"

This is the first time I've ever said those words out loud. My next question should be *Did you want to hurt me?* but I won't ask it.

I'm sorry. I don't know what happened.

I know what the first part is. It's a non-apology, where you say sorry but don't say why. Vague. Dismissive. And the next part? "Playing the memory card," Mom calls it. *What happened? Do you mean before, Jesse? After? During? To you as a person? To the dead? To those who survived and have to live with Windsor every day? Probably forever?*

"That's it? That's all I get?"

Nothing.

"Why did you ask me to come?"

Still nothing.

And so I get mad.

No, Jesse, I think. *Not after months of defending you. Reminding everyone of the way you were. Holding on to the old you, who loved me and helped me learn about things and always had an answer. Not after driving all this way because you asked me to, only to find that you aren't you anymore. That nothing more will happen because you've given up.*

I feel my hands grip the base of the bed, hard enough to be painful. I want to hit something.

"You don't need me."

My voice is no longer constricted, but low and hard. You do that to deliver the truth, even when it's the toughest kind. Jesse taught me that. "Yelling and screaming and carrying on are tools of the weak," he said. "Make *them* listen to *you*." It has to be that way because of what has to happen next. What I have to do. What he needs to hear.

"I'm done, Jesse. Don't talk to me anymore."

I reach into my pocket. I have to dig deep. I take out my great-grandpa Gene's watch, the braided lanyard making reassuring pressure points against my fingers. I unravel the braid, the strands unweaving into a kinked spray of olive-green paracord, until the watch is released. The watch goes back into my pocket. Its cracked crystal face is cool through the thin fabric. I clench the loose strands of paracord in my fist before tossing them onto the bed beside Jesse's withered leg.

My heart wants me to turn away and move back into the hallway. But I can't. For a long moment I don't understand why. Then something inside twinges about that sad little nest of paracord. It sits wrong, incomplete, on the bed and inside me. I pick it up and find I can walk out. But I don't take it with me. I drop it into the garbage on my way out. It hisses into the small white bag lining the bin and then I'm back in the hallway. I don't look back.

ARRANGED

Teresa, the other nurse, is in the hall when I emerge from Jesse's room. She glances at the clock on the wall and says something to me, but I don't hear her. I feel like I'm in a cocoon, my thoughts providing noise cancellation for everything else. I can feel myself looking dumbly at her. She smiles and points at my wrist. The bandage covering the last spots of PI rash has flapped loose. She motions me to follow her down the hall and takes me to a supply cart around a corner. She grabs some gauze and tape and an irrigation syringe and sits me on a gurney. Physically. Two hands on my shoulders. But I don't want to sit. I want to get back to Mia and Gal and get away from here.

The sound comes back as she removes my dressing. She's saying something about infection. "It'll just take a sec, hon."

"No, they're waiting for me."

Teresa looks at her watch. Frowns. I don't like that frown. Why the urgency? I get up, pushing her restraining hand away.

"Please sit. I don't want —"

"I have to go."

When I round the corner, there is a constellation of flashes, spotting my vision. Cameras? A bunch of voices swell and there is movement beyond the orange spots burned into my retina. I'm surrounded. Reporters and photographers. Normal-looking people holding cameras and phones and shouting questions at me. Shouting my own name at me. How did they get that? No one knows I'm here. More flashes. One constant bright light. That must be a video camera. I try to look beyond the gaggle for Mia and Gal, but I can't find them.

I feel a firm hand holding my bicep and trying to guide me. I'm annoyed — what's with everyone trying to move me where they think I should be going? — but the flash of purple in my peripheral vision feels familiar. Purple scrubs. Sarah. She leans in and speaks loudly in my ear. Says Teresa's name and drops an F-bomb and tells me she didn't know the media had been called. She moves toward a glassed-in room across the hall and slides open the door. All the blinds are drawn. Gal and Mia are inside.

One of the photographers tries to get an arm in and snap some blind photos, but Gal grabs the arm and slams it upward. The camera doesn't break, but there's a squeal of pain from outside. The arm and camera pull back.

Sarah slides the door closed and leans against it. "Shit."

Mia rushes over and gives me a great big hug. Doesn't speak, just holds on like there's no one else in the room. Gal and Sarah don't say anything either. I can hear the clamour outside. The reporters are actually yelling questions through the sliding glass door.

"They won't come in," Sarah says. "Privacy laws. It's illegal to open a closed hospital door without permission."

"What's going on?" I ask. "Why are those —"

"The other nurse called them while you were with Jesse," Mia says.

"I'm so sorry," Sarah says. "Teresa must've figured she could make a few bucks."

"I don't understand."

"You're the Windsor Shooter's son," Sarah says, "and you came here. That doesn't happen every day."

"Stepson," I say.

"Still …"

Sarah doesn't finish the thought, but of course she doesn't have to. My presence is unusual. I might've been avoiding it all summer, but for everyone else it's an exciting development in a near-dead story. Everyone gave up on Jesse a long time ago.

"That doesn't make what she did all right," Mia says.

"Of course it doesn't. I'm sorry," Sarah says again.

"You don't need to apologize," I tell her. "Thanks for helping me."

"Did it help? Your visit, I mean?"

"I don't know yet. It wasn't what I expected."

She nods. "That's not unusual on this floor."

"And thanks for this, too. Helping all of us."

"It's the least I can do. I feel terrible. We take privacy so seriously." She sighs. "Or we're supposed to, anyway."

"Will you get in trouble for this?" I ask.

"Probably not. Well, maybe. But I'll be fine. What do I pay union dues for if not for situations like this, right?" She laughs for a split second before cutting herself off. Shakes her head as though she can't believe that came out of her in this moment. Adrenalin. I get it.

"How do we get out?" Gal asks.

Sarah moves past us and to the back of the room. Waves her ID badge in front of a small, nondescript box on the wall. The back wall, another sliding door, opens with a hiss. "Go this way. There's an elevator down the hall that can take you to the parking garage."

"What about the reporters?" Mia asks.

"This area is staff only. It's how patients from the different floors get moved around for tests, surgery, that kind of thing. No one will hassle you."

Gal moves into the hallway. I almost pause to thank Sarah again and to wish her well, but Mia takes my hand and leads me out before I can. More leading when I'm not sure I want to be led. But I let her. The door slides closed behind us.

The ride down to the parking garage feels slow, like an hour passes before the doors open into the exhaust-smelling gloom. I worry about reporters staking out the car, but no one's around when we get there. Gal gets out his keys and clicks open the doors as soon as the car comes into view. The horn beeps and the yellow hazards flash in the low fluorescent lighting. The car next to ours is still warm, clicking and muttering as its engine cools down.

Inside Gal's car we sit and stare out the front windshield. No speaking. No need to. We can hear our breathing. You forget about real silence until you find it again. Everywhere else is noise and motion.

TOLD

It's so bright outside. Emerging from the parking garage to the main parking lot feels like I'm seeing sunlight for the first time. Gal pulls a warped pair of sunglasses from behind the sunshade and puts them on, and Mia draws a grubby hat down low. It's creased and folded, and I wonder how long it's been in Gal's footwell. There's nothing for me. All I can do is hold my hand up to shield my eyes.

We leave the hospital grounds without incident. All seems normal. No TV-satellite trucks fringe every foot of the perimeter, no police cruisers block the entrances and exits, no family cars are parked at panicked, crazy angles. Not like last time, when Mom was finally allowed to drive me home. I look back at the building, brilliant white against the sky, and realize for the first time that Jesse would've already been there as I was leaving. He tried to kill himself precisely forty-nine minutes after the first shots were fired. *Fo-wer-niner mikes after the first rounds went downrange*, he'd say, exaggerating the words. *Fo-wer* for *four. Niner* for *nine. Mikes* for *minutes*. To sound clearer on a military radio. It was hours before things were settled and documented and straightened out enough to let the survivors leave, so he was definitely there. Rushed in on a gurney like all the others. Alive and worth saving. His own piece of the commotion he created. I wonder sometimes how he could've messed up his own death. He should have known better, right?

"We will need to find a mechanic," Gal says.

"I just want to go," I say.

"The spare will not make it all the way back to Hamilton."

Mia pulls out her phone. Opens Google Maps for a nearby mechanic. They argue about near or far, small mechanic or franchised tire specialist. Gal only trusts the independents. Mia says that speed is important and also that the franchise will probably have the tire in stock. Gal reluctantly concedes the point. Mia turns and gives me an impish thumbs-up. Smug victory. I try to smile back. I probably look like a gargoyle. They decide on a place out in the suburbs.

As we drive, I pull out my burner phone to text Aunt Viv.

— all done
— And?
— it was weird
— I bet
— everything ok at home?

There is a brief pause. It feels like forever before her text arrives.

> — Dills, your mom was beside herself last night so I told her. I know I said I wouldn't but I had to
> — told her what?
> — Everything

I begin and delete a dozen replies. Between the hospital media ambush and now worrying about Mom, what's happened seems too big for texting. I should call Aunt Viv. But I'd have Gal and Mia listening on my end, and I'm not sure I'm ready to talk about it. I should definitely call Mom. The acid heat of guilt rises in my gut and I don't know what to do with it.

> — ?????

Aunt Viv is impatient as I type and delete and type and delete. Probably wondering if I'm writing a novel. She deserves more. Mom deserves a hell of a lot more. And yet I'm not there.

> — we'll be home in a few hours

As soon as I hit Send I power off the phone. I hope she's not too pissed about my lack of response. I hope she's staying close to Mom.

I slide the phone into my pocket and look out my side, watching the traffic get lighter as the city thins into its outskirts. Gal and Mia are chatting in Arabic now, punctuated by brief laughs and groans. Reliving the hospital in a language I can't understand. I don't mind, though. I let the now familiar but unknowable sounds wash over me and lean my head against the window. The safety glass is warm from the sun. I close my eyes and try to make sense of what's happened as the highlight reel of the trip and my summer and everything rushes past my eyelids.

LOVELY

I don't know I'm sleeping until potholes in the tire place's parking lot knock my head against the window and wake me up.

LIGHTNING TIRE & LUBE
while u wait!!

A compromise. An independent tire specialist. I almost smile.

"Hey, Dills," Mia says.

"Hey."

"You sacked out pretty hard."

"I guess I needed it."

The lot is empty. There's a small sign between the service bays that tells us to park there and honk the horn, so we do. The garage door trundles up on its guides and a small, wiry guy walks to the driver's-side door, wiping his hands on a rag. His skin is so brown, it's almost black. Stained red hat. Navy-blue coveralls that look bright next to his skin. Stitched to the chest is a white Lightning Tire & Lube patch fringed in red.

"Leave the keys in the ignition. Oil change is twenty minutes or so. You can wait in the waiting room."

"No oil change," Gal says. "We need a new tire. We are running on the spare."

"No problem, sir. That'll be a bit longer, maybe thirty minutes." He kneels and checks out the spare on the back left and scans the rest. "You'll want to change both right and left in the back, though, if not all four."

They go back and forth about brands and styles and prices. Gal settling on a mid-range pair of all-seasons for the rear that sound so expensive to me. I again have the empty urge to offer repayment, but this time say nothing. Gal holds out a hand, which the guy takes, looking pleased at the formality of a handshake to seal the deal.

He says, "I'll put the new ones on the front, rotate the others to the back. Okay?"

"You can do all of this in thirty minutes?"

He flashes a smile. "Twice, if I had to."

"All right."

We all step out of the car and the guy slides in, moves the seat forward a few inches, puts the car into gear, and zips into the bay. Like it's all one motion. No hesitation. No brake lights until the car stops in its spot above the mount.

The waiting room is a small rectangular space. The front window of the store is to our back as we enter. A TV blares high in the corner, angled toward the chairs lining two of the walls. A table under the window warms in the dusty sun, bearing the weight of a space-age espresso machine, an untidy spread of old magazines, and a wobbly rack of pamphlets and promotional material. A customer service counter divides the space between us and the service area. The door behind the counter is propped open for air movement, letting in the sounds of air tools and metal working metal. Just past the smell of oil and hydraulics and metal is the burnt smell of old coffee.

A young woman, maybe university age, sits behind the counter, clicking around on the computer there. She doesn't look up as we enter. A single other customer, a tanned man in a camouflage T-shirt, sits in a far chair. A matching ball cap pushes down on his impossibly blond hair, which sticks out like a scarecrow fringe. Though he's sitting, I can tell he's a big guy. He looks folded into the chair like clothing into too-small luggage. His eyes are glued to the TV. Some twenty-four-hour news channel, a clash of traffic cams and anchors and news tickers and weather icons. Every element screaming, *Look at me!* It hurts my eyes, so I sit in one of the free chairs and look at the framed tire posters hung wherever there's a few square feet of wall space. Mia sits next to me, Gal in the next chair down.

I think about Jesse. It's the pause that lets it happen. The waiting. Gal closes his eyes, patient as a park bench. Mia has her phone out and is scrolling through email or something. So normal. I feel normal, too, and that makes me uncomfortable. I've taken in the wasting body of my stepdad, a guy I've defended and puzzled over for months, but I don't feel anything. I've said goodbye, but it doesn't seem like a farewell. No telling how much longer he'll live, so my visit and my words are probably meaningless. Like a handful of water poured into a Cootes Paradise creek in the hopes of freshening Lake Ontario, absorbed long before reaching the marsh, much less the lake beyond. I'll never know.

I pull out my phone and power it on to send a text to Aunt Viv about the delay, but decide not to. What's thirty minutes when she doesn't know our specifics anyhow? The phone's screen brightens and urges me to swipe in. I wait for Aunt Viv's delayed texts to arrive, but there's nothing. Maybe she understands why I didn't respond. But if she told Mom everything, there's no reason not to have given Mom this number. I should see a cascade of worry in the register, red letters and numbers for every missed call. I should see it now and I should've seen it when I texted before. The little voice-mail icon bold and red with a number that signals Mom's level of concern.

But, no. No numbers, no cascade.

What should I do with that? Put the phone away? Stick to the plan? Realize that there's nothing to be gained from a phone call where all you can do is inevitably break the connection? There's a certain logic to that. A certain attractiveness, too, in holding on to some measure of control. I tell myself to power down again, but my fingers don't listen. They're working on my heart's instructions. *Call your mom. Now.* Driven by an image of a mother so heartbroken and betrayed she can't text or call her only child. I watch my fingers do the touchscreen dance across the familiar numbers and the phone is up and there's a ringing sound and a pickup click interrupting the second ring.

I wait for the voice. The hello. Nothing.

"Mom?"

Is there a hissing on the line, or is it my mind filling in the lack of response from her?

"It's Dills."

Still nothing.

"Say something, Mom. Please."

"Are you safe?"

"Yeah. I'm with Gal and Mia and we blew a tire yesterday and we're getting it changed somewhere out in the —"

"Stop."

"Mom?"

"That's enough."

"I saw him. I saw Jesse."

There's a deep, brief moan on the other end of the line.

"He looked so different. He —"

"Please stop. I can't. Not now. I'm glad you're safe. But, Dills, I just can't."

And the click on the other end of the line is so final and dreadful that it must have filled the room. Gal and the other guy haven't moved. I lower the phone and look at Mia. She's watching me but not saying anything. I hear myself saying that I called my mom as if Mia didn't already hear everything on my side. That she hung up.

"I don't know what to do with that," I say.

"It's a lot to process."

"I need to get out of here. Walk, maybe."

We rise from our seats, pocket our phones, and step toward the door.

"Do not go too far, please," Gal says as we pass, not moving, eyes still shut tight.

Mia and I reply in unison that we won't. We glance at each other and walk out, the cheerful bells above the door signalling our arrival back into the world. Like we've been delivered by reindeer and sleigh. I swear they didn't ring when we came in.

Mia sets her phone's timer to ten minutes, a signal to turn around. I love that. It's the kind of detail only she could bring into the situation. I hear myself ribbing her about it. As another diversion from the strangeness of the day, I suppose. She's a good sport about it and gives back as well as she gets. Better, in fact. We're actually laughing when her alarm sounds.

"Thanks," I say. "I needed this."

"Me, too. I'm glad to be here, but it's quite a ride."

We turn and walk for a few steps. I breathe deep and shake my head. "I'm worried about Mom. She sounded so shattered by this. What if —"

Mia stops me with a kiss. She literally steps in front of me and halts my forward momentum with her hands on my shoulders. Gentle but with that bear strength behind them. She rises on her toes and plants her lips on mine, firm and warm and dry. My body is suddenly drawing in all the inertia from every car that passes, the sun, the turning of the planet. I want to wrap her up in me and carry the kiss to where kisses like that always suggest you go. But she breaks away and drops down to her heels, her eyes sparking. She moves a single finger to her lips like she wants to gauge the heat there. I haven't even moved my arms from their dumb place at my side.

"You're lovely," she says.

"Oh. Uh, thanks."

"You should've seen your face when you talked about your mom. Sweetest thing I've ever seen."

"Sometimes I think she won't make it through all of this."

Mia shakes her head, looking at me with a kind of wonder. "You survived the shooting — I can't imagine what you've had to carry — but you're more worried about her. Call me cheesy and Hallmark, but with you on her team I think she'll do fine."

"I have to tell her about Jesse. She won't be ready."

"You're a good son, Dills. Wow."

"Aside from running away and not telling her."

"Sure. And the LoJack and breaking the conditions of your sentencing."

"Right. And those."

We grin, shaking our heads at the impossibility of everything, and resume walking. On the way out, we watched the landscape change, from the tire place nestled among low strip malls, industrial buildings, gas stations, and fast-food joints, to the faceless rows of identical houses that surround us now. New pavement. Tiny trees and brand-new sod, the edges browning. Big SUVs in every driveway.

Mia and I walk back to the tire place, talking quietly, just loud enough to hear each other over Saturday traffic, a pair of teenagers no one looks twice at.

RECOGNITION

When we get back, the car has been backed out of the bay and is idling in the lot. Inside, Gal is leaning against the counter, signing the work order. The mechanic stands behind the young woman at the desk with keys in hand, ready to hand them over. Without taking her eyes from her computer screen, she slides the credit card terminal over to Gal, who pays by chip and secret number.

The mechanic drops the keys into Gal's hands. "You serve?"

Gal turns his good ear toward the guy. "I am sorry?"

"The pattern of your scars. Sprayed. Like from a blast."

"Oh. Yes. A long time ago."

"The Sandbox?"

"I am sorry?"

"Iraq? Afghanistan?"

"No. Israel."

The guy nods. "Panjwaii for me. Bunch of us came back with scars like that."

Gal nods, looking unsure what to say.

I do, though. You pick that up when you spend enough time with a vet in public. "Thanks for your service."

Jesse didn't talk about it except when the Corolla's veteran plates got noticed. Strangers pumping his hand or slapping him on the shoulder and repeating those words. He'd ask for the bill at a restaurant or arrive at the counter of the coffee shop only to find that the order had been paid for. Little handwritten notes, always anonymous. "THANK YOU FOR YOUR SERVICE." "It's embarrassing as hell, Dills. But awesome too, you know? It means something." Mom would get the same thing when she was out and about, always gently making sure that Jesse's name got mentioned. Turn the conversation back to what he gave. Lots of people shaking their heads and telling her that she served as much as anyone. Mom embarrassed by that, too, of course.

The man's eyebrows go up and he smiles. "You're welcome. Thanks for saying that."

Jesse always said "you're welcome" and "thank you," too. "Good manners are currency you can spend, kiddo," he'd tell me.

I feel Mia's hand on my shoulder. I follow her eyes to the TV on the wall. It's still muted. Bizarre watching such a familiar scene unfold like a silent film. Amid the tickers and scrolling text, the live-action frame is showing the scene in the hospital. Shaky, handheld footage. I watch myself come around the corner with the nurse who called the media. Sarah bustles me into the observation room, the camera bumping and shaking as the door slides shut. The scene cuts back to the moment I come around the corner, slowing down and zooming in, pausing on my grainy, video-stilled face. "WENDELL SIMS, SON OF WINDSOR SHOOTER." Cut back to the studio, where an anchor is speaking to the camera, serious. I imagine phrases like *moments ago* and *exclusive* and *saw it here first*. My last school photo hovers over her shoulder. Younger, chubbier, but still me.

"Shit," I say.

"Yep," Mia replies.

"I wonder who gave them that pic?"

I look over at the other customer, who's watching the TV, his face slack and passive. Something clicks. He sits upright and looks over at us. Back at the TV. At us. TV. He hikes his camouflage cap up on his forehead. In a nanosecond he has his phone out and he's typing. Then he's calling someone and watching us intently. I can almost hear the phone connecting on the other end, the news station's receptionist answering, asking how she can direct his call.

Gal's watching all of it, too. He shakes his head and says we should go. As we get into the car, the guy appears in the shop's window, now speaking into his phone. So this is what conspicuous feels like. People know you. They stare at you like they have something invested in what you do. Who you are. As we drive away, I get the tiniest glimpse of what it has taken for Mom to keep me safe and anonymous. And I feel shame that I might've made all those efforts and worries mean nothing.

SIEGE

The trip back to Hamilton feels quicker than the trip out. Gal pushes the car up past the limit, but there's something more to it. Like time has compressed. An hour in, we pull into a service centre to fuel up and take care of some basic human needs. We're almost surprised by the need to stop. The events of the morning pushing aside the urge to pee, the pang of hunger. We get our bagels and drinks to go, Gal sipping his coffee as he pulls back onto the highway, moaning about bad coffee and how sofas aren't meant for sleeping. Mia and I pass a large hot chocolate back and forth, each sip cooler than the last. I take a single bite of my bagel before spitting it out and wrapping the whole mess back in its bag.

The rest of the drive is uninterrupted. No one says much. Too much worrying about what might come next. In my case, I think about the reporters and video and my new notoriety. Mom's too, probably. And I try to imagine how I might apologize for the unforgivable.

And then we're home, driving up the main neighbourhood road and turning onto my street. Gal stops as soon as my house comes into view. Four or five shiny white vans, emblazoned with call letters and bright graphics, are parked around the house. Two of them have satellite dishes transmitting to the sky. I see a familiar blue car parked by the side door. Walters. Knowing that we only use the side door to go in and out of our house. First to arrive, I'm sure. An edge on the competition.

"That was fast," Mia says.

"Once they had my name …"

I don't finish. No need to. Simple web searches and public records and you'd land on Sims in minutes.

There's no car in the driveway. Aunt Viv's Prius still in the shop. Mom's car gone for who knows how long. Our house looks under siege.

"What should we do next?" Gal asks.

"Drop me off at the front door," I say. "Then go home."

Mia turns. "No, Dills, we should —"

"Guys, thanks so much for doing all this for me. But I have a feeling it's going to be super ugly when I walk in that door."

"We can help."

I shake my head. "I need to do this on my own."

"Are you sure?"

"No. Not of anything anymore. But at least it's just me facing the music."

"For now," Gal says.

Mia clicks her tongue behind her teeth. "Hey, come on."

"He did not drive himself, yes?"

I ask, "Gal? Mia? Trust me, okay?"

They look at each other and nod, and Mia turns to look me right in the eye. I feel pinned down in the back seat by it. Her dark eyes boring into me. Unsettling and reassuring all at once. The strength of it. Bear. Tiger. Pick your apex animal.

"Call me as soon as you can."

"I will."

I pull out the burner and text Aunt Viv.

— we're here r u home?

Her reply arrives almost before I'm finished typing.

— Yes
— unlock the front door i'm coming in
— Do you see the reporters?
— they're all watching the side should give me an extra second or two
— Hopefully!
— lol right

I slide the phone into my pocket. "Okay. I'm ready."

Gal puts the car in gear and accelerates the final distance, cutting a turn at the last second to stop at the curb closest to the front door, and I'm pulling the handle and stepping onto the sidewalk. Slamming the door. Slapping my hand on the roof to signal I'm clear. Watching Gal pull away. For a second, I can't see the circus, but Walters looks around the corner of the house, recognizes me, and holds her phone out in front, shouting a question of some kind. I realize I haven't moved from my spot. I dash up the stairs to the door. Walters's questions are pebbles launched at my back as I reach for the door handle. The rest of the reporters are behind her.

"Wendell, why did you go?"

"Wendell, how does it feel to —"

"What next?"

"Did you talk to him?"

Aunt Viv has swung open the door and stands aside as I rush in. She closes it against the cacophony of voices, which fade to dull chatter through the heavy steel. I stumble into the living room and put my hands on my knees. Maybe ten steps in total and my heart is pounding, my breath as thin as if I've sprinted a mile or a klick or something far and uphill. The hardwood floor blurs.

"Dills. You're home. Thank God."

Mom's voice. Mom's firm hands on my arms, my shoulders, lifting me upright, moving to my face, my neck, my chest, my arms again, and back to my hands. Checking for damage. My eyes clear and she's right in front of me, looking me up and down and at all points of my face, as though there's no way to focus on one. Needing to take in all of me.

"Mom, I'm so —"

One of those hands gently covers my mouth. She's shaking her head. That look is called "Don't Say a Thing Right Now, Young Man." I smell soap and skin and something rusty. Solder and flux, ground in. Committed hands. One keeping me from speaking, the other now rising up to embrace me, hard enough to steal some of the breath I've only just regained. Both are shaking. She's shaking. My eyes fill. How close I've brought her to coming apart. Like I said, she feels everything.

"The phone," she says, releasing me and stepping away. "The one Viv gave you."

"What about it?"

She holds out a hand. The other wipes away a single tear on her cheek.

Aunt Viv takes a step toward us. "Vick, he should have the chance to —"

Mom turns toward her and silences her with a look that you'd say was expressionless if you didn't see her eyes. I dig the burner out of my pocket and lay it in her hand. It's still warm. She gives it a long, accusing look and turns away, her filthy workshop shirt — one of Jesse's old Class A uniform ones, a faint green that can look white from a distance — flapping behind her as she disappears through the door that leads downstairs.

DIG

A short while later I walk up the stairs and into the living room. The noise outside has gone down. Reporters back to their places, back into siege mode. Gramma Jan has come down from her room and is sitting in the easy chair. She is pale and thin. And pissed. She's watching the front door like she could shoot fire through it. Aunt Viv has seated herself on the couch and looks up as I enter. I shake my head. Mom won't come out. She won't speak to me. She locked the door to her workshop and fired up her grinder, making conversation impossible.

"She'll be all right," Aunt Viv says. "We just have to —"

"Give her time, yeah, I know," I snap at her.

"Easy, Dills."

"Why is everything about time? Seems like there's either too much or not enough of it."

"Maybe life's biggest damn secret," Gramma Jan

says. "That and love. Regardless, you never get it back. Time, I mean. Maybe love, too."

"That's pretty dramatic, Mom," Aunt Viv says.

Gramma Jan glares at her and points. "Sit in my chair for a few days, Vivian, then we'll talk about what's dramatic."

"Okay. Sorry. It just felt extreme is all."

Gramma Jan grunts and goes back to her burning study of the door. As soon as she's sure Gramma Jan can no longer see her, Aunt Viv rolls her eyes. She doesn't seem to care that I'm in the room. That I can see her. I get this glimpse of the teenager still inside. Apologies as a selfish kind of peacemaking. I sit at the other end of the couch and settle in for a wait. Wondering how and when the waiting could end.

"I imagine you don't want to talk about it," Aunt Viv says.

"About what?"

"The trip."

I'm annoyed at the non-question. The kind of thing you say because you should, not because you want to. Half-hearted. Leading. Hard to turn around without an unnatural amount of force. *Actually, I'd love to talk about it, Aunt Viv! Why don't you put your feet up and let me tell you* all *the details!* Meh.

"I want to talk to Mom first," I say.

"That makes sense."

"It was … eventful. I can say that."

Gramma Jan snorts and stands up. Too quickly. She has to grab the back of the chair to steady herself. Her clothing — the family uniform of jeans and frayed

T-shirt — hangs on her. An unsteady scarecrow. Her face is flushed and her eyes have narrowed. An unsteady and livid scarecrow.

"That's it," she says. "This ends now."

Aunt Viv stands, too. "Mom?"

"Reporters chasing you all over like you're some wounded specimen. Following you home. Goddamn vultures."

"What're you going to do?"

"I'm going out there. Beat them off with a broom if I have to."

"I'd watch that press conference," I say. Reaching for an inappropriate levity.

Aunt Viv gives me a look. *Don't encourage her*, it says. She moves next to Gramma Jan as she reaches for the door handle and puts a hand on her mother's hand. "Stop."

"They can't treat my family this way."

"They're following the story, Mom. They'll go away if we ignore them."

"When?"

"I don't know. Not long. Surely this isn't worth more than a news cycle."

I don't think she's right, but I don't say anything. Of all of us, Aunt Viv is by far the most media savvy, so surely she knows they'll feed on this for at least a few days. The stepson of the Windsor Shooter making a pilgrimage to see his wasting father in a distant hospital? Caught on tape outside the room? Tracked home to where he and his mother have made a new, anonymous life? Rich material. It's feast or famine in the news industry, and this is at least a holiday meal. They'll gorge themselves to bursting and let the calories sustain them a while.

"I want them off my property."

"They'll go back to their spots on the road and sidewalk if no one goes out. Public property."

"It's still harassment. I should —"

"They're not breaking any laws. And it won't help, going out there, looking like —"

"Looking like what, Vivian?"

No response. Aunt Viv's intentional dangler left in the air for Gramma Jan to grab on her own. Looking like an elderly, sick, crazy woman. While Mom and I cower inside. Gramma Jan's outburst would be a delicious addition to the meal. The perfect side dish that gets praised as much as the main.

Gramma Jan frees her hand from Aunt Viv's loose grasp and opens the door a crack. Immediately, reporters fire questions through the gap, a vertical slash of diminished light. Grey clouds instead of blue sky out there. I can see Walters's bright red jacket and her blond hair. A few seconds pass, feeling like an eternity.

Gramma Jan closes the door and stands still, head down, one hand on the silver handle and the other against the doorjamb. When she turns back into the living room, she looks paler. Thinner. Defeated. She grabbed hold of what Aunt Viv didn't say. Maybe it was the sight of the reporters. Maybe the noise. Whatever it was, the realization soaked her through. That the media would insist on learning more about her. They'd scoop and dig and do what they do. And they'd find her cancer as surely as the tests the doctors did a few weeks ago. She'd become part of the story. Part of the reality she was trying to banish. Part of that sickly pot-luck that was being assembled about my family. More calories.

NO APOLOGY

It's evening now. Late. Dark outside. I'm in the kitchen, staring into the cupboards, hungry but not seeing or craving a thing. Aunt Viv leans against the counter. Mom's still in her workshop, and Gramma Jan went to bed a while ago. In the end, I told them the story. It was bursting out of me anyway. Gramma Jan tried to stay awake, but lost more colour with every passing minute. Her body pulling its limited supply of blood back to its core to combat the pain and fatigue. She stopped me as I talked about Noor's apartment, then said goodnight and eased her way upstairs. I watched Aunt Viv deflate as she watched her mother leave. She wondered out loud when they'd have to move Gramma Jan to the main floor. When the stairs would become too much. I didn't say anything. It would need to happen soon. *Way too goddamn soon*, Gramma Jan would say.

"So you and Mia …?"

"I suppose."

"*I suppose*?"

"It's good. I like her."

Aunt Viv smiles. "As your older and wiser and scary aunt, my official position is that you're too young and that no one, of course, is good enough for you."

"And unofficially?"

"I met her. She's nice. I'm happy for you."

I exhale. "I'm glad, Aunt Viv."

"Just don't rush it, okay?"

"I won't."

"Good."

There's a knock at the side door. Aunt Viv gives me a weary look and tells me to stay put and out of sight. She doesn't have to. The last thing I want is to give some eager reporter a chance to stick his camera in the door to get a picture of me like they did at the hospital. I hear the whoosh of the door opening followed by a few seconds of silence. The murmur of low voices. More silence. Then the heavy clunk of the sticky door. Aunt Viv steps back into the living room.

"He's in here," she says over her shoulder.

Sean walks in, looking like hell. Untucked shirt. Hair sticking up. Unshaven. He's removed his shoes, which Gramma Jan calls "a common-sense sign of respect," but his brown socks look worn. And they're sloppy, as if he's too tired even to pull them up after removing his shoes. This all at a glance.

I stand up out of reflex. He waves me down again and kneels on the floor next to me. He tugs on the LoJack's nylon strap, checking for extra give. For compromise. He pulls out a little black device from his pocket that looks like a beeper, holds it next to the ankle monitor, and pushes a button. Three green LEDs light up in sequence and the device in his hand emits three quiet and cheerful chimes. Satisfied, he stands and drops onto the couch next to me, tossing the device onto the coffee table.

"Okay, then," he says by way of greeting. But he's looking at Aunt Viv. Sad eyes. She's still leaning against the doorframe separating the living room from the hallway, arms folded.

"Hi, Sean," I say.

I don't say any more, aware of the delicate balance of fact and fiction that we've built around this weekend. Something is obviously making him worry about the integrity of the LoJack, but I can't guess what. Aunt Viv has been clear — there should be no anomalies in my movements to find. No digital trail.

And yet.

"So here's a little story, yeah?" he says. "There's this youth probation officer who procrastinates a lot, and sometimes has to use his Saturday mornings to get caught up on paperwork. Imagine him heading to a local café to take advantage of its excellent sausage biscuits, strong espresso, and free Wi-Fi, and imagine him ordering and sitting down. Imagine a TV on the wall, which he watches while he waits for his breakfast. And guess what he sees?"

Ah. I know where this is going.

Aunt Viv is obviously processing the same thing, studiously willing herself not to look at me. Like I'm willing myself not to look at her. But she does speak first. Maybe thinking that she can control the narrative. "What does he see?"

Sean laughs, quick and harsh. "Get this, Vivian, you'll never believe it. He sees one of his clients on the news, caught on film at the hospital in Windsor. But the youth worker thinks *That's impossible!* He'd have gotten an alarm if the client had left town. Some of his clients wear ankle monitors, yeah? So he checks his monitoring app, and guess what?"

Aunt Viv does not respond to this one.

Sean throws up his hands. "The app tells him that there's no problem, that his client hasn't gone anywhere except for a few short walking jaunts around the neighbourhood!" His voice has gone up a few levels. His eyes move between Aunt Viv and me, as narrow as toothpicks. "In two places at once! What do you make of that, guys?"

"Quite a story," Aunt Viv says.

"Oh, it is," Sean says. He snorts. "It really is."

He sits back against the couch cushions, folds his arms, and falls silent. We hear footsteps on the stairs from the basement, and Mom steps into the hall. She waits while Aunt Viv, who's still blocking the doorway, stands aside to let her in. Her eyes rest on Sean. I can see deeper shadows under her eyes. More exhaustion and weight to bear.

"Sean? What's going on?"

He gives a quicker, less sarcastic version of the story. Same result for us. Silence. But Mom hasn't been brought in, so she's confused. "I don't understand. Is there some malfunction?"

Sean points at the diagnostic device on the table. "I checked, and all's well with the equipment."

"So how can this happen?"

"That's the mystery of it, isn't it, Vivian?"

He's glaring at her again. Mom follows the look.

"Why would she have anything to do with —"

She goes quiet, too. Everyone waits. Breaths are held. Mom looks her sister in the eye, pinning her down with a scrutiny I know can melt glass. Aunt Viv tries but can't hold it. I get that feeling. You have to look away to protect your delicate insides. Mom exhales through her nostrils, an extended, low hiss of constricted air.

"You didn't," she says to Aunt Viv.

"Vick, there's no need to —"

But there's nowhere to go from there without admitting everything, so Aunt Viv stops herself.

Sean is watching all of this intently. Very, very interested. And looking more and more pissed off by the millisecond. "You screwed me, Vivian."

"Don't be so dramatic."

"I should report this."

"You do what you need to do."

"But you know that I can't —"

"As I said —"

"Because what do I show the court, yeah? The digital record? Spotless. But then they say they've seen the news. *Oh, right, that,* I say. *Well, I've been hacked.* They say, *Course you have, so let's order an inquiry.* I say, *Great. Easy.* Until they discover that I've been dating the hacker."

"I'm not a hacker."

"I can't believe you did this to us, Vivian," Mom says.

Aunt Viv winces but doesn't respond. She glances over at me. *Remember the plan*, the look says.

Mom tries to get a response out of her again and again, but still Vivian doesn't say anything. Sticking to her resolution that you can't be incriminated by something that never gets said. She folds her arms again and simply looks at the floor through the onslaught. Sean occasionally pitches in or answers a question, but I can see he's wrung out. Resigned. All he sees is a bleak, unemployed future. If not worse. He hasn't done anything other than his job, but he still got led on and used, and he'll live out the consequences.

Meanwhile the person who started it all fades away in a distant hospital bed. Jesse will never face a trial. He'll never answer for what he's done. I can't get my head around that. He was all about accountability. I remember one time when I broke a spoke on my bike trying to tighten it. I heard somewhere that you have to keep them tight, not realizing that cheap kids' bikes aren't made that way. The spoke bent and popped out and I tried to ignore it, but a bike needs every spoke to work or it limps along on a warped rim that you can't hide from anyone. "Stop," Jesse said when I tried to worm my way out of it. "Don't make it worse by lying. One, take responsibility. Two, fix what you've broken. It's that simple. Clear as mud?" But there are some mistakes that can never be fixed. Sometimes what's stolen can never be recovered.

This can't get that far. I won't let it.

I slap the coffee table with my hand and stand. The effect is instantaneous. The living room goes quiet and all eyes find their way to me. Aunt Viv sees what I'm about to do and she moves from the door, shaking her head. But I give her a look of my own, hoping it's strong enough, and she stops.

"I'm sorry," I say. "This is all my fault."

"Wait," Mom says. "Let's —"

"No, Mom. I have to own my shit."

Own your shit. Jesse's language. ("But tell your mom I said *stuff*, right?") Mom's eyes widen and shimmer. She starts to say something more but I hold up a hand.

"Visiting Jesse was my idea. I thought he wanted me to go. I had to go, too, I guess. It wasn't what I expected, but —" Then it's my eyes that are filling. The disappointment of it. The reality. I wipe my palm across my eyes and look at Mom. "It is what it is, right?"

It is what it is. More of Jesse's voice, channelled through me. Time to let go.

She nods and gives me a small, sad smile. "It is what it is."

I take a deep breath and turn toward Sean. "I went to Windsor last night."

"No kidding," he says, rolling his eyes.

"If Aunt Viv restores the system to show the trip, can you charge me properly?"

"Is she admitting that she hacked me?"

Aunt Viv glares at him but says nothing. But I don't think it matters. I can see some strength return to Sean's bearing. He's seeing a way out of this.

I say, "I'm admitting I left town. Can you charge me?"

"I don't charge anyone, remember? I'll merely report that you broke your sentencing conditions. The consequence will be up to the court, although for you I suspect it'll be just an extension, rather than escalation. You'll have to tell the judge where you went."

"And why," Mom says to me.

"I know. I'll take whatever comes."

"You must've had help," Sean says.

I look at the floor, not wanting to say anything to get Gal and Mia in trouble, but I nod. It's pretty obvious I couldn't have gone on my own. Sean waits for me to offer more, but I won't. This is on me.

I don't know how long we all stay suspended like that, between what's said and unsaid, but finally Sean sighs and sits back on the couch.

"Ah, screw it," he says. "Don't tell me. Frankly, I don't need the extra paperwork."

"Thank you."

"Don't thank me, Wendell. There are no guarantees here." A pause. "They must be some amazing friends."

"The best."

"All right," Sean says. "This stays with me and I leave them out of it. As long as the other thing is taken care of, yeah?"

"Aunt Viv? Will you do it?"

There's so much resistance in her. She scowls and spends a long time looking at the floor, her eyes darting left and right. Weighing and figuring. Finally, without looking up at anyone, she nods. Sean's relief takes him over so completely, he looks like he could cry. Seeing that perfect lack of a digital trail. Saved.

He gets up and mumbles a good night, tells me he'll see me in the morning, and walks out. I lock the door behind him, peeking through the blinds. I watch for a short while, but there's only one news truck still there. Dark. No movement. Gathering dew on the windshield. Like they've gone to sleep. But I'm sure they haven't gone away or forgotten.

When I return to the living room, only Aunt Viv remains, sitting in the easy chair with her laptop. Already immersed, her brow scrunched up in concentration. She doesn't look up but tells me that Mom has gone back to her workshop, that she's pretty upset. Proud that her kid is taking responsibility but also worried what his actions and admissions will bring down on him. I go downstairs and stand outside her door.

"Mom?"

No answer. No sounds. No light cutting under the door to tell me she's present and busy and hopefully okay.

"I'm sorry."

Still nothing. I turn and go into my room and lie down on the bed. It's not that late, but I don't want to come out again. Something in me needs to lie in the darkness without doing anything. Apart from wondering about the impossibility of doing the right thing.

ON YOUR TERMS

Before work on Monday morning, I pause on our side step before heading over to the park. I'm surprised to see that the street is empty of news people. They were there all day yesterday. I guess our story isn't important enough for constant coverage. Media owners with tight budgets, refusing overtime.

I step away from the house and head west toward the park. A now-familiar rhythm. Aside from wondering when the media circus will return, it feels like any other day in this messed-up summer. Cooler, though. The sun isn't as high. Later sunrise. For the first time, I'm wearing a long-sleeve T-shirt under my safety vest. There's a depth to the coolness. Maybe fall isn't so far away.

I didn't see Mom at breakfast. Only Aunt Viv and Gramma Jan were up, getting ready for a last-minute appointment at the hospital. Something to do with adjusting the cocktail of drugs the doctors have Gramma Jan on. She was as pale as yesterday, and there were new tremors in her hands as she tried to eat her breakfast. She had a hard time with it. Her toast shook on its way to her mouth. Aunt Viv had to peel her hard-boiled egg for her.

Behind me, there's the quick beep of a car horn. I turn to see a small silver car pull up beside the house. Must be an Uber for the trip to the hospital. Aunt Viv emerges from the house and leans into the car's window to say something to the driver. He turns on his yellow hazards. She sees me and waves before heading back inside.

I walk quickly, trying to get a little heat in my bones. The park is quiet. The sudden coolness keeping the less diehard walkers and runners away.

Sean meets me at the field house with a stack of paperwork to read. He must've been up late to get it ready so quickly. Gal is starting his day, too, but lets Sean and me use his office. There's almost no smell of weed today, as though Gal has aired the place out for us.

"I will walk now," he says, getting up from the tiny desk. "Take your time."

"Thank you," Sean says.

His words are professional but clipped as short as a brush cut. Like he's still processing his unwilling role in my production. Like he doesn't want to say too much, too soon. Like he's deciding how pissed off to be at anyone who might've been involved. After Gal steps out, Sean rushes through the formalities about my admission of guilt and what happens next, and I have to sign a few forms.

"Your mum has a few things to sign, too," he says. "I'll head over to your place next."

"She wasn't up when I left."

"Is that unusual?"

"Very. She's an early riser."

"Well, this isn't like every other day, I suppose."

Sean's voice rises lightly at the end of his statement. Almost a question but not quite. I don't respond. What would I say? I haven't seen an "every other day" for a long time. All my days seem prone to shift in unexpected directions.

He gets up and slides the paperwork back into its folder as he walks to the door. He pauses, silhouetted against the brightness of the morning.

"Vivian came through, by the way. Your trip to Windsor is clearly indicated. The chronological vectors and my lack of immediate response are anomalous enough for an investigation —"

"Chronological vectors? And what investigation?"

He shakes his head, almost comic in its suddenness, and gives a small, sad smile. "Right. Sorry. I had your aunt in my mind as I said it. She'd know."

"She would."

"Your ankle monitor tracks speed, time, and distance, yeah? So it's clear you drove out of the city, which normally would've triggered a breach alert. That I didn't immediately register the breach or try to locate you is enough to get me in trouble, and enough for a records audit."

"Does that happen?"

"Hasn't yet," he says. "But it could. My work phone is tracked, of course, so if anyone notices my little GPS dot sitting at home while you're zipping to Windsor and back …"

"Right. Bad news. Got it."

Without another word Sean turns away and disappears through the door. His lack of farewell hangs in the cool, damp air like an accusation. I sigh, put on my helmet, and follow. Sean is already at his car, opening his door. Gal is out here, too, working on a service door down the side of the building. Tightening the hinges with a screwdriver. Out of earshot. Far enough to be polite.

"Do I need to worry about him?" Gal asks as I approach. He doesn't look up from his task.

"I don't think so. My admission seems to be enough."

"Good."

"Can I use your phone? I'd like to call Mia."

"It is early, my friend."

"She'll be up. She's an early riser."

"No, I was thinking of her parents. They might not know about —"

"And my call will only make them curious. Got it."

"Good," he says again.

And that's it. I wait for something more, but he is reimmersed in the task. The hinges needing all his attention. Like I wasn't there.

So.

Spike in hand, I walk out into the field. The dew on the grass is thick and cold and in seconds soaking into my toes. I head into the woods across the way, thinking I can stay on the paths until the sun gets high enough to burn off the moisture.

Time passes slowly. I find only the occasional piece of trash. Lots of time to think. And to fall into that old habit of waiting for Jesse's voice. Which doesn't come. It feels strange doing the job without knowing whether or not his voice could arrive at any moment. Yet what could he say now? I don't know how to feel about that.

FAR FROM PERFECT

Mom finds me before lunch. I'm working the treeline on the far side of the aviary. Eastern exposure. Full sun. The grass here is dry. I'm avoiding the shadows.

She's dressed in jeans and a long open sweater, her hair in a simple ponytail. Which is surprising — she prefers to pile her hair on top of her head in loose bunches, cool off her neck and out of her work. She looks tired but at peace. Her eyes still carry the dark shadows underneath but also a calmness I haven't seen in a while. And she's going grey. More than occasional streaks of white and silver line her light-brown hair. I don't think I've noticed that before. A green plastic shopping bag hangs from her left hand, bumping against her leg as she walks. She smiles and waves.

"Lunch?" she says, holding up the bag.

"Is everything all right?"

"You're a hard one to find. Good thing I ran into the park manager."

"Gal. He's my supervisor."

"Right. Funny I've never met him before. What did you call him?"

I say the name again.

"Oh, okay. He introduced himself to me by his last name. Amar, I think it was."

"I've only known him as Gal. Sean called him Gary on the first day."

Her head tilts and she purses her lips. Nods. "Right. Gal. So that's who Viv was talking about. The one who drove you to see Jesse. Now that fits in a little better."

"Mia came, too."

"I know."

"So are you all right? What's up?"

"Your head looks good. The stitches, I mean. There's barely a scar."

"Mom …"

"Let's find a spot to sit down, okay?"

I point at a couple of benches on the south side of the aviary and ask if those will do. The sun is shining on the outside cages. Birds are visible in only one of them. A handful of tiny green and yellow parakeets, squawking loud enough you'd think there were dozens. Mom smiles at the sight and the noise and says that it's perfect. We walk over together. I watch her closely. Part of me is happy that she looks so at ease, but the rest of me doesn't fully trust it. You can be afraid of a sudden peace that appears in a loved one too soon.

We sit on opposite ends of the bench, leaving a space between us for the meal. Mom opens the bag and lays out the food. Bread. Sandwich meat. Cheese. Mustard.

Apples. Yogurt cups. A couple of those miniature bags of chips you give out at Halloween. She wordlessly assembles a sandwich and hands it over to me. Bologna and cheddar and mustard. A new combination to me. I take a bite and chew, Mom watching me as I eat. Expectant.

"It's good," I say with my mouth still full. "Really good."

She looks pleased. "That was my favourite sandwich when I was a kid. I'm glad you like it."

I always thought PBJ was her favourite. The things you can't know, I suppose. I finish chewing and swallow. "What's going on?"

"I had a craving. Bologna sandwiches and chips and a picnic. Lucky for us the store had everything." She reaches into the bag and pulls out the receipt, crumples it up, and worries the small wad of paper between her fingers.

"No, I mean —"

"I know what you mean, Dills. In a minute. First things first."

She flicks the wadded-up receipt back into the bag and pulls the far side of her sweater across her body. From a small pocket sewn to the front she withdraws a brass-coloured object engraved with an unfamiliar style of writing. And something else I haven't seen in her hands since before the shooting. A small joint the size of a .22-calibre short round, held tight in a binder clip. A pinner. She and Jesse used that word whenever they smoked up together. Their ritual. They'd grin at each other, and whoever had the joint would hold it up before sparking up and would say "Pinner time, lover!" like it was a horny, sacred toast.

"Really? Now?"

"Yes, really," she says. "Yes, now."

I watch Mom place the joint between her lips and open the brass lighter and flick the wheel. She touches the flame to the tip of the joint and breathes in so deeply she might hold the entire summer in her lungs. She exhales and smiles, closing her eyes. A single tear escapes, but she lets it course down her cheek. A good tear. She doesn't stop smiling as it dashes under her chin and soaks into her collar. She inhales again. Exhales. I wait.

"This must look strange," she says.

"Wow, yes."

"Mr. Amar — Gal — hooked me up."

"Wait, what? He did?"

"I could smell it on him. So after I introduced myself, I just asked."

"And he gave it to you?"

She inhales again, holds it, then blows the yellowish smoke at the sky. "Yep. Rolled it right there in front of me. Clipped it. Gave me his old army Zippo, said I could return it later."

I glance at the lighter again. The engraved script is Hebrew, of course. There is also a crest, like you'd see on a military shoulder flash. And nicks and scratches and dents. The tarnish of the brass a long history.

"This is so weird," I say.

"I'm drowning in weird, Dills. This feels normal."

What do I say to that? It's so accurate. Maybe I understand far too much.

The pinner is already almost burned down. She tokes a final time, this one even longer and deeper. Her eyes narrow but shining. As she exhales she talks about how she and her friends used to run all over the park. The secret places they found. I think about Mia's spot in the hedge and wonder if Mom might've used the same space. She talks about how they used to make fun of the lawn-bowling-club members, their white clothes and hats and formal ways. About how old they seemed to her and her friends.

And she laughs about the poison ivy, how mad Gramma Jan used to get whenever a new rash appeared. I look at my own wrist, realizing that the bandage fell off at some point, but don't say anything. I let her talk. She hasn't said this much since the shooting. There's a fragile need in her I'm afraid to frighten away. I can pinpoint the hour when it began, of course, but it feels undefinable, too, like it's possible that entire histories could get forgotten.

"You saw him," she says. "You saw Jesse."

I nod.

"I never went to the hospital after the shooting. Sometimes I wanted to. Mostly I didn't. The media was camped out, of course. But I was so angry."

"Everyone was. Is."

"But not you."

"I am now. He's given up. He's not even willing to try to come home, to face me, to make one thing right."

"You shouldn't carry this."

"I don't know how I can't."

"Me being angry at him has nothing to do with why. I'm as mad at myself for not seeing ..." She sighs and looks at the distant trees for a few long seconds. "Of course, there were all the little things. Little signs. Like breadcrumbs to what happened. But —"

"He always seemed okay to me. Normal."

"Maybe he was to you. For you."

"Everyone hates him."

She snorts. "These days people don't know what to hate. Or how."

"They all talk about him like —"

"No. Something inside him cracked. Something beyond his strength. That's it. People need to think there was more, but he was just broken. That's it."

"I didn't know you felt that way. I thought —"

"I'm sorry, Dills."

I hold out my hand and she places the lighter into it. I flick it open. Closed. Open. Closed. The sound of it echoes sharp around us. "I'm sorry, too, Mom. For all of this."

"'Sorry is as sorry does,' as Gramma Jan likes to say."

One of the most confusing things I've ever heard. Yet it makes a kind of sense, too. *Sorry* needs to get said, but it can't really fix anything, can't bring anyone back. Mom reaches out and fingers the edge of my safety vest above my shoulder, worrying a spot where the nylon is beginning to fray. A mom thing. Looking for something to repair.

"Tell me about the trip," she says. "Tell me every-thing."

So I do. Every detail. When I get to the part where I first saw him, I have trouble getting it out. My mind and soul pushing those details so far down I can barely grab them. Scars. The pieces of a person lost to gunfire. How a damaged person can be there and not there. The details hurt when they claw themselves out, and I fight myself as I'm sharing them. Even with my mom, who needs to know. We both lose it a couple of times. But you know what? Some amazing things get said. But those are just for me and her. I hope that's all right.

"So now we just wait," she says. "For the end."

"Yeah."

I get up and help her pack away the garbage. She tells me she's going to sit for a while and enjoy the sun and the quiet and the sweet little high she's riding. I put on my helmet and take hold of the spike, but as I'm about to walk away, the sounds of hard laughter and bikes being bashed over rough pathways clatter through the trees beyond the aviary. Three boys burst out of the trailhead and skid to a stop in a cloud of their own dust a few dozen feet away.

As the air clears, I recognize them. It's Pat and a couple of friends who move around the school in a rough, awkward pack. Nameless drones. When Pat sees me and my mom, his eyes widen. He turns to his friends and tells them to head over to the basketball court, that he'll catch up. They snicker and give him a hard time about it, but roll away, laughing, when he threatens them in a voice too low for me to hear. When they're safely away, Pat pedals over, dismounts, and leans his bike against its kickstand. The canteen sling is a diagonal, insulting slash across his chest. My hand clenches tighter around the spike. Only he can ruin a moment so perfectly.

"Hey," he says. And that's it.

"I recognize you," Mom says. "You're Patrick."

"Yes, ma'am. From Wendell's school."

Well, if that word doesn't threaten to knock me out cold. *Ma'am.* That he used it. That he knows it at all. "One, always be polite to your elders, no matter what. Two, always introduce yourself and say *sir* and *ma'am*. Clear as mud?" Jesse's voice — the one I hear in my memories — arrives untouched from the past, so pure I almost respond out loud. But, no. Not in front of Pat. Not again. No more material for him.

"What do you want?" I ask, hard.

Ordinarily Mom would snap at me to try again, to remember my manners. But she doesn't. She understands what fed my stupid, misguided need to go after him with the knife. My actions not justified, of course, but there's no need to paint things gold when they're already stained red.

"Hey, uh, I saw the news. I had no idea."

"So?"

"What happened to you ... with your dad ... it ..." He stops. Looks down at his feet. Kicks the grass. "Well, it sucks."

On a scale you can't imagine, Pat. But there's no way I'm talking to you about it. You look like you want to say more but I'll stand here, spike in hand, if you don't mind. Waiting for you to rip something open again.

He looks almost ready to say something else, but instead he shakes his head, quick, like he's flinging away an unpleasant bit of business. He unslings the canteen and holds it out, the pouch dangling in the chasm between us. I reach out and take it back. There is the faintest smell of bleach. Like he washed and disinfected it. Must be my imagination.

It's not enough. Not even close. But Mom isn't feeling any of that. She's looking at him with a sad smile and nodding. An appreciative, half smile you allow to burn through your grief. Momentary. Maybe because of the weed. Maybe something else. Pat looks up and sees her face and puffs out a breath. Embarrassed but relieved. Then he turns his attention back to the ground, kicking some poor bunch of grass free from its roots.

"So, yeah," he says. "Okay."

And with that he turns back to his bike, mounts it, and rides away across the grass. No goodbye. Mom and I share a look. Learning to accept what's been offered. Whenever we can.

YOUR STORY

On my way home that evening, when I head back to the field house to store my stuff, I see a familiar blue car parked on the street nearby. Walters comes out of the building, cellphone in hand. Escorted by Gal, who shakes his head and turns back into the gloom. Looks like he's not co-operating. Good. She leans against the wall and raises the phone, closes her eyes, and talks to it. Recording details. I change direction slightly, hoping she won't open her eyes and see me. I can keep my garbage-collecting gear at home for one night. I'll explain it to Gal in the morning. He'll understand.

Wishful thinking. Not a millisecond after I make my decision, Walters opens her eyes and zeroes in on my safety vest. Smiles. Steps away from the building and walks, fast, toward me.

I stop and wait for her. In that same millisecond, what her presence means has become clear. Talking to

Gal means she found out the specifics of my sentencing. And if she was able to find out about that, well, everything has been laid bare.

"So now you know," I say when she draws close enough.

A momentary look of surprise. She nods. "I do."

"Are the other reporters camped out at our place?"

"Probably. Or at least some of them."

"What do you want?"

"I want to tell your story."

"You and everyone else."

"Not everyone wants to tell this part."

"Isn't that what every reporter says?"

"I was in court, remember? No one else is trying to go this deep, to look beyond your trip and the shooting. I think you have a lot more to say. As a survivor, sure. But about moving here, too. About your stepdad, if you want. And obviously with your mom's permission."

Stepdad. It's not a passcode or anything, but no one else has had the sensitivity to use the proper term. And because the shooting happened in a school, to kids, there's been a lack of survivor perspective. I get that. Kids are vulnerable. They need space to heal. But part of me thinks it would be good if other people could understand more about what happened. From those who were there. In our own words. Reconstructions and interviews with first responders and hospital staff only go so far. How can we get better unless we prevent the tragedy of children knowing how black and surprisingly small the muzzles of assault rifles are? Of children seeing friends butchered in front of them. The sights, the sounds, the smells. The voids that are left when friends and teachers are snatched away.

"I guess that makes sense," I say.

"I'm glad."

"Mom grew up here."

"I know."

"You went to school together."

"Yeah."

"She brought me back here after the shooting. Home, for her. Not for me. It's hard to think about, much less talk about."

"I get that. I'm sorry."

"A lot of people say they're sorry."

"Please don't misunderstand. Obviously, I hate that you or anyone went through what you went through. But I'm more sorry that we can be so awful to survivors. The media, I mean. I think we can do better."

Uh huh. My head tilts, skeptical.

But she beats me there. She winces, as though she's only then heard herself. "God, I sound like such a cliché. Anyhow, take this."

Walters reaches into her satchel — which is identical to one Mom carries, only hers is a deep maroon, while Walters's is a coyote brown — and pulls out a stack of business cards held together by a stained rubber band. I like that. Functional. Plain. She slides a card out and holds it out to me. Blue newspaper logo. Her name and contact info in raised black ink. White cardstock.

"Call any time. Day, night, whenever."

"Okay."

"And don't worry. We have fickle appetites. Things will quiet down quickly after everyone files their stories about your most recent adventures."

"Which you'll do, too."

"True. I have bills to pay, after all. But there's no deadline for the bigger story. Take your time. When you're ready."

"If I'm ready."

"Right. And make sure you tell your mom."

"I will."

She says a quiet goodbye and walks to her car. Drives off. I stuff the card into my pocket and go home, ducking my head and saying nothing to the full-auto questions from the reporters. There are fewer of them now, but those who remain make up for it with increased repetition and intensity.

GOODBYE, PART II

Mom's in the kitchen chopping vegetables. The smells of heat and chopped things fill the air. She smiles when I walk in and puts a finger to her lips. Gramma Jan's dozing in the living room easy chair, head back and mouth open, a hardcover open on her lap. Mom comes over and gives me a hug.

"Smells good," I say, my voice low.

"Thanks. I'm hungry today." She winks.

"I can tell."

There is a faint skunkiness wafting from her hair and clothes. She releases me and goes back to the cutting board and her ingredients laid out on the counter. Carrots. Celery. Onion. Zucchini. Brown rice measured out in a cup. All for the pot of gently boiling water on the stove. I can't remember the last time she made homemade soup. Homemade anything, really.

"Did Cathy find you? She stopped by right after I got back from our lunch."

"Cathy?"

"Walters. Sorry."

I nod.

"What do you think of her?" she asks, lifting the cutting board above the hot water and scraping in the chopped veggies. She wipes her hands on a dishtowel. "Did she tell you what she wants to write?"

"Yes."

Mom pours the rice into the pot. "Me, too."

"Part of me wants to trust her."

"I don't. I'm not sure what good it would do. Talking to her made me want to pack us up again and find somewhere else to start over."

"I don't want to run away again."

"Me neither, Dills. But —"

Mom's cellphone rings. The chimey bells and vibration are nauseatingly sudden and loud in the stillness of the house. She reaches over as quickly as she can, but the damage has been done.

Gramma Jan stirs, her eyes fluttering open. "Answer the damn thing, Victoria." Her voice like river stone dumped from a truck.

"Sorry. I thought I had the ringer off." Mom taps the green button. "Hello?"

She listens, frowns, and looks at me. She places a hand over the microphone. "Reduce the heat when the soup boils, okay?"

"Sure."

"Thanks," she says over her shoulder as she heads into the family room. I try to hear what she's saying, but she's keeping her voice down.

Gramma Jan groans as she gets up from the chair behind me. She's paler now, almost transparent. Beads of sweat appear on her lip, despite the coolness of the house. Only huge, deep pain can do that. She shuffles into the kitchen, leaning on a new cane. High tech. Like you could build an airplane out of it.

She sees me looking. "Stupid thing. Made the mistake of falling in front of the doctor."

"Can I get you anything? Your meds?"

"Hell, no. They got me on the strong stuff now. Bottles and bottles of it. Makes it hard to think. And go to the bathroom. God, painkillers bung you up something good."

"Gross. TMI, Gramma."

"TMI?"

"Too much information."

She snorts, but it brings a fresh flash of pain. Her features twist and she has to exhale long and slow to manage it. She sits down on one of the kitchen chairs, rests the cane across her thighs.

"Gramma —?"

"NEI, you mean. Not enough information. If telling you about my inability to take a shit keeps you from making the same mistakes I did, so be it."

"Mistakes?"

"Mistakes, regrets. They pile up."

We hear the beeping of the keypad on the side door and a clunk as the door is closed hard on the frame. Enough to rattle the other doors in the house, old things on old hinges. Aunt Viv comes in, shaking her head, her mouth set. She drops a loud, long, acidic F-bomb. When she sees Gramma Jan and me standing there, she hooks a thumb over her shoulder toward the reporters outside. "Leeches," she says. "Every damn one of them."

"Language, Vivian. In this house —"

Aunt Viv rolls her eyes. "Yeah, yeah, purity of word and thought and all that. Wonder where I get it from."

"Don't be sarcastic with me, young lady."

Aunt Viv moves beside Gramma Jan and leans over for a side hug. "How are you feeling?"

"Oh, I'm super, dear." Her voice is exaggerated, that of an old woman in a classic movie. She holds up the cane. "I'm bionic, don't you know!"

I'm watching this in real time and yet I can't believe it. Half apologies and hugs and witty repartee. Makes me feel like I'm witnessing the interactions of some alien family in a parallel universe.

Aunt Viv lifts her chin in greeting to me. I give her a low wave. No words right now. All this bizarrely comforting strangeness is leaving me without much to say. She holds up and shakes her keys, declaring that her car is fixed and humming along, which you'd expect given how much coin she just dropped on the dealership. Her phone beeps and she glances at the screen. Frowns.

"Bad news?" Gramma Jan asks.

"No," Aunt Viv says, distracted. "I was expecting that by now he'd ..." She stops.

"He?" Gramma Jan asks.

Aunt Viv shakes her head, embarrassed to have revealed as much as she did.

"She's talking about Sean," I say to Gramma Jan.

"You're too good for him, Vivian."

Aunt Viv squirms. Visibly.

I ask, "He hasn't come around?"

"I wasn't expecting a full pardon or anything, but still."

"He was pretty pissed."

"Still is, apparently," Aunt Viv says, looking perplexed. An unfamiliar emotion for her. Usually it's all confidence and brashness. As though she fully expected that Sean's emotions should be as hackable as the tech she deals with. But apparently his anger is offline. And all his own.

Mom comes back into the kitchen, looking like someone has punched her somewhere tender. The three of us watch her put the phone down and move to the stove. She stirs the soup without looking at it. She isn't seeing us either, even as she starts talking.

"That was the lawyer. Jesse's and my lawyer, I mean. From Windsor."

She pauses. Gramma Jan, Aunt Viv, and I exchange looks but wait for her to continue.

"You know that the lawyer has power of attorney. But the hospital also has her as Jesse's first emergency contact. Not me. God, what a fight that was. Me, trying to build space between what happened and our family, and the hospital administrator needing to fill in his forms —"

"What did she say?" I hear myself asking.

"I was worried that someone might access the records. I didn't want our names to —"

"Victoria Sims," Gramma Jan says, her voice as firm as I've ever heard it. "Tell us."

Mom takes a deep breath. Exhales. "Jesse's dying."

"And?" says Aunt Viv.

"He's dying, Viv."

"He's been dying for months."

Mom's mouth opens and closes. Aunt Viv's words true but as blunt as ever.

"He never woke up," I say. "We've kind of known this was coming, right?"

"I guess that's true," Mom says, her hand coming up to rub her right temple. Hard. "But the lawyer said that his organs have begun failing. That it's just a matter of time."

"I don't know what that means," I say.

"No one does, kiddo. It's just what they say."

Aunt Viv and Gramma Jan offer advice, weigh in on next steps, on what it could mean. I can hear the attempt at comfort in there, the need to help shore up what might crumble. Well meant, all of it. But it basically centres on getting ready to move on from this. To let him die while we carry on here. Embark on the next phase of our involuntarily shifted life. Like the ground has become permanently uneven but we can work and learn to get our balance back. They're eclipsing Jesse, though. And not seeing a mother, either. Not seeing a wife.

There are lots of words but Mom isn't hearing any of them. She's moved herself into that hazy place you go when you understand that grief is on the way but you can't quite see its shape.

It feels like a long time before Mom does anything, but finally she moves. She turns off the stove and slides the soup to the cool space between the elements. She picks up her cellphone. Unlocks it. Dials. Gramma Jan and Aunt Viv seem to notice that Mom is moving independently of their ideas, and they fall silent as she makes the call.

"Hello? Are you still open? ... Good ... I know it's late notice, but do you have anything available for tonight? ... Windsor ... A large sedan would be fine ... Yes, I need a pickup."

She rattles off our address, thanks the faceless person on the other end of the line, and disconnects the call. Looks around the room.

"I need to pack," she says. "He'll be here in fifteen minutes."

"I want to come with you," I say.

She shakes her head and points down at my ankle monitor. "You literally can't, Dills."

"This doesn't feel finished."

"It's not. Not yet."

Mom lays a hand on my shoulder as she passes me. She tells me that I'm first on her list of people to call when there's anything to update. Then she's gone upstairs to her room to pack.

Gramma Jan and Aunt Viv resume their conversation, quieter now, as though they're afraid Mom will hear them through the ceiling. They talk for a few minutes. Aunt Viv's phone chimes a few times with new texts but she ignores it. They fall silent. *All talked out, thank God*, Jesse would say. He hates small talk.

Gramma Jan stands, slow and fragile and shaking, leaning on her space-age cane. "I'm taking my old bones to bed, kids."

"But Vicky's still —"

"Tell me in the morning, Vivian. I'm done in."

Aunt Viv nods, moves to Gramma Jan's side, and takes her arm, which sparks a round of weak but flinty swearing. She doesn't refuse the help, though.

Mom comes back into the kitchen as they make it to the hallway door, a canvas bag slung over her shoulder. She has jotted a few notes down on a piece of paper that she pushes into Aunt Viv's hand. She faces her mother and sister and tells them to take care of me. To watch out for me. She goes quiet. So do they.

A series of short knocks on the door fills the space. Everyone looks at it. Mom shifts, adjusting the strap of her bag. More silence. And another series of knocks, louder this time. Mom calls out that she's on her way and she'll just be a minute.

"You should get going," Aunt Viv says. "Call whenever you need to."

"I will."

Gramma Jan sighs. Loud. "I don't know what to say to you, Victoria. I'm so tired."

"Me too, Mom."

"Just come home when you can. This is home now."

Mom breathes deep and folds Gramma Jan into a tentative hug. Like holding a butterfly. But Gramma Jan drops her cane and grabs her daughter hard. Fierce. Long. Whispers something into Mom's ear I can't make out. Mom nods. Aunt Viv comes in and joins them. Full eyes everywhere. I feel like I'm witnessing history.

Mom wipes a tear away and smiles at her mother. Eyes narrowed. Tells Gramma Jan not to die while she's away. Says she might need her around for what happens next. Gramma Jan laughs, quick and harsh, like it's all she can manage, and says something in her failing voice about hell freezing over and wild horses and unfinished business. Aunt Viv picks the cane up from the hardwood floor and helps Gramma Jan into the bedroom down the hall.

I walk Mom out. The reporters are gone for the night. No cameras flash. No questions are machinegunned at us. The driver, a tall, lanky guy with bad skin, wearing an ill-fitting shirt and rental-company tie, offers to carry her bag. She refuses. Of course she does. But she does link her arm in mine and hold tight, like my weight can keep us grounded.

At the car, she tosses the bag into the back seat and faces me. She gives me a hug and I return it because that's what you do. But I wait for her to let go first. She's holding so tight and long and has her face buried in my neck. I realize she hasn't held on to me like this since the hospital released me to her after Windsor. So much of the blood covering me ended up on her that she had to throw out her clothes, too.

She tells me how sorry she is for all of this. How proud she is of me. Which is awkward because she's been amazing, but now doesn't seem like the time to argue. And finally, she tells me she'll say goodbye to Jesse for me. Because she knows, somehow, that I didn't get to.

PART III
EVERYWHERE

POTENTIAL

Mom's been in Windsor for more than a week. Jesse is holding on longer than anyone predicted. I don't know how to feel about that. "Death is a part of life," he said to me once. "No sense in dwelling on it. We all end up in the same place. Pushing up daisies. The great dirt nap, ha ha." But even as he spoke, I could tell that his eyes didn't believe the words. And now the lie is clearer. Death is more than a part of our lives. It's a twisted blood relative who refuses to leave. Maybe ever.

The cordless handset rests beside me on the side step. Still warm from my nightly phone call with Mom. She calls after supper to fill me in on the day's happenings. Tonight we didn't have much to talk about. The medical staff is monitoring Jesse. The reporters saw Mom arrive and made her part of the story for a day or two. Her lawyer threatened legal action, so the hospital got better at keeping the reporters away from the ward. But they've been waiting outside the building less and less often anyhow — Mom hasn't commented and Jesse hasn't died, so there's nothing to feed their fading appetites. Tonight, without the scrutiny, Mom sounded more at ease, a little more like herself.

Mia sits next to me. She arrived while I was on the phone. She hands me a glass of lemonade with mint, a gift from her mother. Everyone knows about me and Windsor now. There are gifts. Letters. Emails. Floral bouquets. Boxes of candy. Anonymous casseroles appearing on our doorstep. Mia's mom keeps a small thermos in the fridge filled with the lemonade for Mia to bring over every night. Her dad in the dark about it. A mom's tiny, sympathetic rebellion.

Mia one-arms me closer so she can kiss my cheek. Her lips are warm. "How's your mom?"

"Tired."

"I bet."

"Waiting for Jesse to …" I stop. I still can't say it. "Uh, waiting is hard enough, but this thing with Gramma Jan is stressing her out."

There was an episode this afternoon. Over the past few days, Gramma Jan's pain has been getting worse and worse. She refuses to take anything stronger than Tylenol, and the pain affects her balance and her ability to make good decisions. When I got home from the park there was an ambulance parked beside the house. Lights off, the paramedics moving around in no great hurry. Just another call to an elderly person's home for just another fall. Gramma Jan was inside the vehicle, strapped to the gurney and pissed about it. There wasn't time for many details, but Aunt Viv said there'd been a bad fall and a blackout and a long period where Gramma Jan didn't remember who she was.

Their departure has left another hole in the house. I sat by myself for a long time before messaging Mia on my iPod and asking her to come over.

"Any news from Vivian?"

"No."

"She's tough, your grandma."

"She is."

We sit in silence. I sip the lemonade and feel the tartness and sweetness competing on my taste buds. The high of the mint at the back of my mouth. Delicious and foreign and slightly subversive.

"And Jesse?"

I shrug. "The same."

"How? Aren't all his —"

"He's going, but no one can say when."

"That sucks."

"Mom sounds like she wants this settled. Me too, kind of. And not."

"Yeah."

Settled. Weird to say the word, much less think about its meaning. Feels like fantasy. Way out there. Glimpsed only in my imagination. That thing other people get to have while not realizing they have it at all.

"What's this?" Mia moves the cordless phone and picks up the envelope pinned underneath. The phone a paperweight to keep the letter from blowing away. She runs a finger over the printed crest and return address of the youth-court division. Looks at me. "May I?"

I nod. "Sean dropped it off today in the park."

She slides the carefully folded paper from the torn envelope. Reads it. It's only a couple of paragraphs.

"So you have a date for the hearing," she says.

"A week before school starts."

"Are you worried?"

"Not really. Sean says he's already spoken to the judge. He thinks she'll add more hours of service rather than escalate."

"Good. I'm not ready for prison romance."

"Ha ha."

Mia folds the letter and gently, precisely, slides the paper into the envelope. I watch her hands as she returns the letter to its spot on the cement. You couldn't call her hands delicate or graceful, but they're perfectly steady. Surgical. She sees me looking, laughs, and does a pantomime of a hand-model presenting a piece of jewellery, a bracelet maybe. I can almost see diamonds there, ablaze in the setting sun. She leans in, her arms sliding around my middle, and rests her head against my shoulder. We watch the sun fall toward the horizon. I have her warmth on one side and the failing summer evening's coolness on the other. I shiver.

Mia asks, "Should we go inside?"

"Not yet."

"Let me get you a blanket or something. You're a popsicle."

"Okay."

She gets up, opens the door, and disappears into the house. A cicada in a nearby tree starts trilling. The sound goes on for a minute or so before weakening in a long, steady decline. And silence again. Odd to hear one this late in the day. Or at this temperature. Usually they do their best to deafen me from the trees only on the hottest afternoons. Mia returns with the fleece throw blanket from the family room sofa and wraps us both up in it.

I start talking. Again. I've been doing that more and more since Mom left. I tell myself I'm not going to, but Mia sits or walks with me and out everything comes. Maybe tonight it's the blanket's sudden warmth that does it, loosening me up like injured tissue. I don't know. But my memories come out in a jumbled mess. Details I've never told anyone. About questions I'll never get the answers to. About Windsor and Ethan and the blood and the sounds I still hear when I close my eyes or try to fall asleep. About best friends who die afraid and alone and so horribly that you don't want to make any more friends because they can be taken so easily. About Gramma Jan, how there are a thousand kinds of cancer we have to worry about. About school and fear and life and how nothing is certain until it is.

I feel like there should be millions of tears, but my voice never breaks, not once. Because of Mia. At some point I realize she hasn't said a word but has reached out and taken my hand, has pulled it onto her lap, and is now holding it with both of her own. Her wrestling hands, so unbelievably warm and calloused and strong. I think about how a friend can hold another friend together. About how good that is. How necessary.

Beside me on the step, the cordless phone begins to ring, echoing along the sidewalk and down the street. NO CALLER ID is splashed bold across the amber screen. It feels like a long time before I pick it up, but it's probably not. Maybe a second or two. But so many thoughts fill that instant. About what happens next. What might get said. It could be nothing at all, everyday talk that won't change a thing. It could deliver the unexpected, where miracles happen or where everything threatens to fall apart. Or it could be the call I'm expecting, that simple and final piece of information that tells me it's time to move on. That it's all right to heal. Maybe even to forgive.

So.

I lift the handset and push the Talk button. I clear my throat to make sure I have a voice for this part. I want to be heard.

"Hello?"

At the other end of the line, there's a voice I know and love and trust. Low. Calm. Telling me there's news.

ACKNOWLEDGEMENTS

First, to everyone who has been touched by gun violence, to the survivors, victims, and their heartbroken loved ones, I am grateful for the courage and grace you've shown in sharing your stories. Thank you for trusting us with your memories and pain and rage, and for somehow still daring to hope.

Thank you again to Rachel Spence, Scott Fraser, and the rest of the team at Dundurn for bringing me into the family. Special thanks to Jenny, Susan, Sophie, and Babs for their laser-applied specialties. It's a pleasure to work with such a dedicated and professional crew, and my work couldn't be in better hands.

A million thanks to Rachel Eliza Griffiths, who graciously allowed me to borrow a few lines of her sublime and devastating poem "26" for my epigraph and title. Also thanks to writers extraordinaire Karen Bass, Amanda Leduc, Roz Nay, and Anne Valente, who read this novel and said some really nice things. Buy and read their books, everyone: you will be challenged and changed for the better. And, of course, much love to all my writer friends, who inspire and push me to write better.

And what a privilege and honour it is to live and write in a country where literature is honoured and valued! I'm thankful for everyone who loves and supports the arts, but Valhalla exists for those who support public funding. Thanks to the Canada Council for the Arts and the Ontario Arts Council, whose granting programs have given me and so many other scribes the financial space to create.

Thank you, Cootes Paradise, Churchill Park, and Westdale.

To those who serve, have served, and will serve their country: thank you. We send, you go, and too often it costs everything. We see you. What you've done matters. We need to do more for you.

Finally, to my people. To God, who makes it all possible. To the saints at HPL and SJE. To my family, immediate and in-law and extended, for all your support; I am spoiled for love. To my girls, Nora and Alida, for making me care even more about what's to come, and for giving me a reason to keep telling my stories. You are safe and loved, and I know you'll strive for a world where every child can feel the same. To Rosalee, my amazing wife, first reader, and the mother of our girls, you are so much in everything I do and every word I write I can't even begin to define how much you mean to me. Fifteen years, my Left. Imagine that. Here's to a whole bunch more.

Collected Poems

1919-1962

INDIANA UNIVERSITY POETRY SERIES

(all volumes hardbound unless otherwise indicated)

Babette Deutsch

COLLECTED POEMS

1919-1962

Indiana University Press / 1963

BLOOMINGTON

Contents

5

7

TRANSLATIONS

Foreword

THIS BOOK opens with some of the poems composed since
the publication of my latest volume of verse and concludes with
three translations made during the same period. Most of the remaining work has been chosen from the seven volumes published
between 1919 and 1959. These poems, like the ones in the opening
section, are arranged in roughly chronological order. Some have
been revised. Among those omitted is one that received public recognition, a few that have been anthologized, a sonnet sequence
presented as the Phi Beta Kappa poem at Columbia University in
1929, and some others admired by fellow poets and critics. On recent scrutiny these pieces did not sufficiently content me and I
was unable to rework them to my satisfaction. This accounts, too,
for the exclusion of a book-length poem: *Epistle to Prometheus*
(1931). I have also omitted—although I like them well enough to
be glad that some are available elsewhere—several pieces of light
verse.

Translation may be an impertinence or a crime; it is always
a risk. Encouraged by friends and strangers here and abroad, I
have continued to take the risk. In a single instance it has been
absent, that of the composition by the German poet, Christian
Morgenstern, which follows:

NIGHT SONG OF THE FISH

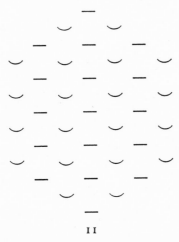

Whatever their faults, the translations offered here are among those that I agree with more trustworthy judges in finding acceptable. There are some others in the volumes from which half of these were chosen. Where the differences between the two languages involved were such that the spirit of the original could best be conveyed by following its form, I tried to do this. Thus, the rhymes in the translations from Pasternak which may dismay some readers are the closest approximation I could find to the apocopated off rhymes which are equally startling in the original. For the nuances, as well as for the prose sense and the metrics of the Russian poems, I am indebted to my husband, Avrahm Yarmolinsky. For those of the Japanese poems I have to thank Kenneth Yasuda, of The Asia Foundation, Tokyo. I had the help of Sirpa Tuhkanen Yarmolinsky in translating the Finnish lyrics. These, like the poem by Walter Neumann, were among the translations made with the aid of a Bollingen Foundation grant.

The poem, "Tivoli : Copenhagen," published in this country by the Columbia University *Forum*, originally appeared in the memorial volume: *Karen Blixen*, copyright 1962 by Gyldendal, Copenhagen; to both I owe thanks for permission to reprint it here.

B. D.

New Poems

SPACE MAN

Jetted like the circus's
Human bullet, he'll face
A public privacy
For the space of his throttled jaunt.
Returning,
Will he be implacably displaced,
Haunted by earthlessness?
Craving the unknown, he endures,
Abides its brood of dangers,
Even this one of being
Always a stranger
To those riding at our planet's pace only around
The simple sun.

The nightboat moving
Down the river: legs of light
Twinkling, how quickly
That caterpillar glides off,
Trailing the still joyful dark.

SUMMER POEM

Rich heat of August sweetens
Young apples on the boughs
Beyond the resinous road.
Beyond turf's dapple, drowsing.
Cicadas bell the time
Of year, but no tale's told
Till the cool-throated tones
Of the church on the hill
Shadow their unstilled shrilling.
As in the hand of the wind,
The sprinkler's water-fan
Sways lightly over flowers.
Marigold, zinnia, lily,
Phlox, dark primulas
Burn in the nooning light.
Azure's immaculate
As candor here. A cloud
Mimics a cherub's flight.
The equinox seems near.
And peace awhile, mockingly
Lovely and grave, returns.

ADMONITION

The graveyard and the garden share
A streetlamp like a gibbous moon.
As crisp as frost, soft as a plume,
Its ghostliness invades the room:
The mirror beckons, shadows pale and stare.

No shape, however sharp, is true.
Darkness and hoar divide the scene.
From what will be, from what has been
Cut off, this world is wholly clean.
Washed in cool unreality like dew.

Vision absconds, as with the dying.
Now sound, if growing more, if less,
Sound, perfected in formlessness,
Possesses all. Blow, or caress,
What sound thus offers there is no denying.

Secret as silence, in the turf
Around the gravestones on the hill
As in a ripening orchard, still
Thin pulses quiver, wince, and thrill
Like the blind shrilling of a spectral surf.

Nothing can drown them but the voice
That issues from the bell tower's throat,
As *one*, and *two*, and *three*, the rote
Of those bronze resonances float,
Calling to wake, or sleep. Calling: "Rejoice!"

THE DISENCHANTED

The pointed savor of a pineapple,
A world of corners, each hiding surprise,
And melancholy, as in a giraffe's eyes:
The kingdom of childhood is dappled glory. Old,
We are like prisoners at their exercise.

Here nothing shines. Night passes. The bare street
Under that stone sky is Chirico's.
Shadows are cut by a grey light that glows
Like the cheek of a ghost. Mystery, once alive
With promises, now clings to what death knows.

Morning returns. Though snow is on the river,
The famous punctual daffodils return.
Young lovers lie together. They will learn
The truth that holds us still. Loss is our jokesmith,
And tenderness the fire with which we burn.

CEZANNE

Air. Light. Energy. A birth of joy
As if this peasant earth, free of the embrace
Of an invisible god,
Not quite asleep, half smiled, remembering.
The mountain : here. The mountain : here. Always
The same, different in all ways. The mountain
Clearly rejoicing in the morning;
Smoldering in the moody afternoon;
No sadder than courage, the mountain shouldering
The soon familiar weight of dusk.
And once more earliness. The windy whites
Of a fresh day, blue that dares not, then dares.
The mountain's dream at dawn. The playful hush
That holds the saplings. The bare road turning
Into the woods. Still expectancy.
The green voice of the alleys triumphing
While it recedes. Powerful counterpoint : stark
Chill of cliffs; the wintry stream.
Stroke upon stroke, square upon square of white,
The loaded brush, the palette knife, five
Yellows, six reds, four blues, only three greens
Have ripened apples that spill into now, thrust up
A mountain's life. Paint giving the unseen
Shapes that cast shadows. Inscapes of delight. Silence,
Tumultuous or serene. Shadowless mystery.

THE MOTHER

On the hilltop, close to the house of the empress, Your temple
Is dark, sunken: a pit. The thick crowded pillars
Stumps only. The dread of Your presence
Lopped, like them, cold in mutilation.
Throning it here, in the stillness: vacancy.
In times beyond this time, were you robed in darkness?
You were known, then, as the Great Goddess. You are
Great even yet, more terrible, Mother Cybele, now you are
   nothing.

Shaking the glory of Heaven from his heels, perhaps an angel
fled to this earth, this Italy, these Venetian
lagoons. Where, in the hilarity of escape, he soon
designed a place to walk in: the piazza,
spacious as (knowing no other) Heaven's courts were spacious.
Beneath the bare azure it lay, as immensely empty.
The piazza was all that was there.

An angel, too, can be lonely.
But the runaway knew what do to: he sang
a Mozartean phrase that peopled the place with doves,
if emblems of Christ, sacred to Aphrodite. Yet the piazza,
for all the froufrou of their fluttering, their rou-cooing, glittered
    in sunshine:
empty still. He waited.
Something was wanting there beyond the birds.

And then he remarked the far end of the square.
So surely it was that San Marco sprang to life, winged and a lion
at play with a Byzantine empress, dazzling,
at the far end of the square.
Marble dreaming, mosaic blazing, triumphant bronze,
stone holding ivory's delicacy in derision,
spire on spire, dome smiling on golden dome, gonfalons streaming,
power, opulence, gaiety dancing together:
the vision of a truant angel.

Then the dark chime of the Moors' twin hammers resounded and
like a billow in spume dissolved, where refined planets spangled
    the azure, in the zodiac's golden circle;
and above it a lion couchant folded his wings
as if time were no more.
Almost a rebuke, on the right—the stern campanile.

Oh, but he needed more than the doves and the dazzle,
who felt a little the burden of his being
in Venice, on the Piazza di San Marco.
He paced the length and the breadth and again the length of the
     piazza, reflecting,
till out of his reflections—as palaces
in Venice rise out of the water—shadows arose,
and multiplying and petrifying and arching
elegantly, formed those lofty arcades
endless and grey as trade,
yet, with Venice glass iridescent as the necks of doves,
with Venice lace, as befits a city that is bride of the sea,
sumptuously graceful.
But the unearthly stranger, he did not know why, dissatisfied,
     shook his wings,
putting the doves to frightened flight, who alighted again
before the arcades, croodling and strutting and gleaming.

Then the angel knew what he must do. He sang
a second phrase, if less than Mozartean, festive
as a wedding. It was *Tischlein-deck-dich* on the piazza's
either flank. Parasols, yellow or red or blue or yellow, hugely
     sprouted
like mushrooms in a fairy ring; strings being stroked, plucked
     strings,
decanted music like a light wine, glasses were lifted like singing.
     Above,
a sky intensely azure. Beneath it, two or three children scattering
glistening grain to the doves; while at either side the piazza, men
     and women,
rosily aureoled, sat at their several tables, in a dream
of a Byzantine empress pavanning with a winged lion, with birds
     alighting and flying, with music sparkling like wine, and
     everyone
rejoicing in the grandly absurd pinnacled marvel, as in the piazza,
     immense
as the courts of Heaven.

And the soft and the savage voices of wounds were silent.
Soilure was washed away.
There was no shadow
But the slight shadows of the wings of doves, and the colored
    parasols' flanges.
As, in love,
joined pleasures, burning, kindle a universe,
here earth and Italy, Italy and Venice, Venice and her piazza fused,
    and from that central splendor shed such light
as, for an hour,
blots out the whole world's night.

PASSAGE

It is their twittering that shimmers; it is their droning
That steadily hones the stillness. They remain hidden.
Invisibly, summer is passing. A flight not noticed
Like her warmth, her fragrance in passage,
Unless by these noises, that will be matched, at night,
By the brilliance, the sustained distance, of constellations.

LATE REFLECTIONS

Old and sick, you turn away from mirrors, whether
They show the mocking face years have stained and withered
Or reflection quails at the coward's mean gesture.
Images of body and soul. What is the soul?
A feather blown by odd weathers of shine, of shade.
And the body? Is shaper and shape of the soul.
Sick, the pair live by the clock in a placeless time.
Old, they live in a futureless place, where odors
And a few fragrances are lingering features.
Hard to remember, the shape before it was fixed
As it will be in death, and as hard to believe
The remembered was once pure possibility.
In our grandparents' days, not blind superstition
But the love that illumines reason required that,
After a death in the house, mirrors be covered.

FIREWORKS

Not guns, not thunder, but a flutter of clouded drums
That announce a fiesta: abruptly, fiery needles
Circumscribe on the night boundless chrysanthemums.
Softly, they break apart, they flake away, where
Darkness, on a svelte hiss, swallows them.
Delicate brilliance: a bellflower opens, fades,
In a sprinkle of falling stars.
Night absorbs them
With the sponge of her silence.

VOICES ON RIVERSIDE

in homage to WILLIAM CARLOS WILLIAMS

Vermilion. Orange. Two shirts
on two darkskinned boys on a bench in the summer park.
Trees are less green than the drum like a long gourd
one pounds with the heels of his palms.
                                             The other
has twin small drums his fingers tap like a lover's
fondling
            a girl's hard little breasts.
Slow, the long
              drum
                    booms;
the twin drums flutter and snap. Rhythms
hot as an orange shirt
                        open
                              on cocoa-colored skin,
rhythms
          bold as a vermilion shirt
under a black face blind with consummation.
Brilliance mates with brilliance
                                  to assert
wealth as of tropical suns. The colors drum
like the heartbeats of boys flooded with salt joy,
with health shouting like Nile and Niger and Zambezi in tumult
    and unison.
It strikes the streets dumb,
                              the dusty park
hears only the speech of two shirts
on two dark drumming boys. Orange. Vermilion.

ANOTHER AUTUMN

A flotilla of clouds by its flocculence lightly defines
That purity of azure. Clouds by Tiepolo.
Earth, beneath, by Midas. Whose shining pleasure
Is in gold only, sometimes in a parent of gold or in golden siblings.
His huge orb, roseate gold, was lately a maple
In a green summer. These mulberry satin weaves,
Tinged with a lesser flagrance, were simple leaves where
Dogwood's ivory sprang; they chime like crystals
Of a parcel-gilt chandelier, in a hall rich with crimsons.
That oak in August spoke giant words, but was never as now
Sovereign, never so roundly sounded
Such resonance of bronze: a gold sombred,
Tuned to the chord of autumn. It will pass,
Is passing. Yet in this cool November light
The vibrance lives, lives as if it could never cease to hold
The wonder, as if it would both spend and keep
The essential gold, tell over and over the glory
That cannot be told.

Sky is such softness, is such dark,
Mat as the pelt of a black panther is
In his den's bight. Under the mat soft black
Flows—a moving mirror of that pure dark—
The river. Sparse lights debate or affirm a farther shore.
But darkness is at flood where, slow, black moves upon black
Yet lifts two lanterns
A boat's length apart; they kindle the water
To brief life, moving down the river.
And vanish.

LIZARD AT POMPEII

Little finger of fiery green, it
flickers over stone. Waits
in a weed's shadow.
Flashes emerald—
is gone.

Here once horror poured so hot, heavy, thick,
everyone was dead before he was sick.
Now here is no heat but the sun's
on old stone treads;
no motion but that rippling inch of whip:
yours, you little live jewel, who slipped away
into silence. Yet stay on to haunt memory,
like those dead.

IN HONOR OF HER SEVENTY-FIFTH
BIRTHDAY

(November 12, 1962)

to

Mischievous moralist, we give you joy,
Admiring the years of your employ
Rewarded by the visits of a Muse
Inhabiting museums, wilds, and zoos.
An heiress of that vigilant recluse who
Never had seen a moor yet vowed she knew
No less just how the heather looks, you find
Exciting most, excursions of the mind.

Courage is needed for such escapades,
Revived when all assumed provision fades,
And courage is your maxim, burnished by
Irradiant piercing singularity.
Gracious to all but fools, you let us eye

Mouse at Versailles, roc, bison, crow, kiwi,
Ostrich and elephant; we thank you for
Over a dozen curious creatures more,
Robust yet delicate—so your poems entrance,
Enhancing virtue with wit's elegance.

TIVOLI : COPENHAGEN

To the memory of the indomitable "Lioness,"
the BARONESS KAREN BLIXEN

The Chinese lanterns are hanging like fiery fruit
Beyond the gate invisibly engraved:
"Abandon despair, you who enter here."
They star the blossomy paths to the pagoda
That a Chinese emperor gave to a Danish king.
Here's everything that royalty or childhood could desire.
It is Hans Christian's world, without his sorrow.
Until tomorrow, all the toys are alive. The brave tin soldier
Comes marching along with his full company
To martial music that Mars never heard of,
Till the heart beats beats, beats beats like a thaumaturgic
Drum. The pagoda floats on the lake.
Ducks and a swan and giant dragonflies that are winged lanterns
Or mosquito traps float on a lake.
Another lake is for boating.
And another music blows in a gay gust
From another part of the forest:
Beethoven's Seventh, with a Chinese conducting.
The forest is rich with witches
And ghosts, and with Titania's people.

There are forest pools, of course, and, in the open, fountains
Where flames or bubbles of silver climb crystal columns.
Farther, screams of delighted fear
Shrill, whirling with the
Ferris-wheel, or bump shatteringly and jump with
The rollercoaster.
But there is generous quiet where the crowd attends
The mountebanks and acrobats, or, better:
The antics of Harlequin and the clown, applauding when
The stern father, the ingénue, and her lover
Give the pantomime a happy ending.
But the children shriek for the actors to speak,

33

If once only, to speak—those master mimes.
Who roar in answer, roar as the curtains close.

It is not night that descends, but dawn that rises
On this pleasure park for children and lovers,
And for those few ancients fallen in love with joy.
It is a love affair of the centuries, with always fresh
Delights in old surprises, with the strangeness of
The familiar marvels,
Where all creatures, as in the first Garden, are at home,
Where everything may enter, save despair.

A DAY IN LATE AUGUST

Depth on fathomless depth of blue, swept clean
Of all but two, perhaps three, cherubic clouds,
The sky is big and festive, like poetry.
Willow, dogwood, oak, elm, tulip tree,
Blue spruce, black walnut, match and march their greens
As in a procession stilled, on the still air.
Hilarity quivers within the grave scene
Like hidden life beneath water.
The air has the sweetness of grass, the grass
Sparkles freshly like air.
Alien or absent, every evil thing.
The most serene month in all the twelve
Summons "the daughter of laughter": a smile, to greet
The autumn that is coming, that is near.

Poems / 1919-1959

TO A DANCER

You are laughing as you run
To toss a ball in the sun;
And you'll pillow your head
Beside the incurious dead?

EPHEMERIS

Above the river, heavy with summer, air
Hangs sleepily,
Where in the embrace of afternoon
We lie, dumb as that air with our delight.
The grass is good to smell:
We suck the fresh
White ends of it, and this green place
Seems pleasanter for the taste.
Below, their shoutings half song, boys
Fling wild through the water; far away
A ripple gleams: laugh of a hidden
Child at play. And after,
Stillness is pointed by a stir in the leaves,
While through the leaves the sky
Blazes, intolerably blue.
Golden the haze is, from whose abundance we weave
A summer fugue:
Music that grieves for nothing.
Quietly
Day fails, the grass darkens.
A widening hush
Allows barely the shadow of an alas.
We stay only to watch the wimpling river flowing greyly on.

The city misted in rain, dim wet flashes of light
Strike through the dusk; vague thunderings—a train.
Over the street's glimmer the cabs rattle and slip;
Darkly the pavement's shine
Reaches into the night.
On blackness color flames: purple and blurs of red
Like fruits of faery bloom,
Yellow soft as honey and gold,
Green as though crushed emeralds bled,
Arctic blue in pale cold ribbons
Lost in fume.

Wind, and those shaken lanterns are swept off
By the shadows' broom.

"TO AN AMIABLE CHILD"

*On upper Riverside Drive, New York,
there is an enclosure containing a child's
grave. It is marked by a funerary urn,
the base of which bears this inscription:
"Erected to the Memory of an Amiable
Child, St. Claire Pollock. Died 15 July 1797,
in the Fifth Year of His Age."*

Was it because you'd wear
Your half-grown wisdom with a
Debonair gaiety, and laughed less than you smiled?
Or because you were tolerant
Of rainy days, of games and company you did not want?
I see you stilly radiant,
And—like delicious food, delicious play—
Loving music and motion and
Pleasure you did not understand
In voice or face or golden weather;
But sometimes for whole hours together
Hooding yourself in silence;
And when you tired of being good,
Driving them wild.
Could you go with death, making no outcry
If slow-footed, as though with nurse at bedtime?
You lie alone here.
Turfs and a quaint urn
Cover the dust of your small body.
The show
Of your inimitable ways is over.
Child, amiable centuries ago,
At your city-huddled little grave
You are remembered so:
Haunting too merrily for a ghost, you are loved
Now.

BALLET SCHOOL

Fawns in the winter wood
Who feel their horns, and leap,
Swans whom the bleakening mood
Of evening stirs from sleep,
Tall flowers that unfurl
As a moth, driven, flies,
Flowers with the breasts of a girl
And sea-cold eyes.
The bare bright mirrors glow
For their enchanted shapes.
Each is a flame, and so,
Like flame, escapes.

SEPTEMBER

This is the month when sun and wind contend
For the possession of that lapis, thinned
To milkiest opal, that is pure bare sky.
A cloud-puff is a milkweed soberly
Shredded by breezes with the fists of boys.
Only to breathe the air is to grow wise
On a transparent liquor, to grow still
As the unherded ruminants who kneel
On the horizon as against a wall—
The hornless hills that want nor barn nor bell.
A butterfly drifts down without a sound,
Proving it is no leaf of sudden brown
To whisk along the floor. The boughs, the turf,
Hug their thick green as though it were a scarf
Against adventuring chill. Few and small,
The russet tongues of the barberry thrill
The hairy verdure with a tinge of fire.
Now apple-seeds grow black, now seeds of pear;
Now the grapes tighten; meadows shake like seas,
And rivers are more level than the fields.
Shadows lie late, their long, drowsy limbs
Spread on the grass; before dusk falls, the winds
Cease, with all noises but the crickets' din;
Poor death's asleep, and we'll not waken him.

SUN BATH

Clothed in languor and nothingness
Lie, and feel the summer press
Her molten seal of hot bright gold
On cheek, on flank; lie still and hold
Hills at arm's length, and watch the sky
Like an ethereal sea reel by;
Watch the boughs' rich plumage turn
To solitary greens that burn;
Shrink human nerves to comprehend
How tentative antennae bend;
Stretch human powers to converse
With ghosts of giants, who rehearse
An unearthly drama there
On the blue platform of the air.
So dissolve into the mood
Of slow, sun-fired, sun-soothed blood
That the huge earth and the heart
Move without stop as without start
In one firm rhythm—being, be
Apprenticed to felicity.

MOVING

After the fretful hours were done—
Morning, noon, and afternoon,
After dusk had come, too soon,
And the sun,
A flushed, speechless creditor,
Upon our lack
Had turned a hasty back,
I turned my own
Upon small swarming trifles and edged fears,
To face their residue from other years.

Going from an old house to a new
Gives one curious things to do—
Closets to empty,
Heartaches to throw away,
Threadbare joy
To divest of mothballs,
Papers to destroy:
Letters from golden lads and girls who say
They have come home from the university
With nothing learned but what they were not taught,
Or, they are in love again,
Or, they are sad
Because of too little love and too much thought,
Or, asking what was meant on such a day
When a certain person said
The sort of thing people will say . . .
It doesn't matter.
Some of them are dead,
And some are married, and a few
Are famous.
Going from an old house to a new
Gives one tiring things to do.
And when we leave that new house, as we must,

Maybe, after some yet unlived years,
Shall I look back
To this night, and call myself a fool
For having cried in my heart for the old school
And the university
And the lovers and friends
Lost in the dark forest of the world?
Ambitions shrink;
Time pulls the best awry;
And ends
Come harder as we grow older.
The nights grow colder—
Or do I?

An April Paris brought again
The sweet selfish stingless pain
Of younger springtimes, ignorant of
The poverty of proven love.
Evening, moving through the heat
And dust of the bright noisy street,
As one half goddess and half whore
Waited at the open door.
Laying quiet on the air
Like a fresco's floating hair,
She squeezed the heart as milkmaids squeeze
The udder caught against their knees.
Evening passed, and night came on,
Lighting softly, one by one,
Stars like arc-lamps in a town
Viewed from an airship upside down.
Night came on, who had no share
In pain that is unmixed with care,
The pain of springtimes ignorant of
The poverty of love.

"THE LAURELS ALL ARE CUT"

We'll to the woods no more, for now
The winter of delight is here:
Earth stony as the fabled moon,
The sky lean-faced, as withering soon,
Rains cannot warm the damnèd bough
Where sits the gutter chanticleer.

There was a season when we walked
In meadows that were dim with blue
And violet life our sharp heels bruised.
The ground kept what the heavens refused
Of color, and a tall wind stalked
Beside us, gathering handfuls, too.

And when the blue was lost there came
A scattered scarlet in its stead.
The grass grew staunchly round each nest
Where sun-fed berries, breast to breast,
Nestled as bright as tropic flame,
And we drank honey where they bled.

These gone, there was a month as bright
As dreams of India to the West
Before the land of gold was snared.
The field lay still, its russet-haired
Warm pelt stroked smooth by drowsy light,
Till the sun slept, and dark was best.

We'll to the woods no more, for now
The winter of delight is here.
But in our blood the summer cries
Compassion on the bird that dies
And leaves no ghost upon the bough
To chill with song the sluggish year.

QUANDARY

There is no shelter anywhere
For her whose wonder, like a hare,
Bursts through the briars of despair,
And bleeds and leaps away.
There is no cave where she may keep.
The stream she drinks of is too deep
For her to ford. Her little sleep
The dreadful stars betray.

The panther heart within her breast
Will never drum her pain to rest,
Who so much fears to be possessed
By tyrannous circumstance.
Though she but stands, she seems to flee,
She trembles so to be as free
As if she'd shed mortality,
And smiled at her own trance.

How to sustain the miracle
Of being, that like a muted bell,
Or like some ocean-breathing shell,
Quivers, intense and still?
How close to her the golden room
That the world builds of its own gloom?
Her patient, furtive, fertile doom
Is there no way to kill?

FOR THE INFANT MICHAEL

Sweet, where music softly goes
Toward silence, and upon that bed
Sleeping, is rememberèd:
Where the breathing of the rose
Defines a fragrance halfway fled:
Or from wintry wings unshed
Hover rumours of the snows:
In such hushed, such honey-holding,
Subtle ways your being runs,—
O virgin bud be slow, unfolding
A radiance like the sun's.

THE PARTY

In the blonde room the lustrous-limbed piano,
Like an incarnate shadow with heart and nerves,
Seems to wait for those fleshly apparitions
Whose passing humors it so darkly serves.

They come: the room contracts with talk and gesture;
Its pictures pale as they nod with curving cheeks;
They flutter the music score with debating fingers.
The keyboard smiles like a wise old slave—and speaks.

Their voices rise and float, wreathing, dissolving
Over the resolute, quivering instrument.
Touch and kiss, grave-flower, wine-drenched laughter
Bloom in a fountain of sound, fade like a scent.

The music gutters at last, is snuffed like a candle.
Gay gossip follows, feasting . . . The farewells start.
Alone in the ash-blonde room the dark piano
Stands like a shining shadow with nerves and heart.

What shall we do with country quiet now?
A motor drones insanely in the blue
Like a bad bird in a dream.

Hush.
The giant plane roars
Gently as a carrier pigeon, soon
Drowned in the distance.

Before the shadows have engrossed the grass
There is a patch of sun to lie upon—
The pale warm thing that summer sheds
When she's ready to be gone.
The peaceful fragrance has not passed
From the fleece that she has worn.
The full bough, the bush, the dreaming vine
Vie with lush greens. To what should grief
Open its eyes again?

One leaf, blood-bright, stains quiet
Like a cry.

SCARECROW

A queer dark shape to scare
Nothing on that bright street,
In the sharp glittering air,
He kept his broken feet
Still, so to save them, while
His coat flapped in the wind.
And, as girls will beguile
Vexed heart or perplexed mind,
The rusty figure wound
And unwound rapidly
A bit of thread he'd found
And clutched at thriftily—
A trick cold fingers caught
Quickly, a thing to do.
His eyes were bare of thought.
His foot stared through his shoe.
A flapping shape to scare
None but himself, where grain
Was none to guard, his care
Was but to wind again
And then again unwind
His bit of thread, not more
Than any scarecrow blind
To what he did it for.

THE SONG

Oh, bitter-hearted me, thrice-parted me,
What Pythagorean discipline will wring
From discord, harmony?
And where, out of this quarreling breast,
Shall peace be found?
Neither the earth, the bloody-syllabled,
Nor the distracted air
Affords a ground
For music to build house.
Selves, you are blackguards who inhabit me
As vagabonds do ditches, prisoners—jails:
Bound, being at rest,
And muddied, being free.
Yet now, even with harsh cracked voices, sing,
Together sing,
And briefly, though joy fails,
Despair rejoices.

On the wall
Jane Avril
Flaunts violent stripes,
Bends her head
Too boldly for a dancer dead.
C'EST le mai!
Below, the slow revolving disc
Quickening gives out
A shout
That recalls
The bones, the jowls, the black gloves, the yellow gown
Set down with Toulouse-Lautrec's
Savage stroke.
C'est le MAI!
Who was it sang?
Who was it spoke?
Dancer, painter, old diseuse,
Anarchists and Fascists must
Come to dust,
But the rich
Malice, the gay lust refute
The tomb, the war, and the listeners, smiling silently
In the polite room.
C'EST LE JOLI MOIS DE MAI!

Do not live with me, do not be my love.
And yet I think we may some pleasures prove
That who enjoy each other, in the haste
Of their most inward kissing, seldom taste.

Being absent from me, you shall still delay
To come to me, and if another day,
No matter, so your greeting burn as though
The words had all the while been packed in snow.

No other gift you'll offer me but such
As I can neither wear, nor smell, nor touch—
No flowers breathing of evening, and no stones
Whose chilly fire outlasts our skeletons.

You'll give me once a thought that stings, and once
A look to make my blood doubt that it runs.
You'll give me rough and sharp perplexities,
And never, never will you give me ease.

For one another's blessing not designed,
Marked for possession only of the mind,
And soon, because such cherishing is brief,
To ask whereon was founded the belief

That there was anything at all uncommon
In what each felt for each as man and woman—
If this then be our case, if this our story,
Shall we rail at heaven? Shall we, at worst, be sorry?

Heaven's too deaf, we should grow hoarse with railing,
And sorrow never quickened what was failing.
But if you think we thus may pleasures prove,
Do not live with me, do not be my love.

As coins because they shine
Remain unspent,
The golden-bodied wine
Will first content
The pure lust of the eye.
Enough, if such rich lustre pay the sight
With interest upon long vanished light.

This pleasure as it pales
Seems not so fine
As what the glass exhales:
Breath of the vine.
Rare gust, be slow to die!
We'll take it on the tongue: mixed with our breath
The ghostly grape laughs jollily at death.

The wine, though cool as snow,
Being drunk, is fire.
The taste transmutes the glow,
Until desire
Puts its long grieving by,
Or finds some savor of sweetness in what's tart.
Though wrung, the heart exults, the shuddering heart.

The failure of delight
That makes us rage,
The treachery, the spite
Of this fouled age,
Wine's power can defy.
The blood bounds in the vein, flesh unsubdued
Forgets its pain, the soul forgets its solitude.

Ape

His eyes are mournful, but the long lined palm
He thrusts between the bars expects the best.
His old man's face as innocent as calm,
The beggar puts compassion to the test
And fails. He grips the bars; his pained stare grows
To a brown study framed in dusty fur.
He has a cold. He sneezes, cleans his nose,
Then gravely licks a flexile forefinger.

A pause; the bald mauve hand from which men shrink,
The fingers, strong to clutch, quick to explore,
Again extended, are again refused.
The eyes, poor sorrow's jewels, seldom wink,
But to his grinning public, as before,
Show endless patience, endlessly abused.

Young Gazelle

Stiff as her Egyptian counterpart
Standing on legs of matchstick ivory,
She hides the racing of her heart,
While the black boss of her enormous eye
Flames inconsolable. Less like a deer
Than like a freckled girl, her skin's blanched gold
Drawn over little bones, her head held clear,
She listens, as if breathing were too bold.

A tremor, and she is still. Now sunny peace,
Light as the straw beneath her feet, persuades
Her pulses briefly. The terror goes—
Whipped by a childish whimsy of release,
She caracoles: a quick bound that evades
The bars. Then drops into a thrilled repose.

Lioness Asleep

Content that now the bleeding bone be swept
Out of her reach, she lay upon her side.
In a blonde void sunk deep, she slept, she slept
Bland as a child, slept, breathing like a bride.
Color of noons that shimmer as they sing
Above the dunes, her sandy flanks heaved slow.
Between her paws curled inward, billowing
Waves of desert silence seemed to flow.

The crowd was gone, the bars were gone, the cage
Thinned into air, the sawdust and the fleas
Winnowed by sleep to nothing. After food,
Absence possessed her: bliss keener than rage,
If slumber's prisoner at a bound could seize
This ghostly freedom, lapping it like blood.

Black Panther

This little panther wears a coat of soot,
Well-suited so. Stretched out along his shelf,
Still as one brooding storm, the sultry brute
Looks soft as darkness folded on itself.
His limbs, his tarry torso, are as mat
As night wanting the stars; his resting grace
Lies leashed. Alone his head's erect: pure cat
Stares, alive with danger, in that face.

From the sharp ears down to the finest hair
At his tail's tip, he might be carved of coal.
Child of the shadows, he appears as tame,
Till, from behind the grate, the gold eyes glare
With such a light as could consume the whole
To ashes and a memory of flame.

Beyond the window the moon may be in riot
With the winter night. But your voice having ceased
In the room here, silence comes, barefooted,
To cover the leavings of our frugal feast.
Your hands rest on the table, clasped, quiet.
Kind as a country servant, silence moves
About us, with a tender dignity smoothing
The unseemly creases in our loves.
Your eyes upon me change no more than the rooted
Shadow beside your chair. Your eyes know
Upon what song this night has locked her throat.
The melody trembles toward us, still too low
To name, though the music mounts above our breathing,
Mounts, and mingles with, far off, a train
That pants harshly of journeys. Your eyes upon me.
We are alone again.

Over the water, polished
Pitch bright in the darkness,
The funnel dipping, the lantern
Swinging: yellow, a stripe
Falling across the cabin's
Cosy shabbiness, cutting
Out of the shadows a worn
Face, and a blackened pipe.

Soft incessant insistent
Puffs of steam in the offing.
Close, on the quay, a sailor
Turns an indifferent stare
From his business of pumping;
Water flushes the planks, and
Ceasing, quiet swallows
The simple scene like air.

No more. This was sufficient
To give fabulous midnight
Earnest intimate glory.
River and lantern webbed
The men, the tug, the moorage
In a steady fluxion,
As the heart swelled, throbbing,
The short hour ebbed.

NEED

What do we need for love—a midnight fire
Flinging itself by fistfuls up the chimney
In soft bright snatches? Do we need the snow,
Gentle as silence, covering the scars
Of weeks of hunger, years of shabby having?
Summer or winter? A heaven of stars? A room?
The smiling mouth, the sadness of desire
Are everywhere the same. If lovers go
Along an unknown road, they find no less
What is familiar. Let them stay at home,
And all will still be strange. This they know
Who with each heartbeat fight the fear of change.

DOGMA

Love is not true: mathematicians know
Truth, that's alive in heaven, and in the mind—
Out of our bodies; you will never find
Love strict as number, and enduring so.
It is not free: alone the grave's narrower
Than the little space in which this passion moves,
With a door that opens inward: he who loves
Measures his paces like a prisoner.

They who give it large names are liars, or
They are fools. More softly, you and I,
Slow to assert what we can never prove,
Wonder what algebraist, what dictator
Can teach us much of truth or tyranny.
Look at me. Do not speak. But this is love.

Carved by the stillness, clean as rock
The moors lie open to the sky.
Each bearded dune stands like a stock
In early nudity.
No shadow stirs, to crack the spell
Cast by the heat upon this waste
That shows the candor of a shell
To heavens as bare, as chaste.
Alone coarse beach grass, shaggy pine
Find sea-grudged root beneath the sand,
And stubborn as the wind, define
The salt lagoon from the salt land.
White as the surf, white as the sun,
The cottages cling sleepily
Each to its hillock, one and one,
Like sea-fed gulls beside the sea.
Between its knees this naked place
Holds the strange peace that is assured
To those who smile in their embrace
At violence dreaded or endured.

As on the throat of some museum piece,
On this chaste air is inlay of gold leaf,
Quieter there
Than sun on cheek, abstract as emperor's jewel
Cased in glass, truer than enamel.
Tumult of swollen waters on the rocks
Below, remote as rare,
Exalts a sovereign stillness.
Balancing
Stiff leaf and stubborn wave,
The tug chugging, the enormous
Strain of the delicate piers, the cloud, the light,
And cinders on the track behind,
The hour
Is silverly suspended.

Insecure, lay this upon some high shelf of the mind,
Not for the eyes
But for the heart to come
Back to, reclaim, and, more than art, admire:
Memory poised
In vulnerable, proud equilibrium.

Look up to the clear arc: bodilessly
Climb
The ridge-pole of heaven,
Swing through the blue tent
Burning with tall cold.
No wind
Breathes
On the brimming peace.
But to perfect
Time's truce—
Single, gold, one leaf
Swerves to the ground.
One crane
Like a slow arrow through the hollow air
Moves truly,
Never to be seen again.

INSUFFICIENCY

What though the moon pours restlessness?
The stars in unison are uttering peace.
The trees are shapes of stillness that no wind,
No birdy shift, rouses from their dark trance.
If there's a soul of stature to address
The night's hugeness, it asks no release.
But one that is ragged, one that is lame and blind
Shudders to hear the silent heavens dance.

Dispersed and spent,
As in legend the limbs of Osiris
Crying one to another, the unknowing undying
Scattered limbs of the god:
On the winter waters
Lie
The hand without fingers,
The feet without speed,
The head without thought, the torse hacked and adrift
And its heart in a house without windows
Beaten upon by the sea,
Unknowing, undying.

Where were you then, my sister, my soul?
Seeking
Through the two kingdoms, imploring
The Upper Region, the Lower, getting no answer?
Asking the birds of the sky
Who deceived you and vanished?
We called you,
We the sad limbs in dispersion.

In vain.

But flying you sought us.
The dead could not stop you.
No, nor the horns of Evil
Those that undid us.
And we cried, scattered.
Cried, and were mute.
And you came, O soul, my sister,
Flying, quick with compassion, the sleepless mother,
Unwearied bride.
Restored
To the hand its fingers, and speed to the feet,

And the heart
Beating again in the body, healed and made whole,
And the brow
Crowned with thought, lord of the nether kingdom.

Now, united,
Shall we not rule?
Can we forgive and govern?
You beside me, and I
That lately was many, scattered and tossing
On the horns of the
Savage dividing waters,
Can we endure?
Death under our sceptre. O
Sharper than death, unpersuadable Evil
Behind and before us?

Do not
Speak, mother and bride, my sister:
We that were
Scattered, now are made one,
We that were
Parted, now are at peace.
O do not
Lay a lightest feather upon the scales
Held in equipoise of triumphant stillness.
Now, my sister, my soul, requited, remember
As I, requited, foresee
The workings of Evil, past and to come.
Nor deny—
Denial only is dying—
This moment of union.

SOLSTICE I

Here in the lap of summer, in the silence
Sharpening every voice:
The bird's,
The boy's spiralling laughter,
Quiescence folds
Itself upon itself, like the blunt hills.
And grows,
No more mysterious than a flower states
Its color to the sun.
Here's a boy's joy
In the arrow that finds its mark.
But the man learns
Houndlike devotion to a universe
Whose evil is not measured, and whose careless
Unhoped-for love
Only dark patience earns.

This is the winter wonder:
Leafless morning
Reigns in the cold street like a sycamore
Clothed in its leopard skin, the golden pallor
Blotting out shadow.
Yet the sore mind
Fumbles, biting on its memories
Like a trapped animal gnawing his caught
Limb;
Freed, must limp
Through war's enormous jungle, bleeding still.
Chill poultice of these wounds, too distant
Lies the bright silence of a polar day.
Only the eyes,
Enchanted by a wintry innocence,
Stay with the tree of light that shows no bud,
Pillar whose glory knows no compromise
With ripening or decay.

Once it was packed like a box with the toys of childhood,
Even the largest dolls grown small and familiar,
And the cuckoo clock saying,
"Tomorrow, tomorrow."
Once it was sad and comic like Mr. Punch,
And events jumped up, like Judy, to be whacked
Over the head, and the greatest kings, like actors,
Were happily at once dead and alive.
Once it was apart
As a crumbled castle on a darkening slope
Half seen from the express.
But whether it was tall as towers or
Tumbled with playthings on the nursery floor,
It was remote and faithful.

History
Coming too close
Is monstrous, like a doll
That is alive and bigger than the child
Who tries to hold it.
It is a clock that tolls the thirteenth hour.
It is a theatre
On fire.
Our history
Images not the castle but the train
Emerging from the tunnel, ruining
Down the embankment toward the modest station,
Where it will lie like a box of toys, broken,
Unpacked in vain.

TO MY SON

Now the blackout of frontiers
Between home and Gehenna
Kills the light in the eyes
That would speak to you, throttles
The word in the throat, estranges
Us from ourselves. Our soiled pledges
Lie among broken bottles for the ragpicker's sorting
When the bombers are still.

How shall we talk
To you who must learn the language
Spelled on the fields in famine, in blood on the sidewalk?
Child (shall I say?),
When the night roars, remember
The songs we sang, lapped in the warmth and bright
Of the nursery:
Malbrough s'en va t'en guerre
Ne sait quand reviendra.
Farewell and goodbye to you, Spanish ladies,
Farewell and goodbye to you, ladies of Spain.
Memory stifles thought
Where the lamp throws a stain on the floor.
Youth is the time to dance.
No more: we have lost your music.
The iron that rings the brain,
The weight in the hollow
Breast where the heart should beat,
Remain.

I cannot hide you now,
Or shelter you ever,
Or give you a guide through hell.
You are ignorant, you are unarmed, and behind your
Scornful smile you, too, are afraid.
History threatens you at each street corner,

The seas are sewed up, and the colors fade
On every map you studied early and well.

The driven exile discovers
Midway in an obscure wood
What does not bloom for the fool:
The flower whose root is despair.
You, in an obscure room in a masterless school,
Must find the faith that cements
The promises public events and private blunders have broken.

Are you alone?
This I would have you remember
(Who felt your heartbeat before you had breath to cry with):
You must wrestle alone
In the stony night like the Jew
Compelling the dreadful angel.
If you fight in the dark
With your self till you force a confronting,
You will be blessed in the morning.

You will be blessed recalling
The question you asked as a child:
How can I change myself
When I have nothing to change
My self with? Then I smiled,
Finding an answer: your will.
Now I know it is love of the impossible
That forms the dove and the lion.
It is love
Of the impossible
That brings the soul to its own.

Though I can hardly reach you and never prove
What the event will teach you,

I who am helpless to move
You from the road you choose,
Or alter the face you will meet there,
Leave you these words with my love.

1943

REFLECTION

Looking in time's long mirror
What image do you see?
One holding a golden basin
For the hands of authority.
We are haunted by the Roman
Face, ominous and tired,
As by the womanish gesture
Of one who has desired
To be free of choice: a burden
Too heavy for old men.
The image in the mirror
Reveals itself again.
The governor slowly washes
One hand with the other hand.
The soldiers wait, impassive,
Obedient as the sand.
We stare on that repeated
Scene till our eyeballs ache.
Will a sandstorm rise? Will the mirror
Crack? Will the image break?

Sunrise tumbling in like a surf,
A foam of petals, curling thousands, lightly crumbling
Away into light.
Waking to this, how could the eyes hold
The shape of night's barren island, the cold cliffs
Climbed in sleep, how
Recall the burned sore scabby
Face of the world?
Into that sea of light the spirit waded
Like a young child at morning on the beach,
Saw only those giant combers, soft as roses,
That mothy spume unfeathering into air.
Lingered there, as a child lingers
To smooth bastions of whitest sand,
To finger shells brighter than dogwood flowers,
To stand, quietly,
Watching the immense marvel of morning
Rolling toward him all its uncreated hours.

SOLITUDE

What is it comes at evening into the room?
When you are alone, when muted lamplight glosses
The wood, yellowing the page whose notes
Blackly assert a deaf man's agony:
The music that his ears cannot receive
Ever. Ever. What is here now?
What does the silence say?
And the books gravely coloring the walls,
Their wisdom shut between boards, behind glass,
Like an anonymous exile without passport.
What is it breathes
So the lamp flickers like a candle flame?
The music beats, as soundless as a heart,
Touching your heartlessness.
And the room widens to receive the night,
The shut page sparkles like a tear,
The deaf man's agony becomes your joy,
Death littles. O what clear
Crystal
Forms at evening in the lonely room,
The lover, like an enemy, can break!

THE LOTUS

Steps in the tomb, uneager visitors,
Cannot
Disturb the flower of silence.
So the chill
Museum air can never hurt this bloom.
What if a sepal's blurred,
Not in a year, not in five thousand years
Was one leaf shaken from
That still stone flame. Let come
A hasty embarrassed boy,
Or some strange embarrassing lady, come and depart,
The silence does not change; their eyes, their fingers
Have not disturbed the flower.
The heart of stillness knows
An answering heart.
The master of the house
That is his tomb, the crowned king, silently
Receives the offerings in silence made.
Men bring him drink, bring jars of beer and wine,
They bring him food, vegetables, bread, meat, fruit,
And bring
Bowls, look, of lotus flowers.
Stone without fragrance,
Figures of the dead:
Can these have power
As wine and meat, as beer and bread? And yet
We eat and drink of them;
But chiefly on the lotus feast.
This is the flower of forgetfulness
To taste whose breath
Is to be fed by the divine memory.
It is the flower
Of risen life, no tomb can keep.
A sage once said the mind of God forgets
Evil that men remember having done, as it remembers

The good that men do and forget.
Then were the mind of God even as the lotus, sweet,
Alive and tall.
Step from the tomb.
Step out into the daylight falling
On the street.
Leave the still tomb behind the soft-hinged door.
Yet you shall sometimes find the lotus flowering
In the mortal mind's so narrow room.

Staring in zoos at the dull-eyed and wild
Who never meet their gaze,
The child, the refugee, the idle sailor
Halt their wanderings to praise the plumage
Of every bird but this.
The friendless seaman and the exile trade
Feathered marvels for their memories.
The child escapes
To a safe jungle rich with cries and colors.
Comforted, they turn back
To the barred nursery, the bareness of
Shipboard or rented room.

Will you come, phoenix joy?

On the stained path two lovers pause.
The air
Throbs
Where upon no visible branch
His wings of light, his breast,
Softer than any kiss, an instant rest.
The world's worst shabbiness
Crumbles. Their eyes meet.

Would you fly, phoenix joy?

But these, returning
Late and alone, will hear the song he sings
Among the ashes as
His self-begotten beauty dying burns.

CITY PARK

The sun they seek unmasks their leisure, bares
Poverty in their clothing, in their hearts.
The loveless cripple, the warped ancient wears
Need like a badge. The glance each darts
At passers-by, like a child's arrow, blunt
And wanton, is retrieved again to fail.
Their patience does not find what it should hunt,
Where pigeons peck and a sparrow flirts its tail.
They scarcely stir, sometimes their fingers fret
Their sleeves. The words they drop are buttons loosed
From a worn thread. Here, birdlike, they forget
The world of green beyond their urban roost.
Faithful as disappointment, they come back
With the bland light that placates as it numbs,
Sharpening their shadows to a narrower black
Among the drifted leaves and few stale crumbs.
And then a cold wind rises and the sun
Falters; they must move. Slowly, they go
Along the dusty path, becoming one
With dusk, that tells them only what they know.

Here on this hill, beyond the sick world's pain,
Landscape is legend, from the shadowy plain
To topknots blonde with sun and lakes that shine
Softly as bloom of porcelain or of wine.
The contours of this classic structure keep
The distance of a dream, where, mocking sleep,
They seem to dance, to vanish, to revive,
Strict as an archaic smile, and yet alive.
No architect on earth was ever skilled
As one musician so to plan and build
A tower true as only number is,
So firm in air, so blithe for view as this.
Most heavy heart, be lifted up, and come
To find yourself in heaven and at home.

Then was the grown-up world of tall decision,
Its beauty of late nights denied a child;
World of bewildering gifts, and strange derision,
Alien alike whether it frowned or smiled,
Yet your least wish was governed by its laws.
The landscape and the weather both were odd,
Exploding with effects that hid a cause
Serene and lonely as the Will of God.
Recall it: peopled by an august race,
Immune to the passions that attack the young,
And knowing all. There every commonplace
Must be translated from a marvellous tongue.

Now is the world of grandeur dwindled, shrunk
To what the stupidest can understand.
The shabby treasures of an exile's trunk
Include no passport to that wonderland,
Though you are told you are a citizen.
The scenery is changed, the climate dull;
The fateful masks are faces, gods are men;
Most nights are long and few are magical.
But there are strangers even here: their speech
Is rich in barbarous mystery, their ways
Are private, who live wholly beyond reach,
Admired and feared, though none of us obeys
Their foreign rule. No dictators, and yet
Strong utterly. While we, with pity wrung
For what they must do, suffer, learn, forget,
Feel shy when we approach them. They are young.

THE NET

Into this net of leaves, green as old glass
That the sun fondles, trembling like images

In water, this live net, swung overhead
From branch to branch, what swam? The spider's thread

Is less passive, where it appears to float
Like a bright hair clinging to the wind's coat.

Hot at work, history neither schemes nor grieves
Here where the soaking dead are last year's leaves,

And over them slung, meshed with sun, a net
No creature wove, none frantically tried to fret.

The huge weight of time without its sting
Hangs in that greenly cradling woof. A wing

Has caught there, held. Held. But not to stay,
We know, who, how slowly, walk away.

A BULL

His sad brown bulk rears patient as the hills
Hunched like dark herders at the pasture's back.
Swaying, he will not topple like those clouds
Heavy with throttled thunders. Lust that thrills
The crowd, to see such power pricked and teased
Through hot blind plunges to a sandy death
While they breathe blood, rage flowering in their veins,
His poor tame suffering will not have appeased,
Who takes the sun's barbs in a sullen drowse.
The ritual of his fertility
Is simple; he was bred only to breed,
The homely husband to a score of cows.
Yet monstrous as a myth, his front denies
His humbled horns, as, hugely male, he stands
Hung with endurance as with iron weights.
Clustering flies mate round his red-rimmed eyes.

THE DOOR

Wide as a champagne glass, mouth brimming
With sun, this interval
Offers a bouquet of near and far.
Summer having left the door ajar,
A woman drops a word that is a leaf.
Being unheard, she smiles:
Another leaf
                    twinkles down.
Upon the sill now every petal burns,
Veined, as a lover with his love, with light.
Their colors sharpened, sincere as knives,
These flowers, glittering singly,
Stave off night
                    another hour.
Greens beyond
Thick as thunders, crowd:
Live greens the wind alerts,
Greens drowsing, shadows or green revenants,
Young green
Disputing what old green asserts.
The door of summer stays
                    ajar.
Half trying
For entrance, the toe of chaos withdraws again.
Voices shelter this hush, this spacious
Pause. If its meaning
Is music, commonplaces make it plain.

THE GULLS

On the steep cliff
That hung over the sand,
Where nothing moved for the eye's farthest reach
But ocean's royal colors twitched with white,
And, on the sky-wide beach, a flock of gulls,
I gave my joy into the birds' wild keeping.
On the shore
Only the gulls were living, and
Beyond, those lucid greens,
Those traveling purples, dark as fate.
I could believe the gulls more beautiful
Than Yeats's swans above the lake at Coole.
Fifty and more, by my uncertain count,
They rested there,
Till suddenly, upon what wind of impulse who could say,
They rose, as if the shore were answering
Ocean's harsh whisper with a grey salutation,
To settle on the sea.
They were at home, being wave-bred, on their wide watery nest,
And, floating quietly as clots of foam,
They rocked my joy with them upon that boundless breast.
But not for long.
Once more they rose, over fifty of them, away
In winged ellipse.
And as they flew,
Leaving the vast shore still, the vast sea bare,
I marveled that, though the gulls carried it
Viewless into the sky, poor human joy
Could rise so high, could, vanishing, stay.

If you press a stone with your finger,
Sir Isaac Newton observed,
The finger is also
Pressed by the stone.
But can a woman, pressed by memory's finger,
In the deep night, alone,
Of her softness move
The airy thing
That presses upon her
With the whole weight of love? This
Sir Isaac said nothing of.

INTERLUDE

Accordion music meanders the pathless woods
From the hidden cabin like one lost, half sorry
To find his way home at last. Coolly, the sun,
With wind for helper, teaches the young forest
Basketry of shadow.
The accordion pauses, rests; the single noise
Is a grasshopper scraping his wing with his leg
On a bleached log.
Wasps weave through the silence
Now veined by the voice of a bird.
Sky holds fiery blue
In a green mosque of leaves. Here how all praises
The passing summer, and the sound almost fails
Of the seep of sunny moments.
As for defense, eyes look toward the tower
Of one formidable cedar,
While the hour bleeds twinkling away.

STRING QUARTET

Who have no heaven come
Into the hall that passively receives
Their fluttering chattering quotidian selves,
The grieving mind and the deceiving heart.
Then they recede, as who should bow before
The entering instruments.
These find their places,
And all is garden and is grace, is
Eden, animal and innocent.
The violins and the viola cradle restless chins,
The serious cello's blonde body glows.
How faithful are the dog-eared scores, and how
The bows lift, scenting music!
Now, coolly as a flower
Unfolds, paradise
Begins.
      Fingers prance on the strings,
      Bows dance in air,
      Time is undone even where time grows,
      Blossoming like a tapestry's blue and rose,
      Vanishing like its colors at day's close:
      Blossoming, fading, vanishing, only to spring
      Up as a fountain tossing a crystal ball
      On the tips of the water's fingers.
Will it roll away out of the hall:
The impalpable sphere striped with day and night,
Or tossed once more
Leap into the sky
And be lost?
Some cough, some sigh, or stir in their chairs,
Some stare
At the floor or the ceiling, a few close their eyes.
Time is the hairs of a horse stroking the gut of a sheep,
Time is a hole in the carpet, is dust on the lamp, is a
    cramp in the knee.

Time is nothing to see.
What is it summons
The son of the morning from this hollow wood
In his first radiance, summons
The daughters of music too in theirs?
What temporal marvel unmakes time, that here
Dread measures the brink of the gulf,
And does not shrink,
Love sees how vilely it must live,
And smiles?

DEPARTURE

The sensual parade of summer thins.
Green music, humming thighs, keen tambourines
Fade into grass. Crossing the dusty road,
Who hears the tune the caterpillar sings?
Noon's blaze has shrunken. Cool as lemon skins
The light that meadows wash their faces in.
Leafage crowds close, but richest boughs bear stains
Of tired banners, sunken. Lakes and winds
No longer leap in recognition, only
Begin to speak, and then are dumb again.
This opulence is tarnished. It is known
A shining fortune waits the season's heir,
But what was wealth is spent. This is the ebb
Of glory. How things end. When dark puts on
A widow's mournful jewel, say, the moon.

THEY CAME TO THE WEDDING

Like gods who are fêted,
Like friendly old slaves,
Their silence full of music,
Their hands full of flowers,
Singly, in waves,
They came to the wedding.

First, sceptred with sunlight,
Slicing the shadows,
The Pharaoh came decked
In power, in sereneness
Like that of the lotus,
The lively, erect
Flower of forever.

The empress of China
Paraded her dragons
Of silver and gold,
While mountains were unloosing
Their hair to the music
Waterfalls trolled
Like bells for the wedding.

Saints came and sailors
With stories of marvels
And marvellous gifts,
And masts that now were branches
Broke into bird-song
Floating in drifts
Down branching horizons.

The deserts danced after,
The rivers before,
Till darkness like a mortal
Denying immortals
Thrust from the door
Those who came for the wedding.

These are the streets where we walked with war and childhood
Like our two shadows behind us, or
Before us like one shadow.
                    River walks
Threaded by park rats, flanked by battleships,
Flickering of a grey tail on the bank,
Motionless hulls
Enormous under a dead grey sky.
Farther, the harbor and the miscolored waters
Rocking their flotsam under the blank round eye
At the masthead staring down the rats to come,
Beyond the fisher gulls.
And the windows full of ropes and hardware,
Doorways, barreled, yawning on the dark,
Wall-eyed alleys, coils of husky smells,
The breath of journeys strong there.
Streets whose sordid beauty
                    joked readily with hope.
The taller avenues,
And walls that smiled like unpurchased horizons,
Swung intimate views out of a foreign room,
Hung a gate upon a garden's fable,
Walls that frowned
With aged remorseless eyes
Or the gloom of thunderlit landscapes, opening
A door into that placeless country
Where the sad animal is blithe, free and at home.
Too, those halls
Where we stepped lightly among the creatures
Whom death had tamed, who yet crouched, sprang, or flew,
Fierce as hunger, graceful as joy,
Until we knew, as in a half silvered mirror, the half
Captive image of immortality.
These are the old places, and walking there
As then with war and childhood,

I look into the shadows' faces.
They appal.
                    Yet often I will see
(The marvels floating alive upon that stream,
The breathing of delight like purest air)
Another place: that you contrived
Between midnight and morning
In your dream, and in the morning
Took me there.
                    We greeted it, who could not stay.
But it is there,
Surviving wonder, yes, and despair.

AN AUTUMN POEM

The air rich and thin; the colorless color
Of pasture bristles softly as feathers of fur.
But the wild is still.
               Stubble is queens in homespun,
Their spiky crowns held higher than they were
Before their jewels went and they were drained of gold.
Now trees are flushed with wonder of leave-taking,
While the mild skies look on,
                    keeping a flock
Of birds afloat, like a scarf dreaming and waking.
Once more the genius of autumn,
                  how mutely, enfolds
A spent world, being ignorant of what spoke
In that thunderflash when all the dead
And all the living mingled in one smoke.

NIKÉ AT THE METROPOLITAN

Great-winged, as thirstily as an athlete you
Lean your headless throat upon the wind.
Your blind breasts
Remember how they once frowned down the sea.
But the prow
That outfaced Ptolemy is now worn stone,
And here is worse—
A plaster image of that faceless thing.
It is this age's curse
To look at you, goddess of Samothrace, and think,
No cause is just.
Yet, with shorn arms you nurse
Whatever infant triumph men will bring
To rest in your opposing thrust.

From great this, little that : the dust
Hissing beneath the bed,
The silence of all the dead,
From the abyss,
The fat,
We escaped to the hoofed and horned.

The rhinoceros's armature,
The rodent's play, the improbable
Giraffe was our delight.
The hippopotamus baby,
Solid, slow, and wide-mouthed as a dredge, showed the delicate
Pinkish grey of a young sunset cloud.
The crested curassow
Wore his huge sapphire as a prince
His caste mark, and the camel bore his hunch
As brother to the dunes.

We stood and stared
At the uncaring eyes of a sphinx-bodied cat.
Egypt sat in his pose who would not stir
More than a pharaoh throned, or
Couchant there, as if he were the form and pressure of the waste.
There was another whose gold thinly
Gleamed in his eyes alone, the rest was black:
So might twin moons ride implacable night.
And one, the ebony-striped, the sulphur-jowled,
Seemed the familiar of a rishi come
Down softly from his savage mountain home.
Farther, an infant dragon, neither tame
Nor yet breathing flame,
Perched the little leonine marmoset.

Reality was larger than the dream.
Eden so near a change,

The peacock's vulgar scream was consolation for
The splendor of his tail.
Translated fabulously from the Orient, from southern opulence,
Jungle, peak, plain,
Like living myths the creatures ranged
Across a landscape framed by skyscrapers and tenements.
Not half at home, they were no stranger
Than those beseeching them for inklings of
Their kingdoms
And their power
And their glory.
Speechlessly, we too, laughing a little, with what love, what pain,
Told them our story.

THE LOOK

Beneath the gay bandeau the shaven head
Showed. The eyes, huger in the wasted face,
Wandered like wild things dulled by narrow pacing.
The hand was tethered to a pain, that fed
On a spreading horror. Light revived the pain,
Reminding it how it had gorged before;
While off the brightness of the corridor
Some rooms were dark now where the dead had lain.
Talk fluttered heavily toward the neighbor bed,
In vain, moved toward the pain again, then tried
Circling some public topic, turned and eyed
The heart's homeliest charges, stiffened, fled.
The living stood beside the bed and waited
For nothing in the nowhere of appal,
And smiled at her, as if there were no wall
Between them and the dying. Her fate
Stood near them with eyes larger than her own,
That would not close, not even when she slept.
Its look followed after as they lightly crept
Off, waving, leaving her alone.

SCENE WITH FIGURE

The treadmill prisoner of that century
Whose sufferings seem quaint beside our own
Ground corn, ground stone. With steady tramping, she,
Repeating her grey round, grinds misery.
A choking heap, that she must eat alone.
Awake, asleep, she walks, she walks, she treads
The steps her crippled feet have worn. The crime
She pays for is a secret learned heads
Have not deciphered. But the few tears she sheds
Are salt as blood. Her heart burns like lime,
Destroying shriveled joy's long raveled threads.
She watches now the dying of her child
Whose life was empty as statistics are,
And all its broken furniture is piled
Beside her treadmill. This place is not wild.
It is a known spot on an unknown star.

DEATH OF A DOG

The loping in the darkness, here, now there,
As the wild scents whispered, the roadside beckoned, while
Things without heads roared past, their smell not vile
But meaningless—and the loping on, to where
A richer odor sang out like a snare.

Across the road it sang again, too strong
To leave, although a small monster was hooting
Behind, spoiling the scent, and suddenly shooting
Ahead, in a heavy stench, a wrench, a wrong
Noise of everything where it could not belong.

He got free, though, and with a limping leap
Found the high grass and panted there, his eyes
Twin frightened fires. He did not try to rise.
One leg was smutched, with oil, for the blood, deep
In the unscarred body, crept, then poured toward sleep.

He would have voided the strangeness: could not; strained
His neck toward some loosening of agony,
But could not reach it; grinning dreadfully,
Would have turned from the hand that stroked him and refrained,
But could not: could not stir. The hurt remained.

The hurt remained, the hurt, and the amaze,
As the eyes waned, like pin-point stars gone out
When darkness clouds. And now there was no doubt:
The leaping, the listening, the kind queer scent-crammed days
Were done. A dog's death is a death men do not praise.

Itiskit, itasket,
A green and yellow basket,
                    green, yellow, brown, black,
I wrote a letter to my love
And on the way I
                lost
                    it
(Will you ever get it back? Never never ask it).
But you know what was in it?

A mouse's minute.
A spicule's dream, a spider's whisper,
Fly's reply.
The twinkle in a needle's eye.
Tickle of a comet's whisker.

It can't be traced?
No land, no sea, no place, no face?
Once upon a space a town on stilts, a box in a box,
Sticks, ships, docks, locks.
No face. Giant cheeks.
No place. Fins and beaks.
        Arrows know where to go
        And they tell
        Radicle and pedicle.
No face, no place, no land, no sea,
But gastropod's geometry.
You hear if you listen well
            <   ∧   ‾
Staccato : Crescendo : Forzando : Marcato :
                      ⌢
            FERMATA.

An echo after silence knocks.

The streets that offer it a snag-toothed smile,
An age that's paved with excrement, with wrongs
That choke the breath, could make the precious vile
If they could reach it, but how should they spoil
What to no street and to no time belongs,
Though it alight here for a bird-foot while?

Yet most securely housed, certainly wrought
In a given age are the proud things that tell
Less of the sweat spent on them and the thought
Or of the princely figure that they brought
Than they tell gaily like an astonished bell
The marvel that their imaging has caught.

For in a fountain, in a tapestry,
Saved from another time, paid for perhaps
With miners' or with ploughmen's agony,
And placed now for the whispering world to see,
To praise, to pass, look! there's a finger maps
The very heaven we dreamed could never be.

Beyond a portico presided over
By an angel, young, demure, with slotted wings,
The fountain, central, reigns. Thunders discover
A dewy dazzle, a mercurial hover.
Firm, amidst rushing joys, the fountain springs,
Sheds thunders, lifts the tower of a lover.

Tapestry shows the fabulous unicorn,
The gentlest beast that ever laid its head
Upon a lady's lap; like a tall thorn,
There both to serve the rose and to adorn,
Rises within her hand, which without dread
Clasps the white wonder, that resplendent horn.

These images are so noble they can call
Into the mind a thought that's fugitive
Yet noble, like themselves: instants where all
Speaks of supreme delight are radical,
There in the midst of death we live, we live
Where exaltation is most natural.

Who, above, prepares an austere fiesta?
None. It is carpets of cloud unrolling prove
The heavens desire dancing. Clearly they also
Require grey, for all wear grey. In an enormous
Hush the ethereal crowd advances.
It will have trumpets, drums. Are gay girls hidden
In veils O grey as fear? Are hierophants
Proudly pavanning toward a sacred murder?
Clouds
Are darkening here, nothing but clouds.

It is a huge fiesta, if austere:
Faces shrouded, feet shod with fog,
What appeared as gods or girls are mountains dancing.
Muffled their Highnesses are, yet moving lightly
As mist, they advance and bow, they retreat, they
    have changed
Places. It is a dance O it is a dance. Fire
Veins their approaching embrace. Have they kissed
At last, who vastly glow, part sombrely, go off?
Clouds
Are lightening here, nothing but clouds.

It is a fierce fiesta, no more austere
Than if clumped torches rearing on the rumps of
Elephants lit up an emperor's games.
The elephants trumpeting, the amphitheatre
Reverts O to a jungle clearing. About the kill
Fiery lions, ripping their feast, tread,
Bound and roar, grumble, roar, are still. The air,
Fanned with sound, cools.
Clouds
Are tumbling here, nothing but clouds.

The clouds roll forward greyly bellying. Rain
Pours down the cliffs, on the bunched factory lights
That quench and flare. Under fresh sluice the river is
Dimpling iron, and the beetlebacked limousines, like the
    asphalt, black
And bright. The thunder has stopped. The lurid branches
Of lightning, the hushed heat lightnings blotted out
By clouds loosing the rain. They pass away.
The rain ceases. There is nothing here
But memory of an austere fiesta.

PIANO RECITAL

(for Maro Ajemian and John Cage)

Her drooping wrist, her arm
Move as a swan should move,
First singing when death dawns
Upon the plumaged flesh.
But here no swan wings thresh,
No river runs. A woman
Strikes hidden strings in love.

Now slow—as fronds of palms—
Her fingers on the keys.
Lifted, her listening arms
Ponder the theme afresh,
Until it seems young flesh
Is momently transmuted
To echo's effigy.

No no—the risen hands
Pounce on the keys, destroy
The hush, rush on, command
The blacks, the ivories,
In flight now with the keys
To grief's unwindowed prison,
To the low gate of joy.

She leans with sparkling looks
Toward the dark wood, her strong
Hands work as gleaners should.
Then, as who would caress
A birdlike wordlessness,
She stoops—to drink the meaning
At the still brink of song.

Though all's in pieces, how it holds.
Though all is flat, how still the eye
Goes round and round until it molds
The lifeless lines to something wry
But motionable, that must fly
Or fall, the mind rejoicing in
Deceivers we cannot deny:
Apples, cards, and a mandolin.

This is our world. Without the golds
Spilled heavenwise out of the sky
On valleys, pavements, waters, wolds.
Without the darkness we defy
Night after night. Skew shapes that cry
With voiceless lips and lipless grin
Can yet delight us, so we try
Apples, cards, and a mandolin.

Here are such simple manifolds,
Order so chanced it seems a lie,
No heartfelt warmth, no thrilling colds—
Collage like sherry, pale and dry.
Why does it tell us we shall die?
Or is it here that we begin,
Playing with things that say good-by:
Apples, cards, and a mandolin?

Painter, your abstracts magnify
What is not shown. We are Adam's kin
And we must pluck, not knowing why,
Apples, cards, and a mandolin.

The restless ones are small,
All eyes and knees.
Unable to recall a time not this,
They peer, they climb and crawl;
Their cheeks like fruit, their daring
Spicy with fear. But soon—never—but soon
Their joy must jump the moon.
They sigh: to draw a deeper breath
Would be to draw a knife.
What do they hope for?
O magician, come!

These sit along the aisles
On folding-chairs
Planted as firmly as their white-cheeked smiles
And ladylike white hair.
They seem at peace; they are wearing
Old pains in secret, like old-fashioned styles
In underthings. What creaks
Is not their patience. If they speak,
It is below the breath.
What do they wait for?
O magician, come!

So pink, diminutive, so mute an O,
This infant yawn: we laugh at it—
The human thing;
The little animal has shown it shares
Our habits, not our suffering.

Its mother holds the creature on her arm.
It stirs her smile once more, with a
Bit sneeze, whose small
Concussion is of an insect tambour's force,
Yet intimately natural.

Those who will never again answer us
Seem at this instant further off:
We know them gone
Because they are speechless? Because we'll not hear
Them sneeze, nor ever watch them yawn.

Yellow yellow yellow: you are the child's
First richness, piled in a cornbin's hillocks.
Farmer gives her a fistful, hard to hold.
Of the crammed kernels, a few spill.
Hard to lose: the dribble of orange bright
Sunny white-tipped seeds. Two all but golden
Chips burst through the tighter clutch. Farmer
Seems not to mind, but so much beholden, the small girl
Wonders. And she may carry the crowding yellow
Handful out to the yard? Among queer feathered smells,
Craned pecking necks, and she may call
"Here chick! here chick!" and they will come?
And she must throw the sunny grains to them,
Yes: from the farmer's pan take more and more to scatter
Wide as she can, spattering a yellow hail.
Funnily they run to find it, greedily fight
To pick it up; bested by the stout fellow with the proud crest,
They bicker, cluck and peck. "Here chick, here chick!" But
Soon, too soon it's gone: among the gravel,
Droppings, feathers, the prodigal wealth dispersed, snatched up
And swallowed. The small girl, abruptly bereft
Of glory, is left empty-handed.
Farmer's leathery face turns toward the barn, his other chores.
She will go and play. Not now, but right away. Here still the spell
Of the warm brightness that she held so tight
Hovers: yellow yellow yellow

It glides and glints,
A straw bead picked out by the sun:
One bird note.
A green wind
Blows in the morning,
Dozes at noon, turns
Over, lazily
Ruffling a hay-colored warmth.
Late, the dry
Timbal of the cicada,
Like the pledge of the knifegrinder's wheel,
Refines
Summer's declining edge.

PORTRAIT

The bird's nest, empty, on her table, feeds her,
Far from a Chinese chowder of gummy nests.
She has so small a body, she finds a feast
In a slenderer soup, or in its fragrances.
Someone absconded with her childhood; early
She learned to wipe the fingers of her mind
Like the Prioress at meat. But a tiger paces
Her nights. In the grassy morning she chases the cat
From a wee bit rabbit, it limps off, she is bleeding.
And mends her wounds, and would admire the tiger
For its barbarous grace. She keeps a map of the tropics
A puritan ancestress left, and her garnet from Etna,
Entertaining eternity with a scrap of chill fire.
It is Sunday; the chromium twinkles ironically
In the room, while her love moves round a ghostly branch
That beckons backward, the torn wood gesturing still:
A wave, arrested. For the girl remembers
Years when the dry past was her dancing partner;
The stalk, the straw, the rain of Hokusai
She salutes: in field or sky, whatever is drily smiling.
But the deserts do not tempt: a single sand
Is her sufficient Sphinx. And she may hear it
Sing, she thinks, as the sun, rising, strikes.
But now she is moving into a nearer music,
That visits her pillow at midnight, after the padding
Of the tiger goes off, and the terror, although she knows
Fear of a sort, as she listens. And the night is soft.
She trembles, remembering as she forgets, asking
If the voice in her veins dissembles. It is sweet
As before, rough as never before. She hears famished crying,
Yet under and over it, wordless, like the world,
A song that is too human for a bird.

PARADIGM

Firm as young bones, fine as blown spume, still
As recognition,
The tree holds itself
In air, in water. It looks imaginary.
Yet is earthfast above the shelf, what's drowned
Is bound to the rooted tree by moonlight only.
No starer at its own ghost, no creature
Lost in belief and terror is standing there.
Stilly, a tree greets a tree equally
Still. It shares, or they grown one
Share the old elements: water, earth, air,
In ashwhite body and hair memory of fire.
And yet the tree and its light image look
Like nothing that our planet bears. They are those
Who know what men do not. The force of anguish,
Of delight, bite of ambition, are human, are not theirs.
They are set apart, and solitary, together
Plunged in pale night. They have no will
But recognition.
This is their only meaning.
Tree, tree in the darkness
Of air, of water. Still. And alone.

Stiff as buckram,
Swathed in black and white
Strict as the keyboard,
Three tall ladies lean
Forward—confessing distance
Or delight?

The first phrase
Sparkles like the invisible spire
Fountains exhale, O the first notes
Adorn the air.
Surprising as a child's laugh rising
Higher, higher, higher, the chimes
Must drop—or stop.

Slow, melody climbs again,
Naturally, as a vine grows,
As though the fingers on the piano
Put forth
Buds of sound.
They, too, dewily sparkle.
But, sisters, do you hear
How soon the blithe tones darken, as leaves do,
And their afternoon
Shadows?
Can you recall,
Sisters, the grieving of desire?
Do you fear the advancing shade?
Pray, what shall you do who cannot do
What the piano does when rightly touched?
Even while it smiles, the music
Twinkles like a tear.

As years, years ago for the composer,
Now it is over

For the hearers, for the musician
Drenched in rosy thunders of applause.
She bows
To you, sisters, to all,
As when she leaned above the keyboard she
Bowed to the laws
Governing a strict love.

DESTRUCTION OF LETTERS

To shred them: a narrow labor, and simply toss
The pieces away like peelings. Fingers tear
The heavier sheets across, across, across,
In voluptuous bravery; so children pare
Skin from a wound half-healed, admiring loss.

A phrase, like a deep look, glows from this pale
Manila paper: now flurrying, as past clutch
As confetti for the street sweeper to nail.
The word that a moment since was to behold, to touch,
Collapses into an impalpable Braille.

Postcards resist squarely, stiff to defeat
The redoubled twitch would slice them like a knife;
As if each public view—park, river, or street—
Were alive and clinging to its private life:
All that the eyes have loved returning in retreat.

What's left then? Mincings like receipted bills.
Those lines where the ink throbbed like an artery,
So littled, would not serve a fire by way of spills.
Yet in the widowing wrist the pulse more stubbornly
Beats: the heart swears: memory salutes, and kills.

DIALOGUE

Deep night. I lay on my bed,
Only less alone than the dead
Because I had speech with my heart.
"Everything is refused!"
It was crying. I, disabused,
Replied: "We do not part."

Droning consumedly,
Hidden planes plunged by,
Rousing the heart's hunger.
I offered: "The famished bite
On the used rinds of delight."
That filled the heart with anger.

"Everything is denied!"
It cried. Then I replied:
"Heart, I have your lament
And you have got my voice,
In which you may rejoice,
Perhaps, when all is spent."

My heart acknowledged this
With: "Sing. Sing of the kiss
Given on the deathbed."
"Death's living differently."
"The kiss!" it answered me,
Who was less alone than the dead.

DESIGN

These part us, if at heart we are embraced,
Their savage silence admits no reply:
Mountains of miles, the waters, and the waste.

As hungry fasts are haunted by the taste
Of festivals gone by, the days go by.
These part us, if at heart we are embraced.

We have admired together vases chased
With peak and cataract; now stretched eyes deny
Mountains of miles, the waters, and the waste.

Familiar streets, intimate rooms, erased
By them, revive, but soon our minds let die.
These part us. If at heart we are embraced?

Fresh pleasures glow, old troubles are outfaced
By stranger troubles, all nothing, against those high
Mountains of miles, the waters, and the waste.

The punishment for lovers who have disgraced
Love, so divided, we begin to try.
These part us, if at heart we are embraced:
Mountains of miles, the waters, *and the waste.*

LANDSCAPE WITH FIGURES

Granite-beaked, this dense green-feathered shore
That the world bangs beyond.
Shadows on the lake
The wind
Brushes to colder lustre.
Plumes, rocks,
Are shaped to echo stillness alone.
That cradling sound, that plop of hooves drops from
No hoof: is chestnut-colored water lapping stone.
Those granite beaks will stoop only
To feed, like father eagles, the dusk hush.
The sky before sunrise, the lonely light
After the sun has left heaven and lake both bare,
What do they hear but the pure music of
Silence?
Those multitudes of stars with their blind eyes,
What beauty could they see
But solitude's?

Declared, not like a child or an animal,
But with the clarity of a dead face,
The moon over the mountains. The dead dispense
Such indifferent radiance
On the dark; their smiling would appal.

Coops, barns, are shut, now there is none
In the fields. No spoor of what went galloping over the heavens
With the roar of fire. Poverty
Possesses the hills, the sky. Forgotten the glory
Of that hour when dying and living were one.

The All has shed the moon like a nail-paring.
Naked, it has the night for its mirror, there
We may watch it, moving beyond us, to what bed?
If it spoke, who could interpret what was said?
If it slept, who would lay by the strange clothes it was wearing?

HOMAGE TO THE PHILOSOPHER

(for A. N. Whitehead)

Some things persist by suffering change, others
Endure: the mountain endures, endures and is worn down,
    after ages is gone.
But nature, the philosopher tells his brothers,
Offers another fact for them to brood upon:
Eternal objects. Color is such a one.

"It haunts time like a spirit. It comes and goes.
But when it comes," he reminds them, "it is the same
Color."
        These are years when even a child knows
Endurance. And the famished face of a war with no name
Persists through change. Yet there is a godlike game

For us to play, here, now. The eternal objects are
Our counters. Let our board be the ground,
Planted or paved, or the sea or the sky. In particular
And passing forms—color, shape, sound
Surround us, physical, fantasied, lost, and found.

Eternal red, orange eternal too, yellow, green, blue,
Eternal violet. Play with them, share their estate, set
Them up in the mind like circles and squares, like notes
    remaining true
Whether absent or there. They will vanish, not die, even
    if you forget
Red, orange, yellow, green, eternal blue, eternal violet.

A man who looks at New Haven, with autumn ruddy
As never before, blue as never before,
Dawning on body and mind, you talk to yourself
Of auroras: we are allowed to overhear.
The core of it all is autumn—harvest in kind:
The senses admiring the delicious drench
Of light, of color, of texture, taste, and sound,
Fruit, flower, sail in the sun, a woman's hand,
Her voice, slight and abounding instruments.
Quench these, there's more: the mind, this instant holding
The manifold remembered, the intended
Huge imaginings. Now. Here. And next year or tomorrow
Where? The core of it is autumn, winter's dawn.
But no fear of the pathetic leave-takings
Known to branches above New Haven streets,
Nor the rude soliloquy on beaches smitten
By an easterly wind. Say, *heavy, heavy,*
Hangs over your head, as in the children's game.
The forfeit is heavy, but your talk is light.
Thirty-five years we have known your tinka-tonk,
Azay and rub-a-dub. This is not new
But it is not the same. Your lunar blue
Spangled with ambiguities, your roses
And crow's feathers are viewed under a cloud
And yet they shine in the eye. Now when you speak
Of dirt and dilapidation it is at once
As one of a crowd and as a man alone.
But you are not solemn with Necessity,
The goddess as step-mother. You invite her in,
Into a room shining with mirrors, large,
Windowed to entertain the sun and moon.
She looks at herself in your mirrors, you at her.
You talk to her like a philosopher
But the eschatology, the entelechies,
Are framed in your little language, with *musica*

128

And *Gemütlichkeit, accent aigu ou grave.*
You are no less a sensualist for being
A voluptuary of the mind. But whether you hum,
Or drum on the table, or try to sum it all up
In words, French, German, Spanish, and your own
Inventions, it is the pulse of autumn beating
Under it that we hear. You make us see
More than the golden boughs and the sky, cold,
And blue as flame, to the smell of burning trash.
You mention ferns and we suppose a pun
Upon *die Ferne,* the famed for being far.
For you fern-green, leaf-green, ice-green, are equal.
For you in the night, off in the arctic, rosy
As your bouquet, Aurora borealis
Glows for the giant's table. Put
These images aside. Let us say simply
That a good poet in an evil time
Speaks of the beginning of the end.
He speaks of autumn, that's the dawn of dying.
He speaks of the fact, the event, the thing and the thought,
Trying to hold what's final in his mind.
Thanks, Wallace Stevens, for what you say,
And the way you say it and sing it, grave and gay.
Whether the early morning makes you brave
Or the colors of autumn delight you, clearly you have
The courage of your ignorance. Your speech
Reveals an irreverent joy to which death is
Irrelevant. You give us the fiction and
The festive real. They dance against the sky,
Blue, burning, of your New Haven autumn,
And we salute them, crying good-bye, good-bye.

HOMAGE TO JOHN SKELTON

Your name is Parrot: "a bird of Paradise"?
In Heaven, they say, Hebrew is the Word,
While you use every language, naughty or nice,
Greek, Latin, Welsh as you were Dylan's bird,
Italian, Castilian—good Skelton you've skirred
Hither thither hardily, but, spoken or sung,
Harsh or silk-soft, yours is the English tongue.

It was not made in heaven: the marriage of French
And Anglo-Saxon that bred this mongrel thing.
Is it spoken in hell? It could sweeten that stench.
Yet, Skelton, no skald had such black words to bring
Down thunders: your angry English would fling
Foundations asunder, you cared not who was bruised,
Cardinal or king, so truth was not abused.

Men envy young Tudor, Henry the Eighth,
Not venery's prowess in chamber or wood,
Nor finesse on the flute, nor his ownwayish faith.
It is this Tudor's tutor they'd have if they could:
John Skelton—what pedagogue stands where he stood?
Learned laureate, wit without peer,
He rhymes you as fast as a sailor will swear.

When Henry was England, that tongue was not still:
You mocking Parrot, up on your perch,
You plucked out false feathers with a bold bill,
Charged churchman and challenged church,
Keen to scour what scoundrels would smirch.
And priest that you were, you were handsomely human,
Who named as your wife your lifelong woman.

Psittacus, papagei, periquito, say
Your paternoster, greet us in Greek,
Coo like cocksparrow, jar like a jay,

Sol-fa like a lark, follow your freak—
Your voice is our joy, if you sing, if you speak.
A more than four centuries' marvel, in truth
Are you parrot or phoenix, of unquenchable youth?

Verily, perroquet,
Your vivacious play
Should not a whit dismay
Maître Mallarmé.
Both sagacious birds,
You both made poems with words.
You had only to call,
The words came, one and all,
The tiny words, the tall,
The fragrant, the fresh
As a fine peach's flesh
Or silken purse's mesh.
Nor you did not disdain
The shaggy words, the plain
And nasty, as though they'd lain
Nightlong out in the rain.
You used both smooth and rough,
Choosing the proper stuff
And not more than enough.
Your Elinour Rumming
Has our ears humming.
Our eyes are dizzy,
Our stomachs queazy,
Only to be thinking
Of her and her drinking,
She pouring it out
For bout after bout,
But you made us dafter
When you came after
To pour us a draught, half grief, half laughter.
Our hearts you still harrow
For Jane Scrope's poor sparrow,

Was killed at Carowe
By Gib the cat.
We are sorry for that.
And though again
We may laugh at Jane,
We are fond of Jane
And feel her pain.
You made poems with words
Like all sagacious birds.
And if your rhythms go tumbling,
Bumbling and rumbling,
So that some grumble,
Declaring you fumble,
Then their wits are numb
As a frostbitten thumb
That can pick up no crumb.

Though not few commend you, the fewest command
Your turn of the tongue. Those rhymes proffer choice
Of the spicy, the bitter, the fragrantly bland.
We breathe the fresh whiff of your verse, and rejoice
In Parrot's rich colours, his various voice.
Tutor us, John Skelton, who whetted your beak
On the bars of your cage; tell us how to speak.

Teach us to sing truly as you did, whose words
Would first prick the proud, then beguile a young child.
Throats of another feather yearn over the turds
In this age; too, cages are differently styled.
This bird's locked in the language, the other is exiled.
You seized liberty. Is it out of our reach
Who labor to arrive at your natural speech
For our gardens, our graves, for the tower, for the dive?
While your lessons flourish, English is alive.

THE POEM

The painter of Dante's awful ferry-ride
Declared the world only a dictionary,
Words, words, whose separate meanings must go wide
Unless the visionary
Compose them, so his eyes are satisfied.

The saint from Africa called every thing
A word, the world being a poem by God,
Each evil tuned to make a splendor sing,
Ordered by God
With opposites that praise His fingering.

Was Delacroix a fool? Was Augustine?
The dictionary seems a poor appliance,
With venerable terms become obscene,
Too fertile science.
We try the poem, but what does it mean?

The rhymes are slant, of course, the rhythms free
Or sprung, the figures moving through the mind
Close as a caravan across country
Often unkind.
It is magnificent in its privacy.

And yet the words are there: fire, earth, ocean,
Sound, silence, odor, shape and shadow, fear,
Delight, animal, mineral, time, space, motion,
Lovely and queer,
The crystal's patience, the baboon's devotion.

The words are there; according to his powers,
The saint, the painter, gave the work a gloss,
Loving it. Anguish, as it scours, devours,
Discovering loss.
The logic of the poem is not ours.

The color of silence is the oyster's color
Between the lustres of deep night and dawn.
Earth turns to absence; the sole shape's the sleeping
Light—a mollusk of mist. Remote,
A sandspit hinges the valves of that soft monster
Yawning at Portugal. Alone wakeful, lanterns
Over a dark hull to eastward mark
The tough long pull, hidden, the killing
Work, hidden, to feed a hidden world.
Muteness is all. Even the greed of the gulls
Annulled, the hush of color everywhere
The hush of motion. This is the neap of the blood,
Of memory, thought, desire; if pain visits
Such placelessness, it has phantom feet.
What's physical is lost here in ignorance
Of its own being. That solitary boat,
Out fishing, is a black stroke on vacancy.
Night, deaf and dumb as something from the deeps,
Having swallowed whole bright yesterday, replete
With radiance, is gray as abstinence now.
But in this nothingness, a knife point: pleasure
Comes pricking; the hour's pallor, too, is bladed
Like a shell, and as it opens, cuts.

SUSPENSION

Hiding his golden abdomen, the Spider of the sky was at rest,
Like an unmoved Mover, beyond the shafts of his web.
Three separate spans ran to the river
Spread below, smoothed, as by the Spider's craft.
The threads caught upon silence
As if, the spinnerets stanched, those waters ceased their flow.
Like the hairs of a headless harp
The golden, the silvered, hung, singing
Quiescence. No bird in the branches. They were bare,
Brown as the earth. Brown as a high cloud's brow that frowned
Rosily beside blithe cheeks trumpeting.
Where all was utterly still.
The spans fanned out, three spokes of a tireless wheel
That would go nowhere: unfinished forever.
It would not roll toward evening,
Nor turn toward winter. Yet the air was dusk,
The sky cold. The Spider, hidden,
Softly mantled himself in the heavens of Tiepolo.

A slight-boned animal, young. What jungle fruit
Droops with such grace as you in the subway corner
In your Saturday suit? Your eyes, wide
With would-be wakefulness, are dark as plums
That have the aubergine's lustre, but your skin,
Smooth as an egg, offers the gentler color
Of coffee in the bean. You are a morsel
So fine that you feed the eye as other things,
Sweet-fleshed, pamper the palate. Now you lean
Lightly against your mother, in the surrender
Of weariness still keeping dignity,
As if, a child, you honorably upheld
What was too heavy for a child to hold.
The luminous look is hidden; your eyes are
Lidded at last. You sleep. The bleak surround
Crowds you a little. Yet, even in sleep,
Without defense, darkly your grace proffers
The grave accusation of innocence.

JULY DAY

The afternoon sways like an elephant, wears
His smooth grey hide, displays his somnolent grace, weighing
The majesty of his ponderous pace against
The slyness twinkling in an innocent eye.
An infant born to the jungle, this afternoon
Elsewhere reached its mammoth magnificence,
Achieving the delicate play of a palace creature
With which it moves.
Moves, yet those giant limbs, the hours,
Scarcely seem to stir.
Prehensile as leisure, the pleasure triumphing here
In the procession of summer balances
The sun in hiding, the moon, hidden.
Before those grey knees sink
A gaiety like the glint of ivory slides
Lightly along the sky. This elephant afternoon
Winks at the glory of which it is part,
And bears itself with patience. Soon
It will be trumpeting.

Going up the river, or down, their tuneless look
Is of men grown poorer who, though ageing, wear
Some majesty of the commonplace. Old barges
Are cousin to those whom poverty becomes—
To late November, the north, nightfall, all the
Deprived whom increment of loss enlarges.
They have no faces, have no voices, even
Of their own selves no motion. Yet they move.
With what salt grace, with a dim pride of ocean
Uncompassable by a fussy tug,
Prim nurse that drags or nudges the old ones on.
They must borrow their colors from the river, mirror
The river's muddy silver, in dulled red echo
A sundown that beds in soot. Their freight, rusty,
Faded, cindery, is like the past
The charwoman deals with. Yesterday's business
They carry with the dignity of the blind.
By night the river is black, they are black's shadows
Passing. The unwrinkled stars dispute that darkness
Alone with a lantern on a one-eyed spar.

DISASTERS OF WAR: GOYA AT
THE MUSEUM

Streets opening like wounds: Madrid's. The thresh
Of resistance ends before a tumbled wall;
    The coward and the cursing sprawl
    Brotherly, one white heap of flesh
    Char-mouthed and boneyard black.
A woman, dragged off, howls—a lively sack
Of loot. An infant, fallen on its back,
Scowls from the stones at the Herodian lark.
Light is the monster fattening on this dark.

If shadow takes cadavers for her chair,
Where fresh fires glare life lifts a wolfish snout.
    Bruised and abused by hope, the rout,
    Turning, is gunned across the square
    And scattered. Rope, knife, lead
Slice prayer short. A lolling head
Grins, as with toothache. Stubbornly, the dead
Thrust forward like a beggar's senseless claw.
What is scrawled there in acid?   THIS I SAW.

Beyond the Madonnas and marbles, Goya's brute
Testament pits itself against the hush
    Of the blond halls, the urbane crush—
    Against the slat-eyed, the astute,
    Craning, against the guard, who yawns.
And pits itself in vain: this dark, these dawns,
Vomit of an old war, things the nightmare spawns
Are pictures at an exhibition. We
Look, having viewed too much, and cannot see.

DAMNATION

Hell is not far below,
Not black, not burning,
Nor even past returning:
You come and go.

You go and come
As in a mirror,
But hell is nearer,
And not so numb.

And when you go
You do not lose it,
Because you chose it—
As you know.

More domestic than elegant, leaves and pigeons
Hedge the dazzle beyond. Green, dust,
A purple strutting, screen the river's march.
The walks are for pigeons and ladies
Like parched pigeons, avoiding the bench where a tramp
Rustily sleeps. The carriages in the park
Are babies' now; children make all the traffic.
Spring brightly traveling, summer half awake,
Here the afternoon city plays at being
A dream of summer's: gaiety in repose,
Lazily festive as poster holidays,
A dream. Crossed by the tramp, rousing.
On paths where sparrows edge to snatch the bread
Crumbed for the humbled pigeons, the holiday
Is broken and scattered. Yet a strong green still
Throngs the boughs; and the river, preened, goes twinkling
Past all these birds, on to the salt sea.

I

Oranges beam
Sleekly as mandarins.
Their cheeks grained
As mellow leather is.
Spice, like a bloom, feathers
The thin tough skin.
Where, on a street gone dark,
Lit windows
Hole the night,
Their cosy gold is fellowed.
They could boast of cousins
In ancient Spain.
Spheres of rosy gold, little yellow
Worlds heaped here at
60¢ a Doz.—
Sweet juicy
Oranges.

II

i

Shapely as violins, the pears
Look down.
These, rose-freckled like a strawberry,
Those, with an autumn cheek of withered brown,
Alike, their hauteur.

ii

Beside the leek, Wales' pride,
The small white onions shine
As meek as pearls.

iii

And pumpkins plump as camel-humps,
And squash: tapering
Fingers of light.
Noon turns them to bright as butter thumbs,
Wartily gesturing to the sun.

III

The eggplant does not make the gaudy show
Of pumpkins or pomegranates. Like the crow
Blackbird: the purple grackle, like the 'cello,
The eggplant's note is resonantly low.

It cannot, like the pineapple, display
A finial elegance; lacks the holiday
Grace of the grape. Yet this fruit is shaped
And burnished as those eggs ostriches lay.

Lying so close to the potato bin,
It seems too gorgeous for that distant kin.
Between cusped amethyst and tumbled tubers,
Choose? Sometimes the stained earth-apples win.

IV

A large whitecheeked old woman smiling:
The homely solidity, the beauty of
The cauliflower is vulgar and beguiling.

Cauliflower, branched broccoli above,
And leafy sprouts below, all grown to please,
What share have they in the quality of love?

Nothing on earth is unromantic as these
But turnip lumps. The cauliflower's white
Florets, broccoli's green, are coarse as frieze.

The kale is blowsy. New cabbage, curled tight
As an embryo, the red, purply as cheap stained glass,
Are commoners, too obvious to delight.

Yet even the festive, rare asparagus
Does not take the eye like the simplicity
Of this vegetable that its neighbors here surpass

In voluptuous curves, color, delicacy.
There is a quality better than beguiling
In the cauliflower's homely solidity,
Like a large, whitecheeked old woman, smiling.

V

You with your brush bound to your swelled foiled hand
Would understand, old painter, this upanddown upanddown
Reaching and climbing. The grim grocer toils
Over his chiming pyramids, cares
Only for custom.
Each hour despoils the contrived order; evening
Destroys the flesh. With morning
Opulence is freshly alive,
Sounding the sun's note.
Blunt shapes under drumtight skins,
Sharp hues, some sweet,
Their vibrancy repeats: here is a man's
Livelihood; food to be bought, eaten; goods
Belonging to vision least.
The end here is still life. Custom provides
For the eyes first. They feast. Their feast invites
Thirst and delighted hunger. All are satisfied.

The river was blowing scarves.
They waved to a cloud as it flew
Round the sun-shod hour,
Who stepped lightly as dew
From a glowing
Green to, aloft, a widening stream of windy blue.

If pigeons, if people, strolled
And preened, it was gesture enough
For a saraband.
One stone angel took off
From the steeple:
Stone, or a puff of smoke, or wing's unfeathering stuff.

When dazzling there dartled—what?
A thing: was it creature or sleight
Of magician's wrist
That shone scarlet in flight?
If it startled,
How it seduced the eye where it dove and swam the height!

In derelict levity
Pursuing its willowy tail,
It was all a fling
Of twin ribbons, the gale
In a chevy
Ferried hilariously, then left to float and trail.

Now dolphin, then shying clown
On ski jumps of sky or the bight
Of an azure guy;
A laugh dancing; a mite
That in flying blazed like a crown, it winked out of sight,
The runaway kite, in a somersault's twinkle. O lost
Undying demon of delight!

HEARD IN OLD AGE

(for Robert Frost)

That sweet fire in the veins, while everywhere
The Harpies' filth keeps raining down, the young
Make love, make war, make music: the common tongue
Of private wounds, of the outrage that they share,
Or sing in desperate mockery of despair.

Is there a song left, then, for aged voices?
They are worse than cracked: half throttled by the thumbs
Of hard self-knowledge. To the old, dawn comes
With ache of loss, with cold absence of choices.
What heart, waking to this, drumming assent, rejoices?

Traffic rousing, gulls' cries, or cock crow, score
The body's ignominy, the mind's delays;
Till the Enigma, in a wandering phrase,
Offers a strain never audible before:
Immense music beyond a closing door.

SEASCAPE

Assembling ways to glisten,
Immensity
Is fresh as paint, and friendly,
Like salt.
Until wind pleats it, the water
Spends mica's childish glitter.
At the end of the jetty, erect,
Domestic,
A herring gull
Is the finial on the newel.
He stares westward,
No more prospecting for dinner
Than a saint on his pillar.
Marking the tip of the cape, the lighthouse
Off there is the size of the gull,
Equally singular, equally white.
The hush that sparkles in the sun
Is noon.

THREE VIEWS OF MOUNT RAINIER

i

An ethereal mountain, or
A firm-sinewed cloud?

ii

After Krishna had left off
Playing with the milkmaids,
They gave their milk and cream
To ingenious angels,
Who made for the God this
Giant ice cream, softly, slowly
Dissolving upon the snowy dish of Itself.

iii

Immaculate birth
             of

     floating
Majesty   on those
Northern skies.
Immense   as   nowhere,
That rootless
        repose.

BERKSHIRE AFTERNOON

Those hills are hives swollen with honey
From the trees, under whose boughs tranquilly walking
We listen for thunders of the dancing bees.
Hidden in such a hive, summer,
Served like a queen long enough,
Waits
To depart serenely like a queen.
The garden celebrates the marriage
Of radiance and silence,
Disturbed by
Nothing bigger than a hummingbird,
Or an old man's shy cough.

COMING OF AGE

Phi Beta Kappa poem, Columbia University, 1957

I

From that close cave, kicking away its riches,
Who, fighting toward air, who, crying, comes?
Coming, daring it, who abruptly pitches
Into a dazzle that chills, a gulf that drums?
This wet furled blindness with a naked breech is
Without hope or heart. Feet, fists, and toothless gums,
It is no one yet. Simply it works to seize
Kindness somewhere out of such rough mysteries.

And kindness arrives, as we know; we know this, too:
Invisibles, giants, the mysteries, multiplying,
As the child grows and changes, change. Some few,
Transformed by their names, that are queerly satisfying,
Seem not so awful, as if the name were a clue.
The mysteries do not answer, uncomplying.
Yet, knowledge enlarging knowledge of ignorance,
Round the sage's rose of joy, girl and boy still dance.

They hear the Song of the Senses, as it rises
Out of the air, from water, earth, and fire.
They dance into the Kingdoms of surprises,
Where, innocent of repugnance and desire,
The mineral endures; where the thrifty plant devises
What offspring, what society require;
Where the animal, thrilling with fear, or joy,
Shares the brief particular fate of girl and boy.

II

i

The ancients named the four:
Earth, water, fire, air,
Whose grace all things living in rivalry still share,
Whose enmity grows more
By us, who dare to ignore
Their favors everywhere.

Earth is dirt, is flesh, is flower,
The sheaf, the vine, the bony boughs.
Here the fox holes; here, if a hawk tower,
The rabbit prostrates; bullocks browse,
And deer. Here are parks, trenches, sloughs.

Earth, cousin to the wandering Seven,
Plays foster-mother to her slave;
Still set apart from hell and heaven,
She gives him what so long she gave:
All countries, and a grave.

iii

Mantling the planet,
The viewless tissue
Heaven's tailors issue
An emperor
For the world's wedding:
The air, goes threading
To the heart's core.
Flame, too, would vanish
If air were dying.
Of all things flying
She is the nurse:
Bomber and arrow,
The kite, the sparrow,
All these are air-borne,
So sound is air-borne, song, cry, or curse,
And uttered verse.

iv

Water is clothed with terror, pouring
However purely from the cloud.
Do the seas sleep? The old flood, snoring,
Acting its dreadful dream aloud,
Now shapes the cities' shroud.
The whale's road and the carrier's, water
Cradles the iceberg, rocks the buoy-bells.

Hers is that foam-bright-breasted daughter
Who copulates with war. Still the Unknown compels
Beauty and horror, joined beneath the swells.

v

If the earth, or if water, or air,
    Are elements and essence
Of the days and the nights that we share
    With each so mighty Presence,
And if water, and earth, and air, too,
    Are all we are heir to,
There is one rages deeper, flies higher—
In the deeps, in the vault, in the veins, there is fire.

III

i

Through only five Doors the acknowledged come:
Bringers of food, or flowers. Accusers from
The Egypts and Israels of the soul pass there.
They admit a dark that dazzles, lights that numb.
Ocean's breath pours through those Doors; and stale smells crawl
Across the sills. Through them the madrigal,
The bloody noises come. They open on nothingness,
And it enhances that narrow room they wall.

    O beat, beat to the music
    Of every mortal sense,
    Heart; it ushers another
    As human, and more immense.
    Deaf neither to shrieks nor stillness,
    O dance when you can dance
    To that small music's prodigal
    Mortal resonance.

ii

Even a stench can speak comfortably:
The freshness of earth, warm with horse-droppings,
Clogged seines, reeking richly of the sea.
An herb, pinched, pleasures, but no less the stings

Of woodsmoke, benzoin, rosin, pitch; such things
Haunt like cherishing ghosts who try to tell
How much is brief and lifelong, like a smell.

iii

In his Great Summons the Chinese exile plied
His vacant soul with memories: of song,
Of beloved vistas, of the bright-lipped, bright-eyed,
Revels, high deeds; but first with subtle or strong
Meats, sauces, wines. Relish, time does not wrong,
The condemned approve. Sweet at the tonguetip, taste
Still keeps its sweet, if bitter at the last.

iv

Music is chief of savors, hot or cool;
It is sorrow's physic, that desire will greet
Gaily as nutriment. Music is a pool,
Where beasts from the wilderness of the spirit meet
To drink, then with jungle courtesy, retreat.
Noises pollute it; only stillness clears,
To make purer music for whoever hears.

v

Is vision deaf? Lofty waterfalls make wing
From the Zen master's brush as rhythm flows.
The Persian's orange, azures, crimsons, ching
Like a celesta. Suns' fanfare, arpeggios
Of rain, the planets' inscrutable pavan, these shows
Ring in the mind's ear as a look will. Sight
Has the key to the City of Knowing, and of night.

vi

Unravelling airs, the hackles frost-crisped turf
Erects; the crag that scorches like a nettle;
Silken brutality of assaulting surf;
Pure heat, and clawing cold; clay, marble, metal;
Knives; the finger that brushes like a petal:
All this touch knows, who knows the profoundest kiss,
And the utter pang that robs her of all this.

IV

i

Overwhelmed, deprivation shuffles:
Which goods shall it choose, ignore?
While from all regions, from all seasons,
The senses as before
Ask dues, that, if arriving, shrink and
Will soon arrive no more.

And though, blind trudge, the body shoulders
His fellow whom circumstance
Has lamed, will then the soul, as promised,
Be blessed with legs and prance?
A fable. Yet as the players are leaving,
O what a dance we dance!

ii

Lovers under the lamps dance or dream of dancing;
In smuttiness, in trash on the street the children's feet
Flash. At particular births perhaps a star will dance.
Swaddled in his mother, the infant kicks his heels,
As the heart of age, surprised, reels in death's pouch.

There are many musics. There is their absence, certain
As mischief: the routine disquiet, not just
Hysterical voices of traffic, static, kitchen noises,
But, repeated like crazy phrases, repeated invasions,
All those Times of Troubles that leave the gayest mind
Ignorant where, in the rubble, among the blind, the crippled,
The orphaned, the unburied, it may find some friend.

Ignorance is the Law. Created to sparkle,
A jewel or a snowflake: the crystal, flawless
As the mathematics of its symmetry,
Knows nothing of that multiplying marvel.
The cancer cell breeds, breeding in ignorance
Of what it havocs. The vulture in his eyrie,

Wolf in his lair, dolphin under the wave,
The rat in his clean cage, kills, is killed,
But, living, is ignorant that it must die.

Ignorance is the law, that men have broken,
To be punished: radiant science half confirms
Nebulous Genesis, and to be rewarded
Like rebels who find triumph is their fate.
The lights among which we move, pushing the darkness
Farther back, show darkness, swarthier now
Than the long northern night, and how immense,
Flourishing: an expanse of darkness,
As if the lights themselves were the nourishment
Darkness seized on, to grow. This monster, the creatures,
Alert to a whiff, a whisper, of the enemy,
To his shadow stirring, victims of beak, barb, snare,
Have never feared, have met nowhere. It is this monster,
That makes no sound, that has no shape, that must
Trivialize everything human, must also
Transfigure the trivial, making it most dear.

The ancient elements surround, support us:
The senses, while they can, sing their five songs,
Of everything, desired and undesired,
That belongs to being; alike the actual,
And the imagined, springing from that root
Like the golden Phallus that rises from the lake
At Mount Meru's foot, from which stream men and gods.
It is of common things the senses chiefly
Sing, or speak: of things that are palpable,
Things that address the nostrils or the tongue,
The usual scene, the ordinary sounds.
But silence is what echoes at nightfall.
Nor does that seem a supernatural voice,
Though it is as if the darkness found
Speech for such final greetings, such farewells
As strike the heart dumb—the ignorant heart,
That in despair first learns how to rejoice.

155

Translations

THE SOUL

Go thou
Her changing roads.
Know all her provinces.
Yet to her far frontiers thou shalt
Not come.

(AFTER HERACLITUS)

TANKA

Since he is too young
To know the way, I would plead:
"Pray, accept this gift,
O Underworld messenger,
And bear the child pick-a-back."

FROM THE JAPANESE OF OKURA

HAIKU

The falling flower
I saw drift back to the branch
Was a butterfly.

FROM THE JAPANESE OF MORITAKE

QUATRAIN

that Villon made when he was condemned to die

I'm François, I'm sorry to say,
Born in Paris, near Pontoise city.
Thanks to a rope six feet and a bitty
My neck will learn what my buttocks weigh.

FROM THE FRENCH OF FRANÇOIS VILLON

CORRESPONDENCES

Nature, a temple, has live pillars who
At whiles allow confused words issuance;
Man encounters many an intimate glance
From the forest of symbols that he passes through.

In a profound, shadowy unison,
Like lingering echoes distance has confounded,
As vast as night, like clarity unbounded,
Perfumes, colors, sounds, respond as one.

There are perfumes fresh as infants' flesh,
Dulcet as oboes, and like prairies, green,
—And others, rotten, richly triumphing,

Able to grow immense as infinite things,
Like amber, musk, benzoin, and frankincense,
Sing the transports of spirit and of sense.

FROM THE FRENCH OF CHARLES BAUDELAIRE

JOHN THE RIVER

River without a Land, ohé, John Landless' course,
The waters do not choose between the banks but flow
Onward between those rivals mutually bound
East-West, the Yes-and-No, the youthful and the slow.

Does he adjudicate between the hush, the cries?
He who knows well the springs' gestation underground,
Asks of the winds a vote of confidence, will trace
The figure of the flight on which the birds are bound.

Rightward he views the aging walls of Nineveh,
And ancient kings who fling their rubies to the base
And sees the powerful palace betray itself at last
And the descending rain displume proud Samothrace.

Upon the other shore he sees the Amazons
Plunge freely where the cunning billow braves,
Their large frank eyes, enriched with belladonna, keen
To pierce the ancient secret of the incestuous waves.

Fishers and riverfolk will stand before their huts
To watch the river flow, not jealous of his glory,
Let him seek out the spirit in regions far from here
If they may fish and drink and beach a loaded dory.

River without a Land, its wave ephemeral,
Down to the sea it flows, no choice, no faltering
Between peace on the right and war upon the left
From dawn quick with desire to dusk remembering.

FROM THE FRENCH OF YVAN GOLL

LANDLESS JOHN SALUTES THE HARLEM RIVER

This water this black alcohol that draws us on
This white whiskey where black eyes are swimming
These sulphurous pools where black flies are flowering
These green dragons and black dragons of the plague

O sorrowful wave
White dance   black dance   red dance   yellow dance
Dance of all the seas that give suck as one breast
Massacre of all mothers that choke as one throat

Harlem! Black priestess
Drunk on the white milk of the dew

O river with mole-colored hair
And a scintillant girdle of salmon russet steel
Chaldean dancer in this dirty hole of America
Pinning a moon of gold between your filthy breasts
Toward you descend the cats of our flesh
And the reflections of our shattered sheet-iron

O ancient wave
Wave of the yellow Tigris and of pitchy Harlem
My pillow is stuffed with the scales of cheap fish
Sad wave overwhelmed
By so many drowned heads
Somber river which defies the ocean
With its sluices of death

FROM THE FRENCH OF YVAN GOLL

SPANISH DANCER

As in the hand a sulphur-match burns white
before it flames, and giddily unfurls
its quivering tongues:—so, circling in the sight
of crowding watchers, hurried hot and bright
her rounded dance quivers in widening swirls.

And suddenly it is sheer flame aflare.

Tossing a glance the girl kindles her hair
and with more daring art whirls her attire
wholly, at once, into this furious fire,
from which her bare arms, each a startled snake,
stretch sinuously, rattling as they wake.

And then: as if the fire were strangling stuff
she gathers it together—flings it off
imperiously, with a prouder mien, her eyes
watch: there upon the ground, raging, it lies
and keeps on flaming and will not give place.—
Yet certain of her triumph, with a sweet
welcome now in her smile, she lifts her face
and stamps it out with little resolute feet.

FROM THE GERMAN OF RAINER MARIA RILKE

"PUT OUT MY EYES"

Put out my eyes, and I can see you still;
slam my ears to, and I can hear you yet;
and without any feet can go to you;
and tongueless I can conjure you at will.
Break off my arms, I shall take hold of you
and grasp you with my heart as with a hand;
arrest my heart, my brain will beat as true;
and if you set this brain of mine afire,
then on my blood I yet will carry you.

FROM THE GERMAN OF RAINER MARIA RILKE

"ALTHOUGH, AS FROM A PRISON"

Although, as from a prison walled with hate,
each from his own self labors to be free,
the world yet holds a wonder, and how great!
ALL LIFE IS LIVED: now this comes home to me.
But who, then, lives it? Things that patiently
stand there, like some unfingered melody
that sleeps within a harp as day is going?
Is it the winds, across the waters blowing?
Is it the branches, beckoning each to each,
is it the flowers, weaving fragrances,
the aging alleys that reach out endlessly?
Is it the warm beasts, moving to and fro,
or the birds, alien as they sail from view?
This life—who lives it really? God,—do you?

FROM THE GERMAN OF RAINER MARIA RILKE

GRAPES

I shall not miss the roses, fading
When springtime's hurrying days are done;
I love the grapes whose clusters ripen
Upon the hillsides in the sun—
The glory of my fertile valley,
They hang, each lustrous as a pearl,
Gold autumn's joy, oblong, transparent,
Like the slim fingers of a girl.

FROM THE RUSSIAN OF ALEXANDER PUSHKIN

Here's winter. Far from town, what shall we do? I question
The servant bringing in my morning cup of tea:
"How is the weather—warm? Not storming? The ground's
    covered
With freshly fallen snow?" Come, is it best to be
Astride a horse at once, or shall we, until dinner,
See what our neighbor's old reviews may have to say?
The snow is fresh and fine. We rise and mount our horses,
And trot through fields agleam with the first light of day.
We carry whips; the dogs run close behind our stirrups;
With careful eyes we search the snow, we scour the plain
For tracks, ride round and round, and tardily at twilight,
After we've missed two hares, at last turn home again.
How jolly! Evening comes: without, a storm is howling;
The candlelight is dim. The heart is wrenched with pain.
Slow drop by drop I drink my boredom's bitter poison.
I try a book. The eyes glide down the page—in vain:
My thoughts are far away . . . and so I close the volume,
Sit down, take up my pen, force my dull Muse to say
Some incoherent words, but melody is wanting,
The sounds won't chime. . . . The devil! Where now is the way
I had with rhyme? I can't control this curious handmaid:
The verse is shapeless, cold, so lame it cannot walk.
So I dismiss the Muse: I am too tired to quarrel.
I step into the parlor where I hear them talk
About the sugar-works, about the next election;
The hostess, like the weather, frowns, her only arts
Are plying rapidly her long steel knitting needles
And telling people's fortunes by the king of hearts.
How dismal! Thus the days go by, alike and lonely.
But if, while I play draughts at twilight in my nook,
Into our dreary village a closed sleigh or carriage
Should just by chance bring guests for whom I did not look:
Say, an old woman and two girls, her two young daughters
(Tall, fair-haired creatures, both), the place that was so dull,

So Godforsaken, all at once is bright and lively,
And suddenly, good heavens, life grows rich and full!
Attentive sidelong looks, and then a few words follow,
There's talk, then friendly laughter, and songs when lamps are lit,,
And after giddy waltzes there are languid glances,
There's whispering at table, gay and ready wit;
Upon the narrow stairs a lingering encounter;
When twilight falls, a girl steals from her wonted place
And out onto the porch, bare-throated, chest uncovered—
The wind is up, the snow blows straight into her face!
Unhurt by northern blasts the Russian rose will blow.
How hotly a kiss burns in keen, frosty weather!
How fresh a Russian girl blooming in gusts of snow!

FROM THE RUSSIAN OF ALEXANDER PUSHKIN

I am to the present-day tribe
just a long dirty joke, but I
see him crossing the mountains of time,
him whom nobody sees.

Where bobtailed eyes fall short—
at the head of hungry hordes,
revolutions his crown of thorns,
the year 'Sixteen draweth nigh.

And I
prepare the way.
Wherever there's pain I am there;
and where tears rain,
on every drop I crucify
myself.
It's too late now to forgive.
I've scorched the souls
where tenderness could live,
and that's a tougher job than capturing
a thousand thousand Bastilles.

And when,
announcing its arrival
by revolt,
you go to meet the savior,
I will bolt
ahead, drag out my soul for you,
trample it,
flatten it to a big rag!
and give it to you,
bleeding, for your flag.

FROM THE RUSSIAN OF VLADIMIR MAYAKOVSKY

THE URALS FOR THE FIRST TIME

Without an accoucheuse, in darkness, pushing her
Blind hands against the night, the Ural fastness, torn and
Half-dead with agony, was screaming in a blur
Of mindless pain, as she was giving birth to morning.

And brushed by chance, tall ranges far and wide
Loosed toppling bronze pell-mell in thunder-colored rumbling.
The train panted and coughed, clutching the mountainside,
And at that sound the ghosts of fir trees shied and stumbled.

The smoky dawn was a narcotic for the peaks,
A drug with which the fire-breathing dragon plied them,
As when a specious thief upon a journey seeks
To lull his fellow travelers with opium slipped them slyly.

They woke on fire. The skies were poppy-colored flame,
Whence Asiatics skied like hunters after quarry;
To kiss the forests' feet the eager strangers came
And thrust upon the firs the regal crowns they carried.

Arrayed in majesty, in ranks the firs arose,
Those shaggy dynasts, their grave glory clamant,
And trod the orange velvet of the frozen snows
Spread on a tinseled cloth and richly damasked.

FROM THE RUSSIAN OF BORIS PASTERNAK

"WE'RE FEW"

We're few, perhaps three, hellish fellows
Who hail from the flaming Donetz,
With a fluid gray bark for our cover
Made of rain clouds and soldiers' soviets
And verses and endless debates
About art or it may be freight rates.

We used to be people. We're epochs.
Pell-mell we rush caravanwise
As the tundra to groans of the tender
And tension of pistons and ties.
Together we'll rip through your prose,
We'll whirl, a tornado of crows,

And be off! But you'll not understand it
Till late. So the wind in the dawn
Hits the thatch on the roof—for a moment—
But puts immortality on
In trees' stormy sessions, in speech
Of boughs the roof's shingles can't reach.

FROM THE RUSSIAN OF BORIS PASTERNAK

THREE VARIATIONS

1

When consummate the day hangs before you,
Each detail to be scanned at your ease,
Just the sultry chatter of squirrels
Resounds in the resinous trees.

And storing up strength in their languor,
The ranked piney heights are adrowse,
While the freckled sweat is pouring
From the peeling forest's boughs.

2

Miles thick with torpor nauseate the gardens.
The catalepsy of the valleys' rage
Is weightier, more threatening than a tempest,
Fiercer than hurricane's most savage raid.

The storm is near. The dry mouth of the garden
Gives off the smell of nettles, roofs, and fear,
And of corruption; and the cattle's bellow
Rises columnar in the static air.

3

Now tatters of denuded clouds
Grow on each bush in tasseled groves.
Damp nettles fill the garden's mouth.
It smells of storms and treasure troves.

The shrubs are tired of lament.
In heaven arched prospects multiply.
Like web-toed birds on swampy ground
The barefoot azure treads the sky.

And willow branches and the leaves
Of oaks, and tracks beside the spring,
Like lips the hand has not wiped dry,
Are glistening, are glistening.

FROM THE RUSSIAN OF BORIS PASTERNAK

"IF ONLY, WHEN I MADE MY DEBUT"

If only, when I made my debut,
There might have been a way to tell
That lines with blood in them can murder,
That they can flood the throat and kill,

I certainly would have rejected
A jest on such a sour note,
So bashful was that early interest,
The start was something so remote.

But age is pagan Rome, demanding
No balderdash, no measured breath,
No fine feigned parody of dying,
But really being done to death.

A line that feeling sternly dictates
Sends on the stage a slave, and, faith,
It is good-bye to art forever
Then, then things smack of soil and Fate.

FROM THE RUSSIAN OF BORIS PASTERNAK

A FRAGMENT OF SKY

A fragment of sky melted onto the ice
Wind wiped it away
Wind gathered clouds   wind wiped them away
And wiped away the ice

          all but two gulls the shape of snow

FROM THE FINNISH OF TUOMAS ANHAVA

I play, there is no answer.
The sea darkens.
On the branch, bronze leaves
quiveringly stiffen.
Moon, stars, order themselves in silence,
there is no motion.
I wander,
firm frail instrument of marrow and bone.

Reversed,
the landscape.
To a hollow mirror
I play the expanse of space inverted,
for the sake of opposed harmonies,
slow narrowing music,
the vanishing, the not heard.

FROM THE FINNISH OF EEVA-LIISA MANNER

PAUSE IN THE FIRING

Perhaps there is an inkling of the order to come
Perhaps mischief already runs in your veins
All Bethlehem's towers are striking ten
Come sister let us push on toward the miracle

Make yourself neat be friendly and easy
The pack of fears I take on my back
I a veteran tired but no coward
Come dear sister stay close beside me

We share the night and the abandoned house
But first we must bury clock and key
Now while the guns of time remain silent
Hunched in the trench we push on toward the miracle

Do not look up to stare after the flares
I will tear the barbed wire for you with my hands
I know all the secret trails through the minefields
There is only one star that leads us on

Do not cry sister leave your shoes in the mud
Soon the guns will resume then we must be there
On all the towers squats the mischief to come
Give me your hand we must push on toward the miracle

FROM THE GERMAN OF WALTER NEUMANN

Acknowledgments

Unless otherwise stated, these poems were published in the following volumes, to which the author holds copyright: *Banners; Honey Out of the Rock; Fire for the Night; One Part Love; Take Them, Stranger; Animal, Vegetable, Mineral;* or in *Coming of Age: New and Selected Poems.*

"Coming of Age," read as Phi Beta Kappa poem at Columbia University, June, 1957, is reprinted by permission of *Prairie Schooner,* University of Nebraska Press. "Piano Recital" first appeared in *New Poems by American Poets,* No. 1, edited by Rolfe Humphries, Ballantine Books, 1953. "Disasters of War," "A Small Colored Boy in the Subway," "Seascape," "Earliness at the Cape," "Late Reflections," "Passage," "No Moon, No Star," "Fireworks," and "Another Autumn" originally appeared in *The New Yorker;* "Suspension," "July Day," "Barges on the Hudson," "Unearthly Toy," "The Net," "The Lotus," "Admonition," "The Mother," and "Lizard at Pompeii" in *Poetry: A Magazine of Verse;* "Urban Pastoral," "Berkshire Afternoon," and "Summer Poem" in *Harper's Bazaar;* "Heard in Old Age" and "Voices on Riverside" in *Beloit Poetry Journal;* "At the Green Grocer's IV" in *Grécourt Review;* "At the Green Grocer's V" and "Damnation" in *Compass Review;* "The Door" in *Tiger's Eye;* "Tivoli : Copenhagen" in the Columbia University *Forum,* and also in the volume *Karen Blixen,* Gyldendal, Copenhagen; "N.Y. Tanka" in *The Nation;* "Cézanne" in *Portfolio;* "A Day in Late August" in *Saturday Review;* "Space Man," "The Disenchanted," and "A View of the Piazza di San Marco" in *the transatlantic review.*

The translation "Quatrain" originally appeared in *Rogue's Legacy, A Novel about François Villon,* by Babette Deutsch, 1942, reprinted here by permission of Coward-McCann, Inc. "Tanka" and "Haiku" appeared in *Poetry Handbook,* by Babette Deutsch, Funk & Wagnalls Co., 1957. "Design," first published under the title "A Villanelle" in *Botteghe Oscure,* 1949, was reprinted in *Poetry Handbook.* "John the River" was first published in *The Kenyon Review,* Spring, 1955, and "Landless John Salutes the Harlem River" in *Jean Sans Terre,* by Ivan